HISTOPLASMOSIS

Proceedings of the Second National Conference

Publication Number 808

AMERICAN LECTURE SERIES®

A Monograph in

The BANNERSTONE DIVISION *of*
AMERICAN LECTURES IN CLINICAL MICROBIOLOGY

Edited by

ALBERT BALOWS, Ph.D.
Bacteriology Section
Center for Disease Control
Atlanta, Georgia

Contributors

Libero Ajello, Ph.D.

Mycology Section, Laboratory Division
Center for Disease Control
Atlanta, Georgia

Padiath A. Aslam, M.D.

Department of Thoracic Surgery
University of Tennessee College of Medicine
Memphis, Tennessee

Allonzo-Rulloda Borja, M.D.

District Two State Tuberculosis Hospital
Louisville, Kentucky

Peter A. Bartels, Ph.D.

Gillet and Siebert
Boulder, Colorado

David S. Bauman, Ph.D.

Department of Preventive Medicine
University of West Virginia School of Medicine
Morgantown, West Virginia
University of Kentucky College of Medicine
Lexington, Kentucky

Martha D. Berliner, Ph.D.

Department of Microbiology
Harvard School of Public Health
Biology Department
Simmons College
Boston, Massachusetts

John W. Brandsberg, Ph.D.

Mycoses Section, Ecological Investigations Program
Center for Disease Control
Kansas City, Kansas

v

Charlotte C. Campbell, S.B.

Departments of Microbiology and Tropical Public Health
Harvard University School of Public Health
Boston, Massachusetts

John W. Chandler, Jr., M.D.

Mycoses Section
Ecological Investigations Program
Center for Disease Control
Kansas City, Kansas

Ernest W. Chick, M.D.

Department of Preventive Medicine
University of West Virginia School of Medicine
Morgantown, West Virginia
University of Kentucky College of Medicine
Lexington, Kentucky

Tom D. Y. Chin, M.D.

Ecological Investigations Program
Center for Disease Control
Kansas City, Kansas

Norman F. Conant, Ph.D.

Department of Microbiology
Duke University School of Medicine
Durham, North Carolina

Arthur F. DiSalvo, M.D.

Bureau of Laboratory Services and Research
South Carolina State Board of Health
Columbia, South Carolina

Judith E. Domer, Ph.D.

Department of Microbiology
Tulane University School of Medicine
New Orleans, Louisiana

Irene L. Doto, M.A.

Statistical and Publications Services
Ecological Investigations Program
Center for Disease Control
Kansas City, Kansas

HISTOPLASMOSIS

Proceedings of the
Second National Conference

Held at the
Center for Disease Control
Atlanta, Georgia

Editorial Board
LIBERO AJELLO, Ph.D.
ERNEST W. CHICK, M.D.
MICHAEL L. FURCOLOW, M.D., Sc.D.

C H A R L E S   C   T H O M A S • P U B L I S H E R
Springfield • Illinois • U.S.A.

Published and Distributed Throughout the World by
CHARLES C THOMAS • PUBLISHER
Bannerstone House
301-327 East Lawrence Avenue, Springfield, Illinois, U.S.A.
Natchez Plantation House
735 North Atlantic Boulevard, Fort Lauderdale, Florida, U.S.A.

© *1971, by* CHARLES C THOMAS • PUBLISHER

Library of Congress Catalog Card Number: 70-143724

With THOMAS BOOKS *careful attention is given to all details of
manufacturing and design. It is the Publisher's desire to present books
that are satisfactory as to their physical qualities and artistic possibilities
and appropriate for their particular use.* THOMAS BOOKS *will be true
to those laws of quality that assure a good name and good will.*

Printed in United States of America

B-7

Charles E. Eastin, D.V.M.

Department of Community Medicine
University of Kentucky College of Medicine
Research Laboratory in Mycology
Veterans Administration Hospital
Lexington, Kentucky

Charles E. Eastridge, M.D.

Department of Thoracic Surgery
University of Tennessee College of Medicine
Memphis, Tennessee

Phyllis Q. Edwards, M.D.

Chief, Tuberculosis Branch
State and Community Services Division
Center for Disease Control
Atlanta, Georgia

Chester W. Emmons, Ph.D.

Retired
Phoenix, Arizona

Lamar Field, Ph.D.

Department of Chemistry
Vanderbilt University
Nashville, Tennessee

Michael L. Furcolow, M.D., Sc.D.

Department of Community Medicine
University of Kentucky College of Medicine
Research Laboratory in Mycology
Veterans Administration Hospital
Lexington, Kentucky

Norman L. Goodman, Ph.D.

Department of Microbiology
Medical University of South Carolina
Charleston, South Carolina

Wayne S. Hanley, Ph.D.

Department of Chemistry
Vanderbilt University
Nashville, Tennessee

Phillip Holland, M.D.

Department of Pediatrics
University of Kentucky College of Medicine
Lexington, Kentucky

Thomas Ruffin Hood, Ph.D.

District Two State Tuberculosis Hospital
Louisville, Kentucky

Felix A. Hughes, Jr., Ph.D.

Thoracic Surgery, Veterans Administration Hospital
Department of Surgery
University of Tennessee Medical Units
Memphis, Tennessee

Dan B. Jones, M.D.

Division of Ophthalmology
Vanderbilt University School of Medicine
Nashville, Tennessee

William Kaplan, D.V.M.

Mycology Section, Laboratory Division
Center for Disease Control
Atlanta, Georgia

Leo Kaufman, Ph.D.

Mycology Section, Laboratory Division
Center for Disease Control
Atlanta, Georgia

Charles H. Kirkpatrick, M.D.

Section of Clinical Immunology
University of Kansas Medical Center
Kansas City, Kansas

George S. Kobayashi, Ph.D.

Department of Medicine
Washington University School of Medicine
St. Louis, Missouri

Howard W. Larsh, Ph.D.

Department of Botany and Microbiology
University of Oklahoma
Norman, Oklahoma

Nathan Levene, M.D.

Kentucky State Tuberculosis Hospitals
Department of Surgery
University of Kentucky College of Medicine
Lexington, Kentucky

Juan E. MacKinnon, M.D.

Instituto de Higiene, Facultad de Medicina
Universidad de la Republica
Montevideo, Uruguay

Robert J. Marshall, M.R.C.P.

Division of Cardiovascular and Pulmonary Diseases
West Virginia University School of Medicine
Morgantown, West Virginia

Martin B. Marx, D.V.M., Ph.D.

Department of Community Medicine
University of Kentucky College of Medicine
Lexington, Kentucky

Sara C. McDearman, Ph.D.

Laboratory Service, Veterans Administration Hospital
Department of Pathology
University of Tennessee Medical Units
Memphis, Tennessee

Ilda McVeigh, Ph.D.

Department of Biology
Vanderbilt University
Nashville, Tennessee

Robert W. Menges, D.V.M. [*]

Environmental Health Surveillance Center
University of Missouri
Columbia, Missouri

W. Marcus Newberry, Jr., M.D.

Mycoses Section
Ecological Investigations Program
Center for Disease Control
Kansas City, Kansas

---

[*] Deceased.

James D. Parker, M.D.

Mycoses Section, Ecological Investigations Program
Center for Disease Control
Kansas City, Kansas

John W. Polk, M.D.

Surgical Service, Missouri State Sanatorium
Mt. Vernon, Missouri

John J. Procknow, M.D.

Barlow Sanatorium and Hospital
Department of Medicine
University of Southern California College of Medicine
Los Angeles, California

Prathapchandra A. Reddy, M.D.

Missouri State Sanatorium
Mt. Vernon, Missouri

Irene Roeckel, M.D.

Department of Community Medicine
University of Kentucky College of Medicine
Research Laboratory in Mycology
Veterans Administration Hospital
Lexington, Kentucky

N. Alexander Saliba, M.D.

District Two State Tuberculosis Hospital
Department of Medicine
University of Louisville School of Medicine
Louisville, Kentucky

George A. Sarosi, M.D.

Mycoses Section, Ecological Investigations Program
Center for Disease Control
Kansas City, Kansas

Jan Schwarz, M.D.

Clinical Laboratories, Jewish Hospital
Mycology Laboratory, Cincinnati General Hospital
Department of Pathology, University of Cincinnati
College of Medicine
Cincinnati, Ohio

John H. Seabury, M.D.

Department of Medicine
Louisiana State University School of Medicine
New Orleans, Louisiana

David J. Sencer, M.D.

Director, Center for Disease Control
Atlanta, Georgia

Coy D. Smith, B.A.

Department of Community Medicine
University of Kentucky College of Medicine
Research Laboratory in Mycology
Veterans Administration Hospital
Lexington, Kentucky

Terrill K. Smith

Laboratory of Clinical Investigation
National Institute of Allergy and Infectious Diseases
National Institutes of Health
Bethesda, Maryland

George Link Spaeth, M.D.

Department of Ophthalmology
Temple University School of Medicine
Philadelphia, Pennsylvania

Ronald F. Sprouse, Ph.D.

Departments of Veterinary Microbiology and Medical Microbiology
University of Missouri, Schools of Veterinary Medicine and Medicine
Columbia, Missouri

Guenther Stotzky, Ph.D.

Department of Biology
New York University
New York, New York

Wheelan D. Sutliff, M.D.

West Tennessee Chest Disease Hospital
Department of Medicine
University of Tennessee
Memphis, Tennessee

Fred E. Tosh, M.D.

Mycoses Section, Ecological Investigations Program
Center for Disease Control
Kansas City, Kansas

Clenon Turner, B.A.

Department of Community Medicine
University of Kentucky College of Medicine
Research Laboratory in Mycology
Veterans Administration Hospital
Lexington, Kentucky

John P. Utz, M.D.

Department of Medicine
Medical College of Virginia
Richmond, Virginia

Robert J. Weeks, B.S.

Mycoses Section, Ecological Investigations Program
Center for Disease Control
Kansas City, Kansas

Warren E. Wheeler, M.D.

Department of Pediatrics
University of Kentucky College of Medicine
Lexington, Kentucky

Foreword

THE genesis of this series, *The American Lecture Series in Clinical Microbiology*, stems from the concerted efforts of the Editor and the Publisher to provide a forum from which well-qualified and distinguished authors may present, either as a book or monograph, their views on any aspect of clinical microbiology. Our definition of clinical microbiology is conceived to encompass the broadest aspects of medical microbiology not only as they are applied to the clinical laboratory but equally to the research laboratory and to theoretical considerations. In the clinical microbiology laboratory we are concerned with differences in morphology, biochemical behavior, and antigenic patterns as a means of microbial identification. In the research laboratory or when we employ microorganisms as a model in theoretical biology, our interest is often focused not so much on the above differences but rather on the similarities between microorganisms. However, it must be appreciated that even though there are many similarities between cells, there are important differences between major types of cells, which set very definite limits on the cellular behavior. Unless this is understood, it is impossible to discern common denominators.

We are also concerned with the relationships between microorganism and disease—any microorganism and any disease. Implicit in these relations is the role of the host which forms the third arm of the triangle: microorganism, disease, and host. In this series we plan to explore each of these; singly where possible for factual information and in combination for an understanding of the myriad of interrelationships that exist. This necessitates the application of basic principles of biology and may, at times, require the emergence of new theoretical concepts which will create new principles or modify existing ones. Above all, our aim is to present well-documented books which will be informative, instructive, and useful, creating a sense of satisfaction to both the reader and the author.

Closely intertwined with the above *raison d'etre* is our desire to produce a series which will be read not only for the pleasure of knowledge but which will also enhance the reader's professional skill and extend his technical ability. *The American Lecture Series in Clinical Microbiology* is dedicated to biologists—be they physicians, scientists, or teachers—in the hope that this series will foster better appreciation of mutual problems and help close the gap between theoretical and applied microbiology.

The second National Conference on Histoplasmosis was held in October,

1969, at the Center for Disease Control in Atlanta, Georgia. This conference was attended by scientists, physicians, and public health and laboratory workers from several countries in this hemisphere. The presentations covered every aspect of histoplasmosis and represented the most recent laboratory, clinical, public health, and therapeutic findings on a disease that has attracted global attention in the past two decades. The roster of speakers contains the names of those individuals who have painstakingly and diligently investigated, pursued, and researched every possible avenue and every area of interest that would yield useful knowledge on the mycology, diagnosis, immunology, epidemiology, and therapy of histoplasmosis. The list of authors represents a significant portion of the authoritative and most knowledgeable investigators of this disease and its etiologic agent in the world today.

Foremost among this distinguished group of people are the three members of the Editorial Board, Libero Ajello, Ernest W. Chick and Michael L. Furcolow. These three, working together with Gerald Eggleston of Lederle Laboratories, planned, assembled, and arranged this conference. It was an overwhelming success.

We are grateful to the sponsoring institutions—Center for Disease Control, University of West Virginia, University of Kentucky, and Lederle Laboratories—for their farsightedness and efforts in making this conference and subsequent publication of proceedings possible.

Hence, we have all of the elements that by design are required for a publication in *The American Lecture Series in Clinical Microbiology*. We are privileged and pleased to present the "Proceedings of the Second National Conference on Histoplasmosis." We are confident that it will be recognized as an outstanding and authoritative collection of papers on a disease that has intrigued and baffled man since 1906, when it was first described by Darling.

ALBERT BALOWS, PH.D.
Editor

Preface

CALLED for many years Ohio Valley Disease, histoplasmosis was thought to be narrowly limited geographically. As a result, many clinicians today do not consider this condition in a differential diagnosis, feeling that it does not occur in their particular geographic areas. Yet, the past years have seen two significant outbreaks in places usually considered outside the endemic area: Montreal, Canada, and Mason City, Iowa. In some states, histoplasmosis is one of the most frequent infections.

This meeting of hundreds of professionals from differing scientific disciplines represents the good that can be achieved when several segments of the health community work together to solve a problem. It is a fine example of what can be done when mutual concerns lead to cooperation among the academies, government agencies, and the pharmaceutical industry. Lederle Laboratories is privileged to have been a part of this conference.

It is hoped that the publication of these proceedings will be influential in continuing to inform the scientific and medical professions and, by way of them, in ultimately helping the public.

GERALD EGGLESTON
Lederle Laboratories

Contents

PART III

ECOLOGY, EPIDEMIOLOGY AND CONTROL

PART IV

CLINICAL AND PATHOLOGICAL ASPECTS

PART VI

PREVENTION AND TREATMENT

PART VII

QUO VADIS

HISTOPLASMOSIS

Proceedings of the Second National Conference

Part I
Introduction

Chapter 1

Welcoming Address

DAVID J. SENCER

ONE of the main functions of the director of the Center is to welcome various groups to the Center for Disease Control. I have a few credentials that I would like to display at this time so that you can see that my welcome is more than just a perfunctory one. My first job in the Public Health Service in 1955 was in the Tuberculosis Program working for Dr. Carroll Palmer (at that time chief of Operational Research, for the Tuberculosis Program, Division of Special Health Services, Washington, D.C.). They did not have enough for me to do and had me off in a corner. My principal job was reviewing chest x-rays that had been taken in Europe. At that time, the Immigration Act read that any person suffering from tuberculosis was excluded, and the Public Health Service had a consultant in the Paris office who had decided that anything that was calcified was tubreculosis. Therefore, all persons with x-rays showing calcification were excluded. Having come from the "hotbed" of histoplasmosis in Michigan, I knew better than that.

My next job was in Muscogee County, Georgia, in the Tuberculosis Research Program. We had a patient there who had cavitary histoplasmosis, and once every six months I drew blood to send to Dr. Loosli because the patient had such a high complement fixation titer.

My final exposure to histoplasmosis was a couple of years later. A young boy came in for a 70 MM chest x-ray, which proved to be full of evidence of disseminated calcification. Normally, out of our own curiosity, we would have called him back to discuss the situation with him and give him a skin test. But since he came a great distance to Columbus, Georgia, we bypassed this opportunity and sent him a card saying that he had a minor abnormality but nothing to be concerned with. Three weeks later we had a very frantic telephone call from the State Health Department, which had received notification from the military that this young man appeared for his draft physical and had miliary tuberculosis. Why had we not done something about it? I swallowed hard. We did get the boy in and found that he had disseminated calcification with a very strongly positive histoplasmin skin test.

So, I think that in the fourteen years since that time, we have come a long way in the field of histoplasmosis, as you can see from the concluding session of this program.

It is a pleasure to welcome this group to Atlanta. We also, I think, should call attention to the fact that this conference is sponsored not only by the Center for Disease Control. It is also cosponsored by the University of Kentucky School of Medicine and the University of West Virginia School of Medicine, with very kind support by the Lederle Laboratories.

Dr. Ajello should have known better than to schedule me for fifteen minutes. He very kindly did not provide me with a program, so I was anticipating the usual five minutes. But, he also scheduled Dr. Furcolow after me with opening remarks and gave Leo only ten minutes. I have known Dr. Furcolow for a good many years and know that was also a mistake. Therefore, we can compensate for getting an early start and a short official welcoming by allowing Dr. Furcolow to extend his opening remarks. We do wish to make you welcome for the two and one-half days you are here. Feel free to call upon our staff, who are scattered around in the back of the room, for any extra things that you might want to do while you are here, or for any appointments that you might wish with our staff who may not be in the room. We look forward to a very profitable meeting.

Chapter 2

Opening Remarks

MICHAEL L. FURCOLOW

LITTLE did I think, after having been through the headaches of arranging and staging the 1952 histoplasmosis conference, that I would ever again be fool enough to be engaged in such a foolhardy enterprise or indeed that anyone else would be fool enough to push me into it after looking at the proceedings of that 1952 conference. I find that they were published in 1956, which is certainly no efficiency record. If you will look at the names of the Conference Committee, however, you will find out that they are great believers in the old adage that "An ounce of taffy is worth a pound of epitaphy"; and they have accordingly poured me the taffy to the point where I am standing up here welcoming you to the Second National Histoplasmosis Conference and assuring you, the same way I assured the conference in 1952, that we were going to have a speedy publication of all the articles and conference proceedings. I feel a little surer of myself this time in making this statement, since we already have almost all the papers in hand and assurance that any we do not have we will have by the end of the conference. We wish also to express our gratitude to Center for Disease Control for providing the facilities and, of course, for helping to finance the conference.

Histoplasmosis is a wonderous disease, and I am afraid those of us who have been bitten by the histoplasmosis bug (and I expect it includes most of you who are here) find themselves suffering from an incurable disease; namely, an insatiate curiosity about the doings of this particular fungus, and a strong feeling that if we could solve the problems connected with this fungus disease, we would be well on the way toward understanding many others which we have known for a longer period of time. We propose today to do our best to bring you completely up to date in the story of histoplasmosis. We have assembled all the experts that can be brought together at any one time. I feel it is indeed timely that the conference is held now because those among us who are pioneers in histoplasmosis remember the early days of the first isolations from any numbers of patients and the defining of the extent of the problem. We rejoice also at the presence of so many promising young men who are interested in forwarding our knowledge of histoplasmosis, not only by studying and improving the older tools, but also by applying newer knowledge and techniques. Their presence bides well for the future of our chosen study. We are delighted too to welcome Dr. Mackinnon and Dr. Conti-Diaz, who have come from Uruguay to present the South American

7

point of view, and we regret that other representatives from other countries were unable by reason of financial limitation to be invited to attend. I think it may well be a good sign that we have already far exceeded the number of pages of the proceedings of the first conference on histoplasmosis in the proceedings of this conference. I am certain that the resulting publication will be a landmark in the history of the disease. Welcome to the Second National Conference on Histoplasmosis.

Chapter 3

The Public Health Importance
of Histoplasmosis

HOWARD W. LARSH

THE keynote address topic for the Second National Conference on Histoplasmosis is an interesting and controversial one. There is divergence of opinion as to the importance of this disease and its place in the spectrum of infections in man and other animals. This has been apparent to me in recent years in discussions with individuals concerned with infectious diseases and epidemiology of fungus infections. There are individuals who express the idea that there has been nothing new since 1952. Is this true or have investigations during the past seventeen years extended our basic knowledge of the public health importance of histoplasmosis?

To be objective in my personal evaluation of the status of histoplasmosis in 1952, I reread the proceedings of the conference published up to that period. Particular attention was given to the summaries and recommendations of the chairman of each section of the conference. In my opinion, most, if not all, the recommendations were followed and definitive results obtained. The subjects to be discussed during the three days of this conference will substantiate that histoplasmosis is not a benign topic but has been a progressive and rewarding one since the 1952 conference.

In my discussion I should like to review some of the investigations that assisted in elevating histoplasmosis from a field of hypotheses to a well-established place in the scientific community. It should be fairly clear that the impact of the First National Conference on Histoplasmosis was significant. Research during the next decade on various aspects of the fungus and the disease was extensive. This is apparent if one lists the number of scientific and popularized publications during this period. It is not my intention to usurp the data to be presented by participants of this conference, so I suggest that these individuals relax and not become too concerned.

Salvin (1950), in his discussions on public health aspects of fungus infections, briefly covered the preliminary facets of histoplasmosis to that date. It is well known that histoplasmosis, from its discovery by Darling (1908) through the 1940's, was considered to be of little importance to man's everyday life. Although the disease had been reported from several areas of the world, most of the cases observed were in the United States. Relatively few cases were diagnosed—some seventy-one reported in the literature up to

1945. However, skin test results of Christie and Peterson (1945) and Palmer (1945) led to the discovery that histoplasmosis was widely present as a benign infection. Then Loosli (1955) estimated that as many as thirty million people in the United States had experienced some type of histoplasmosis infection. The infected individuals lived primarily in north central and south central areas of the United States. Explanations for the long delay in recognizing the high incidence of histoplasmosis was primarily that the infection mimics other diseases and that pulmonary lesions caused by *Histoplasma capsulatum* were for many years considered to be due to the tuberculosis bacillus. Dr. Procknow has a lantern slide, which I am sure most of you have seen, that illustrates the mimicking extremely well. These two conditions resolved, histoplasmosis was no longer considered to be a rare and unimportant public health problem. Unfortunately, histoplasmosis is not a required reportable disease; therefore, it is not possible to unequivocally document morbidity and mortality rates. However, Furcolow (1957) has stated, based upon extrapolation from available data on the conversion of skin test reactions, that approximately 500,000 new infections occur each year. It has been estimated also that at least eight-hundred deaths occur each year because of *Histoplasma* infections. In support of these data, investigations have proved that *H. capsulatum* was the etiological agent of many forms of pneumonia and other cases of active respiratory tract infections since 1952. The fungus has been found in clinically apparent as well as in inapparent respiratory infections. Prior to the availability and the expertise to interpret the histoplasmin skin test, serological reactions, and usefulness of selective culture techniques, these types of infections were reported as "unusual forms of pneumonia or unusual pulmonary disease."

The histoplasmin skin test antigen has been a major tool in delineating the significance of histoplasmosis. It is not without criticism because of the constituents in the antigenic filtrate. In the past there has not been a standard procedure for the production of this antigen. It is in this area that extensive research has begun. Information is available as to the length of time of incubation for the maximum antigenicity of histoplasmins produced by various isolates of the fungus. Further research on the fractionation, isolation, and chemical characterization of skin test active components of histoplasmin suggests that a highly specific antigen may be forthcoming for future skin test surveys. These and other studies may result in a definitive antigen which will eliminate cross reactions between the systemic fungi and permit quantitation of skin reactions through a test dose of histoplasmin.

There have been several epidemics of histoplasmosis dating back to 1938. Many of the earlier epidemics were diagnosed as being due to *H. capsulatum* in retrospect. Nevertheless, one of the important factors in establishing the importance of histoplasmosis as a public health problem came as a result of investigations of epidemics. The medical mycologists consider an epidemic to be a situation in which at least two individuals present the syndrome at a given site. So far we have not been confronted too seriously by other medical professions for our criterion of an epidemic. Since 1952 a rather large number of epidemics of histoplasmosis have occurred, and these have been the bases of interesting clinical, pathological, and epidemiological expressions of the disease. Epidemics have been investigated from several areas in which *H. capsulatum* is considered endemic as well as outside the endemic areas of the United States, Canada, and Panama. One of the most active groups investigating these episodes has been the mycology staff at the Center for Disease Control in Kansas City. This group has followed an interesting epidemic in Mason City, Iowa, and has instituted a control program for the eradication of the fungus from the environs.

Epidemics have permitted extensive study and documentation of various types of histoplasmosis ranging from benign pulmonary through disseminated histoplasmosis. It is true that information was available from patients in epidemics from 1938-1952; however, approximately one hundred cases were studied and many of these some years after the histoplasmosis infection occurred. Knowledge obtained from studies of earlier epidemics and improved laboratory techniques permitted more thorough investigations of epidemics after 1952. Many of the latter epidemics included acute pneumonias and other respiratory tract involvements ultimately diagnosed as histoplasmosis.

Parallel in importance to epidemics was the discovery of histoplasmosis among patients in tuberculosis sanatoria. In 1952 Furcolow and Brasher began an investigation at the Missouri State Sanatorium to determine if histoplasmosis occurred among patients in this institution. Their early findings revealed the possibility, and during a six-month period in 1954 it was established that chronic progressive (cavitary) histoplasmosis was a significant entity in the sanatorium's patients. (Furcolow and Brasher, 1956.) Nineteen cases were documented during this period. In a paper to be presented later in this conference by Dr. Reddy, it will be learned that over five hundred cases of histoplasmosis have been recorded in this sanatorium. The number of cases may not be large, but the important fact is that the patients were referred to the sanatorium as having tuberculosis, not because of their histoplasmosis infection. I am relatively sure if a serious attempt could have been made to obtain the cooperation of physicians referring patients to the Missouri State Sanatorium, the number of histoplasmosis cases may have reached 1500 to 2000 during this period.

The discovery of histoplasmosis in the Missouri State Sanatorium created a great deal of interest in the medical directors of other tuberculosis sanatoria. This enthusiasm and cooperation resulted in skin test and serological surveys among patients in sanatoria throughout the United States and in other areas of the world. Walls, Furcolow and Lehan (1958) reported that of 9,774 sera on which serological tests were performed, 6 percent proved positive. The yeast phase antigen was the most efficient in the complement fixation test. In a later extensive serological study on sera from sanatoria patients, Furcolow, Schubert, Tosh, Doto and Lynch (1962) showed that of 44,682 sera 7.5 percent were positive. Based upon those data it was estimated that 8,200 persons with positive serological reactions to *H. capsulatum* are admitted each year to tuberculosis sanatoria in the United States. At the Missouri State Sanatorium it has been our experience that at least 25 percent of the patients with a complement fixation titer of 1:8 or greater will yield *H. capsulatum* from properly collected specimens. This is particularly evident if six consecutive sputum specimens are processed over the first two weeks of hospitalization.

Several years ago, after it was established that histoplasmosis was a problem in tuberculosis sanatoria, a cooperative mycoses study was initiated between the sanatoria and the Center for Disease Control in Kansas City, Kansas. This group has functioned for many years and has been instrumental in increasing our knowledge of clinical, pathological, and epidemiological aspects of histoplasmosis and other systemic, mycotic infections.

Serological antigens, like skin test antigens, have come under severe criticism as a result of the extensive surveys since 1952. It is evident that over the years little has been accomplished in the standardization of antigens produced in various investigators' laboratories. Procedures for the production of these antigens have varied with the individual, a condition which has prevented meaningful evaluation of serological tests. Cross reactions have been frequent enough to disturb the critical investigator and to confuse most clinicians. It has been most difficult to interpret serological results to the practicing physician. Recently, for example, one of our patients had a negative complement fixation titer to histoplasmin: 1:64 to the yeast phase antigen and negative to blastomycin and the yeast phase blastomyces antigen. We isolated a pure culture of *Blastomyces dermatitidis* from his sputum specimens; however, the physician insisted that his disease was histoplasmosis because of the serological reaction.

In recent years attempts have been made to standardize the production of serological antigens and to adhere to quality control procedures. One of the functions of the antigen study group of the American Thoracic Society is to invite newly devised or modified methods for inclusion in the *Methodology Manual for Investigation of Mycobacterial and Fungal Antigens*. To date no information on histoplasmosis antigens or procedures has appeared in this manual. Salvin (1969) summarizes the efficiency of the complement fixation, precipitation, and fluorescent antibody tests for the detection of *H. capsulatum*. He also briefly discusses cross reactions, serologic tests and skin testing, and purification of antigens. In his opinion, the identity and characterization of the components that are associated with various immunological properties are still not determined.

Although the serological procedures used in the diagnoses of mycoses have changed only slightly, minor modifications have been made. Most of the tests have been adapted to microtechniques. These adaptations have proved successful and have been adopted by several researchers.

A new procedure which we have found efficient as a diagnostic serological tool is the immunocytoadherence test (Roberts, 1969). Preliminary investigations using animals experimentally infected with histoplasmosis and sporotrichosis have yielded promising results. The phenomenon of immunocytoadherence serves as the basis for a simple and quantitative method devised to detect cells producing antibodies among large populations of lymphoid cells. It is based on the fact that cells active in antibody production have surface antibodies which can be detected. This has a particular advantage when only very low antibody titers are produced in the disease process. In our investigations the test detected antibody produced by circulating lymphocytes.

The importance of standardized, serological antigens as tools in the evaluation of the public health importance of histoplasmosis remains a serious problem. Procedures are under investigation in our laboratory attempting to produce a specific yeast phase antigen using less harsh biochemical procedures. This should result in an antigen that has not been subjected to denaturation. In these procedures may lie the solution to specificity. This is the ultimate objective of our current research.

The natural reservoirs of the fungus play a major role in the public health importance of histoplasmosis. To the purist the disease has not been proved until the etiologic agent has been isolated from the disease process. The complete epidemiological significance is not understood until the organism is obtained from the environment. Therefore, the isolation of *H. capsulatum* is imperative if histoplasmosis is the designated syndrome. The rapid expansion of our knowledge of the epidemiology of histoplasmosis followed the isolation of the fungus from soil by Emmons (1949). His successful technique made available to other investigators procedures of obtaining the fungus from highly contaminated specimens from nature. It was soon learned that soil containing organic constituents, such as bird excrement, was an environment conducive to the maintenance of the fungus. The literature abounds with reports of successful isolations of *H. capsulatum* from soil samples containing excrement from many kinds of birds. This source of the fungus in nature has correlated very closely with human epidemics of the disease in areas throughout the world. From these data it has been suggested that *H. capsulatum* is a common soil organism that fortuitously is pathogenic to man and other animals. Perhaps it is not entirely correct to call the fungus a common soil organism; but it is interesting that when the source or sources of the inoculum in epidemics are ascertained, soil is usually the implicated contaminated material. There have been various modifications of the procedures used in the isolation of the fungus from contaminated soils; however, the basic principles of the technique are the same, and no entirely new procedure is known to me. The original technique of Emmons was based on the flotation of infectious units in the diluent physiological saline. Nevertheless, when this procedure is followed and the location of the viable particles quantitated, over 90 percent are found in the sediment. Sufficient numbers of the particles do float, as attested by the number of positive isolations that have been made utilizing this technique.

Smith and Furcolow's (1964) modification of Emmon's method has proved highly successful in the isolation of *H. capsulatum* and other systemic, mycotic agents from diversified specimens. In their modification they use sterile mineral oil as the diluent, and the viable particles released from soil are trapped in this menstruum.

Comparative studies now under investigation will determine the efficiency of various soil methods for the isolation of pathogenic fungi from nature. It is hopeful that the newer modifications will prove highly satisfactory, as the recovery of the fungus from nature remains a difficult area in the epidemiology of histoplasmosis.

Emmons (1958) reported the possible relationship of house-dwelling bats to histoplasmosis. He was successful in recovering *H. capsulatum* from the soil adjacent to a bat-infested house in Maryland. Later reports confirmed his findings, and bat guano was found harboring the fungus in Trinidad and Panama. In addition, there have been several authenticated histoplasmosis cases in individuals visiting or exploring caves. Later Shacklette, Dierck and Gale (1962) reported the recovery of *H. capsulatum* from bat tissue. The significance of the fungus in caves was elucidated by the report of Klite and Diercks (1965). These authors clearly showed that *H. capsulatum* was present in fecal contents and organs of bats in the Canal Zone. These findings opened another area of exploration as to the public health importance of histoplasmosis.

I wonder what my medical acquaintance would say now since he stated after an extensive study of the role birds played in histoplasmosis: "We have now followed histoplasmosis from Darling to starling." Perhaps he would say we finally have gone bats.

The mycological phases of *H. capsulatum* remain essentially the same since the appearance of two important publications on the subject: De Monbreun's paper (1934) on "The Cultivation and Culture Characteristics of Darling's *Histoplasma capsulatum*," and Conant's "A Culture Study of the Life Cycle of *Histoplasma capsulatum*, Darling, 1906 (1941)." Perhaps it is here that our critics could defend "nothing new since '52." However, even here microscopical and macroscopical variants have occurred and do occur.

These forms are highly significant in assessing the public health importance of histoplasmosis. During my career as a medical mycologist, I am relatively sure I have discarded variant forms of *H. capsulatum*. I am not at all sure I would not be guilty of the same practice today if it were not for the highly capable technicians, Mr. Rogers and Mrs. Johnson, with whom I have been associated.

Personally, I am delighted but not entirely satisfied with the progress we have made in understanding histoplasmosis. We have passed through an era in which scientists and administrators had to be shown the public health importance of this and other mycotic infections. Much of the early work was based on hypotheses and inadequate data as a result of our knowledge and limited procedures and techniques. In my opinion, we are on sound basic principles, and the progress during the next few years should be phenomenal.

It is distressing to me, however, to see what little support is given to medical mycology and what is happening to our centers of excellence for this field of specialization. Likewise, it is discouraging to witness the rapid loss of image of medical mycology in the United States since 1952. International scholars have in the past looked to recognized medical mycologists in our leading institutions for assistance and guidance in attacking mycological problems in their respective countries. Many mycologists throughout the world have received specialized training in the United States. This reputation was gained through dedication and perseverance of a few individuals. What is being done today to assure the continuation of well-trained personnel in medical mycology? In my opinion, the obstacles which destroy or fail to encourage capable individuals to enter the profession are rapidly becoming unsurmountable. For instance, in many medical schools the curriculum does not include lectures in medical mycology. In others the microbiology course may have three lectures which cover the entire field of mycology. There are some medical schools in which the microbiology staff considers a guest lecturer for an hour every other year sufficient to orient their students with medical mycology. This in itself is most unfortunate, but even worse, most medical technologists and public health microbiologists receive no training in medical mycology. It is not at all uncommon for a graduate, registered technician to remark he was not permitted to examine fungus cultures, as they might be pathogens. Where do physicians, technicians, and other laboratory personnel receive their training to understand the sign'ficance of fungus infections?

The academic training in medical mycology is grossly inadequate for the average student in the medical sciences to comprehend the basic principles of the subject. Therefore, it is not within the grasp of such individuals to comprehend the public health importance of mycotic organisms.

Support in other more sophisticated areas is not sufficient. Not too long ago Dr. Emmons retired from the National Institutes of Health after a highly successful and distinguished career. With his retirement medical mycology was relegated to a minor role in microbiology, although highly qualified medical mycologists were in residence. A further example of the interest for this field of specialization was evident when this conference was first proposed to be held in Washington. It is my understanding that the conference was not held in Washington because the interest in histoplasmosis was not sufficient to warrant the time or space.

The ecological investigations program at the Center for Disease Control in Kansas City has not been able to expand its activities in medical mycology. This situation may be due entirely to the government's austere program and not to the administrative officers; nevertheless, I cannot help but be of the opinion that the medical mycology program has been seriously handicapped at this installation.

The same situation occurs at the Center for Disease Control in Atlanta. The research and teaching opportunities are unlimited; however, progress cannot be made with the limitations they have in professional and support personnel. Surely the work load has been increased over the past fifteen years, but to the best of my knowledge no significant increase in professional personnel has occurred.

The difficulty is not limited to the federal government. Our medical and graduate colleges have not supported medical mycology to the extent that they should have over the years. Some institutions have been most fortunate in that their programs have received more than adequate administrative and financial support. Most of these have been in departments in which large numbers of clinical cases of mycotic infections are seen each year. This is as it should be, but other institutions, such as medical schools, must include adequate training in medical mycology to assure their graduates basic training in all fields of infectious diseases.

Teaching, research, and training programs in medical mycology will have to receive greater financial support during the next decade if we are to keep abreast with the developments in the profession. Leaders among our younger professionals must be developed to increase our image and maintain congenial relationships with international medical mycologists.

References

Christie, A. and Peterson, J.C. (1945). Pulmonary calcification in negative reactors to tuberculin. *Amer. J. Public Health*, 35:1131-1147.

Conant, N.F. (1941). A cultural study of the life cycle of *Histoplasma capsulatum*, Darling, 1906. *J. Bac.*, 41:563.

Darling, S.T. (1908). Histoplasmosis: fatal infectious disease resembling kala-azar found among natives of tropical America. *Arch. Intern. Med.*, 2:107-123.

De Monbreun, W.A. (1934). The cultivation and cultural characteristics of Darling's *Histoplasma capsulatum*. *Amer. J. Trop. Med., 14*:93.

Emmons, C.W. (1949). Isolation of *Histoplasma capsulatum* from soil. *Public Health Rep., 64*:892-896.

Emmons, C.W. (1958). Association of bats with histoplasmosis. *Public Health Rep.,* 73:590-595.

Furcolow, M.L. (1957). Personal communication.

Furcolow, M.L. and Brasher, C.A. (1956). Chronic progressive (cavitary) histoplasmosis as a problem in tuberculosis sanatoriums. *Amer. Rev. Tuberc. Pulmon. Dis.,* 73:609-619.

Furcolow, M.L., Schubert, J., Tosh, F.E., Doto, I.L. and Lynch, H.J. (1962). Serologic evidence of histoplasmosis in sanatoriums in the United States. *J.A.M.A., 180:* 109-114.

Klite, P.D. and Diercks, F.H. (1965). *Histoplasma capsulatum* in fecal contents and organs of bats in the Canal Zone. *Amer. J. Trop. Med., 14*(3):433-439.

Loosli, C.G. (1955). Symposium on clinical advances in medicine: histoplasmosis: some clinical, epidemiological, and laboratory aspects. *Med. Clin. N. Amer., 39*:171-199.

Palmer, C.E. (1945). Non-tuberculous pulmonary calcification and sensitivity to histoplasmin. *Public Health Rep., 60*:513-520.

Roberts, G.D. (1969). A Comparison of the Immunocytoadherence Test to Standard Serological Procedures in Animals Having Sporotrichosis. Master's thesis, University of Oklahoma, Norman, Oklahoma.

Salvin, S.B. (1950). Public health aspects of fungus infections. *New York Acad. Sci., 50*:1217-1228.

Salvin, S.B. (1969). Analytical serology of microfungi. *Anal. Serol. Microorgan., 1*:534-538.

Shacklette, M.H., Diercks, F.H. and Gale, N.B. (1962). *Histoplasma capsulatum* recovered from bat tissue. *Science, 135*:1135.

Smith, C.D. and Furcolow, M.L. (1964). Efficiency of three techniques for isolating *Histoplasma capsulatum* from soil, including a new flotation method. *J. Lab. Clin. Med., 64*(2):342-348.

Walls, K., Furcolow, M.L. and Lehan, P.H. (1958). Histoplasmosis as a problem in tuberculosis sanatoriums throughout the United States. *J. Lab. Clin. Med., 51*(2): 266-270.

Part II

The Organism—*Histoplasma capsulatum*

Chapter 4

Biological Implications of Morphological Variants in *Histoplasma capsulatum* Primary Isolates

MARTHA D. BERLINER

ABSTRACT

Mycelial and yeast form cultures of primary isolates of *Histoplasma capsulatum* and their subcultures of various morphological types can best be maintained for 12 to 18 months at 4°C in sealed tubes or plates. Room temperature storage does not allow for the survival of B type, whereas storage at -10°C severely curtails survival of all types. Maintenance of the mycelial morphological characteristics can be more reliably obtained by transformation to the yeast form and continuous subculture as yeasts. Nevertheless, in both growth forms there is some uni-directional overtake of B types by A types. Several patterns of nonmendelian inheritance are discussed as possible explanations, with extrachromosomal or cytoplasmic inheritance being the likeliest.

HISTOPLASMOSIS is caused by the fungus *Histoplasma capsulatum.* This simple fact of a mycotic etiological agent is the pivot around which all research on histoplasmosis must turn. *H. capsulatum* must still be regarded as an imperfect fungus (Kwon-Chung, 1968) with the same physiological, cytological, genetical, and chemical characteristics as many other imperfect fungi that are saprophytic in nature but parasitic in man and other mammalians. It is in the study of the organism's biology that we will be able to make progress applicable to epidemiology, serology, and therapy. With this goal in mind, a start at least has been made in our laboratory on characterizing the morphology, physiology, and genetic integrity of primary isolates of *H. capsulatum,* although we yet have a long way to go.

As reported previously (Berliner, 1968) most, if not all, subcultures of *H. capsulatum* can be separated into two main morphological mycelial colonial types which can be correlated with their mycelial micromorphology: the A or albino type with white aerial mycelium and smooth macroconidia, and the B or brown type consisting of masses of tuberculate macroconidia with sparse, thin, contorted hyphae. There is no correlation between the two types and their microconidial production or their yeast form morphology, but there is correlation between B types and increased virulence (Daniels,

NOTE. This research has been supported in part by NIH Grants No. 5 RO1, A 1 07520-03, A 1 00177.

et al., 1968) for rabbits. The growth curves of A and B type yeasts (Reca and Campbell, 1967) are virtually identical, as is their tetrazolium reduction pattern (Reca, 1968). As has been pointed out, separation into A and B types can be accomplished only by pinpoint inoculations of mixed cultures onto solid medium in petri dishes and by vigilant continuous observation. Also, in A and B mycelial types thus stabilized from the same strain, the morphological spore types and their relative abundance have remained constant. Since these preliminary results were reported two years ago, these findings have been extended and corroborated with thirty additional primary isolates from a variety of sources. The following significant findings can now be added to our prior observations.

Isolation of Mycelial Strains of the B Type

This can be accomplished only if petri plates are left unsealed and there is free air passage. When replicate plates are sealed with Parafilm, B types are rarely if ever recovered. Once B type colonies are separated and stabilized by repeated subculture of their hyphal tips, however, their macro- and micro-morphology are not appreciably altered thereafter by sealing the plates with Parafilm, or by maintenance in closed screw-capped tubes.

Maintenance of the A and B Types as Mycelial Cultures

The thirty-six primary isolates initially described (Berliner, 1968) were each subcultured immediately upon receipt onto six modified Sabouraud agar slants (Difco) in screw-capped tubes.

The original isolates were sealed and kept at 4°C. Following an approximately two-week incubation period at room temperature (24°–28°C), two of the tubes were stored at this temperature and two additional tubes each at 4°C and —10°C. As soon as A and B types were separated from each of these thirty-six primary isolates, these also were stored in replicate at the three temperatures. In addition, the B type of each strain was inoculated onto the same medium in small box-type petri dishes, sealed, and maintained at 4°C after initial growth. After fifteen to eighteen months storage at the three temperatures, the tubes were opened and the growth subcultured on modified Sabouraud agar in petri plates. The results are summarized as follows:

1. *At room temperature,* the B type did not survive this length of time in storage. The A type and the original parental P type both survived, but the B type could no longer be reisolated from the P type of any of the thirty-six strains.

2. *At —10°C,* only 30 percent of the cultures survived. These were evenly distributed among the A,B, and P types.

3. *At 4 C*, all types survived for up to eighteen months. In addition, except in one instance, the three types (A,B,P) could be reisolated from either the original specimen or its first subculture kept sealed at 4°C. When placed in storage, the isolated B type colonies were uniformly pigmented and showed no macroscopic evidence of A type mycelium. However, after eighteen months' storage all B colonies contained patches or sectors of A mycelium. Some fungal growth including nuclear migration via septal pores is known to take place at this temperature (Girbardt, 1968). Slow accumulation of A genotypes at one locus would thus give rise to A type sectors which might in time completely overgrow the B colony, even at 4°C.

Maintenance of the A and B Types as Yeast Phase Cultures

Animal Passage

When yeasts recently converted from the P,A and B filamentous types were injected intravenously into rabbits, A filamentous type colonies only and B filamentous type colonies only were recovered from animals injected with these yeasts, whereas animals receiving P yeasts yielded both A and B filamentous type colonies. Thus it became evident when working with rabbits (Daniels *et al.*, 1968) that you can only recover the yeast phase type or types with which that particular animal has been infected (Fig. 4-1, 2, 3). The genetic integrity of the A and B mycelial types is maintained through animal passage as A and B yeasts. The parental P phenotype thus appears to be the result of the multinucleate mycelial condition and does not exist in the uninucleate yeast phase as P but only as A or B uninucleate yeasts.

In the summary of the first conference on histoplasmosis by Habel (1956), the following passage is of particular interest in the light of our more recent findings: "The occasional positive results of attempted isolations from the air in *Histoplasma* laboratories brought up the possibility of air contamination of cultures or experimental animals. All the laboratories' experience was against this as a source of erroneous experimental results." Our recent studies with A and B yeasts of primary isolates (Daniels *et al.*, 1968) revealed that the nasal discharges of infected rabbits were teeming with *H. capsulatum* and that the air in the animal room was continuously being seeded with its viable particles. This undoubtedly is a means of cross infecting or sensitizing animals housed in the same room and perhaps is a heretofore unrecognized hazard to laboratory personnel as well.

Yeast Form Cultures on Brain Heart Infusion Agar + 1% Cysteine

Thirty yeast form cultures of six A and B type primary isolates and eighteen undifferentiated yeasts of old stock strains were incubated for 72 hours at 37°C on BHI + 1% cysteine agar in tubes with paraffined plugs and refrigerated for 15 months at 4°C. They were then subcultured and incubated on

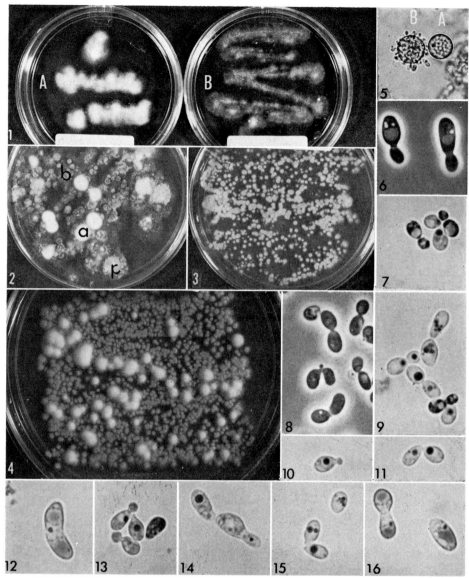

FIGURE 4-1. *1*. G-184A and G-184B on 15% gelatin. 10 d. visible color differences between A and B growth. No liquefaction. ×½. *2*. G-185 P. Mycosel streak plate from nose swab of rabbit infected with yeast phase mixed parental culture. A,B, and P type colonies recovered. 14 d. ×.6. *3*. G-184B. Mycosel streak plate from nose swab of rabbit infected with yeast phase suspension derived from a single B type yeast cell. Pure B colonies recovered. ×.6. *4*. G-184B, modified Sabouraud streak plate from fifteenth weekly subculture on BHI+ cysteine agar of single B type yeast clone. Some A type yeasts have reappeared. ×1. *5*. G-H-1, typical A and B type macroconidia from mixed culture as first isolated from soil. ×750. *6-16*. Typical morphological variations seen in yeast form *H. capsulatum* of both A and B types grown in trypticase soy broth. *6* and *8*, phase contrast. All others vital stained with Janus Green B, which accumulates in the vacuole of living cells. Dead cells in *7, 9* and *13* are completely stained. ×1200.

the same medium at 37°C, as well as streaked thinly onto modified Sabou-raud agar plates for conversion to the mycelial phase at 25°C. All survived storage. The primary isolates grew out as typical A and B filamentous types, as originally isolated. All but two of the old unmonitored stocks grew out as pure A types. Of special interest was the reisolation of a few B type colonies from yeast stocks which had been subcultured at biweekly intervals for thirteen years (G-37) and ten years (G-67), respectively, and which have always yielded only A type colonies when masses of yeast cells were converted to the mycelial phase without appropriate "isolative" streaking. It is now apparent that when isolated yeasts are allowed to convert to the mycelial phase individually, those few of the B genotype still remaining maintain their genetic integrity even when subcultured at least five hundred times in a mass of 90 to 95 percent A yeasts. Interestingly, no B types could be recovered from the mycelial stocks of G-37 and G-67 which had been subcultured for fewer times.

Maintenance of Several Ratios of A to B Yeasts in Weekly Subculture

The stability of various ratios of A to B type yeasts on continuous sub-culture in an optimal *in vitro* environment were studied. Mycelial colonies of strain G-184A, G-184B and G-184P, freshly reisolated from the original plate after one year of storage at 4°C, were converted to the yeast phase at 37°C on brain heart infusion agar (BHI) + 1% cysteine in a 5% CO_2 atmo-sphere. Complete conversion required ten to fourteen days. At this time the yeast phase growth of each type was washed from the BHI slants in trypti-case soy broth (TSB) and grown in TSB on a shaker at 37°C for 48 hours. The growth in TSB was collected aseptically after 48 hours and the optical density adjusted to 50% in a Coleman Jr. spectrophotometer at 560 mμ. Type A and type B yeast suspensions were mixed in the following ratios: pure A, pure B, 1A:1B, 1A:3B, 1A:5B, 1A:9B, 3A:1B, 5A:1B, 9A:1B. Of the above mixtures 0.2 ml of each was streaked over the surface of two slants each of BHI with paraffined cotton plugs. These were incubated at 37°C for one week. The various mixtures were then subcultured on BHI at 37°C at weekly intervals for fifteen weeks and labeled P-1, P-2, P-3, and so on, for each generation. Additionally, prior to each weekly subculture, one loopful from each tube was streaked onto a thin agar plate of modified Sabouraud agar (MSA) and incubated at 25°C for 48 hours to allow yeasts to convert to the mycelial phase, since it is only in this phase that the morphological differ-ences can be ascertained. Two days later, the well-separated single pinpoint mycelial colonies were observed under a stereo microscope at ×70 magni-fication, and assumed to have arisen from single yeast cells, were transferred to plates of MSA for continued growth at 25°C. Thirty-five isolations per plate were made to insure better than a 95 percent degree of confidence in the 1:9 and 9:1 ratios. One and two weeks later the distribution of A and B mycelial types was recorded. The latter numbers were used to plot results in Table 4-I.

Preliminary results are summarized in Table 4-I, with the following additional points. The pure A type yeasts never yielded any other type. No type P colonies ever arose from the presumed single cell isolates. After the second subculture, the "pure" B type always grew a few A type colonies. These appeared late, after at least ten days, and overgrew the B types only slightly (Fig. 4-1, 4).

Conclusions and Discussion

It is apparent that long-term storage of mycelial cultures of *H. capsulatum* is best achieved at 4°C. As long as there is a vigorous growth of B type at the time of storage, it can be reisolated a year or more later. If, on the other hand, the culture at the time of storage has already had its B type sectors overgrown by A type, the former can rarely, if ever, be recovered.

The maintenance of mycelial morphological integrity via the yeast form is of more practical and theoretical importance. The B genotype can be kept more intact by continuous subculture in the yeast phase than in the myce-

TABLE 4-I

Maintenance of A and B Yeasts in Various Ratios for Fifteen Weekly Subcultures

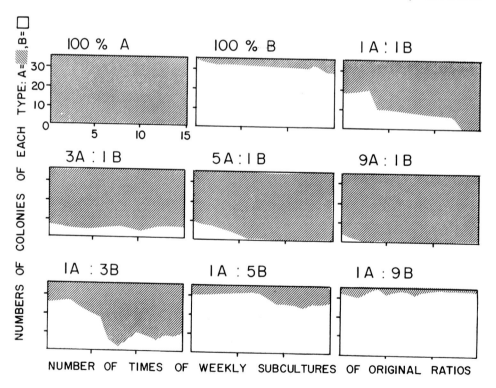

lial, even though some loss does occur. In clonal yeast cell growth the problem of overgrowth by A type is not as irrevocable as in mycelial colonies, since the single yeast cells of the B type can be reisolated. Since no P types were ever found on reconversion of single yeast cells to the mycelial phase, this is a strong indication that the P type is a laboratory artifact and possibly the result of a multinucleate heterokaryotic genome in a plasmone (Esser and Kuenen, 1968) which is continuous via the septal pores.

If we assume that the yeast phase is uninucleate (Edwards *et al.*, 1959) and haploid, then it follows that the A type and B type characteristics are genetically inherited via the chromosomes. Furthermore, it becomes evident that part of the phenomenon of dimorphism is related to the ploidy of the cells or the number of associated genomes. According to Romano (1966), most of the dimorphic pathogenic and saprophytic fungi have multinucleate mycelial phases and uninucleate yeast phases. Whether uninucleate yeasts are haploid or diploid cannot be determined by size or nucleic acid contents (Phaff *et al.*, 1966), but only by direct or indirect genetic evidence. Figures 4-1, *6-16* show the vast range of primary isolate yeast morphologies and division patterns.

Nevertheless, a simple mendelian pattern of inheritance does not explain the eventual take-over by A yeasts, even when they are a small number of the original ratios; nor does it explain the maintenance of A yeasts in 1A:9B ratios. And it does not explain the appearance of A types in supposedly stable B type colonies, with the fairly rapid overgrowth of the latter.

There are several other known genetic pathways in fungi (Esser and Kuenen, 1968) which, combined with mendelian chromosomal inheritance, may explain the present and previous observations (Berliner, 1968). Not yet having a known sexual method of reproduction in *H. capsulatum*, (Kwon-Chung, 1968) makes checking out the following possibilities very difficult, but they should nevertheless be considered. The first is heterokaryosis (Davis, 1966) which eliminates the need for sexual reproduction in adaptation and which can apply only to the mycelial phase. Heterokaryosis and cytoplasmic continuity via the septal pore exists in *H. capsulatum* (Berliner, 1968). Therefore, the mycelial P type may be an unstable genetic mosaic where the rate of division of A type nuclei is greater than that of B types (Davis, 1966). In heterokaryons many nuclei determine the phenotype at any given point in the cytoplasm, even though they may not be localized there. Thus, mutations are usually undetectable in the mycelium. It is unlikely that either A or B types are spontaneous mutations of the mendelian type, since they occur so frequently in virtually all cultures. We do not know what proportions of A and B type nuclei determine each phenotype, and only when a large number of genetic markers are available could this hypothesis be tested.

Since heterokaryosis could not apply to the yeast phase, and since the change is always unidirectional, i.e. B to A, extrachromosomal or cyto-plasmic inheritance (Jinks, 1966) is a more reasonable assumption, since it usually involves a loss of cytoplasmic determinants. Extrachromosomal in-heritance, even if common in fungi, does not occur with a frequency of more than 1 percent in documented cases (Jinks, 1966). We may have a com-pletely new pattern with *H. capsulatum* or the *in vitro* conditions are strongly inductive. The latter is the likelier in a pathogenic organism.

In the morphogenesis from the mycelial to the yeast phase of what pheno-typically appear to be pure type B colonies, extranuclear material is incorpo-rated which may exert considerably more effect on the single haploid nu-cleus in the yeast than on the numerous nuclei in the hyphae. In other words, the cytoplasmic effect is diluted in the mycelial phase. Formation of A types as pinpoints on P type, or more importantly, on B type colonies appears to be a hyphal tip phenomenon which is not carried back to the older myce-lium via the septal pores or by anastomoses. Rather, it confers a suppressive ability which allows the A type to overgrow the B type as found in certain strains of *Neurospora* (Grindle and Pittenger, 1968).

If we do indeed have extrachromosomal inheritance, it appears unusually stable. This has been found only in the *petite* mutant of *Saccharomyces cer-evisiae* where the cytoplasmic genetic determinants have been localized in the mitrochondrial complex (Jinks, 1966) and in certain phenotypic strains of *Neurospora* (Tatum and Luck, 1967) where there is a cytoplasmically inherited cytochrome pattern which is closely related to cell wall synthesis.

Other nonmendelian mechanisms must also be considered in the overtake of B yeasts by A yeasts and for the pattern of mycelial overgrowth. These may be through the mediation of a virus as in bacterial transduction or in-fective DNA as in bacterial transformation. The former has been reported in mycelial fungi (Banks *et al.*, 1968), whereas the latter has been reported once in the *petite* mutant of *S. cerevisiae*. (Tuppy and Wildner, 1965).

★   ★   ★

I wish to thank Dr. Jane Worcester of the Department of Biostatistics for her help in the design of experiments, Dr. Abraham Flexer of the Depart-ment of Biology at Harvard for discussions on cytoplasmic inheritance, and Dr. Morris Grindle of Stanford University for a copy of his unpublished pa-per on cytoplasmic inheritance given at the American Society for Microbiol-ogy Meeting at Detroit, Michigan on May 7, 1968. Drs. Angela Restrepo and Libero Ajello supplied us with recent primary isolates of *H. capsulatum*.

References

Banks, G.T., *et al.* (1968). Viruses of fungi and interferon stimulation. *Nature, 218:* 542-545.

Berliner, M.D. (1968). Primary subcultures of *Histoplasma capsulatum*, I. Macro- and micro-morphology of the mycelial phase. *Sabouraudia*, 6:111-118.

Cozad, G.C. and Furcolow, M.L. (1956). Size of Spores. Proceedings of Conference on Histoplasmosis. Excelsior Springs, Missouri, Nov. 18-20, 1952. *Public Health Monogr.* #39, PHS Publications.

Daniels, L.S., Berliner, M.D. and Campbell, C.C. (1968). Varying virulence in rabbits infected with different filamentous types of *Histoplasma capsulatum*. *J. Bact.*, 96: 1535-1539.

Davis, R.H. (1966). Heterokaryosis. In Ainsworth, G.C. and Sussman, A.S. (Eds.). *The Fungi*. New York Academic Press, vol. 2.

Edwards, M.R., Hazen, E.L. and Edwards, G.A. (1959). The fine structure of yeast-like cells of *Histoplasma* in culture. *J. Gen. Microbiol.*, 20:496-503.

Esser, K. and Kuenen, R. (1968). *Genetics of Fungi*. New York, Heidelberg, Springer-Verlag.

Girbardt, M. (1968). Ultrastructure and dynamics of the moving nucleus. In Aspects of Cell Mobility. *Sympos. Soc. Exp. Biol.*, 12. New York, Academic Press.

Grindle, M. and Pittenger, T.H. (1968). Phenotypic and genetic changes during prolonged growth of *Neurospora* heterokaryons. *Genetics*, 58:337-349.

Habel, K. (1956). Summary. In Proceedings of the Conference on Histoplasmosis 1952. Pub Health Mono. No. 39. Washington D.C.

Jinks, J.L. (1966). Extranuclear Inheritance. In Ainsworth, G.C. and Sussman, A.S. (Eds.). *The Fungi*. New York, Academic Press, vol. 2.

Kwon-Chung, Kyung Joo. (1968). *Gymnoascus demonbreunii* Ajello and Cheng: Evidence that it is not the perfect state of *Histoplasma capsulatum* Darling. *Sabouraudia*, 6:168-175.

Phaff, H.J., Miller, M.W. and Mrak, E.M. (1966). *The Life of Yeasts*. Cambridge, Harvard University Press.

Reca, M.E. (1968). Reduction of a tetrazolium salt in determining growth activity of yeast phase of *Histoplasma capsulatum*. *Appl. Microbiol.*, 16:236-238.

Reca, M.E. and Campbell, C.C. (1967). Growth curves with yeast phase *Histoplasma capsulatum*. *Sabouraudia*, 5:267-273.

Romano, A.H. (1966). Dimorphism. In Ainsworth, G.C. and Sussman, A.S. (Eds.). *The Fungi*. New York, Academic Press, vol. 2.

Tatum, E.L. and Luck, D.J.L. (1967). Nuclear and cytoplasmic control of morphology in *Neurospora*. *Develop. Biol.* (Suppl.), 1:32-42.

Tuppy, H. and Wildner, C. (1965). Cytoplasmic transformation: Mitochondria of wild-type Baker's yeast restoring respiratory capacity in the respiratory defficient "petite" mutant. *Biochem. Biophys. Res. Commun.*, 20:733-738.

Chapter 5

Variation in *Histoplasma capsulatum*

JOHN W. BRANDSBERG

ABSTRACT

Variations among isolates of *Histoplasma capsulatum* have been noted by various investigators. Previously, most of the studies have dealt with gross morphological features. More recently, there has been a tendency for investigators to also consider physiological, pathological, immunological, and genetic differences in these variants. This kind of an approach should be more likely to yield information which will be useful in the determination of "atypical" isolates of *H. capsulatum*.

MOST fungi which have received considerable attention have been found to exhibit a wide range of morphological and physiological variation. *Histoplasma capsulatum* is no exception, and there is a sizeable accumulation of data and comments concerning its physiological and morphological variability as well as differences in the pathogenicity and immunological aspects of different isolates of this fungus.

This discussion will be restricted to a brief consideration of the morphological and pathological variabilities among strains of *H. capsulatum*.

Over the years numerous authors have commented on the morphological aspects of *H. capsulatum*. One of these is DeMonbreun (1934), who demonstrated that the etiologic agent of Darling's disease was a fungus. Howell (1939) did a comparative study of *H. capsulatum* and some morphologically similar genera. Umanzio (1951) studied the various spore forms of *H. capsulatum* and later (1963) described the formation of coremia on certain substrata. O'Hern (1964) found that a white mycelial form which produced both macro- and microspores but would not convert to the yeast phase *in vitro* yielded, on passage through a hamster, a stable variant which would convert *in vitro*. It differed in colony morphology and growth rate and was less virulent than the parental form.

Nielsen (1967) found no correlation between the ease with which a strain converted and the infectivity of the six strains that he studied. He also found no correlation between the tendency of a strain to sporulate and its tendency to convert from the mycelial to the yeast phase.

Anderson and Marcus (1969) found that strains of *H. capsulatum* vary significantly with respect to mouse pathogenicity as determined through different LD_{50} ratios obtained for four of five strains studied. They also noted that the pathogenicity of one of the strains had remained remarkably stable over a thirteen-year period.

Berliner (1968) reported finding four morphologically different groups within thirty-six recent isolates of *H. capsulatum*. Foremost among these were the A (albino) and B (brown) forms which she found to be genetically stable. Daniels, Berliner and Campbell (1968) reported that rabbits inoculated with the yeast phase of types A or B mycelium yielded only the homologous types, while those inoculated with an intermediate (P) type yielded both A and B types which were stable. Berliner (1968) postulates that since the cells of *H. capsulatum* contain from one to four nuclei, some isolates are heterokaryotic. This hypothesis is supported by the fact that stable forms produce only homologous type colonies, while the intermediate types yield more than one type of colony. O'Hern's findings might also be construed as lending support to this idea.

In our laboratory, we have occasionally found a form which produces only restricted, cerebriform colonies which remain sterile on all of the media tried. It sporulates only after repeated serial transfer to fresh media and does not ordinarily convert to a yeast phase *in vitro*. Usually all isolates obtained from a patient infected with such a strain are of one type, and identification becomes a tedious and time consuming process. Animal inoculation is a useful tool in determining these types.

Another problem that we occasionally encounter is the isolation of "atypicals" in mixed infections with *H. capsulatum* and *Blastomyces dermatitidis*, as previously reported (Brandsberg, Tosh and Furcolow, 1964). In the five cases that we reported, we found the typical B type colony of Berliner and a form analogous to her A form. The albino form in this case was invariably sterile and would not convert to a yeast phase *in vitro*. Usually after repeated animal passages, colonies of typical *B. dermatitidis* were isolated and identified. At that time, I was led to make the improbable suggestion that *H. capsulatum* and *B. dermatitidis* might form a heterokaryotic "hybrid." This premise is extremely difficult to prove for various reasons, not the least of which is the difficulty in making cytological studies of either of these fungi.

The study of what are apparently heterokaryotic forms of *H. capsulatum* would be much simpler if they could be differentiated by means other than animal passage. Yeast phase cells would be ideal tools, since they have been reported by Emmons (1959) to be monokaryotic, while the mycelial phase contains several nuclei per cell (Berliner, 1968). Unfortunately, it has not been possible to grow single yeast cells (Scherr, 1957). It seems possible that the A and B forms isolated by Berliner (1968) from the parental strain may have resulted from clones that developed intracellularly from individual yeast cells.

It is quite obvious that we are dealing with a group of individuals which display all the characteristics of individuals; namely, nearly all isolates have a different genotype with a concomitant array of morphological and physiological differences. This is additionally complicated by the possibility of the interplay of any or all of the factors affecting inheritance in the Deuteromycetes, such as mutation, cytoplasmic inheritance, parasexuality, heterokaryosis, and other factors as summarized by Davis (1966), Roper (1966) and Jinks (1966).

Study of these factors is difficult because this fungus is somewhat less than ideally suited for morphological studies: (1) it is a pathogen and requires the use of caution and special equipment if laboratory infections are to be avoided, (2) it is a relatively slow-growing organism, (3) it is dimorphic, the nutritional and environmental requirements varying considerably for the two phases, (4) it does not appear to exhibit convenient genetic markers for the detection of asexual genetic phenomena, and (5) the mycelium and at least the macrospores contain varying numbers of very small nuclei per cell, complicating the isolation of homokaryotic explants for study.

While it seems unlikely that in the near future we will solve the problems associated with "atypical" forms of *H. capsulatum*, the basic studies concerning the origins and nature of these forms should yield information which will be helpful in their identification.

References

Anderson, K.L. and Marcus, S. (1969). Variability in virulence of strains of *Histoplasma capsulatum*. *Amer. Rev. Resp. Dis.*, 99:608-609.

Berliner, Martha D. (1968). Primary subcultures of *Histoplasma capsulatum*. I. Macro- and micro-morphology of the mycelial phase. *Sabouraudia*, 6:111-118.

Brandsberg, J.W., Tosh, F.E. and Furcolow, M.L. (1964). Concurrent infection with *Histoplasma capsulatum* and *Blastomyces dermatitidis*. *New Eng. J. Med.*, 270:874-877.

Daniels, L.S., Berliner, M.D. and Campbell, C.C. (1968). Varying virulence in rabbits infected with different filamentous types of *Histoplasma capsulatum*. *J. Bact.*, 96:1535-1539.

Davis, R.H. (1966). Mechanisms of inheritance. 2. Heterokaryosis. In Ainsworth, G.C. and Sussman, A.S. (Eds.). *The Fungi*. New York, Academic Press, vol. 2, pp. 567-588.

DeMonbreun, W.A. (1934). The cultivation and cultural characteristics of Darling's *Histoplasma capsulatum*. *Amer. J. Trop. Med.*, 14:93-125.

Emmons, C.W. (1959). Fungus nuclei in the diagnosis of mycoses. *Mycologia*, 51:227-236.

Howell, A., Jr. (1939). Studies on *Histoplasma capsulatum* and similar form species. I. Morphology and development. *Mycologia*, 31:191-216.

Jinks, J.L. (1966). Mechanisms of inheritance. 4. Extranuclear inheritance. In Ainsworth, G.C. and Sussman, A.S. (Eds.). *The Fungi*. New York, Academic Press, vol. 2, pp. 619-660.

Nielsen, H.S., Jr. (1967). The dimorphism and infectivity of *Histoplasma capsulatum*. *Mycopathologia*, 31:1-11.

O'Hern, E.M. (1964). Studies on histoplasmosis. I. Comparative virulence of variant and parent strain *Histoplasma capsulatum* in hamsters. *Myopathologia*, 22:167-174.

Roper, J.A. (1966). Mechanisms of inheritance. 3. The parasexual cycle. In Ainsworth,

G.C. and Sussman, A.S. (Eds.). *The Fungi.* New York, Academic Press, vol. 2, pp. 589-617.

Scherr, G.H. (1957). Studies on the dimorphism of *Histoplasma capsulatum.* I. The role of -SH groups and incubation temperature. *Exp. Cell. Res., 12:*92-107.

Umanzio, C.B. (1951). Systemic mycotic infections. V. Further observations on *Histoplasma capsulatum* with brief notes on Darling's histoplasmosis. *J. Osteopath., 58:* 16-23.

Umanzio, C.B. (1963). Histoplasmosis. Part II. Laboratory diagnosis: colonial morphology and coremial formation of *Histoplasma capsulatum. J. Osteopath., 70:*48-62.

Chapter 6

Variation Among Isolates of
Histoplasma capsulatum

HOWARD W. LARSH

ABSTRACT

Macroscopical and microscopical observations of *Histoplasma capsulatum* isolates for many years have revealed variations of different types. These variations have been shown to be fairly common when the isolates were from patients with chronic pulmonary histoplasmosis. On subculturing, the integrity of the variants remained constant over the period studied. These and other studies emphasize the need for awareness of atypical or aberrant forms of the fungus in diagnostic mycology laboratories. Microscopical preparations do not, in many instances, assist in specific identification of the pathogen. The so-called diagnostic or characteristic tuberculated chlamydospore (macroconidium) was not observed in many of the cultures in this study. Conversion from the mycelial to the yeast phase of each isolate in addition to histopathological evidence should be considered for unequivocal documentation of *H. capsulatum*.

FUNGI pathogenic to man and other animals frequently exhibit changes in shape, form, color, or in other characteristics. English (1964), in her nine-year study of variations which occurred in *Trichophyton rubrum* in a routine mycological service, concluded that intermediate isolates will continue to present a real problem to the diagnostic laboratory. Weitzman's genetic study (1964) of pleomorphism in *Microsporum gypseum* further exemplifies the difficulty of determining speciation because of variations among isolates. The literature on superficial fungi adequately reveals the significance of macroscopical and microscopical variations among this group of organisms.

In addition to fungi causing superficial infections, those organisms associated with systemic infections have interesting variants. Spaur (1956) reported pigmentation and failure to produce arthrospores by isolates of *Coccidioides immitis*. Plunkett, Walker and Huppert (1963) corroborated that pigmented isolates of *C. immitis* occur and that identification of this fungus on occasions cannot be done with morphological characters alone. They further showed that it could not be ruled out if spherules were not produced upon initial animal inoculation. Berliner (1968) has studied the colonial and micromorphology of primary subcultures of *Histoplasma capsulatum*. She was able to separate most of the isolates into two main types, based on their colony appearance. Daniels, Berliner and Campbell (1968), using the two types of colonies described by Berliner, showed them to possess varying virulence for female albino rabbits.

Reports can be found illustrating variations among nearly all of the fungi causing systemic infections. These investigations of atypical or aberrant forms emphasize the need for awareness of the occurrence of such variations.

This paper is presented to report experiences over more than a decade in the study of *H. capsulatum* isolated from patients with chronic cavitary histoplasmosis.

Materials and Methods

The isolates of *H. capsulatum* were obtained from clinical specimens submitted to the mycology laboratory for fungus studies. A few of the early isolates were from patients in the Arkansas State Sanatorium; however, most of the investigations were from specimens collected at the Missouri State Sanatorium. Various clinical specimens were cultured; nevertheless, this discussion is limited to isolates obtained from sputum.

Prior to collecting the sputum sample, the patients were encouraged to brush their teeth thoroughly and to use a mouthwash. The sputum was collected in a sterile screw cap jar. Only the early morning specimen was collected and this usually consisted of the first sputum raised. The patient was cautioned to obtain sputum from the lung and trachea and not secretions from the mouth and pharynx. A quantity of 2 to 10 ml was obtained. The amount, consistency, and other characteristics of the specimens were recorded. The specimens were placed on a shaker for thirty minutes or longer before inoculating media. Very thick or mucoid specimens were diluted with sterile, cysteine saline. Sabouraud's dextrose agar without antibiotics, Sabouraud's dextrose agar with 20 units of penicillin and 40 units of streptomycin per milliliter of medium, and blood agar plates were inoculated with 0.5 to 1.0 ml of each specimen. Petri plates were used exclusively; incubation was at room temperature (22° to 25°C) for a period of at least four weeks.

Results

In July, 1957, an organism was isolated from sputa specimens from a patient with a syndrome of histoplasmosis. However, macroscopical and microscopical observations of the culture failed to substantiate the organism as *H. capsulatum*. The colony was not typical, and no characteristic, diagnostic macroconidium was observed. All other laboratory tests and the clinical manifestations were consistent with those described for histoplasmosis. Conversion of the mycelial phase to the yeast phase and histopathological observation of laboratory tissue verified the isolate as *H. capsulatum*. Later, in June, 1958, ten additional isolates were obtained having similar histories, and these were designated as atypical. Since that date a large number of isolates have been obtained from patients with chronic cavitary disease. These, too, have had characteristic growth and color and warrant the designation: atypical or aberrant forms.

Colony and Microscopic Descriptions of Observed Forms of *H. capsulatum*

Typical morphology of *H. capsulatum* on Sabouraud's dextrose agar at room temperature (22° to 25°C) is a slow-growing organism which produces a white, cottony, aerial mycelium. Usually within twenty-one days the mycelium will turn buff to brown in color. Microscopically small, round to pyriform, smooth microconidia may occur as sessile or on short conidiophores on branching septate hyphae. Most descriptions will include that eventually the characteristic round to pyriform, tuberculated macroconidia are produced and the mycological diagnosis is established.

The following colony types have been observed and can be considered atypical since in each instance *H. capsulatum* was proved by conversion and animal studies.

1. Pleomorphic colony type is a frequent one. The mycelium is white, heaped, and cottony within fourteen days. Later the center of the colony turns light buff and is usually crateriform. Very few conidia are present in twenty-one days. Rarely are tuberculated macroconidia found.

2. Glabrous, leathery to waxy colonies of various types are fairly common.
   a. A heaped, cerebriform colony appears within fourteen days. It is deep brown in color and has pleomorphic mycelium later at the edge of the colony. Microscopically, only mycelium has been observed.
   b. The colony is flat, yeasty in appearnce at first, turning waxy with age. Small radial furrows are in the center of the colony. Microscopically, only mycelium has been observed.
   c. The colony has radial furrows and is waxy, heaped and wrinkled in the center. The color of the colony is light brown to beige. Mycelium only has been observed.

3. The colonies have distinct concentric rings and are buff in the center within fourteen days. The remainder of the colony is white at least up to four weeks.

4. The colony is white and glabrous with a small central tuft of cottony mycelium. Later growth becomes velvety and powdery with radiating furrows. Microconidia in small numbers have been observed.

5. The colony is white to velvety with central, crateriform, waxy mycelium. Microconidia usually can be observed.

6. The colony is white when very young, later turning light buff with a slight crateriform center. With age the colony becomes dry and granular. Only mycelium has been observed.

7. The colony grows fairly rapidly and is heaped and buff colored with a concave center. No conidium has been observed.

Discussion

Many of the isolates of *H. capsulatum* obtained from patients with chronic lung disease in tuberculosis sanatoria could not be identified by simple observation of macroscopical growth, color, or colony topography. In addition, microscopical preparations were not of assistance in definitive identification of the cultures in many instances.

It has been our experience that with human, clinical specimens bizarre and varied types of growth can be produced by *H. capsulatum*. This necessitates that extreme care be followed in the examination of Sabouraud's and blood agar plates for suspicious colonies. For these reasons no culture is reported as *H. capsulatum* until it is converted to the yeast phase, and until fairly recently all cultures were proved by animal inoculation.

Interesting aspects of variation have been observed in one human isolate transferred serially on artifical media. This same isolate showed similar variations after having been inoculated into experimental animals and recovered on artificial media. Three distinct colonies developed from the mycelial homogenate and maintained their integrity after subculturing. Microscopical morphology of the three colonies was distinct and type characteristic. There is a need for intensive studies of the various types of variations to ascertain if they are genetically induced or due to environmental or nutritional factors.

References

Berliner, M.D. (1968). Primary subcultures of *Histoplasma capsulatum*. I. Macro- and micro-morphology of the mycelial phase. *Sabouraudia*, 6(2):111-118.

Daniels, L.S., Berliner, M.D. and Campbell, C.C. (1968). Varying virulence in rabbits infected with different filamentous types of *Histoplasma capsulatum*. *J. Bact.*, 96: 1535-1539.

English, M.P. (1964). Variation in *T. rubrum* as seen in a routine diagnostic service. *Sabouraudia*, 3(3):205-210.

Plunkett, O.A., Walker, L. and Huppert, M. (1963). An unusual isolate of *Coccidioides immitis* from the Los Banos area of California. *Sabouraudia*, 3(1):16-20.

Spaur, C.L. (1956). Atypical cultures of *C. immitis*. *Amer. J. Clin. Path.*, 26:689-690.

Weitzman, I. (1964). Variation in *Microsporum gypseum*. I. A genetic study of pleomorphism. *Sabouraudia*, 3(3):195-204.

Chapter 7

Isolation and Characterization of Polysaccharide of *Histoplasma capsulatum*

GEORGE S. KOBAYASHI

ABSTRACT

An immunologically active polysaccharide was isolated from culture filtrates of the mycelial phase of *Histoplasma capsulatum* by procedures employed in the purification of mucopolysaccharides. Such treatment yielded an amorphous white powder with a nitrogen content of 0.39 percent and no detectable amino acids. Glucose and mannose were the only reducing sugars found in acid hydrolyzed samples. The polysaccharide could be further separated into a mannose-rich fraction by treatment with alkaline Fehling's solution.

DIFFICULTIES are frequently encountered in assessing the value of immunologic studies in histoplasmosis (Campbell, 1967). No less important than knowledge of the wide spectrum of disease caused by the fungus *Histoplasma capsulatum* are the antigens which are employed to detect the variable host immune responses. Interpretations of immunochemical studies can be meaningful only where there is some assurance that the antigens being examined are well defined. Several methods have been employed in the characterization of the various components of histoplasmin. In 1948 Cross and Howell isolated an immunologically active polysaccharide from culture filtrates of *H. capsulatum* by precipitation with alcohol. Other workers (Campbell, 1953; Scheff, 1954; Dyson and Evans, 1955; Knight and Marcus, 1958; Salvin and Smith, 1959; Thor and Dray, 1968) have also reported on the use of alcohol for isolating various immunologically active components. Subsequent to these reports, the immunodiffusion studies of Heiner (1958) stimulated several investigators to further fractionate the heterogeneous complex of antigenic substances occuring in histoplasmin. Several active components have been isolated by diethyl amino ethyl cellulose ion exchange chromatography (Greene, DeLalla and Tompkins, 1960; Markowitz, 1964; LaBorde and Abernathy, 1965; Fadula and Larsh, 1967), Pevikon block electrophoresis (O'Connell, Hermans and Markowitz, 1967) disc electrophoresis (O'Connell, Hermans and Markowitz, 1967; Larsh, Bartels and Taha, 1969; Sprouse, 1969) and molecular sieve procedures (Sprouse, Goodman and Larsh, 1969).

This investigation was supported by Public Health Service grant AI 06213 from the National Institute of Allergy and Infectious Diseases and Grant AM 05611.

This report describes the isolation of immunologically active polysaccharide from a culture filtrate of the mycelial phase of *H. capsulatum* by proteolytic methods used in the purification of mucopolysaccharide.

Materials and Methods

Preparation of Culture Filtrate

H. capsulatum, isolate MCM (Kobayashi and Guiliacci, 1967), maintained in our laboratory on 2% glucose, 1% yeast extract (GYE) agar, was inoculated into several 2-liter culture flasks containing 1-liter of GYE broth. After six months' incubation at room temperature in the dark, the cultures were harvested by filtration and the mycelia discarded. The filtrates were further clarified by passage through a Millipore® filter (0.45μ), preserved with thimerosal (final concentration 1:10,000), and stored at 4°C until used.

Purification of Polysaccharide

The procedure employed in the isolation of the immunologically active polysaccharide is summarized in Table 7-I.

Step 1. The culture filtrate was clarified by filtration through a Millipore filter 0.45μ.

Step 2. Dialysis at 4°C for five days against daily changes of distilled water, then lyophilization.

Step 3. Papain treatment (Schiller, Slover and Dorfman, 1961). The crude polysaccharide solution is dissolved in a solution containing crystalline papain, 5 mg/gm dry weight of sample, activated in 30 ml of 0.1 M phosphate buffer, pH 6.5 containing 0.005 M cysteine-HCl and 0.005 M ethylenediamine tetracetate. The enzymic digestion is carried out at 60°C for 18 to 24 hours.

Step 4. Trypsin digestion (Schiller, Mathews, Jefferson, Ludowieg and Dorfman, 1954). Crystalline, trypsin, 5 mg/gm dry weight of original material is added to the papain treated material. The enzyme reaction is carried out in a Visking casing tube suspended in 0.1 M

TABLE 7-I

Isolation of Immunologically Active Polysaccharide from Culture Filtrate
of the Filamentous Phase of *H. capsulatum*

Step	Procedure	Weight of Recovered Material (grams)
1	Filtration	6.702
2	Dialysis vs. distilled water	2.260
3	Papain treatment	1.374
4	Trypsin treatment	1.247
5	AG 50-W	1.165
6	AG 1-2	0.598

phosphate buffer, pH 7.8 at 37°C for three days. Bacterial contamination is controlled by adding 1 to 2 crystals of thymol to the
buffer. The enzymic reaction is terminated by the dropwise addition
of cold trichloroacetic acid to a final concentration of 10%. After
mixing for 30 minutes in the cold, the solution is clarified by centrifugation. The supernatant fluid is neutralized with 1N NaOH and
then dialyzed against frequent changes of distilled water for two
days at 4°C.

Step 5. AG 50 W cation exchange treatment. The solution is mixed batch-
wise with AG 50 W resin at 4°C for 30 minutes and then filtered.

Step 6. AG 1-×2 anion exchange treatment. The filtrate is added to the top
of an AG 1-×2 column and eluted with distilled water. The eluate
is collected and lyophilized.

Chemical Procedures and Analysis

A 7 to 12 ml sample was removed at each step in the purification procedure and analyzed. Total nitrogen, quantitative carbohydrate determinations, paper chromatography, and total recovery values were determined by
methods previously reported (Kobayashi and Guiliacci, 1967).

Ultracentrifugal Analysis[*]

A 6 mg sample of the final product was dissolved in 1 ml of 0.1 M phosphate buffer, pH 7.4, containing 0.15 M NaCl. The polysaccharide solution
was spun in a Spinco Model E ultracentrifuge at 50,740 rpm. Sedimentation
patterns were recorded by photographs taken at 8-minute intervals throughout a 2-hour period of time.

Immunologic Studies

The procedure for obtaining antisera to *H. capsulatum* has been previously reported (Kobayashi and Guiliacci, 1967). Methods for immunodiffusion studies were essentially those of Wadsworth (1957).

Results and Discussion

The yield of active material at various steps in the treatment of the crude
culture filtrate is shown in Table 7-I. Chemical analysis of samples taken at
the various steps showed a decrease in total nitrogen content and an enrichment in carbohydrate (Table 7-II). A major portion of the material removed by the various treatments appeared to be amino acids, which were
demonstrated by descending paper chromatograms of acid hydrolyzed sam-

---

[*] Ultracentrifugal analysis and calculations of the sedimentation coefficient were aided by
Dr. Norma A. Fletcher.

TABLE 7-II

Analysis of Nitrogen and Carbohydrate Content of Various Immunologically Active
Polysaccharide Obtained From Culture Filtrate of *H. capsulatum*

Step	Procedure	%N*	% Carbohydrate†
1	Filtration	5.02	19.06
2	Dialysis vs. distilled water, lyophilized	2.57	16.13
3	Papain treatment	2.12	47.59
4	Trypsin treatment	1.77	51.94
5	AG 50-W (cation)	1.56	57.30
6	AG 1 (anion)	0.39	61.40

* Micro-Kjeldahl method (Kabat, 1961). $(NH_4)_2SO_4$ as standard.
† Anthrone method (Morris, 1948) glucose standard.

ples. Virtually no ninhydrin-reactive material could be found in the hydro-lyzed sample of the final product.

Concomitant with the decreased nitrogen content was an enrichment in carbohydrate-reactive material (Table 7-II). Knight (1958) detected only dextrose in his active polysaccharide fraction isolated from the mycelial phase filtrate, while Salvin and Smith (1959) found their material from the yeast phase filtrate to be composed mainly of mannose with trace amounts of galactose and an unidentified reducing substance. The material recovered in step 6 (Table 7-II) with 0.39% nitrogen and 61.40% carbohydrate contained both mannose and glucose. No other reducing compounds were detected in the final material.

Analytical data on the chemical composition of immunologically active polysaccharides isolated from culture filtrates of *H. capsulatum* have been presented by several authors (Cross and Howell, 1948; Salvin and Smith, 1959; Markowitz, 1964), and the nitrogen content of these substances varies from 0.8 to 4.2 percent. Chromatographic and spectrophotometric data obtained by Salvin and Smith (1959) suggested that protein was the bulk of the nitrogenous component. Attempts made by these authors to separate the protein from the carbohydrate by chemical means were unsuccessful. The present finding (Table 7-II) of low nitrogen content is of further interest in view of the report of Pappagianis, Putman and Kobayashi (1961), who were unable to separate the carbohydrate from the protein of the immunogenic polysaccharide of *Coccidioides immitis*. The nitrogen content of this polysaccharide material could be reduced to levels of 0.5 percent or less, but only when treated with concentrated alkali solutions; such treatment resulted in immunologically inactive materials. In contrast to these findings, all of the samples removed at each step in the treatment of culture filtrate of *H. capsulatum* showed a diffuse band of identity in agar-gel diffusion studies when reacted against sera of rabbits immunized with killed mycelia of *H. capsulatum*.

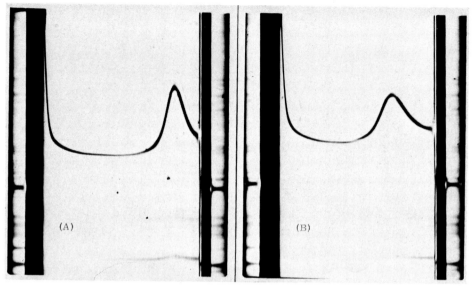

FIGURE 7-1. Sedimentation pattern of purified polysaccharide of *Histoplasma capsulatum*. Frame A was taken at 50,740 rpm after 62 minutes. Frame B was taken at 50,740 rpm after 112 minutes.

Ultracentrifugal patterns of the immunologically active polysaccharide are presented in Figure 7-1. The purified material sedimented with a sedimentation coefficient of 2.53 S corresponding to a molecular weight of about 20,000. The leading edge of the boundry in the sedimentation pattern appeared skewed (Fig. 7-1B), suggesting some heteregeneity in the composition of the purified material. This was substantiated by treating a solution of the polysaccharide with Fehling's solution (Peat, Whelan and Edwards, 1961). A mannose-rich fraction could be precipitated out of solution by the formation of an insoluble copper complex. Salvin and Smith (1959) on the other hand, found their material to be homogeneous in the ultracentrifuge and by immunodiffusion studies, but heterogeneous when subjected to electrophoretic techniques. The sedimentation of this latter material was greater (4.4 S) than those values reported herein. It is possible that this difference may be attributed to the protein associated with the polysaccharide. They were unable to further fractionate this material.

The present studies show that the extracellular polysaccharide of *H. capsulatum* can be treated with proteolytic enzymes to yield a material low in nitrogen content and virtually free of amino acids. The major problem to be solved is the resolution of this material into its component parts so that chemical characterization may be carried out on the reactive moieties.

References

Campbell, C.C. (1967). Serology in the respiratory mycoses. *Sabouraudia*, 5:240-259.

Campbell, C.C. (1953). Antigenic fractions of *Histoplasma capsulatum*. *Amer. J. Public Health*, 43:712-717.

Cross, F.W. and Howell, A., Jr. (1948). Studies of fungus antigens. II. Preliminary report on the isolation of an immunologically active polysaccharide from histoplasmin. *Public Health Rep.*, 63:179-183.

Dyson, J.E. and Evans, E.E. (1955). Delayed hypersensitivity in experimental fungus infections. The skin reactivity of antigens from the yeast phase of *Histoplasma capsulatum*. *J. Lab. Clin. Med.*, 45:449-454.

Fadula, S. and Larsh, H.W. (1967). Separation of specific antigens of two strains of *Histoplasma duboissi* by ion-exchange chromatography. *Bact. Proc. M. 51*:69.

Greene, C.H., DeLalla, L.S. and Tompkins, V.N. (1960). Separation of specific antigens of *Histoplasma capsulatum* by ion-exchange chromatography. *Proc. Soc. Exp. Biol. Med.*, 105:140-141.

Heiner, D.C. (1958). Diagnosis of histoplasmosis using precipitin reactions in agar gel. *Pediatrics*, 22:616-627.

Kabat, E.A. (1961). *Experimental Immunochemistry*. Springfield, Thomas, pp. 476-483.

Knight, R.A. (1958). The chemical, serologic and skin test activities of polysaccharides extracted from *Histoplasma capsulatum* and *Blastomyces dermatitidis*. Ph.D. thesis, University of Utah, p. 37.

Knight, R.A. and Marcus, S. (1958). Polysaccharide skin test antigens derived from *Histoplasma capsulatum* and *Blastomyces dermatitidis*. *Amer. Rev. Tuberc. Pulmon. Dis.*, 77:983-989.

Kobayashi, G.S. and Guiliacci, P.L. (1967). Cell wall studies of *Histoplasma capsulatum*. *Sabouraudia*, 5:180-188.

LaBorde, J. and Abernathy, R.S. (1965). Immunologic and physicochemical studies of the *m* and *h* antigens of *Histoplasma capsulatum*. *Amer. Rev. Resp. Dis.*, 92:322-323.

Larsh, H.W., Bartels, P. and Taha, B. (1969). Fractionation and partial chemical characterization of histoplasmin from four *Histoplasma capsulatum* isolates. *Bact. Proc., M. 34*:166.

Markowitz, H. (1964). Polysaccharide antigens from *Histoplasma capsulatum*. *Proc. Soc. Exp. Biol. Med.*, 115:697-701.

Morris, D.L. (1948). Quantitative determination of carbohydrates with Dreywood's anthrone reagent. *Science*, 107:254-255.

O'Connell, E.J., Hermans, P.E. and Markowitz, H. (1967). Skin-reactive antigens of *Histoplasma capsulatum*. *Proc. Soc. Exp. Biol. Med.*, 124:1015-1020.

Pappagianis, D., Putman, E.W. and Kobayashi, G.S. (1961). Polysaccharide of *Coccidioides immitis*. *J. Bact.*, 82:648-656.

Peat, S., Whelan, W.J. and Edwards, T.E. (1961). Polysaccharides of baker's yeast. Part IV. Mannan. *J. Chem. Soc.*, 56:29-34.

Salvin, S.B. and Smith, R.F. (1959). Antigens from the yeast phase of *Histoplasma capsulatum*. III. Isolation, properties and activity of a protein-carbohydrate complex. *J. Infect. Dis.*, 105:45-53.

Scheff, G.J. (1945). Biochemical and immunological properties of *Histoplasma capsulatum*. No. 650, *Yale J. Biol. Med.*, 18:41-54.

Schiller, Sara, Mathews, M.B., Jefferson, H., Ludowieg, J. and Dorfman, A. (1954). The metabolism of mucopolysaccharides in animals. I. Isolation from skin. *J. Biol. Chem.*, *211*:717-724.

Sprouse, R.F. (1969). Skin test active compounds from *Histoplasma capsulatum. Bact. Proc., M. 33*:115-116.

Sprouse, R.F., Goodman, N.L. and Larsh, H.W. (1969). Fractionation, isolation and chemical characterization of skin test active components of histoplasmin. *Sabouraudia*, *7*:1-11.

Thor, D.E. and Dray, S. (1968) A correlate of human delayed hypersensitivity: specific inhibition of capillary tube migration of sensitized human lymph node cells by tuberculin and histoplasmin. *J. Immun., 101*:51-61.

Wadsworth, C. (1957). A slide microtechnique for the analysis of immune precipitates in gel. *Int. Arch. Allerg., 10*:355-360.

Chapter 8

Antigenic Analysis of
Histoplasma capsulatum

DAVID S. BAUMAN

ABSTRACT

Seven strains of *Histoplasma capsulatum* were examined for the antigen composition of cell wall and cytoplasmic extracts, the chemical composition of the cell wall extracts, and the ability of the extracts to stimulate protective immunity from extrapulmonary dissemination in the hamster. The seven strains were from both human and soil specimens and from widely varying geographic locations.

Seven precipitin bands were detected, six of which seemed to represent distinct antigens (2 from the cell wall, 3 from the cytoplasm, and 1 common to both.) The cell wall extracts contained materials which were between 79% and 85% carbohydrate and between 3.1% and 4.8% protein and had average molecular weights between 9×10^4 and 4×10^5.

The cell wall materials were extractable with dimethyl sulfoxide (DMSO) and protected hamsters against extrapulmonary dissemination to the spleen following challenge with yeast phase cells intratracheally.

FOR the past twenty-nine years medical mycologists have directed most of their "immunologic" efforts toward serologic and skin tests (Van-Pernis, Benson, and Holinger, 1941; Zarafonetis and Lindberg, 1941; Emmons, Olson and Eldridge, 1945; Howell, 1947; Salvin, 1947; Pates, 1948; Salvin and Hottle, 1948; Saslaw and Campbell, 1948; Tenenberg and Howell, 1948; Guy, Panissett and Frappier, 1949; Saslaw and Campbell, 1949; Campbell and Binkley, 1953; Saslaw and Campbell, 1953; Schubert, Ajello, Stanford and Grant, 1953; Salvin and Furcolow, 1954; Salvin, Weber, Lackman, Nishio and Menges, 1954; Sorensen and Evans, 1954; Labzoffsky and Fischer, 1955; Salvin, 1955; Schubert, Ajello, Cooper and Runyon, 1955; Campbell, 1956; Grayston, 1956;Salvin, 1956; Schubert and Ajello, 1957; Heiner, 1958; Knight and Marcus, 1958; Furcolow, 1963; Asgari and Conant, 1964; Kaufman, Brandt and McLaughlin, 1964; Adamson and Cozad, 1966; Campbell, 1967; Chandler, Smith, Newberry, Chin and Kirkpatrick, 1969). The emphasis placed upon patient diagnosis and care is responsible for mycologists using their time almost exclusively in this direction.

We all recognize the drawbacks in the available antigens (i.e. low specificity, low or variable potency, etc.); however, only a small fraction of the

NOTE. Supported in part by a grant from the American Thoracic Society and by grant 1-RO1-A17199-01 from the National Institute of Allergy and Infectious Diseases.

total effort of mycology has been utilized toward development of new antigens and utilization of these antigens for better diagnostic and prognostic tests (Campbell, 1953; Cross and Howell, 1948; Greene, DeLalla and Thompkins, 1960; Knight and Marcus, 1958; Knight, Hill, and Marcus, 1959; Markowitz, 1964; Pine, Boone, and McLaughlin, 1966; Salvin and Smith, 1959).

A complex mosaic of antigens confronts humans and laboratory animals when they are infected with *Histoplasma capsulatum*. The antigenic complexity was best illustrated by Labzoffsky, Fischer and Hamvas (1957), who isolated 8 antigenic fractions from *H. capsulatum* yeast cells, 7 of which seemed to be antigenically distinct, and 3 of which were specific for *H. capsulatum*.

Through the combined use of skin tests, serologic tests, and cultures, diagnosis has been relatively successful on patients submitted for the mycologist's scrutiny. However, far too often a fungus infection is not suspected until late in the clinical course. We need tests which can give accurate prognostic predictions as an adjunct in the decision to treat or not to treat with the available, "toxic," antifungal agents.

It is reasonable to assume that spontaneous recovery from histoplasmosis is, at least in part, due to some type of immunologic response (cellular or humoral?). Conversely, disseminated, progressive disease may be the result of a breakdown in this immunologic response, or a response to only a portion of the antigens, or the wrong type of response (i.e. humoral rather than cellular, or vice versa), or a combination of all three.

If we were able to purify the individual antigenic components of *H. capsulatum* and test the patient for both humoral and cellular immunologic response, we should be able to correlate the patient's clinical course with the type immunologic response to one or more of the fungal antigens. Once this type correlation has been made on a number of patients representing the spectrum of clinical outcomes, then and only then will we be in a position to predict the prognosis of any given patient.

Our research has dealt mainly with laboratory animal infections, and the antigens were purified from *H. capsulatum* yeast cells. Choice of the yeast phase for antigenic analysis, rather than the "classic" histoplasmin approach, is due to the almost exclusive presence of yeast cells in histoplasmosis lesions and the lack of proof that the yeast and mycelial phases are antigenically identical.

Materials and Methods

Organism

Seven strains of *H. capsulatum*, numbers 302 (human case, Furcolow), 341 (soil isolate, Larsh), 342 (soil isolate, Ajello), 344 (human case, Schwarz), 345 (human case, Larsh), 346 (human case, Bauman), 347 (human case, Larsh), were utilized for all infections and antigen extractions. The source, cultivation, and conversion methods for these strains have been previously described (Bauman and Chick, 1969a).

Antigen Preparation

H. capsulatum yeast phase (YP) cells were grown in Eagle minimum essential medium (MEM), modified by adding 10 gm dextrose, 0.05 mg ferric chloride, and 0.05 mg zinc chloride per liter (Eagle, 1955). The cells were disrupted by passing through a bacterial freeze press (Eaton, 1962) at —70°C and 20,000 psi. The YP cell walls were separated from cytoplasmic material by differential centrifugation at 1,000 g for one hour. Cell wall antigen extraction and purification has been described previously (Bauman and Chick, 1969b).

Animals

For immune serum, male albino rabbits (3 per strain) received increasing intravenous doses (0.1 ml up to 1.0 ml) of a suspension containing 10^8 YP cells in saline. The injections were biweekly for one month, and all animals were bled at seven and fourteen days after the last injection.

For immunization-challenge experiments, male Syrian golden hamsters (*Mesocrietus auratus*), thirty-five to forty days of age, were immunized by intramuscular injection of antigen in polyacrylamide gel and challenged by intratrachael injection of YP *H. capsulatum*. Dissemination was detected by spleen culture four weeks after infection (Bauman and Chick, 1969a; Bauman and Chick 1969b).

Serologic Procedures

A semimicro complement fixation test (Lackman, 1964) was performed on all rabbit sera. Optimum antigen concentrations were determined by block titration against pooled immune rabbit sera. Fifty percent (50%) hemolysis end points were determined spectrophotometrically.

Immunodiffusion tests were performed by both micro and macro procedures (3 mm and 6 mm interwell distances, respectively). The diffusion medium contained 1.2% agar, 0.05% sodium azide, 0.8% sodium chloride, and 1 M glycine. Antigens were tested at several dilutions to determine optimum concentrations.

Chemical Determinations

Protein estimations were done by a modified Lowry method (Lowry, Rosebrough, Farr and Randall, 1951) and by the biuret method (Kingsley, 1942). The anthrone method as described originally by Morris (1948) and modified by Seibert, Stacey and Kent (1949) was used for carbohydrate estimation on the extracted antigens.

Molecular Sieve Chromatography

The extracted fractions in 0.15 M phosphate buffer, pH 7.0, were gel filtered through Sephadex G-200 (Pharmacia Fine Chemicals, Inc.). The column bed dimensions were 2.5 × 30 cm for a bed volume of 118 ml. Each packed column was tested with three dextran standards: blue dextran 2,000 (mol wt 3 × 10^6), Ficoll (mol wt 4 × 10^5) and dextran fraction 60,000 to 90,000 (mol wt 6-9 × 10^4). The two latter standards were detected by anthrone determinations and the former by absorbance at 280 mμ. Every third tube from the fraction collector was assayed for protein, sugar, and immunodiffusion bands. All adjacent tubes giving bands of identity were pooled and lyophilized.

Results and Discussion

Comparison of Cytoplasmic and Culture Filtrate Antigens from Yeast and Mycelial Phases

Table 8-I shows the results when freeze press supernates from YP and MP (mycelial phase) were tested in immunodiffusion wells adjacent to HKC-43 histoplasmin against anti-347 (YP) *H. capsulatum* pooled rabbit serum. The YP supernate of strain 347 gave four distinct precipitin bands with the anti-347 serum. These bands were designated A,B,C, and D in order of their relative distances from the antigen well. Single precipitin bands were detected with the freeze press supernate of strain 347 MP and with HKC-43 histoplasmin. These bands showed arcs of identity between each other and the "D" band of the YP supernate.

Strain Differences in Cytoplasmic Antigens

Table 8-II shows the results of immunodiffusion tests with seven strains of *H. capsulatum* (YP freeze press supernates) tested against pooled anti-347 (YP) rabbit sera. The strains were isolated from widely separated geographic areas: 302, Kansas City, Kansas, human; 341, Milan, Michigan, soil;

TABLE 8-I

Comparison of Precipitin Bands from Histoplasmin and Yeast and Mycelial Phases of *Histoplasma capsulatum*

Antigen	No. Bands	Specificity
YP	4	A, B, C, D
MP	1	D
Histoplasmin	1	D

YP = freeze press supernate from strain 347 yeast cells grown in MEM at 37°C.
MP = freeze press supernate from strain 347 mycelial cells grown in MEM at room temperature.
Histoplasmin (Lederle) concentrated to ⅓ volume with dry Sephadex G 25.
A, B, C, D bands designated according to relative position to the antigen well (A nearest the well, D farthest away). The "D" bands of the MP and histoplasmin were designated because of an identity arc with the D band of the YP supernate.

TABLE 8-II

Immunodiffusion Tests with Freeze Press Supernatant Fluids from YP *Histoplasma capsulatum*

Strain*	Precipitin Band			
	A†	B	C	D
302	var.‡	+	+	+
341	+	+	+	+
342	+	+	−	+
344	+	+	−	+
345	+	−	+	+
346	−	−	−	+
347	+	+	+	+

* YP cells of each strain were grown in MEM and glutamine, freeze pressed at 20,000–50,000 psi, −70°C and the broken cell walls removed by centrifugation.

† A, B, D, and D precipitin bands identified by "identity arcs" with antigens in adjacent wells.

‡ Var. = variable (sometimes demonstrable but faint, sometimes absent); + = presence of precipitin band; − = absence of precipitin band.

344, Fredrick, Maryland, human; 345, Mt. Vernon, Missouri, human (Ross); 346, Morgantown, West Virginia, human (Brady); 347, Mt. Vernon, Missouri, human (Scritchfield) and from both human and soil specimens. The "D" band was the only band common to all seven strains and to histoplasmin. Strain 346 was the most recently isolated strain and gave only one precipitin band, even when various dilutions were employed. Strain 302 had been maintained in stock culture the longest of the seven strains (approximately 20 years) and produced three consistent bands.

Strain Differences in Cell Wall Antigens

Tables 8-III shows the elution patterns of DMSO extractable fractions from seven strains of *H. capsulatum*. The peaks (determined by anthrone)

TABLE 8-III

Elution Patterns of DMSO Extractable Fractions Through Sephadex G-200

Strain No.	Elution Volume (ml)*
302	80
341	76
342	96
344	90
345	84
346	88
347	86
BD2000†	56
Ficoll‡	70
Dextran§	130

* Elution volume is the amount of solvent passed through the column after addition of sample until the polysaccharide peak was detected on the fraction collector (peak determined by anthrone sugar determination on every third tube). Column dimensions, 2.5×30 cm bed.

† BD2000 = Blue dextran 2000: molecular weight 2×10^6.

‡ Ficoll: molecular weight 4×10^5.

§ Dextran = Dextran fraction 60,000 to 90,000: molecular weight 6×10^4 to 9.0×10^4.

for all strains were eluted beween Ficoll (mol wt 4×10^5) and Dextran fraction 60,000 to 90,000 (mol wt $6\text{-}9 \times 10^4$). There was some variation from strain to strain of the elution volumes for the peaks (76-96 ml); however, this may or may not represent differences in the mean molecular weight of the antigens, since the precision of the method is low. However, the large elution variation between strains 341 and 342 is suggestive of a difference in the two strains.

The anthrone sugar and Lowry protein estimations on six of the seven DMSO extractable fractions are given in Table 8-IV. All fractions were between 79% and 85% anthrone reactive sugar (Ficoll, a polyglucose molecule, was 99% anthrone reactive sugar) and between 3.6% and 4.8% protein by the Lowry method. The 342 strain extract was not assayed for sugar and protein, since this strain was very difficult to convert and maintain in the YP, and the extract was used only for antigenic analysis throughout these studies. There was no correlation between the values of the sugar and protein determinations and the geographic area where the strain was isolated.

Table 8-V gives the results of immunodiffusion tests with the six DMSO extracts run against all combinations of the seven antisera. The "X, Y, and Z" designations represent a progression away from the antigen wells. The "X" band was common to all antisera; however, it was not demonstrable with the 346 extract. The "Z" band was demonstrable only with 346 extract and strains 345 and 346 antisera.

The "Y" band was demonstrated with extracts and antisera from strains isolated in the central one third of the United States (302, 341, 345, 347), but not from strains isolated in the eastern one third (344, 346) or from outside the United States (342). The "Y" band also correlated with ease of conversion to YP.

TABLE 8-IV

Sugar and Protein Determinations on DMSO Extractable Antigens
from YP *Histoplasma capsulatum* Cell Walls

Antigen Strain*	Sugar†	Protein‡
302	0.80	0.042
341	0.81	0.039
344	0.80	0.048
345	0.85	0.031
346	0.79	0.040
347	0.83	0.036

* Stock solutions of each antigen prepared in 1.0 gm % concentration and dilutions from 1:10 to 1:10,000 tested.

† Expressed in gram per 100 ml of stock solution in comparison to a glucose standard.

‡ Expressed in gram per 100 ml of stock solution in comparison to a BSA (body surface area) standard.

TABLE 8-V

Immunodiffusion Tests with DMSO Extractable, Polysaccharide-rich Antigens
from YP Cell Walls of *Histoplasma capsulatum*

	Antigen Strain*					
Serum	302	341	344	345	346	347
Anti-302†	X, Y‡	X, Y	X	X	O§	X, Y
Anti-341	X, Y	X, Y	X	X	O	X, Y
Anti-342	X	X	O	O	O	X
Anti-344	X	X	X	X	O	X
Anti-345	X, Y	X	X	X	Z	X, Y
Anti-346	X	X	X	X	Z	X
Anti-347	X, Y	X, Y	X	X, Y	O	X, Y

* Antigen extracted with DMSO, alcohol precipitated, gel filtered through Sephadex G-200, and lyophilized prior to use.
† Rabbits immunized with viable YP *H. capsulatum*.
‡ X, Y, and Z bands identified by type are between bands from adjacent antigen wells when tested against the same antiserum.
§ O = No bands formed.

Comparison of Cytoplasmic and Cell Wall Extracts

Table 8-VI compares the cell wall extracts and freeze press supernatant fluids from the seven strains in immunodiffusion tests. The "Y" and "C" bands of strains 302, 341, 345, and 347 showed arcs of identity when the corresponding extracts were placed in adjacent wells. The "X, Z, A, B and D" bands seemed to represent distinct antigenic entities since no identity arcs were formed. The "X" and "D" bands were the only two common to all seven strains.

TABLE 8-VI

Comparison of Cell Wall and Cytoplasmic Antigens of Seven Strains of *Histoplasma capsulatum*

	Antigen Type						
Strain	Cell Wall*			Cytoplasmic†			
	Precipitin Band Designation‡						
	X	Y	Z	A	B	C	D
302	+§	+‖	−	var	+	+	+
341	+	+	−	+	+	+	+
342	+	−	−	+	+	−	+
344	+	−	−	+	+	−	+
345	+	+	+¶	+	−	+	+
346	+	−	+	−	−	−	+
347	+	+	−	+	+	+	+

* Cell wall antigens extracted from washed, broken cell walls with DMSO.
† Cytoplasmin antigens prepared from freeze press supernate after removal of cell walls.
‡ Precipitin bands designated according to their relative position with respect to the antigen wells.
§ + = band present, − = absence of band, var = variable, band was not always demonstrated.
‖ "Y" and "C" bands showed an "identity arc" between the antigen wells.
¶ Presence of antigen inferred from presence of antibody in immunized rabbit sera.

Comparison of Protective Immunization with Different Cell Wall Extracts

Table 8-VII compares dissemination from the lung to the spleen in animals immunized with DMSO extractable cell wall antigens and challenged with 10^5 YP *H. capsulatum* cells intratracheally. All of the strain antigens protected animals very well against challenge with strains 302 and 347. However, animals immunized with strain 342 extract were not well protected against challenge with strains 341 and 345, and extracts from strains 345, 346, and 347 did not solidly protect animals challenged with strain 341 against dissemination.

In immunized animals where dissemination occurred there was an average of 19.8 colonies per spleen, while in control animals there was an average of 192.5 colonies per spleen. The greatest splenic "spillover" occurred in animals challenged with strain 345, the highest virulence strain (ID_{50} = 1.14×10^4 YP cells per animal).

No correlation was found between the antigens detected by immunodiffusion and the ability of an extract to protect an animal from dissemination. In general however, better protection was afforded animals immunized with extracts which produced a "Y" band (strains 302, 341, 345, and 347) than animals immunized with other extracts.

TABLE 8-VII

Hamster Immunization and Challenge with *Histoplasma capsulatum**

Immunizing Antigen Strain[†]	Challenge Strain[‡]			
	302	341	345	347
302	0/5§ (0.024)‖	0/5 (0.004)	1/5 (0.024)	0/5 (0.083)
341	0/5 (0.024)¶	0/5 (0.004)	3/5 (0.222)	0/5 (0.083)
342	0/5 (0.024)	3/5 (0.222)	3/5 (0.222)	0/5 (0.083)
344	0/5 (0.024)	—¶	—	—
345	0/5 (0.024)	2/5 (0.083)	0/5 (0.004)	0/5 (0.083)
346	1/5 (0.103)	2/5 (0.083)	0/5 (0.004)	0/5 (0.083)
347	0/5 (0.024)	2/5 (0.083)	0/5 (0.004)	0/5 (0.083)
Control ¶¶	4/5	5/5	5/5	3/5
Number of ID_{50} Challenge Doses	0.9	1.3	8.9	2.4

* Modified from Bauman and Chick (1969b).
† DMSO extractable cell wall antigens; 0.5 mg in macerated polyacrylamide intramuscularly.
‡ Animals challenged with 10^5 YP cells in 0.1 ml.
§ Number of animals with culturally positive spleens/number of animals challenged.
‖ Numbers in parentheses indicate the probability of obtaining the observed differences between the control animals and the corresponding immunization-challenge groups if in fact there was no protection. Where probability is small, protection is indicated.
¶ —indicates animals sacrificed prematurely, data not available.
¶¶ Control animals received intramuscular injection of polyacrylamide without antigen.

References

Adamson, D.M. and Cozad, G.C. (1966). Immunoelectrophoretic studies of sera from rabbits experimentally infected with *Histoplasma capsulatum. J. Bact.,* 92:887-891.

Asgari, M. and Conant, N.F. (1964). A preliminary note on interraction of skin test sensitivity between histoplasmin and chrysosporin in experimental animals. *Mycopathologia,* 23:321-327.

Bauman, D.S. and Chick, E.W. (1969a). An experimental model for studying extrapulmonary dissemination of *Histoplasma capsulatum* in hamsters. *Amer. Rev. Resp. Dis.,* 100:79-81.

Bauman, D.S. and Chick, E.W. (1969b). Immunoprotection against extrapulmonary histoplasmosis in hamsters. *Amer. Rev. Resp. Dis.,* 100:82-85.

Campbell, C.C. (1953). Antigenic fractions of *Histoplasma capsulatum. Amer. J. Public Health,* 43:712-717.

Campbell, C.C. (1956). Use of yeast phase antigens in a complement fixation test for histoplasmosis. IV. Results with ground yeast-phase antigens in serial specimens of serum from thirty-seven patients. *In* United States Department of Health, Education and Welfare, Proceedings of the Conference on Histoplasmosis, 1952. *Public Health Monogr.,* 39:140-148.

Campbell, C.C. (1967). Serology in the respiratory mycoses. *Sabouraudia,* 5:240-259.

Campbell, C.C. and Binkley, G.E. (1953). Serologic diagnosis with respect to histoplasmosis, coccidioiomycosis, and blastomycosis, and the problem of cross reactions. *J. Lab. Clin. Med.,* 42:896-906.

Chandler, J.W., Smith, T.K., Newberry, W.M., Jr., Chin, T.D.Y. and Kirkpatrick, C.H. (1969). Immunology of the mycoses. II. Characterization of the immunoglobulin and antibody responses in histoplasmosis. *J. Infect. Dis.,* 119:247-254.

Cross, F.W. and Howell, A., Jr. (1948). Studies of fungus antigens. II. Preliminary report on the isolation of an immunologically active polysaccharide from histoplasmin. *Public Health Rep.,* 63:179-183.

Eagle, H. (1955). Nutritional needs of mammalian cells in tissue cultures. *Science, 122:* 501-504.

Eaton, H. (1955). New press for disruption of microorganisms. *J. Bact.,* 83:1359-1360.

Emmons, C.W., Olson, B.J. and Eldridge, W.W. (1945). Studies on the role of fungi in pulmonary disease. I. Cross reactions of histoplasmin. *Public Health Rep.,* 60:1383-1394.

Furcolow, M.L. (1963). Tests of immunity in histoplasmosis. *New Eng. J. Med., 268:* 357-361.

Grayston, J.T. (1956). A Study of the complement fixation reaction in histoplasmosis, employing whole yeast phase cells as antigen. *Public Health Monogr.,* 39:132-139.

Greene, C.H., DeLalla, L.S. and Tompkins, M.N. (1960). Separation of specific antigens of *Histoplasma capsulatum* by ion-exchange chromatography. *Proc. Soc. Exp. Biol. Med.,* 105:140-141.

Guy, R., Panissett, M., and Frappier, A. (1949). Histoplasmin sensitivity. II. A brief study of the incidence of hypersensitivity to histoplasmin in an Indian tribe of northern Quebec. *Canad. J. Public Health,* 40:306-309.

Heiner, D.C. (1958). Diagnosis of histoplasmosis using precipitin reactions in agar gel. *Pediatrics,* 22:616-626.

Howell, A., Jr. (1947). Studies of fungus antigens. I. Quantitative studies of cross-reactions between histoplasmin and blastomycin in guinea pigs. *Public Health Rep.*, 62:631-651.

Kaufman, L., Brandt, B. and McLaughlin, D. (1964). Evaluation of the fluorescent antibody and agar gel precipitin tests for detecting Histoplasma antibodies in anti-complementary sera. *Amer. J. Hyg.*, 79:181-185.

Kingsley, G.R. (1942). The direct biuret method for determination of serum proteins as applied to photoelectric and visual coloimetry. *J. Lab. Clin. Med.*, 27:840-845.

Knight, R.A., Hill, G. and Marcus, S. (1959). Immunization of mice with polysaccharides of *Histoplasma capsulatum*. *Proc. Soc. Exp. Biol. New York*, 100:356-358.

Knight, R.A. and Marcus, S. (1958). Polysaccharide skin test antigens derived from *Histoplasma capsulatum* and *Blastomyces dermatitidis*. *Amer. Rev. Tuberc. Pulm. Dis.*, 77:983-989.

Labzoffsky, N.A. and Fischer, J.B. (1955). A simple method for preparing an antigen from *Histoplasma capsulatum* for the use in the complement fixation test. *Canad. J. Microbiol.*, 1:520-524.

Labzoffsky, N.A., Fischer, J.B. and Hamvas, J.J. (1957). Studies on the antigenic structure of *Histoplasma capsulatum*. *Canad. J. Microbiol.*, 3:975-985.

Lowry, O.H., Rosebrough, N.J., Farr, A.L. and Randall, F.J. (1951). Protein measurement with the Folin phenol reagent. *J. Biol. Chem.*, 193:265-275.

Markowitz, H. (1964). Polysaccharide antigens from *Histoplasma capsulatum*. *Proc. Soc. Exp. Biol. Med.*, 115:697-700.

Morris, D.L. (1948). Quantitative determination of carbohydrates with Dreywood's anthrone reagent. *Science*, 107:254-255.

Newberry, W.M., Jr., Chandler, J.W., Jr., Chin, T.D.Y. and Kirkpatrick, C.H. (1968). Immunology of the mycoses. I. Depressed lymphocyte transformation in chronic histoplasmosis. *J. Immun.*, 100:436-443.

Pates, A.L. (1948). Precipitin reactions in experimental histoplasmosis and blastomycosis. *Science*, 108:383-385.

Pine, L., Boone, C.L. and McLaughlin, D. (1966). Antigenic properties of the cell wall and other fractions of the yeast form of *Histoplasma capsulatum*. *J. Bact.*, 91:2158-2168.

Salvin, S.B. (1947). Complement fixation studies in experimental histoplasmosis. *Proc. Soc. Exp. Biol. Med.*, 66:342-345.

Salvin, S.B. (1955). Hypersensitivity in mice with experimental histoplasmosis. *J. Immun.*, 75:1-6.

Salvin, S.B. (1956). Precipitin and complement fixation tests with whole yeast phase antigen. Proceedings of the Conference on Histoplasmosis. *Public Health Monogr.*, 39:163-165.

Salvin, S.B. and Furcolow, M.L. (1954). Precipitins in human histoplasmosis. *J. Lab. Clin. Med.*, 43:259-274.

Salvin, S.B. and Hottle, G.A. (1948). Serologic studies on antigens from *Histoplasma capsulatum* Darling. *J. Immun.*, 60:57-66.

Salvin, S.B. and Smith, R.F. (1959). Antigens from the yeast phase of *Histoplasma capsulatum*. III. Isolation, properties, and activity of a protein-carbohydrate complex. *J. Infect. Dis.*, 105:45-53.

Salvin, S.B., Weber, R.W., Lackman, D.B., Nishio, J. and Menges, G. (1954). Influence of repeated histoplasmin skin tests on precipitins and complement-fixing antibodies. *J. Lab. Clin. Med.*, 44:56-62.

Saslaw, S. and Campbell, C.C. (1948). The use of yeast-phase antigens in complement fixation tests for histoplasmosis. I. Preliminary results with rabbit sera. *J. Lab. Clin. Med.,* 33:811-818.

Saslaw, S. and Campbell, C.C. (1949). A collodion agglutination test for histoplasmosis. *Public Health Rep.,* 64:424-429.

Saslaw, S. and Campbell, C.C. (1953). Effect of histoplasmin skin testing on serologic results. *Proc. Soc. Exp. Biol. Med.,* 82:689-691.

Schubert, J.H. and Ajello, L. (1957). Variations in complement fixation antigenicity of different yeast-phase strains of *Histoplasma capsulatum. J. Lab. Clin. Med.,* 50:304-307.

Schubert, J.H., Ajello, L., Cooper, J.S. and Runyon, L.C. (1955). Evaluation of histoplasmin and yeast phase antigens derived from a single strain of *Histoplasma capsulatum* in the complement fixation test. *J. Bact.,* 69:558-562.

Schubert, J.H., Ajello, L., Stanford, S. and Grant, V.Q. (1953). Variations on complement fixation antigen production by different strains of *Histoplasma capsulatum* grown on two media. *J. Lab. Clin. Med.,* 41:91-97.

Seibert, F.B., Stacey, M. and Kent, P.W. (1949). An antigenic polysaccharide, "Polysaccharide II," isolated from tuberculin. *Biochem. Biophys. Acta,* 3:632-640.

Sorensen, L.J. and Evans, E.E. (1954). Antigenic fractions specific for *Histoplasma capsulatum* in the complement fixation reactions. *Proc. Soc. Exp. Biol. Med.,* 87:339-341.

Teneberg, D.J. and Howell, A., Jr. (1948). A complement fixation test for histoplasmosis. I. Technic and preliminary results on animal sera. *Public Health Rep.,* 63:163-168.

VanPernis, P.A., Benson, M.E. and Holinger, P.H. (1941). Specific cutaneous reactions with histoplasmosis. Preliminary report of another case. *J.A.M.A.,* 117:436-437.

Zarafonetis, C.J.D. and Lindberg, R.B. (1941). Histoplamosis of Darling: Observations on antigenic properties of causative agent; preliminary report. *Univ. Hosp. Bull.* (Ann Arbor), 7:47-48.

Chapter 9

Partial Chemical Characterization of Histoplasmin H-42

PETER A. BARTELS

ABSTRACT

Fractionation of histoplasmin H-42 using disc gel electrophoresis for separation of components has resulted in partial chemical characterization of a skin test active component. A glycoprotein component was studied, giving identification of a series of carbohydrates as well as several amino acids. Three hexoses have been identified; however, a hexoseamine awaits specific identification, probably by using gas chromatography. At least eighteen amino acid residues have been recognized along with end group analysis. This component, characterized by a Rf 0.7, was the most active as assessed by skin testing guinea pigs sensitized to several different *Histoplasma capsulatum* isolates.

THE skin test antigen histoplasmin, so widely used in epidemiological surveys, is a crude antigenic filtrate of liquid culture media in which *Histoplasma capsulatum* has been grown for varying periods of time. This epidemiologic and clinical tool was employed first by Van Pernis, Benson and Holinger (1941). Emmons, Olson and Eldridge (1945) used the synthetic broth of Smith (1943) as substrate. Palmer (1946) established the pattern of study, employing H-3 for survey of student nurses. Shaw, Howell and Weiss (1950) established the method of standardization of histoplasmin for skin testing. A preparation of this antigen, H-42, has been used until the present time as the product most appropriate for skin testing (Zarafonetis and Lindberg, 1941; Christie and Peterson, 1945; Emmons, 1949; Howell, 1939; Palmer, 1946).

Active skin-testing components found in histoplasmins have been isolated by several investigators, each using methods differing from one another (Van Pernis *et al.*, 1941; Cross and Howell, 1948; Knight and Marcus, 1958; Salvin and Smith, 1959). Greene, De Lalla and Tompkins (1960) have isolated at least two active components on DEAE-cellulose columns. Sprouse (1967) and Fadulu (1968) have completed similar investigations using separate isolates of *H. capsulatum* and *H. duboisii*.

Our laboratory is presently engaged in further chemical characterization of a skin test active component present in H-42 primarily for the purpose of establishing a reference component to be used in selecting a new source for this type antigen. A new source will be required in the near future as a result of the depletion of H-42 supply presently available.

Materials and Methods

Histoplasmin (H-42) was obtained from the United States Public Health Service. The limited supply available necessitated the use of micro-method determinations in several instances. Protein and carbohydrates were estimated on the crude filtrate, dialyzed material, and separate fractions. Total nitrogen was estimated, using the microdetermination of Kjeldahl (Lang, 1958), total protein by the method of Lowry (1951), and total carbohydrates by the anthrone and phenol method (Somogyi, 1945).

Analytical electrophoresis was done on 7.5% separator and 7% stacker gel as described by Canalco (1968).

Preparative electrophoresis was completed on 10% separator gels corresponding to 7.5% separator in the analytical gels and also using a 7% stacker gel system. Tris buffer, pH 7.2, was placed at both terminals while a regulated current of 3.5 mA per column was passed between them.

The method of Sanger (1945) was employed for acid hydrolysis for amino acid determination. Heavy walled Pyrex^{TM} tubes, washed several times with acid and stored in an evacuated desiccator, were used. Lyophilized proteins were suspended in 5.6N double-glass distilled HCl. The tubes were frozen and evacuated to a pressure of 50μ. The solutions were thawed until the vacuum was 60μ; the tubes were immersed again in the freezing solution, letting the air bubbles out. This process was used to degas the hydrolysis mixture. The tubes were shaken gently during the freezing and thawing. The tubes were sealed at 50μ. The hydrolysis was conducted at 110 ± 1°C for 24 hours. After the tubes had cooled to room temperature, liquid on the sides was spun down by gentle centrifugation. HCl was removed on the rotary evaporator, and the residue was redissolved in water and evaporated to dryness three times.

Acid hydrolysis of the carbohydrate moiety was done by the method of Gottschalk (1966). Dry samples of histoplasmin and its fractions were hydrolyzed for 20 hours in 0.25N H_2SO_4 in a sealed tube using a process similar to that described for amino acids. The hydrolysis was conducted at 105 ± 1°C. After hydrolysis the solutions were neutralized with $BaCO_3$ to pH 7, using pH paper. The precipitate was removed by centrifugation. The supernatant was decanted, evaporated in the rotary evaporator, and redissolved in water. Amino acids, peptides, and proteins were removed by passing the solution through columns of Dowex-50-H$^+$ (5 mm × 5 cm). The columns were washed with 1 ml of water, and the washing was added to the eluate, which was evaporated to dryness and redissolved in 26 μl of water.

N-terminal amino acid residues were determined using the procedure of Levy and Chung (1955) and Sanger and Thompson (1953). The dry sample was dissolved to 0.05N aqueous KOH at 40°C, and the pH was adjusted to 8 (addition of 0.05N KOH). DNFB was added and the mixture was stirred vigorously in darkness while the pH and temperature were kept constant by addition of KOH in an incubator. The reaction was terminated when no further base was consumed. The solution was extracted three times with ether and acidified. The precipitated DNP-compounds were centrifuged, washed with water, acetone, and ether, and then dried over phosphorus pentoxide. Total hydrolysis of the dinitrophenyl protein involved the method also described by Sanger *et al.* (1953). DNP-protein was hydrolyzed with 100x quantity of double-distilled 5.7N HCl at 105± 1°C for 16 hours under vacuum. The hydrolysate was diluted to an HCl concentration of 1N. This material (hydrolysate) was extracted three times with peroxide-free ether.

C-terminal amino acid residues were identified using the methods of Guidotti (1960), Harris and Li (1955), Tietze and Gladner and Folk (1957).

Qualitative estimation of amino acids was completed using silica gel for two-dimensionl thin layer chromatography, with n-butanol/glacial acetic acid/water (80/20/20 by volume) as the first solvent and phenol/water (70/30 by volume) as the second solvent. Ninhydrin (0.3 gm ninhydrin + 100 ml n-butanol +3 ml glacial acetic acid) was used to detect amino acids.

Qualitative estimation of carbohydrate was done by using Whatman No. 1 filter paper for descending and ascending chromatography. Descending chromatograms were developed in ethyl/pyridine/water (10/5/6 by volume) and sprayed with benzidine (0.5 gm benzidine, 10 ml glacial acetic acid, 10 ml 40% TCA, and 80 ml ethanol). Ascending chromatograms were developed in isopropano/lacetic acid/water (3/1/1) and sprayed with aniline oxalate reagent.

Qualitative estimation of DNP-derivatives was completed using silica gel. Benzene/pyridine/glacial acetic acid (80/20/20) and chloroform/methanol/glacial acetic acid (95/5/1) were used for the ether-soluble derivatives as described by Brener, Niederwieser, and Pataki (1964). Identification of water-soluble DNP-derivatives was completed using n-propanol/34% ammonium hydroxide (7/3) (Pataki, 1968).

Quantitative estimation of amino acid was performed on a 100µg sample hydrolysate (A-2) dissolved in 0.5 cc of buffer and 10µg of internal standard. Readings were done on a Beckman-Spinco amino acid analyzer Model 120B.

Analytical disc gel electrophoresis of histoplasmin H-42 repeatedly yielded a characteristic pattern of bands. All bands stained with Amido Schwarz protein were located at Rf's 0.05, 0.2, 0.38, 0.64, and 0.7. Only bands 0.38 and 0.7 were positive with Schiff's reagent while none of the bands stained with Sudan Black were positive.

A sample of 8 ml concentrated H-42, corresponding to 2800 Pg protein, was eluted from a preparative column. Fractions were collected and separated into three pooled aliquots. These represented the tracting pool (no band) designated No. 1; the next two showed protein and carbohydrate staining and corresponded to the band with a Rf 0.7 and 0.38, respectively. The minor components with Rf 0.64, 0.2, and 0.5 were not recovered, since preliminary testing of these materials from these bands demonstrated no skin-testing activity.

Figure 9-1 shows the electrophoretic pattern and Table 9-I the corresponding chemical analysis of the dialyzed H-42. Further chemical analysis identified three hexoses to be present: mannose, galactose, and glucose. Both pools 2 and 3 yielded an unidentified hexoseamine. Table 9-II shows the carbohydrate contents of H-42 and its fractions.

Hydrolyzed H-42, 1 mg, in 1 ml HCl was analyzed for amino acid content using thin layer chromatography. Eighteen amino acids were identified. A sample from each pool was also analyzed, with hydrolysates of pool 1 show-

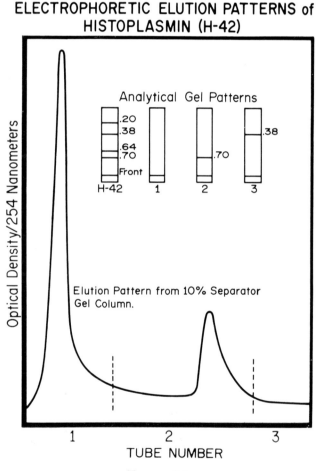

FIGURE 9-1

TABLE 9-I

Chemical Analysis of Histoplasmin H-42 Fractions Eluted from Preparative
Acrylamide Gel Column (10% Separator)

	Fraction Number				
	1	*2*	*3*	*Total*	*% Recovery*
Total protein μg/pool	1100	500	600	2200/2800	78
Total carbohydrate μg/pool	400	200	310	910/2320	39.2
Reducing sugar	+	+	+		
Skin test dilution	100	100	100		
Skin test					
Erythema	6.8	11.6	9.0		
Induration	3.2	9.4	6.4		

ing negative reaction with ninhydrin, while pool 2 and 3 gave similar results.
The molar ratios of the amino acids as compared to histidine residues are
listed in Table 9-III, following separation on the resin column of the amino
analyzer.

End group analysis for amino acids was performed on pooled fraction No.
2, since it was the only pure fraction detected with repeated testing. Di-
DNP-histidine derivative was identified in the N-terminal analysis; however, both serine (RF 0.21) and threonine (Rf 0.18) were detected after 1
minute in the C-terminal analysis, causing difficulty in determining which
amino acid is split off first.

Discussion

Histoplasmin H-42, a composite of different isolates grown in broth culture, demonstrates skin test activity in sensitized subjects. A glycoprotein

TABLE 9-II

Carbohydrate Contents of H-42 and Its Fractions

Fraction	μg hydro- lyzed	Descending Chromatography			Ascending Chromatography			Hexos- amine
		μg Used	No. of Spots	Sugar Identified	μg Used	No. of Spots	Sugar Identified	
H-42	800	400	6	Mannose Glucose Galactose Pink spot Rf 0.04	400	5	Mannose Glucose, Galactose† Spot Rf 0.75	+
S-1	40	40	1	Pink spot Rf 0.04	—	—	—	+
S-2	90	90	3	Mannose Galactose* Pink spot Rf 0.04				
A-1	290	145	1	Pink spot Rf 0.04	145	1	Spot Rf 0.75	+
A-2	390	195	3	Mannose Galactose* Pink spot Rf 0.04	195	2	Spot Rf 0.75 Mannose	+

* Very light spot.
† Appeared as one spot because of poor separation of these two sugars in ascending chromatography.

TABLE 9-III

Amino Acids Composition From Hydrolysate of Protein Fraction With Rf 0.7

Amino Acid	Micromoles×100	Residues/Histidine
Lysine	2.2	3.7
Histidine	0.6	1.0
Ammonia	1.3	2.1
Arginine	1.5	2.5
Unknown	1.0	1.7
Aspartic acid	6.1	10.0
Theronine	5.6	9.3
Serine	5.2	8.7
Glutamic acid	7.8	13.0
Proline	9.6	16.0
Glycine	4.8	8.0
Alanine	4.3	7.1
Half cystine	0.9	1.5
Valine	2.9	4.8
Methionine	0.6	4.3
Isoleucine	1.8	3.0
Leucine	0.6	1.0
Tyrosine	2.4	4.0
Phenylalanine	1.2	2.0

component, characterized by a Rf 0.7 and possessing skin test activity, has been isolated and partially identified chemically. From this partial characterization one can hopefully select from other filtrates one or more which compare favorably with respect to skin-testing activities. Further chemical studies on these glycoproteins, followed by comparison studies using H-42 as the reference, could result in a better preparation of skin-testing material.

It was recognized that the two major components found in dialyzed H-42 are related concerning their composition and activity. When dialyzed material is freshly prepared and applied to columns with a good cooling system, the Rf 0.38 band will predominate. Aged material, allowed to increase in temperature while being subjected to electrophoresis, yields increased amounts of Rf 0.7 bands. This relationship could be explained if the two bands have the same protein moiety but different amounts of carbohydrate residue. The Rf 0.7 band demonstrated the greater specificity and sensitivity when tested on sensitized guinea pigs.

Other studies completed in our laboratory have previously demonstrated the presence of a Rf 0.7 band in dialyzed filtrate obtained from broth inoculated with the Scritchfield and Grand Island isolates. Glycoprotein from District isolate and NCDC No. 267 have predominant Rf 0.38 and 0.63 bands, respectively. Increased levels of activity associated with the Scritchfield component suggest that this isolate could be the choice for future histoplasmin production.

References

Brener, M., Niederwieser, A. and Pataki, G. (1964). *New Biochemical Separations.* London, Van Nostrand Co.

Canal Industrial Corporation. (1968). *Prep-disc Instruction Manual.* Rockville, Maryland., pp. 12-29.

Cross, F. and Howell, A. (1948). Studies of the fungus antigens. II. Preliminary reports on the isolation of an immunologically active polysaccharide from histoplasmin. *Public Health Rep.,* 63:892-896.

Emmons, C.W., Olson, B.J. and Eldridge W.W. (1945). Studies of the role of fungi in pulmonary disease: cross reaction to histoplasmin. *Public Health Rep.,* 60:1383-1394.

Emmons, C.W. (1949). Isolation of *Histoplasma capsulatum* from soil. *Public Health Rep.,* 64:892-896.

Fadulu, S.O. (1968). Biochemical characterization and skin test sensitivity of mycelial growth filtrate of *Histoplasma duboisii.* Ph.D. dissertation, Norman, University of Oklahoma.

Gottschalk, A. (1966). *Glycoproteins.* New York, Elsevier.

Greene, C.H., DeLalla, L.S. and Tompkins, V.N. (1960). Separation of specific antigens of *Histoplasma capsulatum* by ion exchange chromatography. *Proc. Soc. Exp. Biol. Med.,* 105:140-141.

Guidotti, G. (1960). The action of carboxypeptidase A & B on the separated chains of alpha and beta normal adult human hemoglobin. *Biochem. Biophys. Acta,* 42:177-179.

Harris, J.I. and Li, C.H. (1955). Corticotropins (ACTH). *J. Biol. Chem.,* 213:499-507.

Howell, A. (1939). Studies on *Histoplasma capsulatum* and similar form-species. I. Morphology and development. *Mycologia,* 31:191-216.

Knight, R.A. and Marcus, S. (1958). Polysaccharide skin test antigen derived from *Histoplasma capsulatum* and *Blastomyces dermatitidis. Amer. Rev. Tuberc. Pulmon. Dis.,* 77:983-989.

Lang, C.A. (1958). Simple microdetermination of Kjeldahl nitrogen in biological materials. *Anal. Chem.,* 30:1692-1964.

Levy, A.L. and Chung, D. (1955). A simplified procedure for the synthesis of 2, 4 Dinitrophenyl (DNP)-amino acids. *J. Amer. Chem. Soc.,* 77:2899.

Lowry, O.H., Rosebrough, A.L. and Randall, R.J. (1951). Protein measurement with folin-phenol reagent. *J. Biol. Chem.,* 193:265-275.

Palmer, C.E. (1946). Geographic differences in sensitivity to histoplasmin among student nurses. *Public Health Rep.,* 61:475-487.

Pataki, G. (1968). *Techniques of Thin Layer Chromatography in Amino Acids and Peptides.* Ann Arbor, Ann Arbor Science.

Salvin, S.B. and Smith, R.F. (1959). Antigens from the yeast phase of *Histoplasma capsulatum.* III. Isolation, properties, and activity of a protein-carbohydrate complex. *J. Infect. Dis.,* 105:45-53.

Sanger, F. (1945). Free amino groups of insulin. *Biochem. J.,* 39:507.

Sanger, F. and Thompson, E.O.P. (1953). The amino acid sequence in glycyl chain of insulin. *Biochem. J.,* 53:366.

Shaw, L.W., Howell, A. and Weiss, E.S. (1950). Biological assay of lots of histoplasmin and the selection of a new working lot. *Public Health Rep.,* 65(18):583-610.

Smith, C.E. (1943). Coccidioidomycosis. *Med. Clin. N. Amer.,* 27:790-807.

Somogyi, M. (1945). A new reagent for the determination of sugars. *J. Biol. Chem.,* 160:61-68.

Sprouse, R.F. (1967). Ph.D. dissertation, Norman, University of Oklahoma.

Tietze, F., Gladner, J.A. and Folk, J.E. (1957). Release of C-terminal S-(β-aminoethyl)-cysteine residues by carboxypeptidase-B. *Biochem Biophys Acta,* 26:659.

Van Pernis, P.A., Benson, M.E. and Holinger, P.H. (1941). Specific cutaneous reactions with histoplasmosis. *J.A.M.A.,* 117:436-437.

Zarafonetis, C.J.D. and Lindberg, R.B. (1941). Histoplasmosis of Darling: Observations on the antigenic properties of the causative agent. *Univ. Hosp. Bull. (Ann Arbor),* 7:47-48.

Chapter 10

Nutritional Factors That Are Required for the Growth and Sporulation of *Histoplasma capsulatum*

COY D. SMITH

ABSTRACT

Experiments were conducted to determine what elements or compounds were required for the growth and conidia production of *Histoplasma capsulatum* on a defined medium. The fungus was grown initially on a lean defined media containing dextrose, asparagin, phosphate, a mixture of mineral salts, thiamine and biotin, cysteine, and purified agar. In subsequent experiments *H. capsulatum* was cultured on dextrose, asparagin, and phosphate in a purified agar medium with the other ingredients eliminated one by one if they did not prove essential for growth and conidia production. The end result showed that in addition to carbon, nitrogen, and phosphate, only calcium and cysteine were required additives. The fungus would not grow when cysteine or calcium alone was added, but it required both substances. A carbon and nitrogen source as lean as 0.1 percent was apparently sufficient in concentration to permit good growth and sporulation of the fungus.

SEVERAL investigators have studied the basic nutritional requirements for the growth of the mycelial phase of *Histoplasma capsulatum*. These studies have been on such subjects as carbon and nitrogen sources (Scheff, 1950; Negroni, 1946), amino acids (Salvin, 1949), and vitamins (Pine, 1957). It was found that the fungus could utilize several carbohydrate and nitrogen sources and did not require any specific vitamin. Glucose was found to be the carbohydrate of choice, while several of the amino acids served equally well.

Little attention has been paid previously to the requirements for conidia production or the concentration of carbon or nitrogen sources in media needed for growth and sporulation. Is it really necessary to use 4% dextrose such as found in Sabouraud's medium or even 2 percent as used in one modification (Emmons, Binford and Utz, 1963) of medium for *H. capsulatum*? One would not expect to find concentrations of carbon or nitrogen in soil where the fungus occurs naturally as high as that which is commonly used in most laboratory media.

This study was performed for the following purposes: (1) To demonstrate if abundant growth and conidia production of *H. capsulatum* can be obtained on a chemically defined substrate on very low concentrations of nutrients, and (2) in addition to a carbon and nitrogen source, to determine what additional elements or compounds are required for growth and conidia production of the fungus.

Materials and Methods

Basic Medium

The basic medium used in this study consisted of the following composition analytical grade dextrose (Baker) 1.0 gm, asparagin 1.0 gm (Difco), purified agar 20.0 gm (Difco), and distilled water 1,000 ml. The purpose of using a solid medium instead of liquid for studying conidia production was that the fungus does not produce conidia well on liquid media. Of the medium 25 ml was dispensed into 100 × 15 mm plastic petri dishes.

Inoculum

Two recent soil isolates of *H. capsulatum* were used in these studies (PHC and Cyn.). The PHC isolate was used in experiment one and Cyn. in experiments two and three. Preliminary studies showed that the substrate used to produce the seed inoculum was critical in interpreting the test results. For example, if the culture used for seed was grown on a rich medium like Sabouraud's, the inoculum would grow oftentimes for the first transfer on water agar medium devoid of nutrients. Therefore, the medium used for the seed inoculum was a starvation type with minimal nutrients. Beef extract (Difco) 0.5 gm/liter as the sole substrate in a 2% agar base served very well as a seed culture medium. Of this medium 50 ml was dispensed into 250 ml gauze-stoppered Erlenmeyer flasks. After three to four weeks incubation at room temperature, the surface growth was harvested. Added to this were 10 ml of distilled water and twenty to thirty 3 mm glass beads, and the light diffuse growth was harvested by hand-swirling the flasks. A further 1:10 dilution of this seed suspension was made which was used for seed inoculum. Of the inoculum 0.1 ml was placed on each test medium plate and carefully spread, using a curved glass rod.

Harvest and Measurement of Growth from Test Media

Since a great deal of growth and sporulation occurs beneath the surface of a lean medium, a technique was developed for harvesting the entire petri plate contents. This method consists of removing the entire agar disc from two plates for each test and placing it into a sterile 1-pint, screw cap Waring Blender® jar containing 100 ml of distilled water. The contents are blended for 25 to 30 seconds. The end product is a fine gel with the hyphal fragments and spores evenly dispersed in the suspension. Of this 1 ml is removed and placed in a test tube for hemocytometer counts. Prior to counting however,

0.1 ml of concentrated hydrochloric acid and 0.1 ml of lactophenol cotton blue dye is added. The suspension is heated in a water bath to 60°C. The result is an aqueous suspension of stained fungus particles to enhance counts on a hemocytometer at ×450 magnification. The number of hypha and conidia counted are reported as the amount found per milliliters of the original gel suspension, i.e. 100 ml of water plus 40 ml of media (although the two plates originally contained 25 ml each, approximately 10 ml water loss because of evaporation occurred during incubation for four weeks). We have found this method very satisfactory for counting fungus particles and estimating viability.

Preliminary experiments indicated that the fungus would not grow on a dextrose asparagin base medium, especially when using purified agar. Even when a mixture of mineral salts was added, the growth was sparse. The missing ingredient was found to be phosphate. It did not make any difference whether it was monobasic or dibasic sodium, potassium, or the calcium phosphate.

Solutions of 1/5M potassium monobasic phosphate and 1/5 M sodium dibasic phosphate (reagent grade) were prepared, and by combining the two (at the ratio of 87.1 ml of the former with 12.9 ml of the latter), a stock buffer solution was produced with a pH of 6.0. Thus, the amount of phosphate is 27.5 mg/ml. The prepared stock phosphate buffer solution was stored at 5°C.

A lean defined medium was prepared according to the ingredients shown in Table 10-I. It was found that *H. capsulatum* would grow and sporulate very well on this medium.

The following experiments were performed in order to determine what elements or compounds shown in Table 10-I are actually essenital for the growth and sporulation of *H. capsulatum*.

TABLE 10-I

Composition of the Preliminary Defined Medium Used for the Growth of *Histoplasma capsulatum*

	(gm)
Dextrose	1.0
Asparagin	1.0
Phosphate (as Po4 buffer)	0.75
ZnSo4	0.001
MnSo4	0.0005
MgCl₂	0.025
CuSo4	0.0005
Na₂MoO4	0.001
FeNo₃	0.001
CaCl₂	0.025
L (+) cysteine HCl	0.025
Thiamine	0.00005
Biotin	0.00005
Purified agar	20.0
Distilled water	1000.0 cc

Experiment One

Nine different media were prepared, using various combinations of the designated ingredients in the concentrations shown in Table 10-I. The medium designated as the control contained 0.1% dextrose, 0.1% asparagin, 0.055 gm of phosphate and 2% purified agar per liter only. The other eight test media contained these four ingredients plus various combinations of the compounds shown in Figure 10-1. The plates were inoculated with the PHC isolate of *H. capsulatum,* and after four weeks' incubation at 28°C, they were harvested as previously described. There were three media as seen in Figure 10-1 which did not support the growth of *H. capsulatum* (1, 2, 3). The ingredients common to all media where growth was obtained are cysteine and calcium. Medium 5, containing thiamine and biotin, gave less growth than medium 4, which was similar except the two vitamins were left out. Media 4 and 6 have the highest number of total particles, with a hyphal to conidial ratio of almost 1:1. Medium 8 has the highest number of hyphal particles, but the number of conidia is considerably less. The spore to hyphal ratio is the highest in media 9 and 5. In summation, the results from this experiment suggest that perhaps only cysteine and/or calcium is required in addition to the basic medium in order to obtain growth.

Experiment Two

This experiment was performed on five different media as shown in Figure 10-2. The techniques used were similar to experiment one, however,

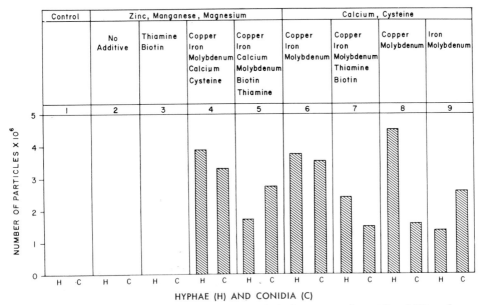

FIGURE 10-1. Comparison of the number of hyphal elements and conidia of *Histoplasma capsulatum* harvested from media containing various mineral salts and/or other compounds.

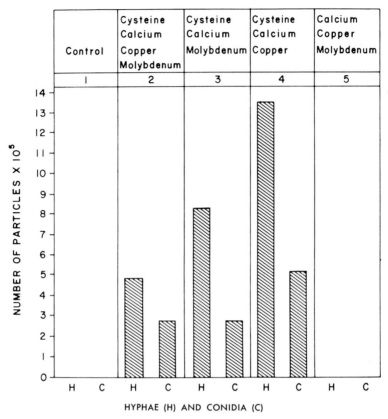

FIGURE 10-2. Comparison of the number of hyphal elements and conidia of *Histoplasma capsulatum* harvested from media containing metallic salts and cysteine.

only calcium, molybdenum, copper and cysteine were studied. The media composition and results are shown in Figure 10-2. Again, essentially no growth was obtained on media without cysteine. The highest number of hyphal particles and conidia were obtained from the medium with cysteine, calcium and copper.

Experiment Three

In order to learn if *H. capsulatum* can grow with the addition of cysteine only to the basic medium without calcium, a third experiment was performed. This experiment was set up using similar methods to that described for experiments one and two. The media were inoculated with the Cyn. isolate of *H. capsulatum* and incubated for one month prior to harvesting. Growth was obtained only on medium 4, containing cysteine and calcium as shown in Figure 10-3. Therefore, either cysteine or calcium when added to the basic medium alone will not permit *H. capsulatum* to grow, but it apparently requires the two in combination.

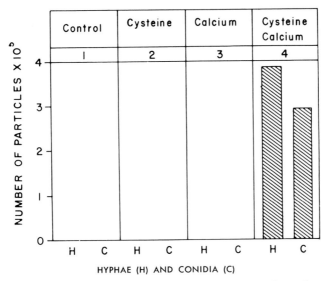

FIGURE 10-3. Comparison of the number of hyphal elements and conidia of *Histoplasma capsulatum* harvested from defined media with calcium and cysteine added.

Discussion

The purpose of this study was not to determine the need for metallic trace elements, but to determine the basic elements or compounds which are an absolute requirement for growth and sporulation. The reason all the various metallic elements were used initially is because of preliminary work which showed a "M" salt mixture containing these elements was required for growth.

The requirement for cysteine for the mycelial phase of *H. capsulatum* may be similar to its yeast phase, in which other organic sulfur sources as well as cysteine serve equally well (McVeigh and Morton, 1965). The requirement for calcium in addition to cysteine is indeed surprising and should be further explored. These data do not show whether calcium is the only metallic salt in addition to cysteine that must be added to the basic medium; perhaps calcium is not specific, and others may do the job as well.

The above experiments were conducted in consideration of growth and sporulation requirements only. Viability of the conidia and hypha were determined in each experiment; however, time does not permit showing these data. It should be emphasized that none of the components of the test medium was prepared in optimal concentrations for growth. All were generally the reverse, i.e. purposely made up to be lean. Most chemicals even when purified contain traces of other elements; therefore, using as lean a medium as practical for these experiments would help reduce chemical contamination. In addition to the required substances for growth shown in this experiment, other elements such as iron or copper may permit improved growth and sporulation as suggested in the results shown in Figure 10-1.

The concentrations of carbon and nitrogen (1.0 gm/liter) in the above media appear to be ample for good growth. While it produces a more diffuse growth than a rich medium such as Sabouraud's, sporulation is generally much higher. Most mycologists, especially medical mycologists, use spores primarily for identifying pathogenic filamentous fungi. Therefore, the use of a lean substrate for growth of these organisms appears advantageous. Finally, the rate of growth of *H. capsulatum* in a defined medium compared to a complex undefined one such as yeast extract is somewhat slower. This is a common biological phenomena, since the enzyme system has to function more efficiently in order to synthesize certain required substances. These substances may already be present, at least in part, in the complex medium.

References

Emmons, C.W., Binford, C.H. and Utz, J.P. (1963). *Medical Mycology*. Philadelphia, Lea & Febiger, p. 347.

McVeigh, I. and Morton, K. (1965). Nutritional studies of *Histoplasma capsulatum*. *Mycopathologia*, 25:294-308.

Negroni, P. (1946). Unnievo caso de histoplasmosis. Estudio Micologico y terapeutico. *Rev. Argent. Dermatosif*, 30:212-219.

Pine, L. (1957). Studies on the growth of *Histoplasma capsulatum* III. Effect of thiamine and other vitamins on the growth of the yeast and mycelial phase of *Histoplasma capsulatum*. *J. Bact.*, 74:239-245.

Salvin, S.B. (1949). Cysteine and related compounds in the growth of the yeast like phase of *Histoplasma capsulatum*. *J. Infect. Dis.*, 84:275-283.

Scheff, G.J. (1945). Biochemical and immunological properties of *Histoplasma capsulatum*. No. 650 *Yale J. Biol. Med.*, 18:41-54.

Chapter 11

Growth Inhibition of *Histoplasma capsulatum* by Organic Sulfur Compounds

ILDA McVEIGH, LAMAR FIELD, AND WAYNE S. HANLEY

ABSTRACT

Representatives of thirteen classes of organic sulfur compounds have been screened for inhibitory action on the *in vitro* growth of yeast phase cells of *Histoplasma capsulatum*. The classes containing the most active compounds were the thiols, thiolsulfonates, thioacids, carbonyl disulfides, dithiocarbamates, trithiopercarbamates and the n-decylaminoethyl disulfides. Correlations of the structure of the compounds with activity are discussed.

THE best source of organic fungicides for control of plant pathogens has been sulfur compounds, particularly the dithiocarbamates (Horsfall, 1956; Rich, 1960). Many of these compounds have been found as inhibitory to fungi as most chemicals used in human therapy, if not more so, and some are less toxic to animals (Thorn and Ludwig, 1962). Rhodanine (2-thioxo-4-thiazolidinone) and several of its derivatives, which also contain the dithiocarbamate linkage,

were reported by Christison, Conant and Bradsher (1955) to inhibit *in vitro* growth of the yeast form of *Histoplasma capsulatum* at concentrations of 10µg/ml or less, but they were too toxic in mice for *in vivo* protection tests against experimental histoplasmosis. Tetraethylthiuram disulfide, which contains the same linkage, was reported by these investigators to inhibit *in vitro* growth of the yeast cells at 5µg/ml and to be less toxic for animals than the rhodanine compounds. However, it failed to protect mice against experimental histoplasmosis at the dosage levels used. Nevertheless, in view of the continued need for a satisfactory drug for the treatment of histoplasmosis and of the significant inhibitory action exerted on *H. capsulatum in vitro* by

NOTE. This research was supported, in part, by Biomedical Science Support Grant, National Institutes of Health Grant Fr-07089-02 to Vanderbilt University and by PHS Research Grants AI-03524 and AI-08916 from the National Institute of Allergy and Infectious Diseases and PHS Research Grant AM-11685 from the National Institute of Arthritis and Metabolic Diseases.

Modified versions of portions of this paper have been published in *Mycopathologia et Mycologia Applicata*, 35, 313-323 (1968) and 37, 349-356 (1969). A detailed report on the carbonyl disulfides is in preparation for publication at an early date.

some of the organic sulfur compounds tested, further investigations of such compounds for effects on this pathogen appear worthwhile. Accordingly, in cooperation with Dr. Lamar Field and some of his associates in the Chemistry Department of Vanderbilt University, a broad screening program of representatives of various classes of organic sulfur compounds for their effects on growth of *H. capsulatum* was undertaken. Further investigation will be made of the classes of compounds which on the basis of the screening tests appear most promising, in endeavors to correlate structure with activity, to decrease animal toxicity, to modify distribution characteristics, and to increase *in vivo* effectiveness.

Materials and Methods

The materials and methods were similar to those described previously by McVeigh and Evans, 1968, and McVeigh *et al.*, 1969, and determinations were made of the effects of each test compound on growth of the yeast form cells of two strains (H-7 and H-25) of *H. capsulatum* in a proteose peptone broth medium containing citrated human plasma. Solutions containing known concentrations of the test compounds were prepared and sterilized by filtration. Appropriate amounts of the solutions were added to portions of the heat-sterilized medium, mixed, and then dispensed aseptically in 10 ml quantities into sterile tubes. The tubes were inoculated immediately using per tube 0.1 ml of a standardized inoculum (2.0-4.5 $\times$ 10^8 cells/ml) prepared by suspending cells from a two-to three-day-old culture in saline solution. The cultures were incubated for seven days at 37°C, after which growth was measured turbidimetrically.

The test compounds not soluble in water were dissolved either in methanol or in dioxane and then diluted with sufficient water or an aqueous solution of Tween® 80 to result in the desired concentration (usually 1000 μg/ml) prior to sterilization. The usual procedure was to test the effect of each compound in triplicate at concentrations of 5μg, 10μg, 15μg and 20 μg/ml. Some compounds were tested at additional concentrations within the range of 0.0μg-20.0μg/ml. Some compounds, because of their sparing solubility in the solvents, were tested only at concentrations of 10μg/ml or less. Controls contained the medium only and the medium plus the solvent at the highest concentration used in the test cultures. Some of the compounds found to be effective in inhibiting growth in the peptone medium were tested also for their effects on growth in the chemically defined medium (McVeigh and Morton, 1965).

Results and Discussion

Representatives of the following classes of organic sulfur compounds have been tested for their inhibitory effects on growth *in vitro* of the yeast form

cells of *H. capsulatum:* thiols, thioacids, disulfides (especially carbonyl disulfides of the general structure $RC(O)SSR'$, and *n*-decylaminoethyl disulfides of the structure $RSS(CH_2)_2NH\text{-}n\text{-}C_{10}H_{21}$), dithiocarbamates, trithiopercarbamates, thiolsulfonates, sulfinates, sulfenamides, aldehyde and
ketone derivatives of aminothiols, penicillamine analogs, thiamine analogs,
and cystine and cysteine analogs. On the basis of results of the preliminary
screening tests, the thiols, thioacids, thiolsulfonates, carbonyl disulfides,
n-decylaminoethyl disulfides, dithiocarbamates, and trithiopercarbamates
appear to offer the greatest promise as sources of inhibitory agents for this
fungus and were therefore selected for further study. It should be noted
that this decision was based on growth determinations made at the end of a
seven-day growth period. Had the growth determinations been made after
a shorter incubation period, it is likely that more compounds would have
appeared to be effective, since several recorded as negative did cause a
delay in growth or partial inhibition at the higher concentrations tested.
The lowest concentration of a compound which resulted in complete inhibition during the seven-day incubation period was considered the minimum
inhibitory concentration.

The thiols and thioacids are relatively insoluble in water, have very dis-
agreeable odors, and those of low molecular weight are quite toxic to animals and volatilize or decompose readily. Thus, they are unlikely to be
useful in the therapy of animals. However, they are very reactive. According to Owens (1969), they act as reducing agents for a wide variety of
substances, including components of biological systems such as disulfide
enzymes and certain coenzymes. A number of metals involved in oxidations
and electron transport may be complexed by them. The thioacids and their
derivatives have been very useful in the control of certain plant pathogens.
The reaction of thioacids $[RC(O)SH]$ with thiols $(R'SH)$ results, in principle, in the formation of carbonyl disulfides $[RC(O)SSR']$, another class
which offers promise as a source of inhibitors of *H. capsulatum.* Thus, such
structures may be a useful means of introducing active groups into compounds having more desirable properties than the original compounds from
which they may be considered to have been made.

Accordingly, sixteen thiols and six thioacids, obtained from commercial
sources, were tested for their inhibitory effects on each of the two strains of
H. capsulatum in an effort to establish a correlation between structure and
activity. Those which were effective in inhibiting one or both strains are
listed in Table 11-I. The aliphatic thioacids appeared to be more active than
the aromatic, and those with short chains more effective than those with
long or branched chains. The alkanethiols, in general, seemed less effective
than the arenethiols. The substitution of an electron withdrawing group in
the aromatic ring of the thiols apparently resulted in increased activity.

In order to obtain a structure-activity relationship in the carbonyl disulfides $[RC(O)SSR']$, twenty-three compounds having different R and R'

TABLE 11-I

Minimum Inhibitory Concentrations (MIC) of Selected Thiols and Thioacids

Compound	R	H-7	MIC ($\mu g/ml$)	H-25
RSH				
Benzenethiol	C_6H_5	*P-10		5
p-Chlorobenzenethiol	$p\text{-}ClC_6H_4$	7.5		2.5
p-Toluenethiol	$p\text{-}CH_3C_6H_4$	>10		10
o-Toluenethiol	$o\text{-}CH_3C_6H_4$	>10		7.5
2-Naphthalenethiol	$2\text{-}C_{10}H_7$	*P-5		5
α-Toluenethiol	$C_6H_5CH_2$	>10		10
1-Dodecanethiol	$CH_3(CH_2)_{10}CH_2$	>10		10
2-(n-Decylamino)ethanethiol	$n\text{-}C_{10}H_{21}NH(CH_2)_2$	10		7.5
3,4-Dichlorobenzenethiol	$3,4\text{-}Cl_2C_6H_3$	15		5
RC(O)SH				
Thioacetic acid	CH_3	15		12.5
Thiopropionic acid	CH_3CH_2	20		10

* P = partial growth.

groups (e.g. short, long, and branched chain alkyl and aryl) have been synthesized so far, sixteen of which were inhibitory for one or both strains. A detailed report of the results is now in press (Field, Hanley, McVeigh, and Evans). Tentative deductions concerning the relation of structure to activity, made on the bases of the results examined to date will be discussed briefly here. For the R group, alkyl was better than phenyl. Short chain alkyls appeared to be most effective. Branching or lengthening of the alkyl chain resulted in decreased activity. For the R′ group, phenyl proved slightly better than short alkyl; again, lengthening or branching of the alkyl chain decreased activity; electron-donating or -withdrawing groups seemed to confer little advantage over the phenyl group itself. Owens (1969) in a discussion relating to thiuram disulfides reported that alkyl groups regulate the strength of the disulfide linkage and determine in part the lipophilicity of the molecule. Thus the ease with which the compound permeates the cells and the rates of reactions within the cells are correlated with the alkyl groups. According to Owens, the data of Klöpping (1951) suggest that size and spatial arrangement of the alkyl groups are critical in toxicity and that, as the number of the carbon atoms in the alkyl group is increased, permeation may become a limiting factor. He also pointed out that the oxidation potential of the disulfide decreases as the alkyl chain increases. This, in turn, may prevent the intracellular reactions which are responsible for the toxic effects.

The inhibitory action of various trithiopercarbamates on yeast cells of *H. capsulatum* has been reported by Buckman, Johnson and Field (1966) and by McVeigh and Evans (1968). Of the eight trithiopercarbamates tested, all

TABLE 11-II

Minimum Inhibitory Concentrations (MIC) of Various Trithiopercarbamates and Dithiopercarbamates

Compound	MIC (μg/ml) Peptone-Plasma Medium		MIC (μg/ml) Synthetic Medium	
	H-7	H-25	H-7	H-25
$H_2NC(S)SSC(CH_3)_3$	>20	>20	>10	>10
$CH_3NHC(S)SSC(CH_3)_3$	15	10	5	>10
$(CH_3)_2NC(S)SSC(CH_3)_3$	20	10 or less	1	2.5
$H_2NC(S)SSC_6H_4$-p-CH_3	10	5	5	10
$CH_3NHC(S)SSC_6H_4$-p-CH_3	7.5	2.5	2.5	10
$(CH_3)_2NC(S)SSC_6H_4$-p-CH_3	7.5	1 to 2.5	1.0 or less	5 to 10
$CH_3NHC(S)SSCH_2CH_2NHC(O)CH_3$	10	10		
$(CH_3)_2NC(S)SSCH_2CH_2NHC(O)CH_3$	10	5		
$CH_3NHC(S)S^-K^+$	5	5		
$(CH_3)_2NC(S)S^-K^+$	10	2.5		

but one was inhibitory at 20μg/ml or less (Table 11-II). The inhibitory action of these compounds was equal to or greater than that of two commercial dithiocarbamate salts when tested under the same conditions. As has been reported for the dithiocarbamates (Owens, 1969), the activity of the trithiopercarbamates is enhanced by the addition of one or more methyl groups to the nitrogen atom.

Six *n*-decylaminoethyl disulfides have been synthesized and tested. Each of these was inhibitory to both strains of *H. capsulatum* at concentrations of 10μg/ml or less (Table 11-III). Further investigations of this group are planned. No reports concerning antifungal activity of members of this class of compounds have been found. This class is of particular interest in that, except for the thiosemicarbazones (Benns, Gingras and Bayley, 1960) and the N-substituted ethylenethioureas (Ross and Ludwig, 1957), organic sulfur

TABLE 11-III

Minimum Inhibitory Concentrations (MIC) of *n*- Decylaminoethyl Disulfides

Test Compounds R-CH_2SS-$(CH_2)_2NH$-n-$C_{10}H_{21}$·HCl	R Group	MIC Strains	
		H-7	H-25
		μg/ml	μg/ml
Benzyl *n*-decylaminoethyl disulfide· HCl	C_6H_5	10	5.0
p-Methylbenzyl *n*-decylaminoethyl disulfide· HCl	p-$CH_3C_6H_4$	5 or less	2.5
p-Methoxybenzyl *n*-decylaminoethyl disulfide· HCl	p-$CH_3OC_6H_4$	5.0	5.0
p-Cyanobenzyl *n*-decylaminoethyl disulfide· HCl	p-CNC_6H_4	10	5.0
m-Nitrobenzyl *n*-decylaminoethyl disulfide· HCl	m-$NO_2C_6H_4$	10	2.5
2-Acetamidoethyl *n*-decylaminoethyl disulfide· HCl	$CH_3C(O)NHCH_2$	10	5.0

compounds containing alkyl groups with long carbon chains have been relatively inactive. Benns *et al.* reported an increase in the fungicidal activity of the thiosemicarbazones with increase of the alkyl chain to ten carbon atoms, above which a decrease in activity occurs.

Tests of the compounds for toxicity to animals and *in vivo* tests for effectiveness in treatment of experimental histoplasmosis are being conducted in other laboratories. Some of the compounds have been found to have rather low toxicities for animals.* For example, the LD_{50} of some of the trithiopercarbamates for mice were in the range of 350 to 1500 mg/kg. The few compounds which have been tested thus far for protection against experimental histoplasmosis have been ineffective.†

A continuation of the program is planned, with major emphasis to be placed on the preparation of functional derivatives of the most promising types of compounds; further explorations will be made of the lipophilic, steric, and electronic factors and the biological activities of the products. For example, investigations will be made of the effects of substitution of groups having water-solubilizing functions, such as NH_3Cl, SO_2Na, and SO_3Na, on the fungicidal activity of the compounds.

★   ★   ★

We are indebted to Drs. M. Bellas, J. D. Buckman, N. E. Heimer, B. J Sweetman, R. B. Barbee and P. M. Giles for their cooperation in supplying various compounds; part of their work was supported by the U.S. Army Medical Research and Development Command (Contract No. DA-49-193-MD-2030).

References

Benns, B.G., Gingras, B.A. and Bayley, C.H. (1960). Antifungal activity of some thio-semicarbazones and their copper complexes. *Appl. Microbiol.,* 8:353-356.

Buckman, J.D., Johnson, B.S. and Field, L. (1966). The antimicrobial activities of carbonyl and thiocarbamoyl disulfides. *Canad. J. Microbiol.,* 12:1263-1267.

Christison, I.B., Conant, N.F. and Bradsher, C.K. (1955). The sensitivity of *Histoplasma capsulatum* to rhodanine and related compounds. In Sternberg, T.H. and Newcomer, V.D. (Eds.). *Therapy of Fungus Diseases, an International Symposium.* Symposium at University of California, pp. 268-278.

Field, L., Hanley, W.S., McVeigh, I. and Evans, Z. Biologically oriented organic sulfur chemistry. Carbonyl disulfides as inhibitory agents for *Histoplasma capsulatum. J Med Chem* (In press)

Horsfall, J.G. (1956). *Principles of Fungicidal Action.* Waltham, Chronica Botanica Co, pp. 171-185.

---

* Tests performed at the Walter Reed Army Institute of Research, Washington, D.C., under the supervision of Drs. D. P. Jacobus, T. R. Sweeney and E. A. Steck.

† Arrangements made by Dr. W. B. Lacefield for tests conducted at the Eli Lilly Company, Indianapolis, Indiana.

Klöpping, H.L. (1951). *Chemical Constitution and Antifungal Action of Sulfur Compounds.* Utrecht, Schotanus and Jens.

McVeigh, I. and Evans, Z. (1968). Effects of various compounds on growth of yeast cells of *Histoplasma capsulatum. Mycopathologia,* 35:313-323.

McVeigh, I., Evans, Z., Field, L. and Hanley, W.S. (1969). Inhibitory effects of organic sulfur compounds on *Histoplasma capsulatum. Mycopathologia,* 37:349-356.

McVeigh, I. and Morton, K. (1965). Nutritional studies of *Histoplasma capsulatum. Mycopathologia,* 25:294-308.

Owens, R.G. (1969). Organic sulfur compounds. In Torgeson, D.C. (Ed.). *Fungicides; An Advanced Treatise. Chemistry and Physiology.* New York and London, Academic Press, vol. 2, pp. 147-301.

Rich, S. (1960). Fungicidal chemistry. In Horsfall, J.G. and Dimond, A.E. (Eds.). *Plant Pathology.* New York and London, Academic Press, pp.553-602.

Ross, R.G. and Ludwig, R.A. (1957). A comparative study of fungitoxicity and phytotoxicity in an homologous series of N-*n*-alkylethylenethioureas. *Canad. J. Bot.,* 35:65-95.

Thorn, G.D. and Ludwig, R.A. (1962). *The Dithiocarbamates and Related Compounds.* New York, Elsevier, pp.207-277.

Chapter 12

Physiology of *Histoplasma capsulatum*
A Review

DAVID S. BAUMAN

ABSTRACT

The physiology of *Histoplasma capsulatum* is reviewed from the literature, and the effects of various carbon, nitrogen and sulfur sources on the growth of both the yeast and mycelial phases are summarized in tables. Where data are available, nutrition is correlated with vegative structures and growth.

IN addition to being the first to cultivate *Histoplasma capsulatum*, De-Monbreun (1934) also established the dimorphism of the organism. Contrary to DeMonbreun's belief that the yeast form could only be obtained through animal passage, Conant (1941), through the use of paraffin-sealed blood agar slants, was able to establish the entire asexual life cycle *in vitro*, including conversion of spores and hyphal elements to the yeastlike form and reversion of the yeast form back to the mycelial form through the production of germ tubes.

All of the researchers who have worked on various aspects of the physiology of this organism are too numerous to detail in this paper; however, most of the work of these individuals is summarized in the tables to follow. Growth and other measures of physiologic effect are approximated from the various systems of reporting that have been used.

Mycelial Phase

The mycelial phase of *H. capsulatum* consists of septate, branching hyphae, 1.5μ to 2.5μ in diameter. Along the hyphae (laterally and terminally) microconidia (2μ-6μ) are produced and may be sessile or on short sterigmata. In addition, there are large smooth-walled spores (7μ-10μ), either lateral branches. With age, these spores develop thick walls with tuberculate sculpturing of the outer wall (Conant, 1941).

The optimum pH for growth of the mycelial phase on synthetic medium is approximately 6.5 (Howell, 1941). At pH 5.5 to 6.5 aerial mycelium and macroconidia are formed, whereas at pH 7.7 to 8.6 there is little or no aerial mycelium and sporulation is negligible.

The optimum temperature range for the mycelial phase is 20° to 30°C. A temperature greater than 32°C is usually inhibitory for the mycelial phase. Based on optical density measurements, Pine (1957) observed a generation time of approximately 12 hours at 25°C in shake cultures.

The organism is a strict aerobe, and growth is greatly inhibited by stoppering the culture tube with a rubber stopper or by growing it beneath the agar surface (DeMonbreun, 1934). Also, high humidity is beneficial to growth on agar media (Menges, Furcolow, Larsh and Hinton, 1952).

Smith (1964) and Smith and Furcolow (1964) stimulated the growth and sporulation of the mycelial phase by adding starling manure extract to an agar medium. Similar stimulation was observed on a medium containing only yeast extract and agar.

Pine (1957), in studies on the vitamin requirements of *H. capsulatum*, observed no diminution of growth for twelve strains when any or all vitamins were deleted from a defined medium. Salvin (1949), however, found one of six strains tested which required biotin for maximum growth when alanine was the sole nitrogen source. McVeigh and Morton (1965) found one out of twenty-five strains deficient for biotin on a defined medium without an organic nitrogen or sulfur source.

Table 12-I summarizes the growth of the mycelial phase on various nitrogen sources. This phase appears to require nitrogen in an amino acid form, with little or no utilization of an inorganic source. No single amino acid or nitrogen source is required for growth, but more luxuriant growth is obtained with certain of the sources.

There are insufficient data in the literature on which to base any assessment of the effect of nitrogen source on sporulation. Where data exist, they seem to indicate that asexual sporulation of all three types occurs when the nitrogen source is not conducive to luxuriant vegetative growth (Smith, 1964).

TABLE 12-I

Effect of Nitrogen Source on the Growth of *Histoplasma capsulatum* Mycelial Phase

Nitrogen Source	Growth*	Spore Types	Reference
KNO₃	+	S, T, M†	Negroni, 1940
(NH₄)₂SO₄	+	S, M	Negroni, 1940
			McVeigh and Morton, 1965
Asparagine	+++	S, T	Negroni, 1940
			McVeigh and Morton, 1965
			Salvin, 1949
Histidine	+++	—‡	Negroni, 1940 and 1946
Cystine (cysteine)	++	—	Negroni, 1940 and 1946
			Salvin, 1949
Glucosamine	+++	—	Salvin, 1949
Acetamid	+++	—	Salvin, 1949
Urea	++	—	Negroni, 1940 and 1946
Peptone	+++	—	Negroni, 1940 and 1946

* Growth estimates approximated from literature.
† S = smooth-walled macroconidia, T = tuberculate (rough-walled) macroconidia, M = microconidia.
‡ Blank spaces indicate absence of results in the literature.

Negroni (1940) investigated extensively the effect of carbon source on growth of mycelial phase *H. capsulatum*. Table 12-II illustrates these results, and as can be seen, glucose, galactose, mannose, and mannitol support luxuriant growth of the organisms, whereas the other carbon sources tested gave only minimal growth.

Mahvi (1965) using cell-free extracts of both the yeast and mycelial phases found that the Embden-Meyerhoff and hexose monophosphate pathways were operative in both phases of growth. This is consistant with the luxuriant growth of *H. capsulatum*, using glucose as a carbon source (Negroni, 1946; Salvin, 1949; Pine, 1954; McVeigh and Morton, 1965).

Morphology and Physiology of the Yeast Phase

As pointed out previously, in tissues of the infected host and under certain cultural conditions, *H. capsulatum* grows as a yeastlike organism. The yeast phase cells are oval bodies which measure approximately 1.5μ to 2.0μ by 3.0μ to 3.5μ (Conant, 1941). Reproduction occurs by budding, with the buds forming at one of the poles of the cell. Usually a single bud will form at a time from each mother cell.

In stained preparations the cell nucleus usually appears as a peripheral crescent-shaped mass (DeMonbreun, 1934). The single nucleus of a budding cell positions itself near the bud, constricts, and divides with one-half going to the daughter cell.

Darling (1906) in his original report described a capsule surrounding the yeast phase cells in tissue; however, this seems to have been an artifact, as a

TABLE 12-II

Effect of Carbon Source on the Growth of *Histoplasma capsulatum* Mycelial Phase

Carbon Source	Growth*
Glucose	+++
Galactose	+++
Mannose	+++
Mannitol	+++
Maltose	+
Lactose	+
Raffinose	+
Trehalose	+
Dextrin	+
Sorbitol	+
Inulin	+
Sodium oxalate	+
Sodium tartrate	+
Sodium citrate	+
Sodium acetate	+

Note: Negroni (1946) was used as reference for these data.
* Growth estimates approximated from results reported in the literature.

capsule is not demonstrable with India ink or capsule stain (Conant, 1941) or on electronmicrographs (Ribi & Salvin, 1956).

In older cultures of the yeast phase, large swollen cells have been observed. These were from two to three times larger than the size of actively growing cells and had a thick cell wall. The swollen forms were resistant to drying, and remained viable for as long as two months at room temperature (DeMonbreun, 1934).

The *in vitro* growth of the yeast phase of *H. capsulatum* was strictly aerobic (Pine, 1954). The generation time of the yeast phase under various cultural conditions was reported as follows: Liquid shake culture, 9 to 11 hours (Pine and Peacock, 1958); blood agar, 6 to 8 hours (Rowley and Huber, 1956); and tissue cultured, mouse histiocytes, 11.2 to 12 hours (Howard, 1965).

The growth of the yeast phase on blood or serum containing media was observed to occur at temperatures between 34° to 37°C. At lower temperatures conversion of the yeast phase to the mycelial phase generally occurred (Conant, 1941). Yet in the presence of cysteine, the yeast phase was maintained, both at 25°C and at 37°C, with as great or greater growth occurring at the lower temperature (Pine, 1957; Pine and Peacock, 1958). Although there has been no report of the optimum temperature determined within small increments for yeast phase growth, these results indicate that it is somewhere below 37°C.

The optimum pH for yeast phase growth is dependent upon the growth medium. On a basal agar medium with added whole blood, the rate of growth of one strain of *H. capsulatum* was the same at pH 5.5, 6.5, and 7.5 (Pine, 1954). However, with serum albumin substituted for blood, the rate of growth increased with increase in pH. In this same study, however, the number of colonies obtained from small numbers of yeast cells was much lower at a pH of 6.5 than at pH 4.5. On a synthetic medium, the rate of growth for the yeast phase increased from pH 4.5, to 6.5, but no growth was obtained at pH 7.0 and 8.0. These results were interpreted as suggesting a requirement for cysteine (Pine, 1954), since at higher pH cysteine is bound by fumaric acid (Pine and Peacock, 1955).

Table 12-III lists the growth response of yeast phase *H. capsulatum* to various nitrogen sources. As in the case of the mycelial phase, inorganic nitrogen sources did not sustain growth of the yeast phase (Negroni, 1940). A rather complex situation exists in that the organism not only requires an organic nitrogen source but also an organic sulfur source (Salvin, 1949; Pine, 1954; Scherr, 1957). McVeigh and Morton (1965) found that cysteine, cystine, and methionine would not simultaneously serve as an organic source of sulfur and nitrogen. This seems to be in disagreement with the work of Salvin (1949), who found that cystine, cysteine, and glutathione would individually fulfill both requirements.

TABLE 12-III

Effect of Nitrogen Source on the Growth of *Histoplasma capsulatum* Yeast Phase

Nitrogen Source	Growth	Reference
KNO₃	N.G.*	Negroni, 1940
		Salvin, 1949
NH₄NO₃	N.G.	Salvin, 1949
(NH₄)₂SO₄	N.G.	Salvin, 1949
Purines	N.G.	Salvin, 1949
Uracil	N.G.	Salvin, 1949
Actamid	N.G.	Salvin, 1949
Glucosamine	N.G.	Negroni, 1940
Asparagine	N.G., +++†	Negroni, 1940
		McVeigh and Morton, 1965
Cystine (cysteine)	+++, N.G.	Salvin, 1949
		McVeigh and Morton, 1965
Glutathione	+++, N.G.	McVeigh and Morton, 1965
Peptone	N.G.	Negroni, 1940
Proteose peptone	+++	Salvin, 1949

* N.G.=no growth, +++=maximum growth.
† McVeigh and Morton found that cystine, cysteine, and methionine served as an organic source of sulfur, but they would not serve also as nitrogen source; however, sodium thioglycollate and glutathione served neither as sulfur no nitrogen source.

Table 12-IV illustrates the effect of mixtures of sulfur-containing and non–sulfur-containing amino acids on the growth of the yeast phase. Cystine, cysteine, methionine, methylcysteine, and dl-homocystine gave maximal growth of the yeast phase in combination with a mixture containing sixteen

TABLE 12-IV

Effect of Mixtures of Amino Acids on the Growth of *Histoplasma capsulatum* Yeast Phase

Amino Acids	Growth	Reference
16 nonsulfur amino acids+cystine	+++*	Salvin, 1949
+cysteine	+++	
+methionine	+++	
+methyl cysteine	+++	
+dl-homocystine	+++	
+sodium thioglycolate	++	
+glutathione	++	
+diglycylcystine	++	
+NaHS	+	
Glutamic, aspartic and cysteine	+++, +++, +++	Salvin, 1949
		Pine, 1954
		McVeigh and Morton, 1965
and methionine	N.G., +++	Salvin, 1949
		McVeigh and Morton, 1965
Casein hydrolyzate and glutathione	N.G., N.G.	Salvin, 1949
		Pine, 1954
		McVeigh and Morton, 1965
Cysteine and glutamine	+++	Pine, 1954
Cysteine and aspartine	++	Pine, 1954

* N.G.=no growth, +=slight growth, ++=moderate growth, +++=maximum growth.

TABLE 12-V

Effect of Carbon Source on the Growth of *Histoplasma capsulatum* Yeast Phase

Carbon Source	Growth	Reference
Glucose	+++*	Negroni, 1940 Pine, 1954
Glycerol	+++	Pine, 1954
Galactose	+	Negroni, 1940 Pine, 1954
Fructose	+	Pine, 1954
Mannose	+++	Negroni, 1940
Ribose	+	Pine, 1954
Maltose	+	Negroni, 1940 Pine, 1954
Lactose	+	Negroni, 1940
Sucrose	+	Negroni, 1940
Inulin	+++	Negroni, 1940
Sodium citrate	+++	Pine and Peacock, 1958
Starch	++	Negroni, 1940
Citrate	+++	Pine and Peacock, 1958
Glucose and citrate	+++	Pine and Peacock, 1958

* N.G. = no growth, + = slight growth, ++ = moderate growth, +++ = maximum growth.

other, nonsulfur amino acids (Salvin, 1949). Pine (1954), and McVeigh and Morton (1965) found cysteine in combination with glutamic and aspartic acids gave maximal growth of the yeast phase; however, Pine, in contrast to McVeigh and Morton's work, was not able to demonstrate methionine fulfilling the sulfur requirement.

Table 12-V shows the effect of carbon source on growth. As in the case of the mycelial phase, glucose and mannose supported maximum growth of the yeast phase. One interesting difference is in the effect of sodium citrate. Sodium citrate would not support growth of the mycelial phase (Negroni, 1946); however, luxuriant growth of the yeast phase occurred on this carbon source (Pine and Peacock, 1958). These results are consistent with those of Mahvi (1965), who found large amounts of aconitase in the cell-free extracts of the yeast phase. Further, Pine (1957) found that in the presence of organic sulfur and nitrogen sources, alpha-ketoglutaric acid supported excellent growth of the yeast phase.

McVeigh and Morton (1965) studied the vitamin requirements of twenty strains of *H. capsulatum* in the yeast phase using a basal medium containing glucose as carbon source and asparagine as nitrogen source. Of these 20 strains, 19 were partially deficient for thiamine, 1 for pantothenic acid, 9 for inositol, 5 for nicotinic acid, and 1 for biotin. The optimal concentration for thiamine was found to be 0.1µg/ml. When deficient amounts of thiamine were present, growth consisted of a mixture of both yeast phase and mycelial fragments, while few if any mycelial elements were observed in those cultures supplied with adequate amounts of this vitamin.

References

Conant, N.F. (1941). A cultural study of the life cycle of *Histoplasma capsulatum*, Darling (1906) *J. Bact.*, *41*:563-578.

Darling, S.T. (1906). Protozoan general infection producing pseudotubercles in lungs and focal necrosis in liver, spleen and lymph nodes. *J.A.M.A.*, *46*:1283-1285.

DeMonbreun, W.A. (1934). The cultivation and cultural characteristics of Darling's *Histoplasma capsultaum*. *Amer. J. Trop. Med.*, *14*:93-116.

Howard, D.H. (1965). Intracellular growth of *Histoplasma capsulatum*. *J. Bact.*, *89*:518-523.

Howell, A., Jr. (1941). Studies on *Histoplasma capsulatum* and similar form-species. III. Effect of hydrogen ion concentration. *Mycologia*, *33*:103-117.

Mahvi, T.A. (1965). A comparative study of the yeast and mycelial phases of *Histoplasma capsulatum*. I. Pathways of carbohydrate dissimilation. *J. Infect. Dis.*, *115*: 226-232.

McVeigh, I. and Morton, D. (1965). Nutritional Studies of *Histoplasma capsulatum*. *Mycopathologia*, *25*:294-308.

Menges, R.W., Furcolow, M.L., Larsh, H.W. and Hinton, A. (1952). Laboratory studies on Histoplasmosis. I. The effect of humidity and temperature on growth of *Histoplasma capsulatum*. *J. Infect. Dis.*, *90*:67-70.

Negroni, P. (1940). Estudio Micologico del primer caso Sud-Americano de histoplasmosis. *Rev. Insti. Bacteriol. (D.N.H.)*, *9*:239-294.

Negroni, P. (1946). Un Nuevo caso de histoplasmosis. Estudio micologico y terapeutico. *Rev. Argent. Dermatosif*, *30*:212-219.

Pine, L. (1954). Studies on the growth of *Histoplasma capsulatum* I. Growth of the yeast in liquid media. *J. Bact.*, *68*:671-679.

Pine, L. and Peacock, C.L. (1955). Reaction of fumaric acid and cysteine. *J. Amer. Chem. Soc.*, *77*:3153-3157.

Pine, L. (1957). Studies on the growth of *Histoplasma capsulatum* III. Effect of thiamin and other vitamins on the growth of yeast and mycelial phases of *Histoplasma capsulatum*. *J. Bact.*, *74*:239-245.

Pine, L. and Peacock, C.L. (1958). Studies on the growth of *Histoplasma capsulatum*. IV. Factors influencing conversion of the mycelial phase to the yeast phase. *J. Bact.*, *75*:167-174.

Ribi, E. and Salvin, S.B. (1956). Antigens from the yeast phase of *Histoplasma capsulatum*. I. Morphology of the cell as revealed by the electron microscope. *Exp. Cell Res.*, *10*:394-404.

Rowley, D.A. and Huber, M. (1956). Growth of *Histoplasma capsulatum* in normal, superinfected and immunized mice. *J. Immun.*, *77*:15-23.

Salvin, S.B. (1949). Cysteine and related compounds in the growth of the yeast-like phase of *Histoplasma capsulatum J. Infect. Dis.*, *84*:275-283.

Scherr, G. (1957). Studies on the dimorphism of *Histoplasma capsulatum*. I. The role of -SH group and incubator temperature. *Exp. Cell Res.*, *112*:92-102.

Smith, C.D. and Furcolow, M.L. (1964). The demonstration of growth stimulating substances for both *Histoplasma capsulatum* and *Blastomyces dermatitidis* in infusions of starling (*Sturnis vulgaris*) manure. *Mycopathologia*, *22*:73-80.

Smith, C.D. (1964). II. Evidence of the presence in yeast extract of substances which stimulate the growth of *Histoplasma capsulatum* and *Blastomyces dermatitidis* similarly to that found in starling manure extract. *Mycopathologia*, *22*:99-105.

Chapter 13

Preliminary Studies of the Readily Extracted Lipid of Cell Walls and Cell Sap of the Yeastlike Form of *Histoplasma capsulatum*

JUDITH E. DOMER

ABSTRACT

Cell wall and cell sap preparations of the yeastlike form of *Histoplasma capsulatum* were extracted with chloroform:methanol, and the readily extracted lipids thus derived were compared. The cell sap preparations were shown to contain 12% to 15% lipid after the removal of nonlipid contaminants; the cell walls contained only 1% to 2% lipid. Chromatographic analysis on glass fiber paper, both qualitative and quantitative, did not reveal any major differences between the two extracts. Phosphatidyl choline and phosphatidyl ethanolamine were the major phospholipids present in both extracts, and the triglycerides were the major neutral lipid. Other components of the extract which were identified were phosphatidyl serine, diglycerides, sterols (ergosterol and other unidentified ones), sterol esters, and free fatty acids. The relative percentages of the fatty acids in the total extracts, as well as the fatty acids of the individual lipid classes, were determined by gas chromatographic methods. The fatty acid patterns of the cell wall and cell sap extracts were relatively simple and very similar. Oleic acid (18:1) was the major fatty acid, followed by moderate amounts of linoleic (18:2) and palmitic acids (16:0), with only small amounts of palmitoleic (16:1) and stearic (18:0) acids.

F OR several years we have been studying the chemical composition of the cell walls of the yeastlike and mycelial forms of *Histoplasma capsulatum*. The results of our studies on the monosaccharide, chitin, and amino acid constituents have already been published (Domer, Hamilton and Harkin, 1967). Lipid, presumably a fourth component of the walls, had been extracted from them during our previous work but had not been characterized. The investigation of the lipids was begun with those of the yeastlike form which were readily extracted, inasmuch as they were removed first from the cell wall preparations with neutral solvents before the extraction of the tightly bound lipids with acidified solvents. Since we have always been concerned with the possibility that the readily extracted lipids of the cell wall preparations might be simply contamination from cell sap (the lyophilized supernate resulting from centrifugation of a homogenate of yeast cells), it was decided to examine comparatively such lipids as derived from

NOTE. This study was supported by USPHS Grant 1 RO1 AI 08588.

the cell walls and cell sap. The depth of our investigation was prompted, in part, by a similar study of cell walls of the ascomycetous yeast, *Nadsonia elongata,* (Dyke, 1964) in which gross differences in the fatty acid composition were found between the cell walls and the whole cell. Work on the characterization of the tightly bound lipids of the yeastlike form, as well as on all the lipids of the mycelial form, is in progress but will not be reported at this time.

Materials and Methods

Cultural Methods

H. capsulatum Sweany B was the same strain used for previous cell wall studies (Domer, *et al.,* 1967). All cultural methods, as well as those methods used in the preparation of cell walls and cell sap, were described in the same publication. Briefly, the yeastlike cells were incubated in a liquid glucose-yeast extract medium at 37°C for 72 hours and were then harvested, washed, and broken by agitation with glass beads in a Braun homogenizer. The cell walls were separated from the cell sap by centrifugation at 450g for 30 minutes, after which the cell sap (supernate) was immediately lyophilized. Following repeated washings of the cell walls with 0.2 M NaCl, 1 M NaCl and distilled water, they, too, were lyophilized.

Lipid Extraction

The readily extracted lipids were removed from the cell walls and cell sap by the method of Folch, Lees and Sloane Stanley (1957) with chloroform: methanol (2:1) under N_2 for two 2-hour extractions at room temperature and then overnight with fresh solvent at 4°C. The cell sap extracts were not washed with water to remove nonlipid contaminants as described by Folch, *et al.,* but were instead purified by passage through a Sephadex G-25 column (Wuthier, 1966). Because of the small amount of lipid present in the cell wall extracts, they were not subjected to any purification procedure.

Lipid Analyses

Total Weights

The total quantity of lipid in the cell sap extracts was determined by weighing evaporated portions of each extract before and after passage through Sephadex. As there appeared to be no appreciable nonlipid contamination of the cell wall extracts, and since the total quantity obtained from a cell wall extraction was small, they were only evaporated and weighed once.

Qualitative Composition of the Lipid Extracts

The lipid classes in the extracts were separated and identified by ascending chromatography on glass fiber paper (Type SG, Gelman Instrument Co.,

Ann Arbor, Michigan) in several solvent systems, using appropriate standards (Supelco, Inc., Bellefonte, Penna.) and detection methods. The phospholipids were separated in two polar solvent systems (Barbosa, 1966) consisting of chloroform:methanol:50 percent aqueous acetic acid (100:9:1) and chloroform:methanol:ammonia (100:9:1). The triglycerides, sterols and sterol esters were separated in two solvent systems consisting of isooctane: isopropyl acetate (100:1.5) (triglycerides and sterols) and isooctane:benzene (100:5) (sterol esters) (Hamilton, Swartwout, Miller and Muldrey, 1961). A fifth solvent system containing isooctane:chloroform:acetic acid (150:49:1) (Dr. James Hamilton, personal communication) was employed to separate the diglycerides from the other lipid components. After the chromatograms had been developed, they were air-dried, sprayed with concentrated reagent grade sulfuric acid and charred on a hot plate to produce carbon from the compounds. Several staining procedures were applied to similar air-dried chromatograms to detect specific compounds or reactive groups. Specific stains used were Rhodamine 6G (Applied Science Laboratories, State College, Penna.) (Marinetti and Stotz, 1956), ninhydrin (Gelman Instrument Co., Ann Arbor, Michigan), Dragondorff's reagent (Brown, Yeadon, Goldblatt and Dieckert, 1957), and aniline phthalate.

Quantitation of Selected Lipid Classes

Phosphatidyl ethanolamine, phosphatidyl choline, and the triglycerides were quantitated by densitometry (Muldrey, Miller and Hamilton, 1959; Swartwout, Dieckert, Miller and Hamilton, 1960). Several dilutions of each appropriate standard were chromatographed with the lipid extracts, and duplicate papers were run at all times to minimize error. Ergosterol was quantitated by spectrophotometric methods (Topham and Gaylor, 1967).

Fatty Acid Determinations

The fatty acid distribution of the total lipid extracts, as well as those of selected lipid classes, was determined. For the total fatty acid pattern, a small portion of each extract was evaporated and taken up in methanol or benzene and the methyl esters prepared (Metcalfe and Schmitz, 1961; Morrison and Smith, 1964). The fatty acid distribution of the lipid classes was determined by a method similar to that described by Bowers, Hamilton, Muldrey, Miyamasu, Reynolds and Schally (1966). A single lipid extract was spotted ten to twelve times across an entire sheet of glass fiber paper. This was then developed in the appropriate solvent system, and a vertical guide strip was cut from one side for spraying with sulfuric acid and detection of the separated compounds. Using the guide strip, horizontal strips could be cut from the remaining chromatogram which contained only the desired compound. Then the strips containing this compound were again developed in an appropriate solvent system (chloroform:methanol:50 percent aqueous acetic acid, 100:18:2, for neutral lipids, methanol for phospholipids) so that the compound would move with the solvent front and collect at one tip of the strip.

After drying, the tip was cut into small pieces and the neutral lipids were eluted with acetone:isooctane (1:1) in a small culture tube while the phospholipids were eluted in a similar manner with methanol. The methyl esters of the phospholipids were prepared directly from the methanol eluate, but neutral lipid extracts were first evaporated and then taken up in methanol for fatty acid preparation. A Barber-Colman gas chromatograph, Series 5000, equipped with a flame ionization detector was used for the detection of the fatty acids. The column was packed with 15 percent EGSS-X, 100/120 mesh Gas Chrom P for most of the work. Some of the fatty acid samples were chromatographed on 3 percent OV-1 (80/100 Chromosorb WH P, Supelco), however, to check the ratio of saturated versus unsaturated acids. The operating conditions of the gas chromatograph were as follows: column temperature, 180°C; injector temperature, 255°C; detector temperature, 235°C. Relative percents of the fatty acids were calculated by determining the areas under the peaks by triangulation.

Results

Yeastlike cells were cultured in large quantities on two distinct occasions and separate cell wall–cell sap preparations made from each lot. All of the data on the cell sap preparations are based on several determinations of each cell sap preparation. However, only enough cell wall material was obtained from each lot of cells to complete the spectrum of analyses once on each cell wall preparation.

Total Weights

The total quantity of lipid in the cell sap preparations after separation of the water-soluble contaminants with Sephadex was 12 to 15 percent (Table 13-I). Approximately 7 percent of the total extract appeared to be nonlipid. Amino acids probably contributed largely to the contamination because

TABLE 13-I

Percentage of Cell Wall and Cell Sap Preparations of the Yeastlike Form of *Histoplasma capsulatum* Soluble in Chloroform:Methanol (2:1) Before and After Passage Through Sephadex

		Before Sephadex	After Sephadex
		(%)	(%)
Cell sap	I	19	12
	II	22	15
Cell walls	I	1	not done
	II	2	not done

when chromatograms containing the "before" and "after" Sephadex extracts were developed in one of the phospholipid solvent systems and then sprayed with ninhydrin, there were many ninhydrin-positive compounds in the initial extract that no longer appeared after the Sephadex procedure. Two phospholipids, phosphatidyl ethanolamine and phosphatidyl serine, are of course ninhydrine positive, but their position and concentration were unaffected by the Sephadex treatment. No reducing sugars were detected in the extracts with aniline phthalate.

The total quantity of readily extracted lipid from the cell walls was 1 to 2 percent. Contaminating compounds, such as amino acids, were not detectable in the wall extracts.

Qualitative and Quantitative Results

There were no differences detected in the qualitative composition of the lipids of the cell walls when compared with the cell sap. Therefore, the following lipid classes were separated and identified in both extracts: phosphatidyl ethanolamine, phosphatidyl choline, phosphatidyl serine, triglycerides, diglycerides, sterols, sterol esters, and free fatty acids. With the methods employed here we were unable to detect phosphatidyl inositol and sphingomyelin in the readily extracted lipids. There were at least three different sterols present, of which ergosterol was one. No attempt was made to identify the others. We can say, however, that the sterol associated with the sterol esters is neither ergosterol nor cholesterol. This conclusion was based on the chromatographic and spectrophotometric properties of the sterol released by saponification of the esters.

The quantitative results with phosphatidyl choline, phosphatidyl ethanolamine, the triglycerides, and ergosterol (Table 13-II) showed no significant differences in distribution between the cell walls and cell sap. There appeared to be a 1:1 ratio of phosphatidyl choline and phosphatidyl ethanolamine in all the preparations, and the triglyceride level was always much higher than the other components.

TABLE 13-II

Quantitative Results for Selected Lipid Classes of Cell Walls and Cell Sap of the Yeastlike Form of *Histoplasma capsulatum*

	Phosphatidyl choline %*	Phosphatidyl ethanolamine %	Triglyceride %	Ergosterol %
I Cell sap	24	20	49	7
Cell walls	21	19	56	4
II. Cell sap	17	16	62	5
Cell walls	16	18	60	6

* Relative percent of the four components quantitated, namely phosphatidyl choline, phosphatidyl ethanolamine, triglyceride, and ergosterol.

Fatty Acid Analyses

The major fatty acid in both the cell wall and cell sap preparations was oleic acid (18:1) (Table 13-III), followed by linoleic (18:2) and palmitic (16:0) acids, respectively. Stearic (18:0) and palmitoleic (16:1) acids were present but always in relatively low quantities. Again, there appeared to be little in the way of differences between the cell walls and the cell sap. The results of the fatty acid analyses of the cell sap preparations, as presented in Table 13-III, are averages of several determinations on cell sap obtained from a single lot of cells. As was mentioned previously, it was possible to do only a single determination on the cell walls obtained from one cell wall–cell sap preparation. The fatty acid analyses of the second lot of cells show basically the same pattern in both cell walls and cell sap. In fact, we now have data on four separate lots of cells prepared under the same conditions and have found that the only variation from lot to lot is in the exact levels of oleic (18:1) and linoleic (18:2) acids. The oleic acid (18:1) level, however, is never less than 50 percent of the total and never greater than 70 percent, with a proportionate increase or decrease in linoleic (18:2) acid. The precise levels of these two fatty acids, within the limits indicated, seem to be a reflection of the exact metabolic state of the cells at the time of harvest. This

TABLE 13-III

Fatty Acid Distribution in Lipid Classes of Cell Walls and Corresponding
Cell Sap of Yeastlike Form of *Histoplasma capsulatum*

Total	Relative %*				
	16:0	16:1	18:0	18:1	18:2
Cell sap	14	1	2	50	33
Cell walls	14	1	2	55	29
Free fatty acids					
Cell sap	9	4	3	52	33
Cell walls	10	tr	tr	70	20
Triglycerides					
Cell sap	13	2	4	61	21
Cell walls	10	tr	tr	68	21
Diglycerides					
Cell sap	18	2	7	52	21
Cell walls	21	tr	3	55	21
Phosphatidylcholine					
Cell sap	11	2	2	61	24
Cell walls	21	3	3	52	21
Phosphatidylethanol					
Cell sap	24	2	4	48	23
Cell walls	28	2	2	52	16
Sterol Esters					
Cell sap	8	2	2	57	31
Cell walls	8	2	—	67	23

* The percentages of the fatty acids for all total samples and for the lipid classes of the cell sap are averages of several determinations. The fatty acid percentages of the cell walls are from a single experiment.

statement seems valid in the light of experiments whereby cells were harvested at two-, three-, four- and six-day intervals and the fatty acid patterns determined. In these cells, the oleic acid (18:1) level at two days was approximately 50 percent and increased progressively to a high of 70 percent at four days where it remained stationary.

Discussion

Our initial interest in the lipids of *H. capsulatum*, as was mentioned earlier, was to obtain a more complete picture of the cell wall. From the results presented here, we conclude that the readily extracted lipids of the cell wall preparations of the yeastlike form of *H. capsulatum* do not seem to be a part of the cell wall. In fact, since the quantitative results of the several lipid classes examined, plus the fatty acid analyses of the extracts and lipid classes, are so similar, it would appear that the readily extracted lipids are indeed contaminated with cell sap. This is a quite different picture from that seen in a similar study with *N. elongata* (Dyke, 1964) where the cell wall fatty acids contained no palmitoleic acid, compared with the whole cell fatty acids which contained 57 percent of the same. It may be, of course, that we have simply not examined the one component that is different. However, the qualitative chromatographic patterns are so similar that the possibility seems remote. An additional factor to consider is the fact that of the four classes examined quantitatively, presumably three of these, phosphatidyl choline, phosphatidyl ethanolamine, and ergosterol, are components of the cell membrane which might well be the major contamination in the cell wall preparations. Electron microscopic examination of the yeastlike form cell wall preparations previously revealed occasional pieces of cell membrane adhering to cell walls (Domer, *et al.*, 1967) which would correlate with these findings. In addition, the fourth component, the triglycerides, constitute a major portion of the cell sap extracts, and if there is cell sap contamination, it presumably would be present in relatively high concentration.

The qualitative findings in the phospholipids and neutral lipid classes were not surprising, and they correlate reasonably well with the findings on other pathogenic fungi, e.g. *Blastomyces dermatitidis, Paracoccidioides brasiliensis* (Kanetsuna, 1967), *Candida* (Monilia) *albicans* (Combs, 1968; Peck and Hauser, 1939) and *H. capsulatum* (Nielsen, 1966). With respect to *H. capsulatum*, Nielsen examined the phospholipids of several strains in detail, and contrary to his findings, we did not find sphingomyelin or phosphoinositides. However, we have not yet examined closely the tightly bound lipids. In Nielsen's investigation, the readily extracted phospholipids were mixed with the tightly bound ones before separating them on a column of silicic acid, so those specific compounds may have been contributed by the tightly bound extract. It is of interest, however, that in one of his strains he found no phosphatidyl choline, and in the other it was only 8 percent of the phospholipid extract. We have examined in preliminary fashion several other strains of *H. capsulatum,* (the specific results have not been presented here) and have always found phosphatidyl choline; from chromatographic appearances it is present in at least as great a concentration as phosphatidyl ethanolamine.

It is interesting to speculate, also, on the usefulness of the lipid patterns of pathogenic fungi in demonstrating phylogenetic relationships. As can be seen from the results, the fatty acid pattern of *H. capsulatum* is relatively simple and is strikingly similar to those reported by Peck *et al.* (1938, 1939) for the yeastlike form of *B. dermatitidis* and *C. albicans.* The major fatty acid in all three is oleic (18:1), with smaller amounts of palmitic (16:0), linoleic (18:2) and stearic (18:0). By comparison, however, the fatty acid patterns of several ascomycetous yeasts examined, *Saccharomyces cerevisiae* (Longley, Rose and Knights, 1968; Suolmalainen and Keränen, 1968), *Hanseniaspora valbyensis* (Haskell and Snell, 1965), and *N. elongata* (Dyke, 1964) are different in that palmitoleic acid (16:1), constitutes approximately 50 percent of the total fatty acids and linoleic (18:2) seems to be absent. There is an exception to this generalization, in that one ascomycetous yeast so far examined, *Lipomyces lipoferous* (Jack, 1966) has a fatty acid pattern similar to that observed thus far with the imperfect yeasts. It should be stressed that it is somewhat difficult to generalize concerning the lipid patterns of fungi because of the effect that different cultural conditions, variant strains, and so forth, may have on such patterns (See Shaw, 1966 for a review of the fatty acids of fungi). However, by examination of the results obtained by various investigators along with our own findings, there does seem to be something of a pattern developing with those pathogenic fungi thus far studied. The imperfect yeastlike organisms appear to have as their major fatty acid, oleic acid (18:1), whereas in the mycelial forms, there is a shift in dominance to linoleic acid (18:2) (e.g. Audette, Baxter and Walker, 1961; Wirth and Anand, 1964). Several nonpathogenic mycelial forms, *Penicillium pulvillorum* (Nakajima, 1968) and *Neurospora crassa* (Todd, Stone, Hechter and Nussbaum, 1957) show a similar pattern with linoleic acid (18:2) being dominant. In addition, the fatty acids of *N. crassa* include a large proportion of linolenic (18:3) acid which is seen in only small amounts or not at all in the other fungi mentioned here.

One final consideration of the lipids of pathogenic fungi is their possible involvement in the disease process. This idea initially grew out of the early work with the phospholipids of the tubercle bacillus (Sabin, 1932; Thomas and Dessau, 1939-1940) showing that tubercles could be produced by the injection of the phosphatides derived from the bacillus. Baker (1942) attempted a similar study with *B. dermatitidis* and was able to show a reaction to the phosphatides, but it was not as extensive or as characteristic as that seen with the living organism. Di Salvo and Denton (1963) showed much later that there seemed to be a correlation between total lipid content and virulence of *B. dermatitidis*, but they could not show a correlation between phosphatide level and virulence. The possibility exists that a lipid component other than phosphatides is related to this phenomenon. With a better understanding of the total lipid picture of the fungi, perhaps more extensive studies into the possible relationship of lipid and the disease process could be initiated.

References

Audette, R.C.S., Baxter, R.M. and Walker, G.C. (1961). A study of the lipid content of *Trichophyton mentagrophytes*. *J. Gen. Microbiol.*, 7:282-283.

Baker, R.D. (1942). Experimental blastomycosis in mice. *Amer. J. Path.*, 18:463-478.

Barbosa, E. (1966). Comparative studies of cell walls and cytoplasmic lipids of wild-type and the osmotic-mutant of *Neurospora crassa*. Dissertation thesis, Tulane University, New Orleans.

Bowers, C.Y., Hamilton, J.G., Muldrey, J.E., Miyamasu, W.T., Reynolds, G.A. and Schally, A.V. (1966). The simultaneous determination of both the quantity and the fatty acid composition of the triglycerdies in three to ten microliters of plasma. *J. Amer. Oil Chemists' Soc.*, 43:2-6.

Brown, M., Yeadon, D.A., Goldblatt, L.A. and Dieckert, J.W. (1957). Chromatography of phospholipides and related compounds on glass paper impregnated with silicic acid. *Anal. Chem.*, 29:30-31.

Combs, T.J., Guarneri, J.J. and Pisano, M.A. (1968). The effect of sodium chloride on the lipid content and fatty acid composition of *Candida albicans*. *Mycologia*, 60:1232-1239.

Di Salvo, A.F. and Denton, J.F. (1963). Lipid content of four strains of *Blastomyces dermatitidis* of different mouse virulence. *J. Bact.*, 85:927-931.

Domer, J.E., Hamilton, J.G. and Harkin, J.C. (1967). Comparative study of the cell walls of the yeastlike and mycelial phases of *Histoplasma capsulatum*. *J. Bact.*, 94:466-474.

Dyke, K.G.H. (1964). The chemical composition of the cell wall of the yeast *Nadsonia elongata*. *Biochim. Biophys. Acta*, 82:374-384.

Folch, J. Lees, M. and Sloane Stanley, G.H. (1957). A simple method for the isolation and purification of total lipides from animal tissues. *J. Biol. Chem.*, 226:497-509.

Hamilton, J.G., Swartwout, J.R., Miller, O.N. and Muldrey, J.E. (1961). A silica gel impregnated glass fiber filter paper and its use for the separation of cholesterol, triglycerides and the cholesteryl and methyl esters of fatty acids. *Biochem. Biophys. Res. Commun.*, 5:226-230.

Haskell, B.E. and Snell, E.E. (1965). Effect of vitamin B_6 deficiency on the composition of yeast lipids. *Arch. Biochem. Biophys.*, 112:494-505.

Jack, R.C.M. (1966). Lipid patterns in the major classes of fungi. *J. Bact.* 91:2101-2102.

Kanetsuna, F. (1967). Estudio bioquimico del *Paracoccidioides brasiliensis*. *Acta Cient. Venez.* (Suppl.), 3:308-317.

Longley, R.P., Rose, A.H. and Knights, B.A. (1968). Composition of the protoplast membrane from *Saccharomyces cerevisiae*. *Biochem. J.* 108:401-412.

Marinetti, G.V. and Stotz, E. (1956). Chromatography of phosphatides on silicic acid impregnated paper. *Biochem. Biophys. Acta,* 21:168-170.

Metcalfe, L.D. and Schmitz, A.A. (1961). The rapid preparation of fatty acid esters for gas chromatographic analysis. *Anal. Chem.,* 33:363-364.

Morrison, W.R. and Smith, L.M. (1964). Preparation of fatty acid methyl esters and dimethylacetals from lipids with boron fluoride-methanol. *J. Lipid Res.,* 4:600-608.

Muldrey, J.E., Miller, O.N. and Hamilton, J.G. (1959). Quantitative glass paper chromatography: phosphatidyl choline and sphingomyelin. *J. Lipid Res.,* 1:48-52.

Nakajima, S. and Tanenbaum, S.W. (1968). The fatty acids of *Penicillium pulvillorum. Arch. Biochem. Biophys.,* 127:150-156.

Nielsen, H.S., Jr. (1966). Variation in lipid content of strains of *Histoplasma capsulatum* exhibiting different virulence properties for mice. *J. Bact.,* 91:273-277.

Peck, R.I. (1947). In Nickerson, W.J. (Ed.). *Biology of Pathogenic Fungi.* Waltham, Chronica Botanica, pp.167-188.

Peck, R.L. and Hauser, C.R. (1938). Chemical studies of certain pathogenic fungi. I. The lipids of *Blastomyces dermatitidis. J. Amer. Chem. Soc.,* 60:2599-2603.

Peck, R.L. and Hauser, C.R. (1939). Chemical studies of certain pathogenic fungi. II. The lipids of *Monilia albicans. J. Amer. Chem. Soc.,* 61:281-284.

Sabin, F.R. (1932). Cellular reactions to fractions isolated from tubercle bacilli. *Physiol. Rev.,* 12:141-165.

Shaw, R. (1966). In Paoletti, R. and Kritchevsky, D. (Eds.). *Advances in Lipid Research.* New York, Academic Press, vol. 4, pp.107-174.

Suolmalainen, H. and Keränen, A.J.A. (1968). The fatty acid composition of baker's and brewer's yeast. *Chem. Phys. Lipids.,* 2:296-315.

Swartwout, J.R., Dieckert, J.W., Miller, O.N. and Hamilton, J.G. (1960). Quantitative glass fiber paper chromatography: a microdetermination of plasma cholesterol. *J. Lipid Res.,* 1:281-285.

Thomas, R.M. and Dessau, F.I. (1939-1940). Experimental tuberculosis in mice. The cellular response to the chemical fractions of the tubercle bacillus. *Yale J. Biol. Med.,* 12:185-198.

Todd, D., Stone, D., Hechter, O. and Nussbaum, A. (1957). The component fatty acids of *Neurospora crassa* lipides. *J. Biol. Chem.,* 229:527-533.

Topham, R.W. and Gaylor, J.L. (1967). Anaerobic formation of ergosterol from a 5 α-hydroxysterol by cell-free preparations of yeast. *Biochem. Biophys. Res. Commun.,* 27:644-649.

Wirth, J.C. and Anand, S.R. (1964). The fatty acids of *Trichophyton rubrum. Canad. J. Microbiol.,* 10:23-27.

Wuthier, R.E. (1966). Purification of lipids from non-lipid contaminants on Sephadex bead forms. *J. Lipid Res.* 7:558-561.

Part III

Ecology, Epidemiology and Control

Chapter 14

Histoplasmin Sensitivity Patterns Around the World

PHYLLIS Q. EDWARDS

ABSTRACT

Judging from results of skin test surveys, millions of people become infected with *Histoplasma capsulatum*, but only a small proportion of the infected develop clinical disease. Many parts of the world seem to be free of infection, whereas in other regions most of the native populace has had experience with the fungus.

Although extensive areas of the globe have not been studied, accumulated evidence indicates that the majority of endemic foci are within the tropics and subtropics. An exception is found in central United States, where skin test studies show high rates of sensitivity prevailing over a large area.

Soil, especially when enriched with chicken, bat, or starling droppings, appears to be the reservoir of infection. More study is needed in order to clarify the ecology and epidemiology of histoplasmosis.

AFTER three decades of studies on histoplasmosis and other systemic fungus diseases, the mechanism interacting between the causative organisms and the human host, i.e. the epidemiology of human infection, remains obscure. Several types of studies continue to yield information that may eventually provide the elusive key to the puzzle. These studies include the following:

1. Skin test surveys of human populations for evidence of infection.
2. Studies of localized outbreaks of acute disease for indications of "point sources" of infection.
3. Examination of soil and other inanimate elements of the natural environment for isolation of *Histoplasma capsulatum*.
4. Examination of birds and other wild and domestic animals for evidence of sources and transmission of infection.
5. Reported cases of disease in humans for histories of residence or occupation that may suggest the presence of infectious sources in a localized area.

Early thinking on the epidemiology of histoplasmosis was influenced to a large extent by findings obtained in sudden outbreaks of acute clinical disease among small groups of people. In such situations, history of a recent common exposure indicated the likely source of infection. Collection of soil samples at such sites and subsequent isolation of *Histoplasma capsulatum* from these samples confirmed the presence of a reservoir, or a "point source," of infection. Further studies on soil samples led to the belief that soil is the natural habitat of *H. capsulatum,* that growth and multiplication of the fungus are enhanced in soils enriched with the droppings of bats and birds, that infection of man and susceptible animals results from inhalation of spores or germinative mycelial fragments from soil, and that infection probably is not transmitted from man to man or from animals to man.

Only after a skin test antigen was developed and survey data began to accumulate did we realize that vast numbers of mild or subclinical cases occur and that the localized sharp outbreaks account for only a negligible fraction of all histoplasmosis. Skin testing soon led to another discovery—place of residence is an important factor in the epidemiology of histoplasmosis. Among lifelong residents of some regions, none of the people becomes infected and no cases of histoplasmosis are seen. In other areas, most of the people have experienced infection by early adulthood and clinical disease is common.

Skin test surveys are the major epidemiologic tool presently available. Positive reactions to histoplasmin in an area indicate that the fungus is present in the local environment and that people are being exposed to the point sources of infection. Conversely, negative reactions (and investigators' reports should document the negative as well as the positive) indicate that sources of infection are absent or, if they exist, that people are not contacting them or that some yet-undefined force, possibly some ecological or environmental factor, prevents infection.

This paper updates information published earlier on world wide distribution of histoplasmin sensitivity (Edwards and Kiaer, 1956). In its preparation, current information was drawn from published reports and obtained through correspondence with individual investigators. An accompanying map shows the distribution and prevalence of skin sensitivity where testing has been done and identifies the great areas of the world from which information is still fragmentary or entirely lacking. The data on which the map is based are presented in detail and referenced in full elsewhere (Edwards and Billings, 1970).

The world picture of histoplasmosis shows that most endemic foci are in the tropical and subtropical zones. However, there are several large foci in temperate regions, the largest or possibly the best documented of these being in the United States. In this map black indicates localities where more than 30 percent of the population tested were reactors to histoplasmin. The striped pattern represents areas where 10 to 30 percent of the people tested were positive; the crosshatch pattern is for 2 to 10 percent positive; and the dotted pattern indicates only an occasional reactor (less than 2%) or no re-

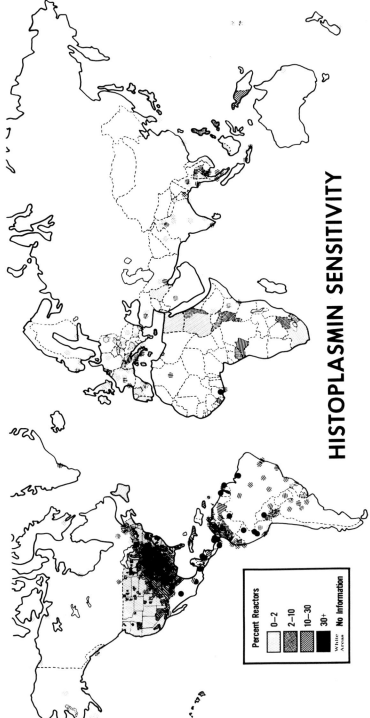

FIGURE 14-1. Worldwide patterns of skin sensitivity to histoplasmin, 1969.

actors at all in the population tested. The white areas—and much of the world map is white—are the areas where testing has not been done or information has not been made available.

A round patch placed approximately in the center of a country represents a study reported but without identification of the place of residence of the people tested. This same round symbol is also used to represent selected study groups such as tuberculosis patients, clinic patients, prisoners, or policemen.

The black areas on the map, showing that more than 30 percent of the population were reactors, are seen principally in the Americas. Even within these high-prevalence areas, however, infection rates may show wide variations, from very high to very low, over relatively short distances.

An area of high prevalence, perhaps the highest in the world, lies in the middle of the North American continent. Along the Mississippi and Ohio rivers—Missouri, Illinois, Indiana, Kentucky, Tennessee, Mississippi—more than 80 percent of the population in many localities become infected by the time they reach adulthood. Irregular and scattered foci extend out from this major endemic area into southeastern Canada—Ontario and Quebec—across the Appalachian mountains into Maryland and Virginia, and southwestward into the Central Plains. However, cross reactions owing to coccidioidal infection account for much of the sensitivity in the southwestern United States.

Histoplasmosis is also endemic throughout most of Central and South America. The first cases of the disease were reported sixty years ago from Panama, where the frequency of infection is well above 30 percent in young adults. There are also high-prevalence areas north of Panama, in southern Mexico, Guatemala, Honduras, and Nicaragua, as well as to the south in Venezuela, Surinam, Columbia, Peru, Bolivia, Brazil, and Argentina.

Histoplasmal infection is uncommon in lifelong residents of Europe and the eastern Mediterranean zone, although recent studies are pointing to small, localized foci in Italy, in two instances with rates between 10 and 30 percent.

Great reaches of Africa remain untested. Where testing has been done, the highest rates continue to be reported from the western tropical regions —Liberia, Ivory Coast, and the Congo basin near the coast. Information on Uganda provided by Bezjak (1969) but received too late for mapping would change the picture somewhat. He reports skin test results varying from 1.1 percent in cotton factory workers to 31.4 percent in one group of sawmill workers.

In the African continent, many cases of clinically recognized disease are attributed to *H. duboisii*, a disease more commonly seen as an involvement of the mucocutaneous tissues than as the pulmonary form generally associated with *H. capsulatum*. However, both species of *Histoplasma* may coexist in Africa, with one predominating over the other in a given area. In South Africa, for example, *H. capsulatum* is the predominant cause of disease. So far as is now known, both species produce skin sensitivity to the histoplasmin derived from *H. capsulatum*.

In Asia, histoplasmosis is prevalent in scattered foci throughout most of the southeast. Reactor rates ranging between 10 and 30 percent have been reported from localities in East Pakistan, Burma, Thailand, Malaysia, and Indonesia. Lower levels of sensitivity—the areas marked by cross-hatching, which represent 2 to 10 percent reactors—appear in the New Delhi area, in central Burma, and in Thailand and the Philippine Islands. Clinical cases of the disease are now being recognized in these regions.

The geographic patterns of histoplasmin sensitivity raise important questions about the epidemiology of systemic fungus infections in human populations. Judging from results of skin test surveys, millions of persons have been infected with *H. capsulatum*, yet only a small proportion of those infected develop clinical disease. Is this a function of the size of the infecting dose or of the route of infection? Do most infections involve such small numbers of organisms that development of skin sensitivity is the only sign, whereas clinical disease develops from an unusually large infecting dose?

Where do you collect soil samples when there is no history of common exposure pointing to a particular spot, as is most commonly the situation? Variations in the frequency of histoplasmin reactors in different parts of a community may sometimes be of help, but this is not an infallible guide. In one city, for example, sensitivity rates among school children were appreciably higher on one side of town than on the opposite side, yet among several hundred soil samples collected from all over the city, only one was positive—that one from the part of town where sensitivity rates were the lowest (Edwards *et al.*, 1960). Suppose the positive sample had been from the side of town with high prevalence? Would we have thought we had found the point source of infection?

These and a multitude of other problems concerning histoplasmosis are yet to be solved. For example, consider the following:

Where do the vast numbers of people who become infected but do not develop clinical illness get their infections?

Why, in a given locale, can the soil at one spot be heavily infected while a spot only inches away yields no fungus?

How can the presence or absence of chicken, bat, or starling droppings be a major determinant for the presence or absence of *H. capsulatum* in the soil?

Why are entire native populations in many parts of the world completely free of infection with *H. capsulatum*, as skin test results indicate?

Are present methods of measuring skin test reactions and evaluating cross reactions valid?

Does experience with one agent of systemic mycotic infection sensitize the victim to skin test antigens for other systemic fungus infections?

In order for skin test results to be comparable and valid, do we need to establish international standards for skin test antigens?

Answers to these and other questions must be sought if we are to gain a better understanding of the ecology and epidemiology of histoplasmosis and other fungus infections.

References

Bezjak, V. (1969). Personal communication.

Edwards, P.Q. and Kiaer, J.H. (1956). World-wide geographic distribution of histoplasmosis and histoplasmin sensitivity. *Amer. J. Trop. Med.*, 5:235-257.

Edwards, P.Q. and Billings, E. (1970). Worldwide pattern of skin sensitivity to histoplasmin. *Amer. J. Trop. Med.*, (In press.)

Edwards, P.Q., Ajello, L., Moore, J., Jacobs, C.F. and Aronson, D.L. (1960). Soil sampling in an urban focus of histoplasmin sensitivity. *Amer. Rev. Resp. Dis.*, *81*: 747-751.

Chapter 15

Distribution of *Histoplasma capsulatum* in the United States

LIBERO AJELLO

ABSTRACT

All available data on the occurrence and distribution of *Histoplasma capsulatum* within the United States were critically reviewed. There is firm evidence, based on cultural studies of human and animal cases as well as soil isolations, that *H. capsulatum* is endemic in thirty-one of the forty-eight contiguous states: Alabama, Arizona, Arkansas, Connecticut, Florida, Georgia, Illinois, Indiana, Iowa, Kansas, Kentucky, Louisiana, Maryland, Michigan, Minnesota, Mississippi, Missouri, Nebraska, New Mexico, New York, North Carolina, Ohio, Oklahoma, Pennsylvania, South Carolina, Tennessee, Texas, Vermont, Virginia, West Virginia, and Wisconsin. There is reason to believe that eventually this fungus will be found to exist in suitable habitats in most, if not all, of the states.

IN the United States the tendency exists to overlook the fact that *Histoplasma capsulatum* is indigenous to areas outside of the east central endemic region. It is as if we were so mesmerized by the high prevalence of histoplasmosis in that section of the country, that we forget, in reality, *H. capsulatum* has a much wider geographic distribution.

Data from the most extensive and well-planned histoplasmin skin test survey ever carried out within the forty-eight contiguous states of the United States (Edwards, Acquaviva, Livesay, Cross, and Palmer, 1969*) indeed clearly show that *H. capsulatum* flourishes in the central part of our country. In four states the overall percentage of positive reactors for both rural and urban areas exceeded 50 percent—Arkansas (57.8%), Kentucky (67.3%), Missouri (53.4%), Tennessee (65.1%), (Fig. 15-1). In the adjacent states of Illinois (73.0%), Indiana (67.7%), Ohio (50.4%) and Oklahoma (59.8%) more than 50 percent of all those tested in farm areas had positive reactions (Fig. 15-2).

In addition to these high-prevalence states, others had one or more counties whose lifetime residents had prevalence rates of 50 percent or more. The states with localized high-prevalence areas were Alabama, Kansas, Louisiana, Maryland, Mississippi, Texas, and West Virginia (Fig. 15-3).

The high prevalence of histoplasmin sensitivity in these fifteen states (Fig. 15-4) is paralleled by numerous reports of culturally confirmed human

---

* Unless otherwise noted all citations of histoplasmin sensitivity reactions are derived from this publication.

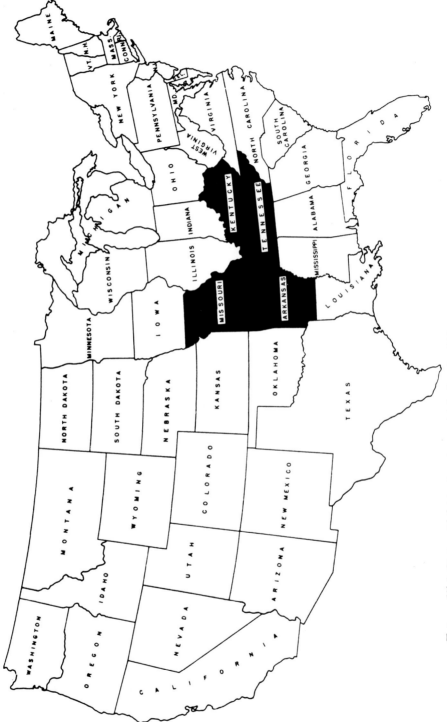

FIGURE 15-1. State with histoplasmin sensitivity levels of 50 percent or more in both rural and urban areas.

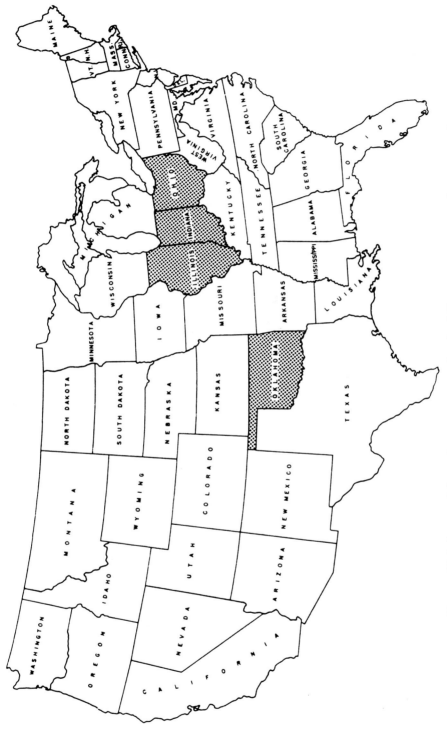

FIGURE 15-2. State with histoplasmin sensitivity levels of 50 percent or more in farm areas only.

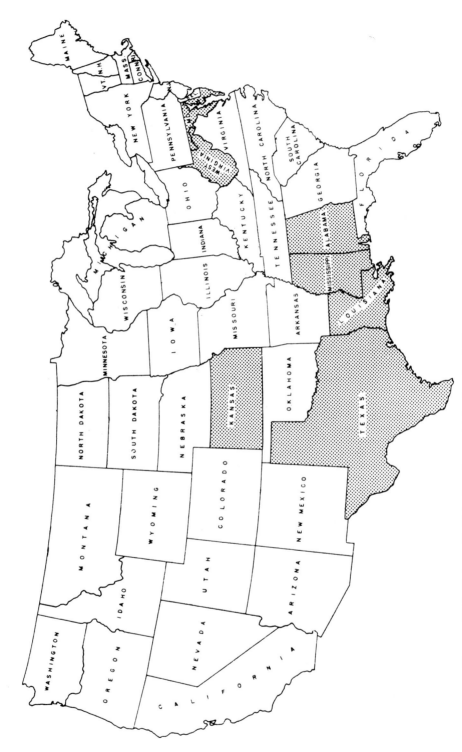

Figure 15-3. States with histoplasmin sensitivity levels of 50 percent or more in one or more counties only.

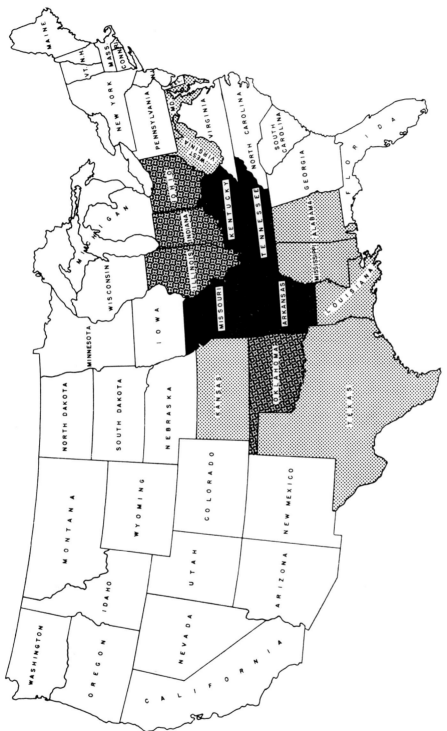

Figure 15-4. Principal histoplasmosis endemic areas.

cases of histoplasmosis, isolations of *H. capsulatum* from animals, and most fundamental of all, recoveries of that fungus from a great number of soil specimens. *H. capsulatum* has been isolated from soils collected in all of the previously mentioned states, with the sole exception of Louisiana (Ajello, 1960a, b).

These fifteen states, then, are the components of the major histoplasmosis region. Within their confines the general population is at high risk, and the incidence and prevalence of infection reach their peaks.

Peripheral Histoplasmosis Endemic Areas

However, *H. capsulatum* is not restricted to these fifteen states. Beyond their limits, soil and other types of studies have revealed that *H. capsulatum* is native to states where its existence was little suspected. These peripheral endemic areas have been uncovered in an additional thirteen states as well as the District of Columbia (Fig. 15-5): Connecticut, Florida, Georgia, Iowa, Michigan, Minnesota, Nebraska, New Mexico, New York, Pennsylvania, South Carolina, Virginia, and Wisconsin. In these states the presence of *H. capsulatum* is not always reflected by morbidity in the resident population nor by the data gathered in histoplasmin sensitivity surveys.

Connecticut

The existence of *H. capsulatum* in Connecticut was discovered quite by accident by Kaplan and his co-workers in 1961 (Kaplan, Ajello, Di Bitetto and McDonough, 1961). While searching for the point source of infection of a feline case of cryptococcosis, they isolated *H. capsulatum* from a flower pot. The potting soil had originally come from an old orchard. Soil specimens collected in the orchard proved to be negative.

There are no cases of human histoplasmosis recorded for Connecticut. This fact is correlated with the finding that the average histoplasmin sensitivity level for the whole state is 1.0 percent.

Florida

Florida's histoplasmin sensitivity level is 4.7 percent, but two cases of histoplasmosis have occurred in native Floridians (Johnson, Radimer, DiSalvo, Ajello and Bigler, 1970). Both individuals had explored caves that sheltered bats. In 1955 Conant isolated *H. capsulatum* from bat-cave soil collected near Floral City in Citrus County. More recently Tesh and Schneidau (1967) recovered *H. capsulatum* from bats collected in Alachua and Citrus counties. In a more extensive Florida survey DiSalvo *et al.* (1970) isolated that fungus from bats collected in seven counties—Alachua, Citrus, Hernando, Hillsborough, Jackson, Marion, and Orange. In addition, soils from

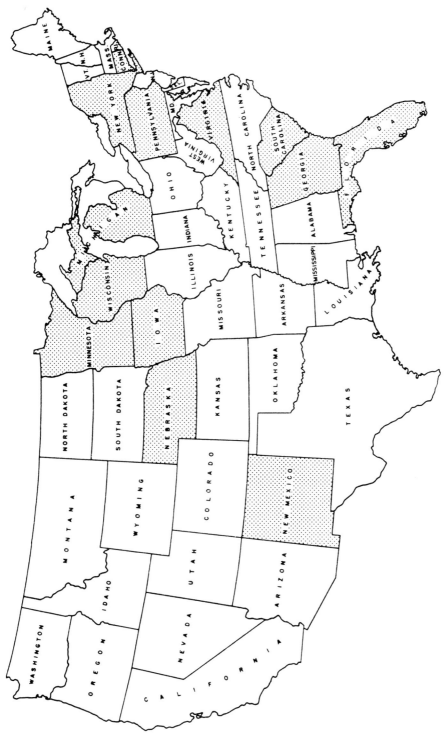

FIGURE 15-5. Peripheral *H. capsulatum* endemic areas based on soil isolations.

bat caves in Jackson, and Marion in Alachua Counties were positive for *H. capsulatum.*

Georgia

Currently available data indicate that *H. capsulatum* is erratically distributed in Georgia. This fungus has been isolated from soil in two sites: one in Dalton, a town in Whitfield County, located in the northwestern part of the state (Edwards *et al.*, 1960); and the second in the vicinity of Augusta, Richmond County, situated in the east central region (Denton, 1969). The Dalton soil specimen came from a grassy area between two houses with no signs of bat or bird activity. In contrast, the Augusta specimens were obtained in an old abandoned chicken coop.

The only other nonhuman isolations of *H. capsulatum* for Georgia were made from two groups of domestic and feral animals. The first had been collected in Brooks, Decatur, Grady, and Thomas Counties, all located in the southern part of the state close to the Florida border (Emmons, Morlan and Hill, 1949). The positive animals were brown (*Rattus rattus*) and Norwegian (*R. norvegicus*) rats and spotted skunks (*Spilogale putorius*). In a more extensive survey of south Georgia animals, Dr. Charles S. Richards and I recovered *H. capsulatum* from a large series of domestic and feral animals: cat (*Felis domestica*), grey and red foxes (*Urycon cinereoargenteus, Vulpes fulva*), opossum (*Didelphis virginiana*), raccoon (*Procyon lotor*) and two species of skunk (*Mephitis mephitis* and *S. putorius*). The positive animals were trapped in the extreme southwestern corner of the state in the counties of Decatur and Seminole.

Although the statewide histoplasmin sensitivity level averages 7.3 percent, surveys conducted in Whitefield County (Edwards *et al.*, 1958) revealed that 55 percent of the children tested in Dalton gave positive reactions. In one section of the city more than 80 percent of the high school students were histoplasmin positive (Edwards *et al.*, 1960). In south Georgia, despite the high prevalence of histoplasmosis in animals, the local population has a histoplasmin sensitivity level of only 13.4 percent.

Reports of only two human cases of histoplasmosis that presumably originated in Georgia have been published (Michael and Vogel, 1954; Peeples and Spence, 1954). Michael and Vogel's patient was a resident of Walker County in the northwestern part of the state, and Peeples and Spence's patient was a resident of Muscogee County in the western part. Walker County has a histoplasmin sensitivity level of 17.6 percent in contrast to Muscogee's 2.8 percent.

Iowa

Iowa has the distinction of being the locale of the first successful isolation of *H. capsulatum* from a human. This was accomplished in 1932 by Hansmann and Schenken (1933a, b, 1934). These investigators classified their isolate in the genus *Sependonium* and failed to equate it with Darling's *H. capsulatum*. Because of this and because of the more thorough description of the second isolate of *H. capsulatum* by DeMonbreun (1934), the priority of Hansmann and Schenken's work is generally ignored.

The overall histoplasmin sensitivity level in Iowa is 21.2 percent, but several regions have sensitivity rates that exceed 25 percent. In addition, thirty-eight cases of histoplasmosis were reported from Iowa in 1961 (Cazin *et al.*, 1962).

In 1951 and 1962 *H. capsulatum* was recovered from soils collected in Jackson County, (Grayston *et al.*, 1953) and in Wapello County, (Cazin *et al.*, 1962). In the latter county the histoplasmin sensitivity rate is 45.3 percent.

The only other Iowan soil isolations were from Mason City, Cerro Gordo County (D'Alessio *et al.*, 1965, and Tosh *et al.*, 1966). This city was the site of two major outbreaks of histoplasmosis associated with a starling (*Sturnus vulgaris*) roost. There 298 clinical cases of histoplasmosis with two deaths were diagnosed. *H. capsulatum* was isolated from 152 of 273 or 56 percent of the soil specimens collected in the city. Twenty-nine percent (29%) of the Mason City school children were found to be histoplasmin positive.

Michigan

Michigan is another of those states, situated outside of the major histoplasmosis region, with at least one area infested with *H. capsulatum*. The endemic site was located in Milan, Washtenaw County. There three different groups of investigators isolated the fungus from soil gathered in and around a starling roost. (Dodge, Ajello and Engelke, 1965).

Although the statewide prevalence of histoplasmin is 5.9 percent, surveys carried out in Milan revealed that 61 percent of 1,300 school children were positive reactors (Engelke, Hemphill, Bushell and McKinney, 1960).

Hickey and Todosijczuk (1968) list forty-seven cases of histoplasmosis for the state of Michigan. But all may not represent indigenous infections.

Minnesota

The first reported case of histoplasmosis in the United States originated in Minnesota. In 1926 Watson and Riley described a fatal infection in a fifty-two-year-old woman who had lived in Minnesota for forty-two years. On the basis of histological studies the disease was attributed to Darling's *H. capsulatum*. Since that historic date, thirty-four other cases have been recorded in Minnesota (Hickey and Todosijczuk, 1968).

Not until 1951 was *H. capsulatum* recovered from Minnesotan soil. In that year Grayston and Furcolow (1953) isolated it from a sample collected under a farmhouse in Becker County near Detroit Lakes. Becker County is situated in an area with a histoplasmin prevalence level of 1.7 percent. The state averages 5.3 percent reactivity.

Nebraska

Until recently there was little cause to believe that *H. capsulatum* was endemic in Nebraska. Only five cases had been reported from that state. The diagnosis in only one of these (Nejedly and Baker, 1955) was supported by the isolation of *H. capsulatum*.

In a 1947 histoplasmosis case (Conlin and Hankins, 1947), described as the first for Nebraska, there is reason to believe that the victim in reality died of coccidioidomycosis. Puckett's three cases (1953) were diagnosed only by histology. On the basis of the residency data given, probably only two of the patients were infected in Nebraska.

All doubt concerning the endemicity of *H. capsulatum* in Nebraska was ended when this fungus was isolated from soil collected in Grand Island, Hall County, by Goodman, Sprouse and Larsh (1968). Hall County is in a group of counties with 10.5 percent histoplasmin sensitivity. An area in the southeast has 26.1 percent sensitivity, and the state as a whole averages 10.9 percent.

New Mexico

Histoplasmin sensitivity in New Mexico averages 11.7 percent, with a high of 20.5 percent in the lower third of the state. This is an area endemic for *Coccidioides immitis,* and it is impossible to state what percentage of the histoplasmin reactions represent cross-reactions to coccidioidomycosis. There is firm evidence, however, that *H. capsulatum* is indigenous to New Mexico. In 1962 *H. capsulatum* was isolated from two soil samples collected in an abandoned mine near the town of Hobbs, Lea County (Varga, 1962).

More recently bats collected in the state have yielded *H. capsulatum* (Studier, 1969).

New York

The existence of endemic foci of *H. capsulatum* in New York state is well documented. In 1953 Grayston and Furcolow, in a retrospective follow-up of an outbreak of pneumonitis among workers who had demolished a school building in Plattsburg, Clinton County, New York, isolated *H. capsulatum* from soil collected in a nearby church basement. The acute pulmonary pneumonitis had afflicted twenty-three men who had been exposed to dust from the wrecked school tower. The tower "was filled with dead pigeons of various sizes and with pigeon droppings to a height of about four feet" (Nauen and Korns, 1944; White and Hill, 1950).

In 1956 during an investigation of two acute cases of histoplasmosis, *H.*

capsulatum was isolated from two sites in the Mohawk Valley (Hazen, Little and Mordaunt, 1956; Cullen, Hazen and Scholdager, 1956).

Prior to this, in 1953, the first case of histoplasmosis in a lifetime resident of northeastern New York state had been reported by Monroe and Kurung (1953).

In 1967 Gordon and Ziment documented the first occurrence of histoplasmosis in western New York state. They isolated *H. capsulatum* from chimney dust that was believed to contain bat guano. This positive site was located near Conesus Lake in Monroe County.

New York state has a statewide level of 2.6 percent histoplasmin reactivity. The area comprising the counties of Clinton, Essex, Franklin, Jefferson, Lewis, and St. Lawrence has 15.3 percent reactivity.

Pennsylvania

Evidence that *H. capsulatum* is endemic in Pennsylvania rests on the isolation of that fungus from soil collected near Kennett Square, Chester County (Emmons and Campbell, 1957). Hickey and Todosijczuk (1968) list thirty-one cases of histoplasmosis for this state. Histoplasmin sensitivity levels average 5.7 percent for Pennsylvania, with a high of 30.5 percent for Adams, Franklin, and Lebanon counties. Three other areas—Cumberland and Dauphin counties, York County, and Lancaster County—had the following percentages of reactors, respectively, 20.7, 21.5 and 25.7 percent.

South Carolina

On the basis of skin test surveys, South Carolina must be classified as a state with a low incidence and prevalence of histoplasmosis. The statewide percentage of histoplasmin reactors is 7.8 percent. A high of 21.4 percent occurs, however, in Greenville County, and levels of 17.1 and 15.3 percent were found in Oconee and Pickens counties and Anderson, Greenwood, Laurens, and Spartanburg counties, respectively.

Hickey and Todosijczuk (1968) cite only one recorded case of histoplasmosis for South Carolina. It had been diagnosed in 1954 by Terry and Matthews (1956). However, in 1965, Sellers, Price and Newberry isolated *H. capsulatum* from three starling roosts in the Greenwood area while investigating an outbreak of histoplasmosis with erythema multiforme and nodosum that involved forty-two patients.

Three years later DiSalvo (1968, personal communication) isolated *H. capsulatum* from soil collected in a starling roost in Laurens County.

Virginia

Virginia has a relatively high rate of histoplasmin reactors—19.3 percent with rates reaching 48.9 percent in the north. In Loudoun County 73 percent of 1,449 individuals skin tested gave positive reactions (Mattern, Bell, Olson, Emmons and Powell, 1956).

It was from Loudoun County that Emmons (1949) isolated *H. capsulatum* from soil for the first time, thus revealing the saprophytic existence of this pathogen in nature. Subsequently, he repeatedly recovered *H. capsulatum* from other soil samples and from a series of domestic and feral animals in Loudoun County (Emmons and Campbell, 1957).

Soils collected in Fairfax and Fauquier counties have also yielded this fungus (Emmons and Campbell, 1957). Fauquier County is located among a group of counties with 43.6 percent histoplasmin reactivity. In contrast Fairfax County has a 16 percent reactivity.

Forty-five cases of human histoplasmosis are registered for that state (Hickey and Todosijczuk, 1968).

Wisconsin

H. capsulatum has been isolated from soil in three counties in the state of Wisconsin: Columbia, Dane, and Walworth (Grayston and Furcolow, 1953; Lehan and Furcolow, 1957; Wilcox, Waisbren and Martin, 1958).

Columbia and Walworth counties are in a region with 6.5 percent histoplasmin reactivity. The prevalence of histoplasmin sensitivity in Dane County is 10.6 percent. The whole state has an average of 4.5 percent reactivity.

District of Columbia

In 1961 Emmons revealed the fact that our nation's capitol is an endemic area for *H. capsulatum*. In that year he isolated this fungus from eleven of fifteen soil samples collected in downtown Washington.

Lifetime residents of the District of Columbia have a 20 percent reactivity to histoplasmin.

Presumptive Histoplasmosis Endemic Areas

On the basis of evidence other than soil isolations, there is reason to believe that *H. capsulatum* occurs in still other areas of the United States. These are in the states of Arizona, Montana, North Carolina, North Dakota, and Vermont.

Arizona

Although there are no published cases of autochthonous human histoplasmosis for the state of Arizona, histoplasmin sensitivity levels are relatively high. Prevalence rates average 28.7 percent for the state and attain levels of 33.8 and 39.6 percent, respectively, for Maricopa and Pima Counties.

The first definitive proof that *H. capsulatum* occurs in Arizona was obtained in 1967 by DiSalvo and his co-workers (DiSalvo, Ajello, Palmer and Winkler, 1969). In that year they isolated *H. capsulatum* from 15 of 555 bats. The positive bats had been collected in three counties: Cochise, Greenlee, and Pima. The percentage of histoplasmin reactors in Cochise and Greenlee Counties averages 19.2 percent.

In 1957 Palmer, Edwards, and Allfather speculated that Arizona histoplasmin reactions were probably nonspecific. They attributed the cross-reactions to fungus infections by unidentified organisms. More recently Lydia Edwards and her co-workers (1969) stated that the reactions are due to infection by both. *C. immitis* and *H. capsulatum*.

Montana

The basis for suspecting that at least one edemic focus of *H. capsulatum* exists in Montana rests on histological findings in a bat. Klite and Diercks (1965) cited Bell's unpublished observation of finding a lymph node in a little brown bat (*Myotis lucifugus*) that contained *H. capsulatum*-like cells.

Histoplasmin skin test surveys have revealed a level of only 2.0 percent for the state of Montana.

North Carolina

North Carolina presents a paradox concerning histoplasmosis. Although it is surrounded by states in which the presence of *H. capsulatum* has been established, there are no published reports of the isolation of that fungus from an autochthonous case or from a natural site.

Belief that *H. capsulatum* does occur in North Carolina is based only on case reports and personal communications. In 1943 Thomas and Morehead presented histological evidence that supported the diagnosis of histoplasmosis in a patient suffering with a concurrent infection of tuberculosis. In a personal communication Conant kindly gave me unpublished data on native cases on histoplasmosis diagnosed at Duke University and at the Bowman-Gray School of Medicine. Twenty-one cases have been registered at Duke. The diagnosis in twenty was based on histological findings only. But in the twenty-first patient a culture of *H. capsulatum* was obtained.

At Bowman-Gray's hospital twenty-three cases have been recorded. Data regarding the basis of the diagnosis were not available.

In 1955, an outbreak of an acute respiratory disease in Warrenton, Warren County, North Carolina, was diagnosed as histoplasmosis solely on the basis of serological findings. Attempts to isolate *H. capsulatum* from the patients and soil ended in failure (Parrott, Taylor, Poston and Smith, 1955; Lehan and Furcolow, 1957).

Histoplasmin sensitivity levels in North Carolina average out to 2.7 percent, with a high of 15.7 percent in a group of northeastern counties. However, a survey carried out in 1951 (Murphy, Peck and Vincent) disclosed

that 43 percent of a random group of 338 residents of Hyde County gave
positive reactions. One hundred forty-seven individuals with pulmonary calcification were found in a mass x-ray survey in Beaufort County; 76 percent
of these gave a positive histoplasmin reaction.

North Dakota

In 1952 an acute pulmonary disease occurred in four workmen, following
exposure to dust created while wrecking an old building in Mandan, North
Dakota (Smith, 1953). Clinical symptoms and immunological studies were
compatible with a diagnosis of histoplasmosis. Attempts to culture *H. capsulatum* from clinical and soil specimens ended in failure (Grayston, and Furcolow, 1953).

In North Dakota histoplasmin sensitivity averages 1.8 percent.

Vermont

Histoplasmin sensitivity levels in Vermont are low, with a statewide average of 4.2 percent. However, two cases of histoplasmosis have been diagnosed in lifetime residents. Both cases were confirmed by culture (French,
Jellison, and Crispell, 1953; Parenteau and Ahmed, 1958).

Unsubstantiated Endemic Areas

In reviewing the literature on histoplasmosis, one must be aware that
some case reports are misleading or are in error. Close scrutiny of reports of
histoplasmosis in California, Colorado, Hawaii and Washington revealed
that they fall into either of these two categories. Some described cases were
merely diagnosed in a state, the individuals having been infected in known
endemic areas beyond its borders; others did not provide convincing mycological data, or necessary travel and residency information, or they presented cases mistakenly diagnosed as histoplasmosis (Adler, 1950, Eby and
Ringen, 1955; Hickey and Todosijczuk, 1968; Lam and Price, 1947; Wyborney, Walch, Loeffler and Wiita, 1966).

Discussion

It is obvious that within the United States ecological conditions favorable
for the propagation of *H. capsulatum* exist virtually from coast to coast and
from border to border. Clinical, ecological, epidemiological, and immunological studies have revealed with certainty that *H. capsulatum* is endemic
in thirty-one of the forty-eight contiguous states (Fig. 15-6).* However, it is

---

* Alabama, Arizona, Arkansas, Connecticut, Florida, Georgia, Illinois, Indiana, Iowa, Kansas,
Kentucky, Lousiana, Maryland, North Carolina, Michigan, Minnesota, Mississippi, Missouri, Nebraska, New Mexico, New York, North Carolina, Ohio, Oklahoma, Pennsylvania, South Carolina, Tennessee, Texas, Vermont, Virginia, West Virginia, and Wisconsin.

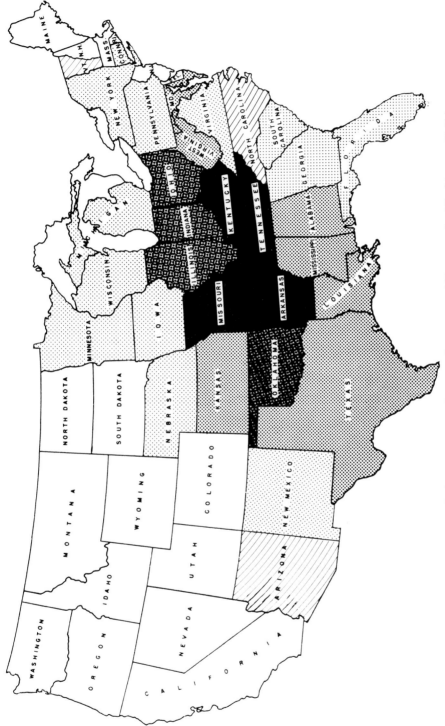

FIGURE 15-6. Currently known *H. capsulatum* endemic areas (31 states plus Washington, D.C.).

also clear that the size of the endemic areas and the intensity of colonization by *H. capsulatum* vary tremendously from state to state. Densities are greatest in the central states of Arkansas, Kentucky, Missouri, and Tennessee, with a graded diminution in prevalence extending from this core area of high infestation.

Away from the major endemic region, the size and frequency of areas seeded with *H. capsulatum* diminish until only small pockets of colonization exist at the edges of its extensive domain. In fringe areas such as Arizona and Florida, favorable environmental conditions for *H. capsulatum's* survival and growth seem to be available solely in bat habitats. It is possible that microclimatic conditions suitable for the propagation of *H. capsulatum* occur in most, if not all, of the twenty states* where the fungus has yet to be found in soil.

Mass skin-testing surveys have been of great value in characterizing the areas where *H. capsulatum* exists. The survey conducted by the Tuberculosis Branch of the National Communicable Disease Center (Edwards *et al.,* 1969) on naval recruits from forty-eight states defined areas within each state where reactors to histoplasmin resided. This information can guide field investigators to specific localities in which to search for *H. Capsulatum*. It suggests that positive sites may occur in California, Colorado, Delaware, North Carolina, Nevada, New Jersey, and South Dakota—eight of the twenty states with no soil isolations of this fungus thus far.

It must be emphasized, however, that a low level of sensitivity does not necessarily rule out the presence of *H. capsulatum* in a given area. Because of practical limitations, surveys are likely to miss small communities of sensitized people living near a very restricted focus of infestation, or certain isolated fungus habitats such as bat caves may be visited so infrequently that the rare sensitized individual is not included in the population sample.

Through use of the sensitivity data in the NCDC survey, a numerical estimate of the magnitude of the histoplasmosis problem in the United States is possible. Exclusive of Alaska and Hawaii, the national histoplasmin sensitivity level averages 20 percent. Using the latest Census Bureau population estimate of 200,845,000† people for the forty-eight states surveyed, and making two assumptions, (1) that the yearly histoplasmin sensitization rate is constant, and (2) that the histoplasmin reaction is specific, one comes to the conclusion that approximately 40,169,000 of our fellow Americans have been infected by *H. capsulatum*.

Truly, *H. capsulatum* is the most widely distributed of the dimorphic, sys-

---

* Arizona, California, Colorado, Delaware, Idaho, Maine, Massachusetts, Montana, Nevada, New Hampshire, New Jersey, North Carolina, North Dakota, Oregon, Rhode Island, South Dakota, Utah, Vermont, Washington, and Wyoming.

† Derived from the 1969 Census Bureau data published in *The New York Times,* September 7, 1969.

temic, pathogenic fungi that live in soil. Its spores have literally infected millions of people within the United States.

These is no way of knowing how many individuals develop active forms of the disease and require hospitalization nor how many die of histoplasmosis each year. Over the ten-year period of 1957 to 1966, 746 deaths* have been attributed to that disease. But the actual figure may very well be higher, since lamentably many cases of histoplasmosis still remain undiagnosed or misdiagnosed.

A concerted effort must be made by all public health workers to disseminate and apply the information that is currently known about histoplasmosis. Only through such action can we hope to have all cases promptly and accurately diagnosed and treated with the most effective therapeutic agents. Concurrently, research studies must continue to be encouraged and supported so that our knowledge of *H. capsulatum* will increase. In this way, we may learn how to significantly reduce the effect this organism has on our well-being.

References

Adler, H.E. (1950). Generalized infection with a yeast-like fungus in a range bull. *N. Amer. Vet.*, 31:457-458.

Ajello, L. (1960a). *Histoplasma capsulatum* soil studies. *Mykosen*, 3:43-48.

Ajello, L. (1960b). Geographic distribution of *Histoplasma capsulatum*. In Sweany, H.C. (Ed.). *Histoplasmosis*. Springfield, Thomas, pp.88-98.

Ajello, L. and Richards, C.S. (1958). Unpublished data.

Cazin, J., McCulloch, W.F. and Braun, J.L. (1962). Isolation of *Histoplasma capsulatum, Allescheria boydii* and *Microsporum gypseum* from Iowa soil. *J. Iowa Med. Soc.*, 52:348-351.

Comstock, G.W. (1959). Histoplasmin sensitivity in Alaskan natives. *Amer. Rev. Taberc. Pulman, Dis.*, 79:196.

Conant, N.F. (1969). Personal communication.

Conlin, F.M. and Hankins, C.R. (1947). Histoplasmosis case report. *Nebraska Med. J.*, 32:101-103.

Cullen, J.H., Hazen, E. and Scholdager, R. (1956). Two cases of histoplasmosis acquired in felling a decayed tree in the Mohawk Valley. *New York J. Med.*, 56:3507-3510.

D'Alessio, D.J., Heeren, R.H., Hendricks, S.L., Ogilvie, P. and Furcolow, M.L. (1965). A starling roost as the source of urban epidemic histoplasmosis in an area of low incidence. *Amer. Rev. Resp. Dis.*, 92:725-731.

DeMonbreun, W.A. (1934). The cultivation and cultural characteristics of Darling's *Histoplasma capsulatum*. *Amer. J. Trop. Med.*, 14:93-125.

Denton, J.F. (1969). Personal communication.

DiSalvo, A.F., Ajello, L., Palmer, J.W. and Winkler, W.G. (1969). Isolation of *Histoplasma capsulatum* from Arizona bats. *Amer. J. Epidem.*, 89:606-614.

---

* From Morbidity and Mortality, Weekly Report, National Communicable Disease Center, Atlanta, Georgia. Annual Supplement, Vol. 16, No. 53, Issued November 1968.

Di Salvo, A.F., Bigler, W.J., Ajello, L., Johnson, J.E. and Palmer, J. (1970). Bat and soil studies for sources of histoplasmosis in Florida. *Public Health Rep.* 85:1063-1069.

Dodge, H.J., Ajello, L. and Engelke, O.K. (1965). The association of a bird-roosting site with infection of school children by *Histoplasma capsulatum. Amer. J. Public Health,* 55:1203-1211.

Eby, C.H. and Ringen, L.M. (1955). Canine histoplasmosis in the Pacific Northwest. *Amer. Vet. Med. Assoc., 127:*250-251.

Edwards, Lydia B., Acquaviva, F.A., Livesay, Verna T., Cross, F.W. and Palmer, C.E. (1969). An atlas of sensitivity to tuberculin, ppd-b, and histoplasmin in the United States. *Amer. Rev. Resp. Dis.,* 99:1-132.

Edwards, P.Q., Jacobs, C.F. and Barfield, D. (1958). Sensitivity to tuberculin, histoplasmin and coccidioidin among high school students in northwestern Georgia. *Dis. Chest,* 34:467-483.

Edwards, Phyllis Q., Ajello, L., Moore, J., Jacobs, C.F. and Aronson, D.L. (1960). Soil sampling in an urban focus of histoplasmin sensitivity. *Amer. Rev. Resp. Dis.,* 81:747-751.

Emmons, C.W. (1949). Isolation of *Histoplasma capsulatum* from soil. *Public Health Rep.,* 64:892-896.

Emmons, C.W. (1961). Isolation of *Histoplasma capsulatum* from soil in Washington, D. C. *Public Health Rep.,* 76:591-595.

Emmons, C.W., Bell, J.A., and Olson, B.J. (1947). Naturally occurring histoplasmosis in *Mus musculus* and *Rattus norvegicus. Public Health Rep.,* 62:1642-1646.

Emmons, C.W. and Campbell, C.C. (1957). Histoplasmosis in the District of Columbia, Maryland and Virginia. *Clin. Proc. Child. Hosp.,* 13:225-235.

Emmons, C.W., Morlan, H.B. and Hill, E.L. (1949). Histoplasmosis in rats and skunks in Georgia. *Public Health Rep.,* 64:1423-1430.

Emmons, C.W., Rowley, D.A., Olson, B.J., Mattern, C.F.T., Bell, J.A., Powell, E. and Marcey, E.A. (1955). Histoplasmosis. Proved occurrence of inapparent infection in dogs, cats and other animals. *Amer. J. Hyg., 61:*40-44.

Engelke, O.K., Hemphill, F.M., Bushell, E. and McKinney, E.B. (1960). A survey of tuberculin and histoplasmin reactors among school children of Washtenaw County, Mich. *Amer. J. Public Health,* 50:368-376.

French, E.E., Jellison, O.F. and Crispell, L.S. (1953). Histoplasmosis in a life-long resident of New England. *New Eng. J. Med.,* 249:270-272.

Furcolow, M.L. (1965). Environmental aspects of histoplasmosis. *Arch. Environ. Health,* 10:4-10.

Goodman, N.L., Sprouse, R.F. and Larsh, H. (1968). Histoplasmin potency as affected by culture age. *Sabouraudia,* 6:273-284.

Gordon, M.A. and Ziment, I. (1967). Epidemic of acute histoplasmosis in western New York State. *New York J. Med.,* Jan. 15, pp.235-243.

Grayston, J.T. and Furcolow, M.L. (1953). The occurrence of histoplasmosis in epidemics—epidemiological studies. *Amer. J. Public Health,* 43:665-676.

Hansmann, G.H. and Schenken, J.R. (1933a). New disease caused by a yeastlike organism. *Science* (Suppl.), 77(2002): 8.

Hansmann, G.H. and Schenken, J.R. (1933b). A unique infection in man with a new yeast-like organism. *Amer. J. Path.,* 9:925.

Hansmann, G.H. and Schenken, J.R. (1934). A unique infection in man caused by a new yeast-like organism, a pathogenic member of the genus *Sepedonium. Amer. J. Path.,* 10:731-738.

Hazen, Elizabeth L., Little, G.N. and Mordaunt, Verna. (1956). Isolation of *Histoplasma capsulatum* from two natural sources in the Mohawk Valley; one the probable point source of two cases of histoplasmosis. *Amer. J. Public Health,* 46:880-885.

Hickey, M.A. and Todosijczuk, D. (1968). Sensitivity and incidence of histoplasmosis reported in the literature up to and including 1965. Supplement to a scientific exhibit. Copyright 1968.

Johnson, J.E., Radimer, G., DiSalvo, A.F., Ajello, L. and Bigler, W. (1970). Histoplasmosis in Florida. I. Report of a case and epidemiological studies. *Amer. Rev. Resp. Dis.,* 101:299-305

Kaplan, W., Ajello, L., Di Bitetto D.B. and McDonough, E.S. (1961). The discovery of *Histoplasma capsulatum* in Connecticut soil incidental to the investigation of a case of feline cryptococcosis. *Mycopathologia,* 14:1-8.

Klite, P.D. and Diercks, F.H. (1965). *Histoplasma capsulatum* in fecal contents of bats in the Canal Zone. *Amer. J. Trop. Med.,* 14:433-439.

Lam, F.K. and Price, S. (1947). Histoplasmosis in man. *Hawaii Med. J.,* 6:313-315.

Lehan, P.H. and Furcolow, M.L. (1957). Epidemic histoplasmosis. *J. Chron. Dis.,* 5:489-503.

Mattern, C.F., Bell, J.A., Olson, B.J., Emmons, C.W. and Powell, Erma P. (1956). Continued observation on histoplasmin sensitivity and calcified pulmonary lesions in a rural county. *Public Health. Monogr.* 39:217-220.

Michael, M. and Vogel, R.A. (1954). Histoplasmosis. Report of a case, with observations on management. *New Eng. J. Med.,* 251:884-887.

Monroe, J. and Kurung, J.M. (1953). Histoplasmosis with review of the literature and report of a case, proved by culture, with involvement of the upper lobe of each lung simulating active bilateral optical pulmonary tuberculosis. *Ann. Intern. Med.,* 38:206-222.

Murphy, R.J., Peck, W.M. and Vincent B. (1951). Preliminary report of histoplasmin and other antigen sensitivity in North Carolina. *Amer. J. Public Health,* 41:1521-1525.

Nauen, R. and Korns, R.F. (1944). A localized epidemic of acute miliary pneumonitis, associated with the handling of pigeon manure. Presented at the annual meeting of the American Public Health. Association, New York, N.Y., October.

Nejedly, R.T. and Baker, L.A. (1955). Treatment of localized histoplasmosis with 2-hydroxystilbamidine. *Arch. Intern. Med.,* 95:37-40.

Palmer, C.E., Edwards, P.Q. and Allfather, N.E. (1957). Characteristics of skin reactions to coccidioidin and histoplasmin, with evidence of an unidentified source of sensitization. *Amer. J. Hyg.,* 66:196-213.

Parenteau, Sister Corona M. and Ahmed, M.J. (1958). *Histoplasma capsulatum.* A brief report of its isolation from a recent case. *Vermont J. Med. Tech,* 3:12-13.

Parrott, T., Taylor, G., Poston, M.A. and Smith, D.T. (1955). An epidemic of histoplasmosis in Warrenton, North Carolina. *Southern Med. J.,* 48:1147-1150.

Peeples, W.J. and Spence, M.J. (1954). Pulmonary cavitation due to *Histoplasma capsulatum. Amer. Rev. Tuberc.,* 69:111-115.

Puckett, T.F. (1953). Pulmonary histoplasmosis. A study of twenty-two cases with identification of *H. capsulatum* in resected lesions. *Amer. Rev. Tuberc.,* 67:453-476.

Sellers, T.F., Price, W.N., Jr. and Newberry, W.M. (1965). An epidemic of erythema multiforme and erythema nodosum caused by histoplasmosis. *Ann. Intern. Med.,* 62:1244-1262.

Smith, C.C. (1953). Histoplasmosis in North Dakota. *J. Lancet, 73*:352.

Studier, E. (1969). New Mexico Highlands University, Las Vegas, New Mexico. Personal communication.

Terry, R.T. and Matthews, J.H. (1956). Histoplasmosis: treatment of two cases with beta-diethylaminoethyl fencholate. *Dis. Chest, 30*:570-575.

Tech, R.B. and Schneidau, J.D. (1967). Naturally occurring histoplasmosis among bat colonies in the southeastern United States. *Amer. J. Epidem., 86*:545-551.

Thomas, W.C. and Morehead, R.P. (1943). Histoplasmosis: Report of a case in North Carolina. *N. Carolina Med. J., 4*:378-382.

Tosh, F.E., Doto, I.L., D'Alessio, D.J., Medeiros, A.A., Hendricks, S.L. and Chin, T.D.Y. (1966). The second of two epidemics of histoplasmosis resulting from work on the same starling roost. *Amer. Rev. Resp. Dis., 94*:406-413.

Varga, D.T. (1962). Final report-epidemic investigation-Hobbs New Mexico. *Public Health Ser. Epidem., 62*:52-3.

Watson, C.J. and Riley, W.A. (1926). A case of Darling's histoplasmosis originating in Minnesota. *Arch. Path. Lab. Med., 1*:662-667.

White, F.C. and Hill, H.E. (1950). Disseminated pulmonary calcification. *Amer. Rev. Tuberc., 62*:1-16.

Wilcox, K.R., Waisbren, B.A. and Martin, J. (1958). The Walworth, Wisconsin, epidemic of histoplasmosis. *Ann. Intern. Med., 49*:388-418.

Wyborney, V.J., Walch, H., Loeffler, A.B. and Wiita, R.M. (1966). Histoplasmosis. A review of three cases studied in San Diego County. *Calif. Med., 105*:265-270.

Chapter 16

Histoplasmosis Outbreaks: Their Patterns

GEORGE A. SAROSI, JAMES D. PARKER AND FRED E. TOSH

ABSTRACT

Epidemics of histoplasmosis continue to present excellent opportunities for the study of this disease. Review of the North American experience with epidemics of histoplasmosis since the last comprehensive study revealed certain noteworthy deviations from previous experience.

There was a decrease in the reported outbreaks traceable to chicken manure, but it is difficult to say whether this is more apparent than real. Contaminated starling roosts, especially in urban areas of relatively low endemicity, have appeared as a significant factor in producing epidemics.

The recognition of erythema nodosum and multiforme as an integral part of acute histoplasmosis infections may become a valuable aid in the early detection of histoplasmosis outbreaks.

CLINICAL histoplasmosis still constitutes an important health hazard in the endemic area of the Middle and South Central United States. In fact, this infection probably has involved more people than any other single infectious disease in recent years, with the possible exception of the influenza pandemics (Loosli, 1955). Most of the important information pertaining to histoplasmosis, however, was obtained from a very small proportion of cases in the United States, that is, from the study of epidemic histoplasmosis.

The excellent studies of the 1950's, principally those of Grayston and Furcolow (1953), Loosli (1955), and Lehan and Furcolow (1957), established the pattern of infection: exposure to soil contaminated by chicken, pigeon, or bat droppings.

Since the last review of epidemics in 1957, certain previously unrecognized factors have emerged. The purpose of this communication is to point out these changes in epidemic histoplasmosis.

Results

The North American literature from 1957 to date was reviewed. Fifteen epidemics of histoplasmosis have been reported during that time. Table 16-I shows these epidemics and the pertinent details in chronological order. Figure 16-1 shows the geographic location of these in relation to the known distribution of histoplasmin sensitivity in the United States.

Histoplasmosis

TABLE 16-I

Reported Epidemics of Histoplasmosis 1957–1969

Location and Date of Outbreak	Source	Isolation of H. capsulatum from Soil	Histoplasmin Skin Test Positive/Tested	Serology Positive/Tested	No. Persons Ill Adults M	F	Children	Total	No. With Erythema M	F
Johnstown, N. Y. (Mohawk Valley), 1954 (Cullen et al., 1956)	Debris from fallen tree	+	2/2	2/2	2	—	—	2	—	—
Central Missouri, 1956 (Rubin et al., 1957)	Chicken coop	+	2/2	2/2	1	—	1	2	—	—
Walworth, Wisconsin, 1956 (Wilcox et al., 1958)	Building site (was a starling roost)	+	18/18	18/19	18	1	—	19	—	—
Sturgis, Miss., 1958 (Hagstrom, 1959)	Dirt from a blackbird roost	+	11/12	12/12	—	1	11	12	—	—
Mexico, Missouri, 1959 (Furcolow et al., 1961)	Starling roost	+	10/10	9/9	—	—	10	10	—	—
Baltimore Co., Md., 1959 (Scalia, 1961)	Chicken coop	+	4/4	4/4	3	—	1	4	—	—
Columbus, Ohio, 1960 (Perkins et al., 1962)	Starling roost	+	9/10	9/10	2	2	4	8	—	—
Alexandria Bay, Thousand Islands, N. Y., 1961 (Gordon et al., 1961)	Silo	+	U*	U	U	U	U	3	U	U
Mason City, Iowa—first outbreak, 1962 (D'Alessio et al., 1965)	Starling roost	+	25/25	25/25	U	U	U	28	U	U
Greenwood, S. C., 1962–1963 (Sellers et al., 1965)	Starling roost	+	38/40	33/35	6	31	5	42	6	36†
Montreal, P. Q., Canada, 1963 (Leznoff et al., 1964)	Unknown	—	37/41	32/39	19	23	—	42	1	11
Northwest Illinois, 1963 (Younglove et al., 1968)	Starling roost	+	5/5	10/10	4	1	7	12	—	—
Mason City, Iowa—second outbreak, 1964 (Tosh et al., 1966)	Starling roost	+	78/83	70/82‡	35	44	8	87	4	26
South of Rochester, N. Y., 1964 (Gordon et al., 1967)	Bat guano	+	8/8	8/8	4	3	1	8	—	—
Adair County, Ky., 1965 (Beatty et al., 1967)	Chicken coop	+	1/2	2/2	2	—	—	2	—	—

* U—Unknown.
† Five children.
‡ 4 Anticomplementary

Of these 15 epidemics, 3 were due to exposure to chicken manure, 8 were associated with inhalation of spores from contaminated soil under starling or blackbird roosts, 1 was traced to a point source of bat guano, 1 to a silo, and 1 to debris associated with a fallen tree. In one instance, no definite point source could be identified.

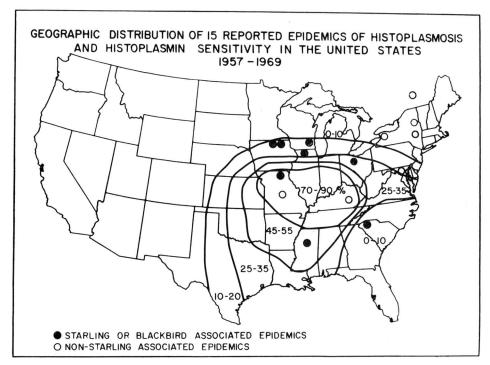

GEOGRAPHIC DISTRIBUTION OF 15 REPORTED EPIDEMICS OF HISTOPLASMOSIS AND HISTOPLASMIN SENSITIVITY IN THE UNITED STATES 1957 – 1969

● STARLING OR BLACKBIRD ASSOCIATED EPIDEMICS
○ NON-STARLING ASSOCIATED EPIDEMICS

FIGURE 16-1.

Two hundred and eighty-one individuals were involved in the fifteen outbreaks. Age and sex were reported for 250 of the cases. Forty-eight were children under the age of sixteen and 202 were adults. Of the 202 adults, 96 were men, 106 were women.

Eighty-four (30%) of the 281 patients had erythema nodosum and/or erythema multiforme. Eleven were adult men, sixty-eight were adult women, and five were female children. All eighty-four patients were part of three large urban outbreaks, one of which reported only the patients with erythema.

Discussion

These results illustrate several important differences when compared with the previous experience. While the majority of the outbreaks were still rural, the largest number of cases came from urban epidemics, which were fewer in number but involved a much larger number of patients per outbreak. In the earlier days, all reported epidemics were essentially rural and involved small numbers of cases.

A very important shift has taken place in the source of the fungus. Lehan and Furcolow (1957) found eighteen proven chicken- and pigeon-dropping associated outbreaks, but only one point source was traceable to a starling roost. Parenthetically, this was not mentioned in their paper but was discovered only after their work was published. In the more recent epidemics, only three were due to working in or around chicken houses, while eight were due to starling or blackbird roosts (Table 16-II). The importance of this finding is that all but one of these occurred in a definite urban setting, unlike the chicken coop associated epidemics, which were universally rural.

The outbreaks of histoplasmosis traceable to disturbed starling or blackbird roosts were notable in one more respect—they tended to occur in areas of otherwise low endemicity (Fig. 16-1), which further accounts for the larger total number of people infected and also for the markedly different age and sex distribution.

When one compares the age and sex distribution during the two periods, i.e., pre- and post-1957 (Table 16-III), the difference is readily apparent. In the earlier period, epidemic histoplasmosis was largely an "occupational" disease of outdoor workers, mostly men or rural children, with only a very small proportion of women. In the more recent largely urban epidemics, adult women were involved much more frequently.

This observation helps to explain an added feature of the more recent epidemics—the frequent occurrence of the allergic skin manifestations of the infection by *Histoplasma capsulatum*.

The association of erythema multiforme and nodosum with specific infectious diseases has been well recognized, especially in tuberculosis, streptococcal infections (Löfgren, 1946; Weinstein, 1969), and perhaps more important, with the acute pulmonary infection caused by *Coccidioides immitis* (Dickson and Gifford, 1938). That these dermatologic syndromes could accompany acute histoplasmosis was not generally appreciated until the three large urban outbreaks in Montreal, Canada (Leznoff, Frank, Telner, Rosensweig and Brandt, 1964), Greenwood, South Carolina (Sellers, Price and Newberry, 1965), and the second Mason City, Iowa (Medeiros, Marty, Tosh and Chin, 1966) epidemic, though isolated cases were reported as early as 1950 (Heilbrunn and Cain, 1950).

In the areas of California hyperendemic for coccidioidomycosis, the incidence of allergic manifestations—the erythemas and joint pains—among Caucasian women is around 25 percent, while it is only 4 percent for Caucasian men, about six times as common among women as in men (Winn,

TABLE 16-II

Point Source of Epidemics of Histoplasmosis in North America

Source of *H. capsulatum*	Reported Outbreaks	
	Lehan and Furcolow (1957)	Current Review
Chicken and pigeon excreta	18	3
Starling and blackbird roosts	1	8

TABLE 16-III

Age and Sex Distribution of Reported Cases of Epidemic Histoplasmosis

Age and Sex	Source of Cases			
	Lehan and Furcolow (1957)		Present Report	
	No.	%	No.	%
Male (over 16)	175	49	96	38
Female (over 16)	13	4	106	42
Children	171	47	48	20
Total	359	100	250	100

1967). From our figures, the allergic manifestations in histoplasmosis are 7 to 8 times more common among women, a figure comparable to that in coccidioidomycosis.

In greater Greenwood, South Carolina, there were an estimated eight thousand infections, with forty-two cases of erythemas, or a ratio of 1:200. In Mason City during the second outbreak, we estimated six thousand infections, with thirty cases of erythemas. Once again, the ratio is 1:200. This infrequent occurrence, coupled with the much higher incidence of these manifestations in women, may explain why this association went unrecognized for so long. While the erythemas can certainly occur in children, it is apparently less common than in adult women, and the virtual absence of adult females among victims of the early epidemics just did not provide a large enough number of susceptibles for these manifestations to become apparent.

While the incidence of these dermatological manifestations is probably common, we think that our figures are too high for the calculation of the true frequency. It certainly follows that in endemic and epidemic situations the reporting of these skin manifestations are near complete, while the much more common pneumonic form does not get reported in its entirety. Nevertheless, they are very important in detecting epidemics; because of their highly visible nature they invariably bring the patient to a physician, therefore serving as excellent sentinels for recognizing epidemics of histoplasmosis.

References

Beatty, O.A., Zwick, L.S. and Paisley, C.G. (1967). Epidemic histoplasmosis in Ohio with source in Kentucky. *Ohio Med. J.*, 63:1470-1473.

Cullen, J.H., Hazen, E. and Scholdager, R. (1956). Two cases of histoplasmosis acquired in felling a decayed tree in the Mohawk Valley. *New York J. Med.*, 56: 3507-3510.

D'Alessio, D.J., Heeren, R.H., Hendricks, S.L., Ogilvie, P. and Furcolow, M.L. (1965). A starling roost as the source of urban epidemic histoplasmosis in an area of low incidence. *Amer. Rev. Resp. Dis.*, 92:725-731.

Dickson, E.C. and Gifford, M.A. (1938). Coccidioides infection (coccidioidomycosis): II. Primary type of infection. *Arch. Intern. Med., 62:*853-871.

Furcolow, M.L., Tosh, F.E., Larsh, H.W., Lynch, H.J., Jr., and Shaw, G. (1961). The emerging pattern of urban histoplasmosis. Studies on an epidemic in Mexico, Missouri. *New Eng. J. Med., 264:*1226-1230.

Gordon, M.A., Greene, C.H. and Elliott, J.C. (1961). A small outbreak of histoplasmosis. Annual report, Division of Laboratories and Research, State of New York Dept. of Health, Albany, p. 86.

Gordon, M.A. and Ziment, I. (1967). Epidemic of acute histoplasmosis in western New York State. *New York J. Med., 67:*235-243.

Grayston, J.T. and Furcolow, M.L. (1953). The occurrence of histoplasmosis in epidemics—Epidemiological studies. *Amer. J. Public Health, 43*(1):665-676.

Hagstrom, R. (1959). Epidemiologic studies by county health departments. *Miss. Doctor, 37:*141-145.

Heilbrunn, I.B. and Cain, A.R. (1950). Mild histoplasmosis clinically resembling atypical pneumonia and accompanied by erythema nodosum and arthritis. *J. Missouri Med. Assoc., 47:*503-504.

Lehan, P.H. and Furcolow, M.L. (1957). Epidemic histoplasmosis. *J. Chronic Dis., 5:*489-503.

Leznoff, A., Frank, H., Telner, P., Rosensweig, J. and Brandt, J.L. (1964). Histoplasmosis in Montreal during the fall of 1963, with observations on erythema multiforme. *Canad. Med. Assoc. J., 91:*1154-1160.

Löfgren, S. (1946). Erythema nodosum. Studies on etiology and pathogenesis in 185 adult cases. *Acta. Med. Scand.* (Suppl. 174), *124:*1-197.

Loosli, C.G. (1955). Histoplasmosis—some clinical, epidemiological and laboratory aspects. *Med. Clin. N. Amer., 39:*171-199.

Medeiros, A.A., Marty, S.D., Tosh, F.E. and Chin, T.D.Y. (1966). Erythema nodosum and erythema multiforme as clinical manifestations of histoplasmosis in a community outbreak. *New Eng. J. Med., 274:*415-420.

Perkins, R.L., Saslaw, S. and Ockner, S.A. (1962). Migration histoplasmosis. *Ann. Intern. Med., 57:*363-372.

Rubin, H., Lehan, P.H. and Furcolow, M.L. (1957). Severe nonfatal histoplasmosis. *New Eng. J. Med., 257:*599-602.

Scalia, S.P. (1961). An outbreak of histoplasmosis in Baltimore County. *Maryland Med. J., 10:*614-619.

Sellers, T.F., Jr., Price, W.N., Jr., and Newberry, W.M., Jr. (1965). An epidemic of erythema multiforme and erythema nodosum caused by histoplasmosis. *Ann. Intern. Med., 62:*1244-1262.

Tosh, F.E., Doto, I.L., D'Alessio, D.J., Medeiros, A.A., Hendricks, S.L. and Chin, T.D.Y. (1966). The second of two epidemics of histoplasmosis resulting from work on the same starling roost. *Amer. Rev. Resp. Dis., 94:*406-413.

Weinstein, L. (1969). *Erythema Nodosum. Disease-A-Month.* Chicago, Year Book Medical Publishers, June, 1969.

Wilcox, K.R., Jr., Waisbren, B.A. and Martin, J. (1958). The Walworth, Wisconsin, epidemic of histoplasmosis. *Ann. Intern. Med., 49:*388-418.

Winn, W.A. (1967). A working classification of coccidioidomycosis and its application to therapy. In Ajello, L. (Ed.). *Proceedings of Second Coccidioidomycosis Symposium, Phoenix, Arizona, Dec. 1965.* Tucson, University of Arizona Press, pp.3-9.

Younglove, R.M., Terry, R.M., Rose, N.J., Martin, R.J. and Schnurrenberger, P.R. (1968). An outbreak of histoplasmosis in Illinois associated with starlings. *Illinois Med. J., 134:*259-263.

Chapter 17

Histoplasmosis in Latin America

JUAN E. MACKINNON

ABSTRACT

Histoplasmosis occurs in very wide areas of Latin America in places where periods of high ambient temperatures under adequate hygrometric values favor the growth of *Histoplasma capsulatum*. These areas extend from Mexico at latitude 32°N to Uruguay and Argentina, up to a latitude not yet determined but exceeding 35°S. The rates of sensitization to histoplasmin have been found to vary from very low to almost 100 percent in adults in some tropical and subtropical humid areas, especially in the valleys and deltas of rivers.

The disease appears as protean as in the United States. Some features make evident that the clinical and epidemiological manifestations of histoplasmosis show different patterns in countries with different climates. These differences may be partially explained by early or late contamination of the population. Experiments in animals give support to the hypothesis that permanent high temperatures in tropical lowlands without alternation of seasons may also contribute to the inhibition or modification of some manifestations of the infection.

IN this paper I shall summarize the main facts recorded in Latin America concerning the clinical aspects and frequency of the infection by *Histoplasma capsulatum*, the parasite discovered by Darling (1906) and regarded as a fungus by Da Rocha-Lima (1912). We shall also discuss the probable causes of the different patterns shown by histoplasmosis in different countries.

Clinical Records

Baliña, Negroni, Bosq and Herrera (1941) observed a case of disseminated histoplasmosis in Argentina. This publication was anticipated by a mycological study of the isolated strain by Negroni (1940). In Brazil, Almeida and Lacaz (1939 and 1941) isolated *H. capsulatum* from lesions of chromoblastomycosis and from the sputum of a patient with tuberculosis. Villela and Pará (1941) were able to see the parasitic form in examining a liver specimen from a child during routine histopathological control of yellow fever. Pará (1946) reports four more cases and isolated the fungus from a dog with histoplasmosis. Shortly thereafter, the disease was recognized in other countries: in Mexico by Perrin and Baez (1943); in Uruguay by Alonso and Cancela-Freijo (1944); in Colombia by Gast-Galvis (1947); in 1951 in Cuba by Sanguly Fernandez and Leon-Blanco (Fuentes 1958); in

Chile, by Olivares, Ahumada, Vaccaro, Paredes and Pozo (1952); in French Guiana by Floch (1953); in Venezuela by Campins and Scharyj (1953); in Ecuador by Rodriquez (1953) and by Alvarez and Leone (1954); in Paraguay by Maas and Riart (1954); in Peru by Arellano and Galvez (1955); in Puerto Rico by Torres, Figueras and Sifontes (1960); in Surinam by Wiersema (1963); and in Costa Rica and El Salvador by Trejos and Guardian (1967).

New cases were recorded in many countries. Negroni (1960) noted 51 cases among adults in Argentina, 48 of the 51 showing the mucocutaneous lesions so frequently found in disseminated forms. Rey, Rubinstein, Bertelli and Negroni (1968) added 43 more cases, among adults, recorded during a period of five years at the Hospital Muniz in Buenos Aires. Most of the cases are disseminated forms and some are chronic pulmonary forms.

Conti-Diaz and da Luz (1968) collected 23 cases among adults in Uruguay, 17 disseminated and 6 chronic cavitary. Other chronic pulmonary cases, with serologic diagnosis, are not included. In two cases Navarrete and Yarzabal (1966) found an interstitial myositis underneath ulcers of an eyelid and of the upper lip and correlated this finding with experimental features observed by Mackinnon and Conti-Diaz (1959) and Mackinnon (1961).

In Brazil the disease appears to have been more rarely observed. In a survey by Londero (1968) twenty-three cases and two epidemics are quoted. One epidemic involved a teacher, twelve scholars, and one dog, (Paula 1959) and the second one, eight persons (Fava-Netto, Silva, Chammas and Lacaz, 1967). The two epidemics are related to bat droppings.

Fifty cases have been recorded in Colombia according to Restrepo-Moreno (1968). Nine cases were known in Ecuador (Rodriguez, 1962).

Histoplasmosis is protean in Venezuela. Rangel, Barnola, Torres, Gomez and Villalobos (1959), as well as Salfelder and Capretti (1961), described primary and disseminated cases in children under two years of age. Angulo-Ortega and Lares (1960) observed primary regressive complexes and later histoplasmomas (Angulo-Ortega, 1961). Chronic, pulmonary, and cavitary cases have been reported by Rodriguez, Angola, Angulo-Ortega, Pollak and Kezes (1960). Campins, Zubillaga, Gomez-Lopez and Dorante (1956) studied an epidemic in twelve persons who visited a cave with bats. Vellutini, Borelli and Rodriguez-Garcilaso (1955) described a disseminated form in an adult with mucocutaneous lesions. Baldo, Campins and Ayala (1961) published a revision and reported that up to 1959, 34 cases of primary histoplasmosis, 11 cases of disseminated forms, 8 of them in children, and 15 chronic pulmonary, had been diagnosed in Venezuela. Among the 15 chronic pulmonary there are 12 histoplasmomas and 3 cavity forms.

The Mexican contribution is marked by numerous epidemic outbursts. Gonzalez-Ochoa (1957) described three epidemics in visitors of caves and abandoned mines; 3 patients out of 12 died. Del Valle, Pedroza, Alcantara and Weber (1957) reported another epidemic involving 18 of 22 workers who collected bat guano in an abandoned mine; 3 men died. More recently Gonzalez-Ochoa (1961) refers to 10 epidemics, all related to bat guano, involving a record of many pulmonary acute forms; 74 cases among 212 persons exposed to the infection; 21 men died, that is to say, a mortality rate of 28.4%.

Floch and Andre (1955), based on hypersensitization to histoplasmin, presume the occurrence of epidemics in French Guiana, the infection being contracted in the open air, simulating influenza.

In Panama, Draheim, Mitchell and Elton (1951) described the first case in a Panamaian, a three-month-old child, who died after dissemination. Moreover, Zimmermann (1954) refers the finding in the lungs of a Panamnian four-year-old child, who died in 1931, of yeast cells similar to those of *H. capsulatum.* Young, Cleve and Vicente-Mastellari (1957) examined surgical specimens from non-Panamanian adult patients transferred from Panama to the Fitzsimons Army Hospital for thoracotomy for nodular lesions due to *H. capsulatum.* They report that at Gorgas Hospital 45 cases of presumed pulmonary histoplasmotic lesions were recorded during a period of twenty-two months: 44 benign forms with symptoms, radiologic picture, and serological reactions similar to those observed in histoplasmosis. However 41 of these 44 cases occurred in non-Panamanians, young adults, and 3 in children. One of these children was a Panamanian. The other patient died with dissemination after the administration of cortisone. The same authors found in materials from autopsies 8 cases of disseminated histoplasmosis; 7 in non-Panamanian adults and 1 in a three-month-old Panamanian child. The absence of cases among Panamanian adults is a feature which is emphasized in the above work. The severe effects of the infection in children is also demonstrated by the finding of fourteen cases in necropsies of children under eighteen months of age in El Salvador and Costa Rica (Trejos and Guardian, 1967).

Rates of Sensitization

In all the countries the rates of sensitization to histoplasmin vary according to particular regions and sites. In Mexico the positive reactors are 55.3 percent in Yucatan (Gonzalez-Ochoa, Esquivel and Caceres, 1948). In Mexico City Glusker, Fuentes and Gomez del Campo (1950) recorded only 3.4 percent, but they found higher rates in the lowlands.

In Guatemala Taylor and Dobrovolny (1960) found 81 percent among residents in the Caribbean lowlands, in a tropical rain forest belt, and a minimum of 23 percent in the highest and dryest areas close to the Mexican borderline. Even higher rates were recorded by Diercks, Kelly, Klite, Fuentes,

Miranda and Alleyne (1965) in some zones of Panama where 50 percent of the ten-year-old population reacted to histoplasmin.

In Venezuela high rates have been recorded in humid, alluvium lowlands by Principe, Convit and Pifano (1961): in Tacarigua-Carabobo 50.5 percent; in Cumanacoa-Miranda, a zone of sugar cane plantations, 60.1 percent; in Yumare-Yaracuy 69.1 percent, and so on. In a list of twenty-nine sites by Albornoz (1963), there are rates as low as 6.6 percent in Yumaroe-Yaracuy, including all age groups.

In Colombia Restrepo-Moreno, Posada, Posada, Abad, Borrero, Calle and Velez (1961) found high rates, 40 percent, in the valley of the Magdalena River. Also high, although dissimilar, rates are prevalent in the valley of the Cauca River (Orozco, Lennox and Hayes, 1964), 44 percent of school children in Candelaria but only 12 percent in Cali.

In Surinam Collier and De la Fuente (1953) recorded 51.2 percent among males and 35.1 percent among females. These rates are as high as 60.7 percent and 53.7 percent in the 30 to 39 years age group. Ways, Bryant and Guicherit (1956) recorded 34.8 percent among bush Negroes.

The rate of reactors is also high in some zones of Peru: 43 percent among school children of Tingo Maria (Villa, Perez and Vargas, 1956), 37 percent in Iquitos. The rates are low in Lima, 4.7 percent, and in Ica (Bouroncle, 1955). High rates were recorded in eastern Peru near the Ucayali river (Rieth and Binder, 1965).

In Ecuador moderate rates, 11.1 to 41.9 percent have been reported in adults from several provinces (Rodriguez, 1958 and 1962).

Moderate rates were found in Paraguay, 18 percent (Gines, Gould and Melgarejo de Talavera, 1949), and in South Brazil. In Rio Carvalho (1961) found 2.4 percent among preschoolers, 18.8 percent among adolescents, 28.3 percent in the eighteen to forty years ago group. According to Lacaz, Almeida, Cury, Mendes and Salomão (1958), the rate amounts to 19 percent in Sao Paulo. Lacaz, Padim and Minami (1967) recorded 19 percent in Arraias-Goias, central Brazil, and 27 percent in Araguaja-Para, north Brazil. A lower rate, 14.7 percent is found in the southernmost Brazilian state of Rio Grande do Sul by Marsiaj, Py and Pegas (1950).

Farther to the south, in Uruguay, Cancela (1949) recorded 8.9 percent of positive reactors and Mackinnon, Artagaveytia and Arroyo (1953), 11.1 percent. Purriel and Navarrete (1964) have confirmed this general rate for the rural population among 23,341 persons. According to those authors low rates prevail in the west of Uruguay, 4 to 9 percent, but higher rates, 24.3 percent, in central Uruguay.

In Argentina Rey *et al.* (1968) recorded rather important rates, 34.5 percent, in Zarate-Buenos Aires in the delta of the Parana River and 35.5 percent in Santa Fe, a port of the same river.

In central Chile, in a rural zone, Colliguay, Honorato and Cruz-Plaza recorded 5.1 percent according to Olivares *et al.* (1952).

In Cuba a moderate rate prevails, 20% according to Pardo, Pardo-Castello and Tucker (1952); in Puerto Rico 12.7% and in Guadeloupe 2 positive and 6 equivocal reactors were found among 255 soldiers (Audebaud, Escudie and Courmes, 1964).

Comments

The skin sensitivity to histoplasmin exhibits the wide distribution of histoplasmosis. The rates of positive reactors show differences in neighboring sites. In areas of Panama, Guatemala, Venezuela and probably in other countries, practically all adults are sensitized. The highest rates are recorded in humid, alluvium lowlands. In these sites most of the ten-year-old population reacts; this feature indicates an early infection by *H. capsulatum*. Skin sensitization to histoplasmin is observed from Mexico down to Uruguay and Buenos Aires. Despite the lack of data, we think that histoplasmosis does not prevail in the high plateau of Bolivia and other high regions as well as in the southernmost part of South America and in arid zones. For the growth of *H. capsulatum* in nature, appropriate high temperatures and high hygrometric values are necessary during some time of the year.

Attention is drawn to the absence of starlings, *Sturnus vulgaris*, in Latin America. The droppings of starlings has a big influence on the growth of the fungus and on the epidemiology of the disease in the United States. The starling has invaded almost all of the territory of the United States after its importation from England. It would be obvious that every effort should be exerted to prevent the access of this bird to Latin America, as it would very likely deteriorate the situation in the area. The oil bird, *Steatornis caripensis*, has an interesting but not important role in the epidemiology of histoplasmosis in the northern countries of South America (Ajello, Lazarus, Cornejo and Moore, 1961).

We have made little reference to histoplasmosis diagnosed by serological methods because they have been carried out only for the last few years in few places. Nevertheless, we think that these methods must be used if we wish to evaluate the true importance of the primary and chronic pulmonary forms, so far as public health is concerned.

The coincidence of the rate of sensitivity to histoplasmin in a certain region, with the frequency of the finding of residual histoplasmotic lesions in autopsies (Salfelder and Reyes de Liscano, 1965), deserves due note and so does the hypersensitization to histoplasmin during an epidemic regarded as influenza because of its symptomatology (Floch and Andre, 1955). The concept that primary histoplasmosis is usually asymptomatic may be due to the lack of diagnosis.

There are some differences between the clinical observations recorded in some countries. In Panama the diagnosis has been routinely carried out among children (Young *et al.*, 1957), and probably the same is true of El Salvador (Trejos and Guardian, 1967). In these countries not a single evolutive case has as yet been recorded among native adults. On the other hand, in Argentina and Uruguay 120 evolutive cases in adults have been found but not even one case among children. Some cases may escape diagnosis, but the difference looks already too marked to disappear. Young *et al.* (1957) wrote: "The natives having been exposed in childhood to the fungus apparently develop a resistance or immunity and the acute phase of histoplasmosis is not observed in adult life." This is certainly a wise explanation for the situation in Panama, but in other hyperendemic zones as those of the United States there exist chronic fibrocavitary forms and even disseminated histoplasmosis among adults, (Furcolow, 1965). Consequently, we must look for another cause which may act simultaneously with a resistance acquired through multiple contaminations since childhood.

Some experiments demonstrate an inhibitory effect of high ambient temperatures on the evolution of some systemic mycoses; they have been surveyed by Mackinnon (1968). One of these experiments refers to histoplasmosis and was published by Mackinnon and Conti-Diaz (1962), who demonstrated that in mice inoculated intraperitoneally, the fungus disappears more rapidly, or it is more difficult to recover in cultures, three months later, from animals kept at 35° to 37°C than from animals kept at temperatures below 10°C. More recently Salfelder, Sethi and Schwarz (1965) inoculated *Cricetus auratus* with the yeast phase of *H. capsulatum;* as a result of exposure to temperature close to 0°C, they observed a disseminated, severe and often fatal disease in contrast to slight dissemination in animals kept at room temperature. In this experiment the hamsters were in a state of partial hibernation.

According to Menges, Furcolow, Larsh and Hinton (1952) *H. capsulatum* does not grow at 40°C, and we observed that it grows poorly at 39°C. Small variations in the temperature of the tissues may have decisive effects on the growth of species of fungi showing a low thermal tolerance. Low temperatures may act through different ways in the evolution of an infection, but the experiments with *Paracoccidioides brasiliensis* in the guinea pig and with *Sporothrix schenckii* in the rat and the mouse show a peripheral effect, the evolutive lesions being in the tail, distal parts of the limbs, muzzle, eyelids, ears, eyeballs and testicles. A physiological effect of cold would have provoked a more general effect, not limited to the periphery of the body. We think that these experiments give support to the hypothesis that permanent high ambient temperatures in low tropical humid zones may inhibit or diminish the clinical manifestations of histoplasmosis. The alternancy of seasons, humid summers and cold winters, may explain the frequency of the sensitization and the severe manifestations of the infection. A similar effect might be observed in tropical zones with humid lowlands and high mountains or tablelands; in fact, in Venezuela the histoplasmosis is rather severe and proteiform.

Histoplasmosis is classed by Furcolow (1965) among the hypersensitivity diseases. The habitat of *H. capsulatum* is not the body of vertebrates where it may grow, provided that the temperature of the tissues is not too high. The thermal barrier for the fungus in cultures is between 39° and 40°C, but in the tissues, an abnormal place for the fungus, it might be lower because the antibodies would add their inhibitory effects to that of the temperature.

The frequency of severe symptoms in young children in tropical lowlands might be due to early infection and to the special sensitivity of the very young but also to the poor development of thermoregulation during the first postnatal months. Moreover, protection against cooling is neglected in warm countries.

The absence of cases among children in Uruguay and Argentina may be due to the rarity of the condition due to limited chances of infection. Purriel and Navarrete (1964) recorded 4.7 percent of positive reactors to histoplasmin in Uruguay among children aged from five to nine years. Ballardini de Morera (1966) found no reactors among 136 children under one year of age, no reactors among 45 children aged one to five years and, again, no reactors among 38 children aged six to nine years; she found two positive reactors among 31 children ten to thirteen years of age. These surveys show that the infection is not contracted during the first years of life in Uruguay. However, the possibilities of early infections cannot be discarded, and some cases may appear.

Other differences are not real. In Uruguay almost all the cases on record were disseminated forms with mucocutaneous lesions up to 1961. Diagnosis is readily reached in these cases. In 1962, 1963, Conti-Diaz, Yarzabal and Mackinnon (1963) studied 142 patients in a tuberculosis hospital. The serologic study, made at the Kansas Field Station of the Communicable Disease Center, showed a positive complement fixation test in nine patients. *H. capsulatum* was isolated from the sputum of two of these nine patients. They showed fibrocavitary lesions without *Mycobacterium tuberculosis*. The skin test with tuberculin cannot be used for discrimination between tuberculosis and histoplasmosis in Uruguay because almost all the individuals react to tuberculin due both to tuberculosis and to the general use of BCG vaccine.

References

Ajello, L., Lazarus, A.S., Cornejo, A. and Moore, Jane C. (1961). Studies on the occurrence of *Histoplasma capsulatum* in Peru. *Sabouraudia*, 1:83-86.

Albornoz, Maria (1963). Aspectos clinicos e inmunologicos de la histoplasmosis en

Venezuela. *Actas Finales VCongreso Ibero-Latinoamericano Derm.* Buenos Aires, pp. 261-275.

Almeida, F. and Lacaz, C.S. (1939). Cogumelo do genero *Histoplasma* isolado de lesoes de cromomicoses. *Folia Clin. Biol. (S. Paulo), 11*:65-69.

Almeida, F. and Lacaz, C.S. (1941). Consideraçoes em torno de duas amostras isoladas de dermatite verrucosa e de escarro. *An. Fac. Med. S. Paulo., 17*:561-575.

Alonzo, J.M. and Cancela-Freijo, J. (1944). Histoplasmosis de Darling. *Arch. Uruguay Med., 24*:193-210.

Alvarez, J. and Leone di Vanna, G. (1954). Histoplasmosis y blastomicosis sudameri-cana. *Gac. Med. (Guayaquil), 9*:283-291.

Angulo-Ortego, A. (1961). Las formas circunscritas de histoplasmosis pulmonar (his-toplasmomas). *Mycopathologia, 15*:217-230.

Angulo-Ortega, A. and Lares-Gomez, A. (1960). Complejo primario pulmonar regresivo de etiologia histoplasmosica. *Revista Tisiol. Neumonol. (Caracas), 2*:85-92.

Arellanor, C. and Galvez-Brandon, J. (1955). El agente etiologico de la fiebre de "Tingo Maria." *An Fac. Med. Lima, 38*:1092-1098.

Audebaud, G., Escudie, A. and Courmes, E. (1964). Les mycoses humaines en Guadeloupe. *Bull. Soc. Path, Exot.* 57:1012-1017.

Baldo, J.I., Campins, H. and Ayala-Paez, C. (1961). Histoplasmosis en Venezue'a. *Mycopathologia, 15*:177-216.

Baliña, P.L., Negroni, P., Bosq, P. and Herrera, J. (1941). Histoplasmosis de Darling; primer caso sudamericano. *Rev. Argent. Dermatosif., 25*:491-516.

Ballardini de Morera, S. (1966). Investigacion sobre sensibilidad cutanea a la histo-plasmina en grupo de ninos. *Arch. Pediat. Uruguay, 37*:227-234.

Bouroncle, A. (1955). Sensibilidad a la histoplasmina en algunas localidades del Peru. *An. Fac. Med. Lima, 38*:1099-1112.

Cancela-Freijo, J. (1949). Histoplasmosis. Enfermedad de Darling. *An. Fac. Med. Montev., 34*:1049-1152.

Campins, H. and Shary, J.M. (1953). Comprobacion de la histoplasmosis en Vene-zuela. *Gac. Med. Caracas, 61*:67-75.

Campins, H., Zubillaga, Z., Gomez-Lopez, L. and Dorante, M. (1956). An Epidemic of histoplasmosis in Venezuela. *Amer. J. Trop. Med., 5*:689-695.

Carvalho, A. (1961). Sobre a histoplasmose na cidade de Rio de Janeiro; Est. de Guanabara. *Rev. Serv. Nac. Tuberc. (Brazil), 5*:5-58.

Collier, W.A. and De la Fuente, A.A. (1953). The histoplasmin test in Surianm. *Docum. Med. Geogr. Trop. (Amst.), 5*:103-108.

Conti-Diaz, I.A. and Da Luz, Silvia. (1968). Histoplasmosis en el Uruguay. *Torax, 17*: 46-49.

Conti-Diaz, I.A., Yarzabal, L.A. and Mackinnon, J.E. (1963). Encuesta sobre histo-plasmosis en un hospital de tuberculosos del Uruguay. *An. Fac. Med. Montev., 48*: 361-366.

DaRocha-Lima, H. (1921). Beitrag zur Kentnis der Blastomykosen, lymphagitis epizoo-tica and Histoplasmosis. *Zbl. Bakt. (Orig.), 67*:233-249.

Darling, S.T. (1906). A protozoan general infection producing pseudotubercules in the lungs and focal necrosis in the liver and spleen, and lymphnodes. *J.A.M.A., 46*:1283-1285.

Del Valle, J., Pedroza, S., Alcantara, R. and Weber, R. (1957). Histoplasmosis pul-monar en La Laguna. *Rev. Mex. Tuberc., 18*:521-532.

Diercks, F.H., Kelley, H.B., Klite, P.D., Fuentes, J.J., Miranda, E.A. and Alleyne, L.A. (1965). Prevalence of histoplasmin sensitivity among school children in Panama City, Republic of Panama, 1962-1963, *Arch. Med. Panamen. 14*:53-59.

Draheim, J.H., Mitchell, J.R. and Elton, N. (1951). Histoplasmosis: fourth case report from the Canal Zone. *Amer. J. Trop. Med., 31:*753-760.

Fava-Netto, C., Silva, U.A., Chammas, F. and Lucaz, C.S. (1967). Histoplasmose epidemica. Estudo clinico, radiologico, micologico e imunologico de surto ocorrido no Estado de Sao Paulo, Brasil. *Rev. Inst. Med. Trop. Sao Paulo, 9:*222-232.

Floch, H. and Andre, J. (1955). Un aspect de l'histoplasmose de primo-infection. *Bull. Soc. Path. Exot., 48:*463-469.

Fuentes, C.A. (1958). Revision de las investigaciones sobre micologia medica y de la literatura en Cuba durante el decenio de 1945 a 1955. *Mycopathologia, 9:*207-223.

Furcolow, M.L. (1965). Histoplasmosis. In Samter, M. *Immunological Diseases.* Boston, Little, Brown, pp.448-454.

Gast-Galvis, A. (1947). Histoplasmosis en Colombia. *An. Soc. Biol. Bogota, 2:*203-207.

Gines, A.R., Gould, E. and Melgarejo de Talavera, S. (1949). Intradermorreaccion con histoplasmina. *Hoja Tisiol., 9:*354-363.

Glusker, D., Fuentes-Villalobos, P. and Gómez del Campo, C. (1950). Ocurrencia de intradermorreaccion a la coccidioidina, brucelina, histoplasmina, haplosporangina y tuberculina con relacion a los rayos-X en conscriptos del Ejercito Mexicano. *Bol. Ofic. Sanit. Panamer., 29:*715-722.

Gonzalez-Ochoa, A. (1957). Histoplasmosis pulmonar aguda primaria. *Gac. Med. Mex. 87:*733-744.

Gonzalez-Ochoa, A. (1961). Histoplasmosis primaria pulmonar aguda *Mycopathologic, 15:*299-305.

Gonzalez-Ochoa, A., Esquivel-Medina, E. and Caceres, M. (1948). Investigaciones de la reactividad a la histoplasmina, tuberculina y coccidioidina relacionada con catastro toracico en Yucatan. *Rev. Inst. Salubr. Enferm. Trop., 9:*55-63.

Lacaz, C.S., del Almeida, Inah E., Cury, I., Mendes, E., and Salomão, Therezinha, A. (1958). Novos resultados sobre a prova de histoplasmina em Sao Paulo, Brasil. *Rev. Hosp. Clin. Fac. Med. S. Paulo, 13:*194-196.

Lacaz, C.S., Padim, Irma M.V. and Minami, P.S. (1967). Reacoes a Histoplasmina em dois provoados brasileiros: Arraias (Estado de Goias) e Conceicao do Araguaia (Estado do Para). *Hospital, 71:*97-100.

Londero, A.T. (1968). Las micosis brocopulmonares en Brasil. Revision critica. *Torax, 17:*224-232.

Maas, L.C. and Riart, G.A. (1954). Un case de histoplasmosis. *Arch. Pediat. Uruguay, 25:*5-21.

Mackinnon, J.E. (1961). Miositis en la blastomicosis y en la histoplamosis. *Mycopathologia, 15:*171-176.

Mackinnon, J.E. (1968). The effect of temperature on the deep mycoses. In *Systemic Mycoses.* Ciba Symposium. London, Churchill, pp.164-178.

Mackinnon, J.E., Artagaveytia-Allende, R.C. and Arroyo, L. (1953). Micosis profundas endemicas. *An. Fac. Med. Montev., 38:*428-445.

Mackinnon, J.E. and Conti-Diaz, I.A. (1959). Miositis en la histoplasmosis experimental. *An. Fac. Med. Montev., 44:*608-609.

Mackinnon, J.E. and Conti-Diaz, I.A. (1962). The effect of ambient temperature on experimental histoplasmosis of the mouse. *Sabouraudia, 2:*31-34.

Marsiaj, J.N., Py, A. and Pegas, N. (1950). Primeiras pesquisas sobre sensibilidade cutanea a histoplasmina no Estado do Rio Grande do Sul. *Rev. Brasil Med., 7:* 157-163.

Menges, R.W., Furcolow, M.L., Larsh, H.W. and Hinton, Agnes, (1952). Laboratory studies on histoplasmosis. I. The effect of humidity and temperature on the growth of *Histoplasma capsulatum. J. Infect. Dis. 90:*67-70.

Miranda, H. and Troncoso, M. (1958). Revision de los casos de micosis estudiados en el Peru en el decenio 1946-1956. *Mycopathologia, 9:*56-64.

Navarrete, E. and Yarzabal, L.A. (1966). Histoplasmosis diseminada. *Torax, 15:*158-164.

Negroni, P. (1940). Estudio micologico del primar caso sudamericano de histoplasmosis. *Rev. Inst. Bact. Malbran., 9:*239-294.

Negroni, P. (1960). *Micosis Profundas. Histoplasmosis.* Buenos Aires, Artes Graficas B. U. Chiesino, Vol. II, 143pp.

Olivares, O., Ahumada, J., Vaccaro, H., Paredes, L. and Pozo, S. (1952). Histoplasmosis generalizada; primer caso autoctono en Chile, aspectos clinicas e immunologicos. *Rev. Med. Chile, 80:*746-757.

Orozco, G., Lennox, R.H. and Hayes, G.S. (1964). A study of histoplasmin skin tests among school children in Cali and Candelaria (Valle de Cauca), Colombia. *Amer. J. Trop. Med., 13:*443-448.

Para, M. (1946). Histoplasmosis in Brazil. *Amer. J. Trop. Med., 26:*273-292.

Pardo, O.A., Pardo Castelló, V. and Tucker, H.A. (1952). Histoplasmin, coccidioidin and tuberculin sensitivities in Cuba; A study of 195 patients. *Bull. Pan. Amer. Sanitary Bureau.* 32:527-530.

Paula, A. (1959). Microepidemia de histoplasmosis. *Rev. Serv. Nac. Tuberc., Brazil, 3:*11-20.

Perrin, G. and Baez, M.M. (1943). Nota sobre el primer caso de histoplasmosis en Mejico. *Rev. Clin. Esp., 9:*396-401.

Principe, A., Convit, J. and Pifano, F. (1961). Resultados de las encuestas epidemiologicas sobre histoplasmosis, coccidiodomicosis y tuberculosis realizada en algunas regiones de Venezuela. *Mycopathologia, 15:*11-52.

Purriel, P. and Navarrete, E. (1964). Epidemiologia de la histoplasmosis investigada en 23,341 personas procedentes de areas ruralas. *Torax, 13:*271-279.

Rangel, G.E., Barnola, J., Torrex, Graciela, Gomez, E. and Villalobos Montel, H. (1959). Histoplasmosis diseminada mortal en un nino de cinco meses. *Arch. Venez. Pueric., 22:*19-31.

Restrepo-Moreno, A. (1968). Las micosis en Colombia. *Torax 17:*99-103.

Restrepo-Moreno, A., Posada, H., Posada, A., Abad, H., Borrero, J., Calle, G. and Velez, P. (1961). Encuesta epidemiologica sobre histoplasmosis en Codazzi (Magdalena). *Antioquia Med., 11:*562-573.

Rey, J.C., Rubinstein, P., Bertelli, J.A. and Negroni, R. (1968). Experiencia en histoplasmosis en el "Hospital F. J. Muniz" y en el Centro de Micologia. *Torax, 17:*50-55.

Rieth, H. and Binder, T. (1965). Reihenuntersuchungen uber das Vorkommen von Histoplasmose in Tiefland Urwald Ostperus. *Mycopathologia, 25:*109-118.

Rodriguez, C., Angola, T., Angulo-Ortega, A., Pollak, L. and Kezes, A. (1960). Formas cavitarias de la histoplasmosis. *Rev. Trisiol. Neumonl. (Caracas), 2:*93-105.

Rodriguez, J.D. (1953). Primer caso comprobado de histoplasmosis en el Ecuador. *Rev. Ecuat. Hig., 10:*7-12.

Rodriguez, J.D. (1958). Revision de las micosis profundas en el Ecuador. *Rev. Ecuat. Hig., 15:*177-188.

Rodriguez, J.D. (1962). Revision critica de investigaciones y literatura micologicas durante los anos 1950-1960 en Ecuador. *Mycopathologia, 17:*185-202.

Salfelder, K., Sethi, K.K. and Schwarz, J. (1965). Experimental histoplasmosis in temporarily "hibernating" hamsters. *Mycopathologia, 27:*289-300.

Salfelder, K. and Reyes de Liscano, T. (1965). Lesiones Histoplasmoticas autopsicos como indice epidemiologico de la enfermedad en los Andes venezolanos. *Mycopathologia, 26:*19-30.

Taylor, R.L. and Dobrovolny, C.G. (1960). The distribution of histoplasmin sensitivity in Guatemala. *Amer. J. Trop. Med.,* 9:518-522.

Torres-Blasini, Gladys, Figueras, E.R. and Sifontes, J. (1960). Histoplasmosis in Puerto Rico. *Bol. Asoc. Med. P. Rico,* 52:136-142.

Trejos, A. and Guardian, J.L. (1967). Generalizad histoplasmosis in El Salvador, C. A. A report of 13 cases in Children under two years of age. *Rev. Biol. Trop. (S. Jose),* 15:315-322.

Villa, M., Perez, F. and Vargas, R. (1956). Intradermorreaccion a la histoplasmin entre los escolares de Tingo Maria. *Rev. Med. Exp. (Lima),* 10:3-16.

Villela, E. and Para, M. (1941). Histoplasmose em crianca no Estado de Minas Cerais. *Rev. Brasil Biol.* 1:449-456.

Ways, P., Bryant, J. and Guicherit, I.D. (1956). Histoplasmosis sensitivity among bush Negroes of Surinam. *Docum. Med. Geogr. Trop. (Amst.).* 8:383-391.

Wiersema, J.P. (1963). A case of histoplasmosis in Surinam. *Trop. Geogr. Med.,* 15: 356-360.

Young, R.V., Cleve, E.A. and Vicente-Mastellari, A. (1957). Acute pulmonary histoplasmosis on the Isthmus of Panama. *Arch. Intern. Med.,* 100:430-435.

Zimmermann, L.E. (1954). A missing link in the history of histoplasmosis in Panama. *U.S. Armed Forces Med. J.,* 5:1569-1573.

Chapter 18

The Role of Birds in the Ecology of
Histoplasma capsulatum

COY D. SMITH

ABSTRACT

Chicken excreta were analyzed in order to determine if they contained substances either nutritional or inhibitory that would allow *Histoplasma capsulatum* to have a competitive advantage over other soil microflora. It was found that chicken excreta were considerably more concentrated than barnyard manure in carbohydrates and nitrogen. The total water-soluble carbohydrate concentration found in various chicken excreta samples ranged from 3 to 16 percent. Upon separation and purification of the carbohydrates, it was found that several were present and could be utilized as carbon sources for the fungus.

The concentration of phosphate and cationic salts were also much higher than is normally found in barnyard manure or loam soil. *H. capsulatum* was shown to be stimulated in growth and sporulation by high concentration of phosphate. High concentration of cationic salts in media did not appear to benefit the fungus directly. However, it was shown that *H. capsulatum* can grow and sporulate well on media containing high salt concentrations, especially if an external source of humidity is supplied.

It was concluded that chicken excreta contained nutritional (carbohydrates and high levels of phosphate) and inhibitory (high cationic salts) substances that may perhaps give it a competitive advantage over many other organisms normally found in soil.

THE first isolation of *Histoplasma capsulatum* from a natural reservoir was obtained from soil contaminated with chicken excreta (Emmons, 1949). However, it was later that chicken droppings were shown to play a role in natural reservoirs (Zeidberg, Ajello, Dillon and Runyon, 1952). Subsequently, this fungus has been isolated from soils containing excreta from several species of birds, such as pigeons (Grayston and Furcolow, 1953), grackles (Ajello, 1960), starlings (Furcolow, Tosh, Larsh, Lynch and Shaw, 1961), and oil birds (Ajello, 1960). Indeed it is a rare instance when the fungus is found in nature that the soil has not been contaminated with avian excreta with the exception of isolations associated with bat guano.

The droppings of birds or bats appear to contain a substance or substances that are either nutritional in nature or gives the fungus a competitive advantage over other micro-flora or -fauna in soil or both.

This investigation was performed in an attempt to demonstrate substances in avian manure that can serve as a substrate for *H. capsulatum* to grow on and sporulate as well as perhaps inhibit many of the competitive fungi and bacteria in soil.

It has been shown that starling excreta are an excellent substrate to promote sporulation with a light diffuse mycelial growth in *H. capsulatum* (Smith and Furcolow, 1964). The substrate acting as a nutrient is at least partially water soluble.

When comparing the constituents of excreta from chickens to barnyard manure, there are several differences, chiefly of concentration rather than chemical. Chicken droppings are more concentrated in cationic salts, nitrogen, and carbohydrates. One of the reasons for this difference is the rate of ingesta passage in chickens is 2.5 to 26 hours compared to ruminant animals which is 12 to 240 hrs. (Sturkie, 1954). Indeed, in small birds the rates of passage are generally faster than in larger birds. This rate varies according to the diet; for example, if birds are eating berries, the rate of passage may be as short as 30 minutes. Therefore, the difference in time for the ingesta passage permits a more complete digestion and absorption of food in the ruminant animal and allows a longer period for bacterial degradation. Another factor that makes the droppings in birds more concentrated than that of ruminant animals is that the urine is expelled with the feces in a concentrated semisolid state. Much of the water is reabsorbed within the cloaca (Sturkie, 1954).

The concentration of elements or compounds will vary in bird droppings depending on whether they are actively laying eggs, young growing birds or the particular diet they are ingesting.

Analysis of Chicken Manure

Carbohydrates

Water-soluble extracts were made of ten different chicken dropping samples. Each was tested for total carbohydrates using the anthrone method.

One extract of chicken droppings was run through a column containing Sephadex G-10 dextran beads, and fractions were collected using a fraction collector. The carbohydrate fractions were detected by the anthrone method and used in equal concentrations as carbon sources in culture media for *H. capsulatum* containing asparagine, phosphate, and mineral salts. A similar medium containing dextrose was used as a standard control. Only one peak or crude fraction was utilized well by the fungus as a carbon source. This crude fraction was further purified by running through another column containing P-2 Bio-gel (California Biochemical Co.) using similar methods, and again its value as a carbon source for the fungus was determined. Further purification of the active carbohydrate fraction was done using paper chromatography techniques.

Results of Carbohydrate Analyses

The total carbohydrate concentration found in water-soluble extracts of ten different samples of chicken droppings ranged from 38 mg/gm for actively laying hens to 163 mg/gm (16%) for brooder chickens. All birds were on commercial diets proven for their highly efficient utilization.

Results of the purified carbohydrate study indicated that several different sugars make up the carbohydrate spectrum in chicken droppings. While several sugars were utilized as carbon sources, only one carbohydrate supported rapid growth and sporulation of *H. capsulatum*. This one sugar comprised less than 10 percent of the total carbohydrate. Using dextrose as the standard carbon source for comparison, this one carbohydrate permitted the fungus to grow and produce excellent sporulation in ten days. The dextrose medium required four weeks before comparable growth was obtained. Since the fungus does not appear to be highly selective in its carbon sources and can use other compounds as such (Scheff, 1950), further work was not pursued in this area.

Other Substances that Affect Growth of *H. capsulatum* Found in Bird Droppings

Phosphate

According to other sources the amount of phosphate found in chicken litter ranges from 1.0 to 1.68 percent and in fresh hen cage manure as high as 2.70 percent (Quisinberry, and Bradley, 1969). These values are over five times higher than that for barnyard manure (*Yearbook of Agriculture*, 1938). In studying the effect of phosphate on *H. capsulatum*, it was found that this compound is an absolute requirement for the growth of the fungus (Smith, 1969) as is true with other organisms and plants. The values found for chicken manure are from 16 to 64 times higher in phosphate than generally found in red-yellow podzolic loam soil (Marbut, 1935).

It is reported in one study on the analysis of bird and bat guano samples that the concentration of phosphoric acid ranged from 10 to 25 percent, depending upon the amount of leaching that occurred from rainfall (*Yearbook of Agriculture*, 1938).

The following experiment was performed to study the effect of high concentrations of phosphate on the growth and sporulation of *H. capsulatum*.

Materials and Methods

Yeast extract medium (Smith, 1964) was used as the control basic substrate. This medium consisted of 1.0 gm yeast extract and 20.0 gm of agar per liter of distilled water. The medium was adjusted to pH 6.5, using 1N KOH. The following amounts of NaH_2PO_4 were added per liter to six samples of the above medium: 0.25, 0.5, 1.0, 4.0, and 6.0 gm, respectively. The pH was adjusted to 6.5, using 1N KOH, and the medium was sterilized by autoclaving. The above medium without added phosphate was used as the control. After cooling to 45°C, it was dispensed into 15 × 100 mm petri dishes. A recent soil isolate of *H. capsulatum* (P.H.C.) grown on a lean beef extract seed medium (Smith, 1969) was inoculated onto the plates. The cultures were incubated for fourteen days at 28°C. and then harvested by blending the entire agar dish in a blender using techniques as described in a separate report (Smith, 1969). Hemacytometer counts were performed on each medium of the numbers of hyphal elements and spores.

The results of using high concentrations of phosphate in culture medium are shown in Table 18-I. The highest numbers of hyphal elements was obtained on the medium containing 1.0 mg/ml of phosphate. The number of hyphae was almost two times that obtained from the control, and the number of conidia were over five times the control. Concentrations of phosphate higher than 1.0 mg/ml still permitted good growth, but the number of hyphae and conidia begins to decrease slowly. The optimum concentration of phosphate for growth and sporulation appears to be approximately 1.0 mg/ml. It is significant to note that growth did occur on all concentrations of phosphate. Even at 6.0 mg/ml the growth was not inhibited significantly and was only slightly less than that of the control.

The use of yeast extract medium as the basic medium for phosphate sensitivity studies may be misleading to some extent, since this salt is probably high in the medium to begin with. This medium also is known to be excellent for the stimulation of sporulation in *H. capsulatum*. If the amount of phosphate already present in yeast extract were known, the above values would no doubt be greater. However, at a concentration of 1.0 gm/Liter of yeast extract, the values of phosphate perhaps are not elevated significantly.

The highest concentration of phosphate used here was 0.6 percent, which is somewhat less than is found in bird excreta. However, all the salt was in solution here, whereas in bird excreta or in soil it is not all in solution. In

TABLE 18-I

Comparison of Growth of *Histoplasma capsulatum* on Yeast Extract
Medium Containing Varying Concentrations of Phosphate

	Number	
	Hyphal Particles	*Conidia*
Control (mg/ml Phosphate)	2.8×10^5	5.6×10^5
0.25	3.0×10^5	8.3×10^5
0.50	3.3×10^5	1.1×10^6
1.0	4.8×10^5	1.5×10^6
2.0	3.4×10^5	1.8×10^6
4.0	2.8×10^5	8.0×10^5
6.0	2.2×10^5	3.0×10^5

other words, the calcium salts of phosphate are not very water soluble at a near neutral pH, even sodium and potassium monobasic phosphate may require heat to be freely water soluble. Therefore, the amount of phosphate in solution in soil would depend on several factors such as pH, water-holding capacity, chemical combination, rainfall, and so on.

Several soils from chicken houses were analyzed, and all were found to be high in cationic salts and phosphate. No correlation could be found between chicken houses that contained *H. capsulatum* compared to negative ones. Concentrations of salts were higher wherever the soil was contaminated with bird droppings. It was the amounts of droppings that were present or protection from direct rainfall that seemed to control the concentrations. These findings are in agreement with those of others (Elconin, Egeberg and Egeberg, 1963) who demonstrated soil salinity to be a factory in the ecology of *Coccidioides immitis*.

Nitrogen Analyses

The total nitrogen of hen cage manure is reported to range from 3.0 to 4.0 percent and bat guano up to 12.0 percent (*Yearbook of Agriculture*, 1938). A great deal of this element occurs as uric acid and urea. Our experience is that *H. capsulatum* does not utilize urea as a nitrogen source in a defined medium, which is contrary to the findings of others (Negroni, 1946). Neither does the fungus use uric acid. In addition uric acid is not very water soluble. Since the fungus does not appear to be very selective in its utilization of nitrogen sources (Salvin, 1949), further studies were not carried out on this element.

Calcium, Sodium, Potassium, and Chloride Analyses

Analyses of chicken droppings for potassium was made using flame emission and an autoanalyser on the water-soluble extracts.

Sodium and chloride analysis was determined on the same samples as above by atomic absorbtion techniques.

The concentration of potassium was found to be 2.2 percent, sodium, 0.4 percent, and chloride, 1.8 percent. Since most calcium salts are not readily soluble in distilled water at a near neutral pH, this analysis was not determined by our laboratory, but concentration of this cation in pure hen manure is reported to be 6.5 percent (Quisinberry and Bradley, 1969).

The three above cations generally occur as salts, the most common are phosphates and chlorides. The value for chloride is probably higher than is shown here, since CaCl is not readily water soluble at a near neutral pH.

Chloride Studies with *H. capsulatum*

It was reported previously that *H. capsulatum* can tolerate high salt concentrations (Smith and Furcolow, 1969). Using yeast extract medium and harvest techniques described previously (Smith, 1969), *H. capsulatum* had a two-fold increase in viable particles with 3 percent sodium chloride added to the medium, compared to the control as seen in Table 18-II. There was no growth on 5 percent salt at room environment, but when humidity was supplied, growth was obtained. The use of salt in the medium did not show a marked increase in viable particles when the plates were incubated in a humidity chamber. The increase in viable particles at room environment is thought to be due to the decrease in relative humidity because of the sodium chloride in the medium. A 3 percent concentration of NaCl reduces the relative humidity from near 100 percent to 98 percent (Robinson, 1945). This decrease in humidity resulted in a higher number of viable particles with an increase particularly in sporulation.

Another experiment was performed using a very lean 1 percent (weight/volume) water-soluble chicken manure extract medium with varying concentrations of NaCl ranging from 1 to 5 percent. The media was dispensed in petri plates and incubated at 28°C for four weeks. A duplicate set of plates was incubated at 32°C. Harvest techniques were similar to those described above. After four weeks part of the plates were harvested; the remainder were held for six weeks.

The number of viable particles per milliliter are shown in Table 18-III. On this lean substrate the plates incubated at 28°C did not have sufficient numbers of total particles for accurate hemacytometer counts and therefore are not included in these data. With increasing concentrations of NaCl the number of viable particles appeared to decrease as though the NaCl was slightly inhibitory, although growth was obtained even at 5 percent. At 32° C, the number of total particles were higher after both periods of incubation with 1% NaCl compared to the control. A more significant finding, however, is that the percent viability appeared to increase with increasing salt concentrations with exception of the 5 percent at six weeks. The reason for higher viabilities with salt is that the number of conidia was higher in all the salt medium compared to the controls. The salt in the medium appeared to also stimulate conidia production, as was true in yeast extract medium, a fact which explains the increase in viability. This increase of viability is a

TABLE 18-II

Comparison of Number of Viable Particles of *Histoplasma capsulatum* Grown on Yeast Extract Medium With Sodium Chloride Added (Room Environment Versus Humidity Chamber Both at 22° to 25°C)

Salt Concentration	Viable Particles Room Environment	Viable Particles Humidity Chamber
Control (%)	1.9×10^5	2.3×10^6
1	2.4×10^5	2.9×10^6
3	4.1×10^5	2.7×10^6
5	N.G.	1.2×10^6

TABLE 18-III

Growth Determinations of *Histoplasma capsulatum* on Varying Concentrations of NaCl in
Medium Harvested After Four and Six Weeks' Incubation

| | *(Four Weeks' Incubation)* | | | |
| | *28°C* | | *32°C* | |
Salt Concentration (% NaCl)	Viable Particles	Total Particles	Viable Particles	Percent Viable
Control	8.45×10^3	2.37×10^5	4.02×10^4	12.8
	5.55×10^3	4.25×10^5	1.68×10^5	39.2
	3.0×10^3	3.37×10^5	1.33×10^5	38.6
	4.5×10^2	2.12×10^5	1.08×10^5	50.9
	5.25×10^3	1.62×10^5	1.47×10^5	90.7
	(Six Weeks' Incubation)			
Control	3.87×10^4	4.62×10^5	2.54×10^5	55
	8.55×10^3	9.83×10^5	3.89×10^5	38.5
	3.5×10^3	4.12×10^5	1.47×10^5	35.6
	3.25×10^3	3.0×10^5	1.99×10^5	66.6
	7.45×10^3	1.5×10^5	3.05×10^4	20.3

result of spores being more viable than hyphal particles. The better growth
obtained at 32°C compared to 28°C is a result of higher humidity resulting
from more rapid water evaporation from the media at this temperature.
Therefore, it appears that it is the reduction in relative humidity using 5%
salt in media that is more inhibitory than hypertonicity.

Discussion

The high concentration of salts found in the excreta of birds is thought to
play a role in the ecology of *H. capsulatum*. Phosphate is the only salt shown
by these data that benefits the fungus directly. Perhaps the relation is similar to that suggested previously for *C. immitis*, i.e. the salts are merely more
inhibitory to other competitive organisms found in soil (Egeberg, Elconin
and Egeberg, 1964). Sodium chloride was used in the above experiments
because of convenience; similar results have been obtained with potassium
and calcium chloride. The high concentrations of phosphate in bird excreta
however appears to benefit the fungus directly, since a stimulation of
growth can be obtained with high concentrations of this compound.

Concentrations of salts are known to be higher in the great river valleys
because of leaching from the higher plateaus and settling in the lower basins. This is one reason the land is often more fertile in the basins. It is interesting to note that the major endemic areas of *H. capsulatum* have been
found previously to be located in the river valleys (Manos, Ferebee and
Kerschbaum, 1956; Furcolow, 1960). Emmons (1954) was able to isolate *H.
capsulatum* repeatedly from the floor of an old house used previously for the
curing of meat. Even though a chicken house was nearby containing the

fungus, the birds had no access to the meat house, nor was there any evidence of contamination by bird excreta. Salt (NaCl) is frequently used to cure meat. One can only speculate as to whether the soil contained high salt concentrations.

H. capsulatum is found more often in old chicken houses and sheltered areas more than open ones (Zeidberg *et al.*, 1952). Even bird roosts are frequently in sheltered areas or heavily wooded ones. The excreta of birds are generally more water repellent than barnyard manure. All these conditions reduce leaching by rainfall, thereby preserving the salts. Once the fungus is established well in a soil reservoir, it does not seem to matter whether there are any bird droppings remaining or the area is sheltered.

In summation, bird excreta are highly concentrated in cationic salts, phosphates, carbohydrates, and nitrogen. Whether any of these compounds play an active role in the ecology of *H. capsulatum* can only be surmised. However, their mere presence means that the fungus certainly has to contend with them.

References

Ajello, L., Briceno-Maaz, T., Campins, H. and Moore, J.C. (1960). Isolation of *Histoplasma capsulatum* from an oil bird *(Steatornis caripensis)* cave in Venezuela. *Mycopathologia, 12:*199-206.

Ajello, L. (1960). *Histoplasma capsulatum* soil studies. *Mykosen, 3:*43-48.

Egeberg, R.O., Elconin, A.E. and Egeberg, M.C. (1964). Effect of soil salinity and temperature on *Coccidioides immitis* and three antagonistic soil saprophytes. *J. Bact., 88:*473-476.

Elconin, A.E., Egeberg, R.O. and Egeberg, M.C. (1963). Significance of soil salinity on the ecology of *Coccidioides immitis. J. Bact., 87:*500-503.

Emmons, C.W. (1949). Isolation of *Histoplasma* from soil. *Public Health Rep. 64:* 892-896.

Emmons, C.W. (1954). The significance of saprophytism in the epidemiology of the mycoses. *Trans. N.Y. Acad. Sci.* (Series II), *17:*157-166.

Furcolow, M.L. (1960). Epidemiology of histoplasmosis. In Sweany, H.C. (Ed.): Histoplasmosis, Springfield, Thomas, pp.113-148.

Furcolow, M.L., Tosh, F.E., Larsh, H.W., Lynch, H.J. and Shaw, G. (1961). The emerging pattern of urban histoplasmosis. Studies of an epidemic in Mexico, Missouri. *New Eng. J. Med., 264:*1226-1230.

Grayston, J. and Furcolow, M.L. (1953). The occurrence of histoplasmosis in epidemics epidemiologic studies. *Amer. J. Public Health, 43:*665-676.

Manos, N.E., Ferebee, S.H. and Kerschbaum, W.F. (1956). Geographic variation in the prevalence of histoplasmin sensitivity. *Dis. Chest, 29:*1-20.

Marbut, C.F. (1935). Soils of the United States. Atlas of American Agriculture, U.S. Department Agriculture, Advance sheets No. 8, part 3.

Negroni, P. (1946). Un nuevo caso de histoplasmosis. Estudio micologico y terepeutico. *Rev. Argent. Dermatosif., 30:*212-219.

Quisinberry, J.H. and Bradley, J.W. (1969). Nutrient recycling by laying hens. *Feedstuffs, 41:*19.

Robinson, R.A. (1945). The vapor pressures of solutions of potassium chloride and sodium chloride. *Proc. Roy. Soc. New Zeal.,* 75:(2) 203-217.

Salvin, S.B. (1949). Cysteine and related compounds in the growth of the yeast-like phase of *Histoplasma capsulatum. J. Infect. Dis.,* 84:275-283.

Scheff, G.J. (1945). Biochemical and immunological properties of *Histoplasma capsulatum. Yale J. Biol. Med.,* 18:41-54.

Smith, C.D. and Furcolow, M.L. (1964). The demonstration of growth stimulating substances for both *Histoplasma capsulatum* and *Blastomyces dermatitidis* in infusions of starling *(Sturnis vulgaris)* manure. *Mycopathologia,* 22:73-80.

Smith, C.D. and Furcolow, M.L. (1969). Growth of *Histoplasma capsulatum, Blastomyces dermatitidis* and *Coccidioides immitis* on medium with varying concentrations of sodium chloride. (Abstract) *Proc. Amer. Soc. Microbiol.,* pp. 113.

Smith, C.D. (1964). Evidence of the presence in yeast extract of substances which stimulate the growth of *Histoplasma capsulatum* and *Blastomyces dermatitidis* similarly to that found in starling manure extract. *Mycopathologia,* 22:99-105.

Smith, C.D. (1969). Nutritional studies of factors required for the growth and sporulation of *Histoplasma capsulatum.* Proceedings Second National Conference on Histoplasmosis.

Sturkie, P.D. (1954) *Avian Physiology.* Ithaca, Cornell.

Yearbook of Agriculture (1938). Soils and Man. U.S. Department of Agriculture p.450 and 517. Washington, D.C.

Zeidberg, L.D., Ajello, L., Dillon, A. and Runyon, L.C. (1952). Isolation of *Histoplasma capsulatum* from soil. *Amer. J. Public Health,* 42:930-935.

Chapter 19

The Role of Bats in the Ecology of
Histoplasma capsulatum

ARTHUR F. DiSALVO

ABSTRACT

Cave disease, a clinical entity compatable with acute histoplasmosis, has been described as early as 1895. In recent years *Histoplasma capsulatum* has been isolated from bat guano collected from around the world. To date, the fungus has been recovered from the tissues of New World bats only. Twenty-five chiropteran species has been reported to harbor this organism. Social behavior of certain species, diet, and environmental factors of the bat harborage may influence the presence of *H. capsulatum* in bat tissue or guano. Studies of the possible cycle of the fungus from bat to soil to bat may contribute to the understanding of the dissemination of *H. capsulatum*.

The Bat

FROM time immemorial the bat has been the victim of controversy and superstition (Allen, 1939). Egyptian tombs from 2000 BC were decorated with drawings of this animal, the Mayas of Central America worshipped the bat as a powerful god, and to the ancient Chinese the bat represented a symbol of happiness and good luck. Perhaps the Chiroptera may bring good luck in our studies of the ecology of histoplasmosis.

Most of the legends about this flying mammal surround the nocturnal activities of this strange creature and attribute them to the dual nature of the bat. In a variation of the theme presented by Aesop (600 BC), the war between the animals and the birds was about to commence. The bat, wishing to be on the winning side, is unsure of whether to join the animals as a mouse, or because of his wings, to ally himself with the birds. Because of his indecision, he is discredited by each side and is forced to hide during the day to avoid the wrath of both kingdoms.

Bats have been accused of causing everything from pimples and boils to rabies, and conversely, potions made from bat blood, urine, or guano have been used by some primitive people to enhance eyesight, avoid blindness, or cure ophthalmic lesions. Perhaps these substances will aid our insight into the ecology of histoplasmosis.

It is interesting to note that Samuel T. Darling, who first described histoplasmosis, also studied another bat-associated disease in Panama in 1909 (Allen, 1939). A common, often lethal disease of horses and mules called murrina was prevalent in this area. He discovered that murrina was caused by a blood parasite he named *Trypanosoma hippicum*. Other investigators pursued these studies and demonstrated that the trypanosome was transmitted by the bite of the vampire bat, *Desmodus rotundus*.

Cave Disease

Gonzales-Ochoa (1963), in reviewing the relationship between bat habitats and histoplasmosis, cited the early description by Mexicans of an acute, febrile respiratory disease in employees of bat guano mines. This association was noted in public health records as long ago as 1895 and again in 1930. The illness was generally referred to as "cave disease." Aguirre Pequeño (1959) succeeded in isolating *Histoplasma capsulatum* from bat guano in the states of Nuevo Leone and Coahuila in northern Mexico.

Washburn, Tuohy and Davis (1948) described a new disease entity (compatable with acute histoplasmosis) in twenty-one of twenty-five persons digging in a cave in southwestern Arkansas. Later investigation of this site indicated a retrospective diagnosis of histoplasmosis when *H. capsulatum* was isolated from soil obtained in this location (Grayston and Furcolow, 1953).

"Tingo Maria Fever," a disease of unknown etiology, plagued the residents of Tingo Maria, Peru, particularly those engaged in collecting the oil bird (*Steatornis caripensis*). This nocturnal, frugivorous, cave inhabitant is valued as a commercial source of oil. In 1955, Lazarus and Ajello (1955) isolated *H. capsulatum* from soil obtained in these caves.

Since the geographic distribution of the oil bird is very limited, these studies were extended to other *S. caripensis* habitats. *H. capsulatum* was then isolated from an oil bird cave in Venezuela (Ajello, Briceño-Maaz, Campins and Moore, 1960) and in Trinidad (Ajello, Snow, Downs and Moore, 1962). Pursuing these findings in Trinidad, *H. capsulatum* was sought and found in a cave inhabited by six species of bats (no oil birds) and in the guano collected in hollow trees which served as bat roosts (Ajello, Greenhall and Moore, 1962). At this time it was thought that bat guano, like chicken droppings, served only as a suitable substrate for this pathogen and that the substrate was seeded by wind-borne spores of *H. capsulatum*.

In 1957, a well-documented study in South Africa by Murray, Lurie, Kaye, Komins, Borok and Way (1957), demonstrated that histoplasmosis occurred in speleologists when a certain cave was visited. The floor of the cave was covered with bat guano and the air was dry and dusty. These investigators succeeded in isolating *H. capsulatum* from the air and from sentinel animals exposed in the cave.

At the same time, workers in other parts of the world were associating epidemics of histoplasmosis in cave explorers with bat guano. Isolations of the infectious agent from bat droppings were reported from Venezuela (Campins, Zubillaga, Gomez-Lopez and Dorante, 1956; de Montemayor, Heredia Osio and de Bellard Pietri, 1958); Tanzania (Ajello, Manson-Bahr and Moore, 1960); Panama (Taylor, Shacklette and Kelley, 1962); Southern Rhodesia (Gelfand, 1962) and Mexico (Jackson, 1961).

A diffuse lobular pneumonia occurred in two workers who had been employed to paint bridges in Maryland. As part of their preparation of the structure, they had to eject roosting bats and then scrape off a 0.5- to 3-inch crust of guano. The two workers were exposed to heavy clouds of dust. Four weeks later symptoms developed. A positive histoplasmin skin test and complement-fixing antibodies to *H. capsulatum* were present in both patients (Englert and Phillips, 1953).

In 1958 Emmons (1958) reported the first isolation of *H. capsulatum* from bat guano that was not obtained from a cave. The contaminated soil was collected on ground surrounding a house in Clarksburg, Maryland, where the big brown bat, *Eptesicus fuscus*, dwelled in the attic. Attempts to isolate the fungus from the liver, lungs, and spleen of sixteen of these bats were unsuccessful at that time. In subsequent studies, the isolation of this fungus from one specimen was reported (Emmons, Klite, Baer and Hill, 1966).

Expanding these findings to other house-dwelling bats, Emmons and Greenhall (1962) investigated guano-laden soil collected from houses in Trinidad selected because contamination with chicken manure was *not* present. Their findings demonstrated that *H. capsulatum* could be found in bat habitats other than caves or hollow trees.

In 1962 the spotlight of *H. capsulatum* shifted back to the site of the first description of this pathogenic fungus—Panama. Shacklette, Diercks and Gale (1962) reported the isolation of *H. capsulatum* from tissues of the bat *Chilonycterus rubiginosa fusca* (*Pteronotus rubiginosa*).

Bats and *H. capsulatum*

In the seven years since the first report of the isolation of *H. capsulatum* from chiropteran tissue, an extensive search for the ecological niche of this fungus has been pursued. Worldwide reports of the isolation of the fungus from guano have come from Malaya (Ponnampalam, 1963), Puerto Rico (Torres-Blasini and Carrasco-Canales, 1965), New Mexico (Kajihiro, 1965) Romania (Alteras, 1966), Brazil (Fava Netto, Andrade E. Silva, Chammas and Lacaz, 1967) and Texas (Al-Doory and Rhoades, 1968). Isolation of the organisms from bat tissue, however, has only been reported so far from the Western Hemisphere.

The most extensive investigations have been reported from Central and

South America. This area is most abundant in both numbers of bats and in variety of species because of climatic conditions (Allen, 1939). Therefore, the organs of Neotropical bats (i.e. those Chiroptera native to the neotropical region of Central America and South America) have been cultured in large quantities. The fungus has been isolated from resident bats of Panama (Klite and Diercks, 1965; Diercks, Shacklette, Kelley, Klite, Thompson and Keenan, 1965; Klite and Young, 1965; Klite, 1965a), El Salvador (Klite, 1965b), and Colombia, South America (Tesh, Arrata, Schneidau, 1968; Marinkelle and Grose, 1965).

Isolations of *H. capsulatum* from bats captured in the United States have been extensive (Emmons, Klite, Baer and Hill, 1966; Ajello, Hosty and Palmer, 1967; Tesh and Schneidau, 1967; Di Salvo, Ajello, Palmer and Winkler, 1969; Di Salvo, Bigler, Ajello, Johnson and Palmer, 1970; Bryles, Cozad and Robinson, 1969).

The first isolations of *H. capsulatum* from Nearctic bats (i.e. native to North America) was reported by Emmons, Klite, Baer and Hill in 1966. This was from *E. fuscus* captured in Maryland and *Tadarida brasiliensis* obtained in Texas. This was rapidly followed by isolations of the organism from bats captured in ten states, Alabama, Arizona, Florida, Indiana, Maryland, Mississippi, Oklahoma, Tennessee, Texas and Virginia, with a report of histological evidence of the organism in the lymph node of a *Myotis lucifugus* from Montana (Di Salvo, Ajello, Palmer and Winkler, 1969). The finding of this organism in Arizona (Di Salvo, Ajello, Palmer and Winkler, 1969) and Tampa, Florida (Di Salvo, Bigler, Ajello, Johnson and Palmer, 1970) constitute the most remote isolations of *H. capsulatum* from the area considered to be endemic for histoplasmosis.

Ecological Factors

Not all attempts to isolate *H. capsulatum* from Chiroptera are successful. When cultural studies are performed on bats randomly captured in an area endemic for histoplasmosis, the recovery of this fungus is entirely unpredictable. A wide variation in recoveries has been demonstrated in the same species and within the same bat harborage. There are many factors to consider which may have some influence on the presence of *H. capsulatum* in these mammals.

Some questions have been raised about the possibility of there being a species specific susceptibility or resistance. At the present time twenty-five chiropteran species have been reported as harboring this organism (Table 19-I). In their study of Colombian bats, Tesh, Arrata and Schneidau (1968) examined thirty-one species of neotropical bats from that South American country. Only three species yielded *H. capsulatum*. In a study of eight spe-

TABLE 19-I

Bat Species Found to be Spontaneously Infected With *Histoplasma capsulatum*

Species	Localities
Artibeus jamaicensis (Lesser Trinidad fruit bat)	El Salvador
Carollia perspicillata (Short-tailed fruit bat)	Panama, Colombia
Chilonycteris rubiginosa (Greater mustached bat)	Panama
Desmodus rotundus (South American vampire bat)	Panama, Colombia
Eptesicus brasiliensis (Brazilian brown bat)	Colombia
E. fuscus (Big brown bat)	Maryland, Indiana, Tennessee
Glossophaga soricina (South American long-tongued bat)	Panama, Colombia
Leptonycteris sanborni (Long-nosed bat)	Arizona
Lonchophylla robusta	Panama
Lonchorhina aurita (Long-eared bat)	Panama
Micronycteris megalotis (Little big-eared bat)	Panama
Mollosus major (Small free-tailed bat)	Panama
Myotis austroriparius (Southeastern myotis)	Florida
M. grisescens (Gray myotis)	Alabama, Tennessee, Virginia
M. lucifugus (Little brown bat)	Montana, Indiana
M. sodalis (Indiana myotis)	Tennessee
Noctilio labialis	Panama
Nycticeius humeralis (Evening bat)	Mississippi
Phyllostomus discolor (Long-tongued spear-nosed bat)	El Salvador
P. hastatus (Greater spear-nosed bat)	Panama
Pteronotus suapurensis	Panama
Tadarida brasiliensis mexicana (Mexican free-tailed bat)	Arizona
T. cynocephala (Florida free-tailed bat)	Alabama
T. yucatanica	Panama
Tonatia bidens (Greater round-eared bat)	Panama

cies of bats from the southeastern United States (Tesh and Schneidau, 1967), it was found that six chiropteran species harbored this fungus. The authors suggested that with more extensive studies, more species would be found to be infected with *H. capsulatum*. This impression has been supported by subsequent reports of additional species found naturally infected with this organism.

Conversely, Shacklette and Hasenclever (1969) isolated this fungus from 337 of 2,280 bats. They found that the rate of infection varied greatly with the different species. The infection rate was reported to range from 1.2 percent of 652 *Carollia perspicillata*, a fruit eating bat, to 25 percent of 1,124 *P. rubiginosa*, an insect eating species. In a study of Florida bats (Di Salvo, Bigler, Ajello, Johnson and Palmer, 1970) none of 101 *Pipistrelle subflavus* harbored *H. capsulatum* while 82 of 170 (48%) *M. austroriparius* harbored this fungus. These two species were captured in the same cave.

In general, bats eat either fruit or insects. Many species of neotropical fruit-eating bats have yielded this organism. The Nearctic bats, all of which are insectivorous, have shown a great variation in their susceptibility to histoplasmosis.

Bats may be classed in two social groups. Solitary bats roost as individuals frequently in trees or under eaves but always alone. The other group, known as colonial bats, is gregarious and crowds together in large numbers, often in caves or attics. The colonial species roost in juxtaposition in such a mass that with some species, the density has been estimated to be three hundred bats per square foot, and the colony will often contain hundreds of thousands or millions of individuals.

H. capsulatum has been readily isolated from the colonial species. The nature of the chiropteran congregation makes capture of these specimens in large numbers a relatively easy task. Only one extensive study of solitary bats (Tesh, Arrata, Schneidau, 1968) was made. In this report 36 percent of 1,001 bats studied were solitary bats and none harbored the fungus. In the Florida study referred to previously (Di Salvo, Bigler, Ajello, Johnson and Palmer, 1970), the *Pipistrelles* (a solitary species) which hung as individuals in the cave were not infected with *H. capsulatum*, while *M. austroriparius* (a colonial species) in the same cave yielded this organism in a large percentage of those examined.

Probably of more importance is the habitat selected by the colonial or solitary bat. A good example of this is the Mexican free-tailed bat, *T. brasiliensis*, which is a colonial bat. The first isolation of *H. capsulatum* from a Nearctic bat (Emmons, Klite, Baer and Hill, 1966) was from *T. brasiliensis* captured in a Texas cave. Tesh and Schneidau (1967) were not able to isolate the fungus from 161 bats of this species and attributed this lack of recovery to the fact that these bats inhabited a hot dry attic—not a suitable habitat for the fungus. On the other hand, Ajello, Hosty and Palmer (1967) isolated the fungus from this species in Alabama where the bats roosted in a hot, dry attic; and Di Salvo, Ajello, Palmer and Winkler (1969) recovered *H. capsulatum* from *T. brasiliensis* found under bridges in the hot, dry Arizona desert. Conversely seventy-one free-tailed bats from an attic in Brooksville, Florida, failed to yield the fungus (Di Salvo, Bigler, Ajello, Johnson and Palmer, 1970).

The climate of the area where the bat harborage is located probably has little or no effect on bat susceptibility to *H. capsulatum*. The elevation of the habitats in which naturally infected bats have been captured ranged from 15 feet above sea level in Tampa, Florida (Di Salvo, Bigler, Ajello, Johnson and Palmer, 1970) to 5,100 feet above sea level in Arizona (Di Salvo, Ajello, Palmer and Winkler, 1969).

An appropriate temperature and humidity is essential for the saprophytic existence of *H. capsulatum* (Goodman and Larsh, 1967). Most of the isolations of this organism have come from guano or bats which were in warm or tropical climates. All the recoveries of *H. capsulatum* in the United States have been from bats captured in the southern area. The arid, hot air of the Arizona desert was moderated by the shade of bridges or the deep recesses

of caves or abandoned mines. While the appropriate humidity has been considered essential for growth, naturally infected bats have been collected in
Arizona where the annual rainfall is 9 inches per year and in the tropical
rain forest of Colombia, South America, where the annual precipitation may
be as high as 400 inches per year. Isolations of the fungus from both guano
and bats have been made from humid as well as very dry environments.

If the bat does play a role in the dissemination of histoplasmosis in nature,
the migration habits of this flying mammal would greatly enhance its capabilities of distributing the organism far from a natural focus. For instance, *T.
brasiliensis* is known to spend the winter in Mexico where *H. capsulatum* is
abundant and then migrate in early spring 800 miles north to Arizona, New
Mexico, Oklahoma, and Texas (Villa, 1956). Studies of banded bats have
shown that these mammals will often return to the same habitat for as long
as seven years (Di Salvo, Ajello, Palmer and Winkler, 1969). Thus, the possible role of the bat in the dissemination of histoplasmosis must be studied
more extensively.

There have been few reports on the serological examinations of bats for
fungal disease. Oels, Branum and Zollman (1968) performed hemagglutination absorption tests on the sera of twelve *E. fuscus* captured in southeastern
Minnesota. Using a 1:4 dilution as the minimum response considered positive for histoplasmosis, they found seven or 58 percent of these bats had antibody to *H. capsulatum*. Klite and Diercks (1965) examined forty bats by
the agar-gel precipitin test. Eight flying mammals were positive by culture;
however, all were serologically negative. Di Salvo, Ajello and Kaufman
(1967) examined twenty-eight pools of chiropteran sera with antigens to *H.
capsulatum* and *Blastomyces dermatitidis*. Each pool contained the serum
from five bats. One pool had a 1:8 titer to histoplasmin; 3 pools had a 1:8
reaction to the yeast form of *H. capsulatum;* 13 pools reacted to the yeast
form of *B. dermatitidis* at a 1:8 dilution and 3 pools reacted to the *B. dermatitidis* antigen at a dilution of 1:16. It is obvious that these serological examinations are very sketchy and that further studies of the immunology of bats
may prove informative.

In most studies where tissue has been cultured for isolation of this pathogenic fungus, the bats have been captured alive. Usually they are either
brought to the laboratory and sacrificed just prior to culture, or they are
placed in a deep freeze for varying periods of time until the necropsies
can be performed. Tesh, Schneidau and Erwin (1967) experimentally infected guinea pigs with *H. capsulatum*. Their studies demonstrated that the
recovery of this fungus from animal tissue frozen at —24°C was diminished
after 72 hours. Many other investigators kept their dead bats at —24°C for
at long as six weeks before attempting to isolate this organism. In our
Florida study the bats were frozen in dry ice at —78°C at the collection site

TABLE 19-II

Frequency of Isolation of *Histoplasma capsulatum* from Bats by Organ

Number Ex-amined	Num-ber Posi-tive	Organs Cultured					Reference
		Lung	Liver	Spleen	Kid-ney	Intes-tinal Con-tents	
10	3	3	0	1	0	1	Klite and Young, 1965
623	62	29	10	22	2	29	Klite and Diercks, 1965
820	26	19	21	22	8	6	Klite, 1965a
259	11	4	3	4	0	2	Klite, 1965b
413	51	42	21	20	2	8	Emmons, Klite, Baer and Hill, 1966
1120	154	135	111	113	ND	56	Tesh and Schneidau, 1967
1001	3	1	1	3	ND	ND	Tesh, Arrata and Schneidau, 1968
2424	337	157	97	129	24	65	Shacklette and Hasenclever, 1969
555	15	10	2	10	ND	ND	Di Salvo, Ajello, Palmer and Winkler, 1969
371	82	23	37	64	ND	ND	Di Salvo, Bigler, Ajello, Johnson and Palmer, 1970
Total 7569	744	423	303	388	36	167	
Percent	100	57	41	52	7	26	

0—Negative
ND—Not Done

and were autopsied within six days after capture (DiSalvo, Bigler, Ajello, Johnson and Palmer, 1970). This latter method proved to be quite satisfactory.

Table 19-II shows the frequency of isolation of *H. capsulatum* from 7,569 bats by organ systems. The data were compiled from ten studies where such information was available. *H. capsulatum* was recovered by culture from 744 bats. The organism was isolated from the lungs in 57 percent of these. The liver and spleen was the source of the fungus in 41 percent and 52 percent, respectively. The yield from the kidney was only 7 percent and seems to indicate that this organ is not a good source of the fungus in naturally infected bats. It was found that 26 percent of the bats yielding *H. capsulatum* did so in cultures of the intestinal contents.

In the study of Arizona bats where the Chiroptera were obtained in a hot, dry atmosphere, it was found that ten of the fifteen positive bats harbored the organism in their lungs. In the studies on bats from wet Florida caves, only twenty-three of eighty-two positive bats contained the organism in their lungs. It appears that in a dry atmosphere there may be constant re-infection by exposure to aerosol particles and therefore the lungs often contain the organism. Whether this represents infection or simple contamination is not known.

In bats from the wet caves, where an aerosol is not as likely to occur, the organism was found most often in the spleen and liver (Di Salvo, Bigler, Ajello, Johnson and Palmer, 1970). This is not unexpected, as histoplasmosis is a disease of the reticuloendothelial system and the spleen and liver have abundant reticuloendothelial tissue.

It is imperative to emphasize that prolonged incubation of the culture tubes is essential for recovery of the organism from bat tissue. In one study, the cultures of 181 bats were kept for twelve weeks and the time (in weeks) macroscopic growth of *H. capsulatum* was first noted was recorded. While a large number of the cultures (42%) grew out in three weeks, 47 percent were not evident until the third to fifth week. Holding the cultures beyond five weeks increased the yield of this infectious agent by another 10 percent.

In those instances where intestinal contents were cultured, the yield was quite low (26%). Eleven of twenty *T. brasiliensis*, experimentally infected with *H. capsulatum* by the intraperitoneal route, shed the fungus in their feces between the tenth and thirtieth postinoculation day (Tesh and Schneidau, 1966). The presence of the organisms in feces or the intestinal wall may provide some information as to whether the bat is actively excreting the fungus in its feces.

The histological examination of intestinal tissues for the presence of *H. capsulatum* has not been rewarding. In many reports where tissue sections have been examined, the fungi were seldom seen histologically, even when the organs were culturally positive (Klite and Diercks, 1965; Emmons, Klite, Baer and Hill, 1966; Tesh and Schneidau, 1967; Di Salvo, Ajello, Palmer and Winkler, 1969; Hasenclever, Shacklette, Hunter, George and Schwarz, 1969). Two groups of investigators described the inflammatory reaction as very mild with a slight lymphocytic infiltration, and the mucosa appeared to be intact (Emmons, Klite, Baer and Hill, 1966; Hasenclever, Shacklette, Hunter, George and Schwarz, 1969). Tesh and Schneidau (1966) found that eleven of their twenty *T. brasiliensis* experimentally infected with *H. capsulatum* by intraperitoneal inoculation contained histological evidence of the fungus in the intestinal tissue. They suggested their findings might indicate direct invasion of the organs from the peritoneal cavity. A granulomatous reaction, typical of infection with this fungus, was not evident in either the experimentally or naturally infected bats.

The possibility that *H. capsulatum* cycles from bat to guano to bat has been suggested. That the bat acquires his initial infection by the respiratory route, as in man, is supported by the many isolations of the organism from the lungs of this flying mammal. There is also evidence that the bat intestine contains the yeast form of this organism in its tissue. Experimentally infected bats have shed the organism in their feces without any prior manipulation of the gut (Tesh and Schneidau, 1966). Although this infection was not acquired by the natural route, it does demonstrate that bats can shed this agent in their feces.

Bats, as spelunkers, are susceptible to histoplasmosis if they enter an infective focus. In all the reports of the isolation of *H. capsulatum* from bats, the mammals yielding the fungus have always appeared to be in good health. Only one bat, which harbored *H. capsulatum* in all organs cultured, appeared ill at the time of capture (Shacklette and Hasenclever, 1969). The effect, if any, on a normal chiropteran host harboring the fungus is not known.

Whether the bat can disseminate this fungus or is just another incidental host for the organism is unknown also. The dissemination of *H. capsulatum* by the bat would be an acceptable explanation for the seeding of guano deep in the recesses of the caves where the organism has been isolated. Although it is possible that these areas were seeded by wind-born spores or mycelial fragments, some of the isolations of this fungus have occurred from so deep in these caverns that this method of spread would seem unlikely.

In the remote areas of Arizona where this fungus was isolated, the population density is very low. The hazards of infection with this organism would be greatest for spelunkers, miners, tourists, or guano collectors. However, in areas where infected bats and guano are found under houses (Emmons and Greenhall, 1962; Emmons, 1958) or in school attics (Ajello, Hosty and Palmer, 1967) a health hazard to the general public would be present.

These previous remarks must not be construed to mean that all bats have histoplasmosis or disseminate this disease. *H. capsulatum* was not isolated from over 500 bats captured in Georgia (Denton, 1969). Similarly, the examination of an equal number of specimens from California was unsuccessful in the isolation of the fungus (Ajello, 1969). Both surveys included those species known to be susceptible to *H. capsulatum*. It does seem likely that *H. capsulatum* must be present in the environment before the bats become infected. That is, the cave may possibly be the source of the infective agent. The guano, like chicken manure or oil bird droppings, would provide the nutrients for the saprophytic existence of this organism.

Whether the bat is the source of the infective agent (Campbell, 1965) or not, it does serve as a more sensitive sentinel animal for detecting possible endemic foci of this agent. The isolations of this organism from Arizona and Florida should alert physicians in these areas of the possibility of histoplasmosis in their patients and encourage them to include it in their differential diagnoses of pulmonary disease.

The exact role of the bat in the ecology of *H. capsulatum* remains uncertain, and its determination will have to await further study by mycologists and mammologists. Additional knowledge of the physiology, migration, hibernation, and other habits of bats is essential before it can be determined whether the bat is a vector or a victim. Further studies in these areas will undoubtedly contribute to our understanding of the dissemination of histoplasmosis.

References

Aguirre Pequeño, E. (1959). Aislamiento de *Histoplasma capsulatum* del guano de murcielago en cuevas del noreste de Mexico. *Gac. Med. Mexico*, 99:243-253.

Ajello, L. (1969). Unpublished data.

Ajello, L., Briceño-Maaz, T., Campins, H. and Moore, J.C. (1960). Isolation of *Histoplasma capsulatum* from an oil bird *(Steatornis caripensis)* cave in Venezuela. *Mycopathologia*, 12:199-206.

Ajello, L., Greenhall, A.M. and Moore, J.C. (1962). Occurrence of *Histoplasma capsulatum* on the Island of Trinidad, B. W. I. II. Survey of chiropteran habitats. *Amer. J. Trop. Med.*, 11:249-254.

Ajello, L., Hosty, T.S. and Palmer, J. (1967). Bat histoplasmosis in Alabama. *Amer. J. Trop. Med.*, 16:329-331.

Ajello, L., Manson-Bahr, R.E.C. and Moore, J.C. (1960). Amboni Caves, Tanganyika, A new endemic area for *Histoplasma capsulatum*. *Amer. J. Trop. Med.*, 9:633-638.

Ajello, L., Snow, D.W., Downs, W.G. and Moore, J.C. (1962). Occurrence of *Histoplasma capsulatum* on the island of Trinidad, B. W. I. I. Survey of *Steatornis caripensis* (Oil Bird) habitats. *Amer. J. Trop. Med.*, 11:245-248.

Al-Doory, Y. and Rhoades, E.R. (1968). Isolation of *Histoplasma capsulatum* from a Texas cave. *Mycopathologia*, 35:201-207.

Allen, G.M. (1939). *Bats.* New York, Dover.

Alteras, I. (1966). First Romanian Isolation of *Histoplasma capsulatum* from the soil. *Derm. Int.*, 5:69-71.

Bryles, M.C., Cozad, G.C. and Robinson, A. (1969). Isolation of *Histoplasma capsulatum* from bats in Oklahoma. *Amer. J. Trop. Med.*, 18:392-399.

Campbell, C.C. (1965). The epidemiology of histoplasmosis. *Ann. Intern. Med.*, 62: 1333-1336.

Campins, H., Zubillaga, Z.C., Gomez-Lopez, L. and Dorante, M. (1956). An epidemic of histoplasmosis in Venezuela. *Amer. J. Trop. Med.*, 5:690-695.

de Montemayor, L., Heredia-Osio, B. y de Bellard and Pietri, E.P. (1958). Aislamiento del *Histoplasma capsulatum* en el suelo de dos cavernas en Venezuela. Nuevas técnicas de investigación por "Método doflotación." *Rev. Sanid. Asistencia Soc.*, 23: 39-54.

Denton, J.F. (1969). Personal communication.

Diercks, F.H., Shacklette, M.H., Kelley, H.B.,Jr., Klite, P.D., Thompson, S.W. II, and Keenon, C.M. (1965). Naturally occurring histoplasmosis among 935 bats collected in Panama and the Canal Zone, July 1961-February 1963. *Amer. J. Trop. Med.* 14: 1069-1072.

DiSalvo, A.F., Ajello, L. and Kaufman, L. (1967). Complement-fixing antibody to pathogenic fungi in Arizona bats. Unpublished data.

DiSalvo, A.F., Ajello, L., Palmer, J.W.,Jr., and Winkler, W.G. (1969). Isolation of *Histoplasma capsulatum* from Arizona bats. *Amer. J. Epidem.*, 89:606-614.

DiSalvo, A.F., Bigler, W.J., Ajello, L., Johnson, J.E. and Palmer, J.W. (1970). Bat and soil studies for sources of histoplasmosis in Florida. *Pub. Health Rep.*, 85: 1063-1069.

Emmons, C.W. (1958). Association of bats with histoplasmosis. *Public Health Rep.* 73: 590-595.

Emmons, C.W. and Greenhall, A.M. (1962). *Histoplasma capsulatum* and house bats in Trinidad, W. I. *Sabouraudia*, 2:18-22.

Emmons, C.W., Klite, P.D., Baer, G.M. and Hill, W.B. (1966). Isolation of *Histoplasma capsulatum* from bats in the United States. *Amer. J. Epidem.*, 84:103-109.

Englert, E.,Jr. and Phillips, A.W. (1953). Acute diffuse pulmonary granulomatosis in bridge workers. *Amer. J. Med., 15*:733-740.

Fava Netto, C., de Andrade Silva, U., Chammas, F. and Lacaz, C.S. (1967). Epidemic histoplasmosis. Clinical, Radiologic, Mycologic and Immunologic Study of an outbreak which occurred in the State of Sao Paulo, Brazil. *Rev. Inst. Med. Trop. S. Paulo, 9*:222-232.

Gelfand, M. (1958). Cave disease: A report of three cases from Southern Rhodesia. *Cent. Afr. J. Med., 8*:461.

Gonzalez-Ochoa, A. (1963). Relaciones entre el habitat del murcielago y el *Histoplasma capsulatum. Rev. Inst. Salubr. Enferm. Trop., 23*:81-86.

Goodman, N.L. and Larsh, H.W. (1967). Environmental factors and growth of *Histoplasma capsulatum* in soil. *Mycopathologia, 33*:145-156.

Grayston, J.T. and Furcolow, M.L. (1953). The occurrence of histoplasmosis in epidemics-epidemiological studies. *Amer. J. Public Health, 43*:665-676.

Hasenclever, H.F., Shacklette, M.H., Hunter, A.W., George, E. and Schwarz, J. (1969). The use of cultural and histologic methods for the detection of *Histoplasma capsulatum* in bats: absence of a cellular response. *Amer. J. Epidem., 90*:77-83.

Jackson, D. (1961). Histoplasmosis. A "spelunker's" risk. *Amer. Rev. Resp. Dis., 83*: 261-263.

Kajihiro, E.S. (1965). Occurrence of dermatophytes in fresh bat guano. *Appl. Microbiol., 13*:720-724.

Klite, P.D. (1965a). The focal occurrence of histoplasmosis in house-dwelling bats on the Isthmus of Panama. *Sabouraudia, 4*:158-163.

Klite, P.D. (1965b). Isolation of *Histoplasma capsulatum* from bats of El Salvador. *Amer. J. Trop. Med., 14*:787-788.

Klite, P.D. and Diercks, F.H. (1965). *Histoplasma capsulatum* in fecal contents and organs of bats in the Canal Zone. *Amer. J. Trop. Med., 14*:433-439.

Klite, P.D. and Young, R.V. (1965). Bats and histoplasmosis. A clinico-epidemiologic study of two human cases. *Ann. Intern. Med., 62*:1263-1271.

Lazarus, A.S. and Ajello, L. (1955). Aislamiento de *Histoplasma capsulatum* del suelo de una cueva en el Peru. *Rev. Med. Exp. Lima, 9*:5-15.

Marinkelle, C.J. and Grose, E. (1965). *Histoplasma capsulatum* from the liver of a bat in Colombia. *Science, 147*:1039-1040.

Murray, J.F., Lurie, H.I., Kaye, J., Komins, C., Borok, R. and Way, M. (1957). Benign pulmonary histoplasmosis (cave disease) in South Africa. *S. Afr. Med. J., 31*:245-253.

Oels, H.C., Branum, E.L. and Zollman, P.E. (1969). Antibodies to *Histoplasma capsulatum* in human and animal populations of Southeastern Minnesota. *Amer. Rev. Resp. Dis., 99*:443-446.

Ponnampalam, J. (1963). Isolation of *Histoplasma capsulatum* from the soil of a cave in Central Malaya. *Amer. J. Trop. Med., 12*:775-776.

Shacklette, M.H., Diercks, F.H. and Gale, N.B. (1962). *Histoplasma capsulatum* recovered from bat tissue. *Science, 135*, 1135.

Shacklette, M.H. and Hasenclever, H.F. (1968). The natural occurrence of *Histoplasma capsulatum* in a cave. 3. Effect of flooding. *Amer. J. Epidem., 88*:210-214.

Shacklette, M.H. and Hasenclever, H.F. (1969). Variation of rates of natural infection with *Histoplasma capsulatum* in bats. *Amer. J. Trop. Med., 18*:53-57.

Shacklette, M.H., Hasenclever, H. F. and Miranda, E.A. (1967). The natural occurrence of *Histoplasma capsulatum* in a cave. 2. Ecologic aspects. *Amer. J. Epidem. 86*: 246-252.

Taylor, R.L., Shacklette, M.H. and Kelley, H.B. (1962). Isolation of *Histoplasma cap-*

sulatum and *Microsporum gypseum* from soil and bat guano in Panama and the Canal Zone. *Amer. J. Trop. Med.,* 11:790-795.

Tesh, R.B., Arrata, A.A. and Schneidau, J.D.,Jr. (1968). Histoplasmosis in Colombian bats, with a consideration of some of the factors influencing the prevalence of natural infection in chiroptera. *Amer. J. Trop. Med.,* 17:102-106.

Tesh, R.B. and Schneidau, J.D. (1966). Experimental Infection of North American insectivorous bats *(Tadarida brasiliensis)* with *Histoplasma capsulatum. Amer. J. of Trop. Med. Hyg.,* 15:544-550.

Tesh, R.B. and Schneidau, Jr.,J.D. (1967). Naturally occurring histoplasmosis among bat colonies in the southeastern United States. *Amer. J. Epidem.,* 86:545-551.

Tesh, R.B., Schneidau, J.D. and Erwin, C.A. (1967). The effect of freezing and storage at $-24°C$ on the survival of pathogenic fungi in excised tissue. *Amer. J. Clin. Path.,* 48:100-103.

Torres-Blasini, G. and Carrasco-Canales, J.A. (1965). A human pathogenic fungus recovered from soil for the first time in Puerto Rico. *Mycopathologia,* 29:177-181.

Villa, R.B. (1956). *Tadarida brasiliensis mexicana* (Saussure), el murcielago guanero, es una subespecie migratoria. *Acta Zool. Mex.,* 1:1-11.

Washburn, A.M., Tuohy, J.H. and Davis, E.L. (1948). Cave sickness. A new disease entity. *Amer. J. Pub. Hlth.,* 38:1521-1526.

Chapter 20

Clinical Manifestations of Animal Histoplasmosis

ROBERT W. MENGES

ABSTRACT

A summary of the data available concerning the clinical manifestations of animal histoplasmosis is presented. The clinical features of the disease in domestic, wild, and captive animals are included. The clinical picture could only be described adequately in the dog, since so few cases have been reported in other animals.

HISTOPLASMOSIS, caused by *Histoplasma capsulatum*, may be characterized by a variety of clinical manifestations in animals and may be benign or disseminated. Since 1938, when *H. capsulatum* was first isolated from a dog (DeMonbreun, 1939), naturally acquired histoplasmosis has been found to occur in several species of domestic, wild, and captive animals (Menges, Habermann, Selby, Ellis, Behlow and Smith, 1963). Among the domestic animals, in addition to the dog, the disease has been reported in the cat, cattle, swine, and horses.

The species of wild or captive animals in which histoplasmosis has been reported include the yellow baboon *Papio cynocephalus* (Courtois, Segretain, Mariat and Levaditi, 1955; Mariat and Segretain, 1956; Mariat and Gardini-Tuesta, 1959), African baboon *Papio papio* (Walker and Spooner, 1960), badger *Meles meles* (Burgisser, Frankhauser, Kaplan, Klingler and Scholer, 1961), several species of bats (Ajello, Hosty and Palmer, 1967), big brown (Kodiak) bear *Ursus middendorffi* (Cross, 1950), chinchilla *Chinchilla laniger* (Burtscher and Otte, 1962), gray fox *Urocyon cinereoargentus* (Emmons, Rowley, Olson, Mattern, Bell, Powell and Marcey, 1955), red fox *Vulpes fulva* (Ajello, 1960), house mouse *Mus musculus* (Olson, Bell and Emmons, 1947), woods mouse *Peromyscus leucopus* (Menges, Furcolow, Habermann and Weeks, 1967), common opossum* *Didelphis marsupialis* and four-eyed opossum *Philander o. fuscogriseus* (Taylor and Shacklette, 1962), raccoon *Procyon lotor* (Menges, Habermann and Stains, 1955), Norway or brown rat *Rattus norvegicus* (Emmons, Bell and Olson, 1947), roof

---

* Emmons (1950), has reported histoplasmosis in an opossum *Didelphis virginiana*. This opossum is considered by Hall (1955), to be a subspecies of the common opossum *D. marsupialis*. He used the name *Didelphis marsupialis virginianus* for the subspecies.

or black rat *Rattus rattus* (Emmons, Morlan and Hill, 1949), spiny rat *Proechimys semispinosus* (Taylor and Shacklette, 1962), short-tailed shrew *Blarina brevicauda* (Menges, Furcolow, Habermann and Weeks, 1967), spotted skunk *Spilogale putorius* (Emmons, Morlan and Hill, 1949), striped skunk *Mephitis mephitis* (Menges, Habermann and Stains, 1955), thirteen-lined ground squirrel *Citellus tridecemlineatus* (Menges, Furcolow, Habermann and Weeks, 1967), and woodchuck *Marmota monax* (Emmons, Rowley, Olson, Mattern, Bell, Powell and Marcey, 1955). A disease which may have been histoplasmosis has been reported in the ferret *Mustela furo* (Levine, Dunlap and Graham, 1938) and guinea pig *Cavia porcellus* (Correa and Pacheco, 1967). The clinical picture can only be described adequately in the dog, since so few cases have been reported in other animals.

Dog

The disease in the dog may be characterized by a variety of clinical manifestations; it may be benign or disseminated (Menges, 1951). In the benign type, primarily the lungs are involved. Healing results in encapsulation and often calcification of the lesions. These cases show no evidence of an illness, but chest radiographs usually reveal pulmonary nodules. Evidence that the benign type is quite common in dogs has been presented by Rowley (Rowley, Habermann and Emmons, 1954). *H. capsulatum* was isolated from the cervical and peribronchial lymph nodes of several dogs showing no obvious illness.

Characteristics of the disseminated disease in the dog are emaciation, persistent diarrhea, ascites, chronic cough, weakness, and irregular pyrexia. There is frequently hepatomegaly, splenomegaly, lymphadenopathy, and ulcerations in the naso-oral-pharyngeal cavities and intestines. Dogs with the disseminated type of the disease may have had a mild respiratory illness and developed a chronic cough several months prior to the onset of severe illness.

Cat

Studies on cats in Loudoun County, Virginia (Rowley, Habermann and Emmons, 1954), have indicated that benign histoplasmosis may be quite common in the cat. Lesions in the cats were found to be minimal, and isolations were made most frequently from the cervical and peribronchial lymph nodes.

The disease has been reported in a one-year-old female cat associated with a human epidemic (Menges, Furcolow and Habermann, 1954). The cat showed anorexia and severe diarrhea.

Cattle

Based on the syndromes in dogs, one might expect the disease in cattle to be characterized by a variety of clinical forms and that it might be benign or disseminated. The natural occurrence of histoplasmosis has been reported in at least three cattle, the first of which involved a range bull on a ranch near Kaupo on the Island of Maui in Hawaii (Adler, 1950). *H. capsulatum* was demonstrated in lung tissue.

The second case occurred in 1950, and involved a nine and a half year-old Aberdeen Angus cow from a farm in Boone County, Missouri (Menges and Kintner, 1951). This cow had gradually lost weight over a period of four to five months before exhibiting dyspnea, diarrhea, grinding of the teeth, poor hair coat, and swelling of the brisket. She became progressively worse and died shortly thereafter. At necropsy, *H. capsulatum* was demonstrated in liver tissue.

A third case occurred in 1960, and involved a male, five-month-old Hereford calf (Menges, Habermann, Selby and Behlow, 1962). He was born and had spent all of his life on a farm located in Fayette County, Kentucky. The calf was found dead without having exhibited noticeable signs prior to death. *H. capsulatum* was demonstrated in lung tissue by using the fluorescent antibody technic and isolated from bronchial lymph node tissue.

A possible fourth case, reported in 1967, involved a cow (Correa and Pacheco, 1967). The cow came from a farm in Brazil located next to a farm which supplied grass for feeding laboratory guinea pigs. Possible cases of histoplasmosis were reported to have occurred among the guinea pigs at the laboratory. *H. capsulatum* was reported to be demonstrated in a subpleural granuloma in a piece of lung from the chronically diseased cow.

Swine

The clinical features observed in swine have been reported for only one pig (Menges, Habermann, Selby and Behlow, 1962). The animal was a two-month-old male, Hampshire pig from a farm located in Madison County, Kentucky. In 1960, the farmer purchased twenty-seven, one-month-old pigs and three sows at a sales barn in Fayette County, Kentucky. Two days later he transported the swine to his farm where they were kept with chickens in a large chicken house. Two weeks later the pigs developed an intermittent anorexia and a slight diarrhea. The sows developed a severe illness and died, but the pigs lingered along and according to the farmer, they acted like they were "smothering to death."

The pig, proved to have histoplasmosis, first appeared sick ten days after he arrived on the farm. He showed fever, anorexia, loss of weight, slight diarrhea, and marked dyspnea. He was necropsied at two months of age, and both lungs showed consolidated and atelectatic areas. Fluorescent antibody studies showed the lung and bronchial lymph node tissues to be positive for histoplasmosis. *H. capsulatum* was isolated from the bronchial lymph node tissue.

Horse

The clinical features observed in horses with histoplasmosis were variable. Histoplasmosis has been reported in five horses, the first of which occurred in 1946 in a six- to seven-month-old Tennessee walking horse filly from Rutherford County, Tennessee (Richman, 1948). Fever, anorexia, depression and dyspnea were evident, and the conjunctival membranes were slightly icteric. *H. capsulatum* was demonstrated in tissue sections of the lung.

Randall (Randall, Orr and Schell, 1951) reported the second case and the first isolation of *H. capsulatum* from horse tissues in 1951. The animal was an apparently healthy five-year-old pregnant mare from Tennessee. The fungus was isolated by a tissue culture technic from spleen and apparently normal amnio-allantoic membrane.

Three horse cases were found in 1960 during a fungus disease study done at Lexington, Kentucky (Menges, Habermann, Selby, Ellis, Behlow and Smith, 1963). *H. capsulatum* was demonstrated in lung tissue sections of all three horses, and fluorescent antibody studies showed the lung and bronchial or cervical lymph node tissues to be positive for histoplasmosis. One case, sacrificed in August 1960, involved a two-month-old, male thoroughbred from a horse farm in Fayette County, Kentucky. The horse had been treated for acute intestinal salmonellosis one month before necropsy. He had fever and a draining abscess at the left hock (tarsal) joint. No gross lung lesions were observed, but microscopic lesions were found.

The second case, sacrificed in July, 1960, involved a three-month-old, male thoroughbred cross obtained from a dealer in Garrard County, Kentucky, for experimental work. Two weeks before necropsy he had been inoculated with nasal washing from a horse showing signs of heaves and pneumonia. The horse showed depression and dyspnea, and at necropsy, two granulomatous lesions were observed the cardiac lobe of one lung. The apical lobes of both lungs were atelectatic, and the remaining portions of the lungs were emphysematous.

The third case, also sacrificed in July, 1960, involved a two-year-old, male thoroughbred from a horse farm in Bourbon County, Kentucky. The horse showed lameness, swollen, inflamed joints, and incoordination. He had enlarged hock (tarsal) joints and erosion of the synovial membranes. No gross lung lesions were observed, but microscopic lesions were found in the lung and liver.

Wild or Captive Animals

Although *H. capsulatum* has been isolated from numerous wild animals, the clinical aspects of the disease in these animals have not been reported. It is quite probable that these animals had an inapparent infection. Some workers reported clinical features, and these are presented under each species.

Baboon

The baboons were all from Africa, and they had African histoplasmosis caused by the large-cell variety of *Histoplasma, H. capsulatum* var. *duboisii.* The yellow baboons *Papio cynocephalus* were captured at Kindia in French Guinea in 1953 and 1954 (Courtois, Segretain, Mariat and Levaditi, 1955; Mariat and Segretain, 1956; Mariat and Gardini-Tuesta, 1959). The animals had chronic skin lesions with fistulous tracts which drained a yellowish exudate.

The African baboon *P. papio* was a female, three to four years old when she was acquired from a collector in the Gambia in 1955 (Walker and Spooner, 1960). In February, 1959, she had cutaneous lesions on a finger and on her tail. Scrapings from the lesions showed typical *Histoplasma* of the large-cell variety.

Badger

The one badger in which the disease was reported was killed by accident near Berne, Switzerland (Burgisser, Frankhauser, Kaplan, Klingler and Scholer, 1961). *H. capsulatum* was demonstrated in a submandibular lymph node.

Big Brown (Kodiak) Bear

The one bear in which the disease was reported was a male, five years old when he died in the spring of 1950 (Cross, 1950). The diseased bear showed evidence of an illness less than a week. The first signs observed were anorexia and drowsiness. The bear was one of two Alaskan peninsular brown bear cubs born in the Detroit Zoological Park on February 3, 1945. Their parents, purchased from a doctor at Cordova, Alaska, in August, 1929, both lived to be approximately twenty years of age. In 1947, the two bear cubs were sold to the Municipal Zoo of Columbus, Ohio. Three years later, the one bear became sick and died.

Chinchilla

Histoplasmosis has been reported in a two-year-old, male chinchilla from Switzerland (Burtscher and Otte, 1962). The chinchilla had been in a group of eighteen imported from the United States to Switzerland one year prior to the onset of illness. The dead chinchilla was taken to a laboratory in Vienna, in January, 1962. One month before death, in December, 1961, the chinchilla was weak, inactive, and appeared to have no vitality. Two weeks later he showed marked loss of weight, and at necropsy, he was emaciated and anemic. The lungs showed emphysema, and the spleen, liver, and some lymph nodes were enlarged. *H. capsulatum* was isolated from spleen, liver, kidney, and lymph node tissues, and demonstrated in tissue sections.

Raccoon

Isolation of *H. capsulatum* from four raccoons which had a distemperlike disease has been reported (Menges, Habermann and Stains, 1955). In these cases, the etiology of the disease was probably distemper virus, and the fungus was not the cause of the signs which were observed.

Ferret

A disease was reported in a ferret which had been used for hunting rats and rabbits near Peoria, Illinois (Levine, Dunlap and Graham, 1938). In March, 1938, the ferret was ill for a week or more, its temperature was subnormal, and it manifested pain in the abdominal region. On examination, an intracellular parasite was found in spleen, liver, and lung tissues. In 1940, Meleney (1940) indicated that the photomicrograph published in the report was very suggestive of histoplasmosis, and other workers (Skulski and Symmers, 1954; Ajello, 1967) have either mentioned or included the ferret among animal cases of histoplasmosis.

Guinea Pig

Possible cases of naturally occurring histoplasmosis in laboratory guinea pigs have been reported from Brazil (Correa and Pacheco, 1967). The adult guinea pigs had a chronic disease and showed emaciation and lameness of their hind limbs. The guinea pig less than three months old showed a rough hair coat, abnormal dorsal curvature of the back, and conjunctivitis. They died in two to four weeks. The principal lesions were ulcerative gastritis, hemorrhagic and catarrhal enteritis, enlarged spleen and mesenteric lymph nodes. *H. capsulatum* was reported to be demonstrated in blood, spleen, lymph node, and intestinal wall tissues, and the fungus was isolated.

In general, the clinical signs of histoplasmosis in animals are not specific enough to be diagnostic. The signs are usually obscure in the benign disease, but chest radiographs may reveal pulmonary nodules. The signs observed in the disseminated disease may lead one to suspect histoplasmosis. Emaciated animals with a persistent diarrhea, intermittent fever, and characteristic changes in their chest radiographs should be suspected. These animals can be skin tested with histoplasmin and blood specimen obtained for serologic tests. A definite diagnosis can only be established by culturing the organism from tissue specimens or by demonstrating it in tissue sections.

References

Adler, H.E. (1950). Generalized infection with a yeast-like fungus in a range bull. *N. Amer. Vet.*, 31:457-458.

Ajello, L. (1960). Geographic distribution of *Histoplasma capsulatum*. In Sweany, H.C. (Ed.). *Histoplasmosis*. Springfield, Thomas. pp.88-98.

Ajello, L., Hosty, T.S. and Palmer, J. (1967). Bat histoplasmosis in Alabama. *Amer. J. Trop. Med.*, 16:329-331.

Ajello, L. (1967). Comparative ecology of respiratory mycotic disease agents. *Bact. Rev.*, 31:6-24.

Burgisser, H., Frankhauser, R., Kaplan, W., Klingler, K. and Scholer, H.J. (1961). Mykose bei einem dachs in der Schweiz: histologisch histoplasmose. *Path. Microbiol.*, 24:794-802.

Burtscher, H. and Otte, E. (1962). Histoplasmose beim Chinchilla. *Dtsch. Tierärztl. Wschr.*, 69:303-307.

Correa, W.M. and Pacheco, A.C. (1967). Naturally occurring histoplasmosis in guinea pigs. *Canad. J. Comp. Med.*, 31:203-206.

Courtois, G., Segretain, G., Mariat, F. and Levaditi, J.C. (1955). Mycose cutanée a corps levuriformes observée chez des singes Africains en captivité. *Ann. Inst. Pasteur*, 89:124-127.

Cross, R.F. (1950). Histoplasmosis. A review of the literature. *Speculum* (Ohio State Univ.), 4:5, 28.

DeMonbreun, W.A. (1939). The dog as a natural host for *Histoplasma capsulatum*. *Amer. J. Trop. Med.*, 19:565-587.

Emmons, C.W., Bell, J.A. and Olson, B.J. (1947). Naturally occurring histoplasmosis in *Mus musculus* and *Rattus norvegicus*. *Public Health Rep.*, 62:1642-1646.

Emmons, C.W., Morlan, H.B. and Hill, E.L. (1949). Histoplasmosis in rats and skunks in Georgia. *Public Health Rep.*, 64:1430-1433.

Emmons, C.W. (1950). Histoplasmosis: animal reservoirs and other sources in nature of the pathogenic fungus, *Histoplasma*. *Amer. J. Public Health*, 40:436-440.

Emmons, C.W., Rowley, D.A., Olson, B.J., Mattern, C.F.T., Bell, J.A., Powell, E. and Marcey, E.A. (1955). Histoplasmosis. Occurrence of inapparent infection in dogs, cats, and other animals. *Amer. J. Hyg.*, 61:40-44.

Hall, E.R. (1955). Handbook of Mammals of Kansas. University of Kansas Museum of Natural History, Lawrence, Kansas. Misc. Pub. No. 7, 10-13.

Levine, N.D., Dunlap, G.L. and Graham, R. (1938). An intracellular parasite encountered in ferret. *Cornell Vet.*, 28:249-251.

Mariat, F. and Segretain, G. (1956). Étude mycologique d'une histoplasmose spontanée du singe Africain (*Cynocephalus babuin*). *Ann. Inst. Pasteur*, 91:874-891.

Mariat, F. and Gardini-Tuesta, W.E. (1959). Pouvoir pathogéne expériméntal d'une souche d' *Histoplasma capsulatum* isolée du singe Africain. *Ann. Inst. Pasteur*, 96: 669-679.

Meleney, H.E. (1940). Histoplasmosis (reticulo-endothelial cytomycosis): a review with mention of 13 unpublished cases. *Amer. J. Trop. Med.*, 20:603-616.

Menges, R.W. (1951). Canine histoplasmosis. *J. Amer. Vet. Med. Assoc.*, 119:411-415.

Menges, R.W. and Kintner, L.D. (1951). Bovine histoplasmosis: case report. *N. Amer. Vet.*, 32:692-695.

Menges, R.W., Furcolow, M.L. and Habermann, R.T. (1954). An outbreak of histoplasmosis involving animals and man. *Amer. J. Vet. Res.*, 15:520-524.

Menges, R.W., Habermann, R.T. and Stains, H.J. (1955). A distemper-like disease in raccoons and isolation of *Histoplasma capsulatum* and *Haplosporangium parvum*. *Trans. Kansas Acad. Sci.*, 58:58-67.

Menges, R.W., Habermann, R.T., Selby, L.A. and Behlow, R.F. (1962). *Histoplasma capsulatum* isolated from a calf and a pig. *Vet. Med.*, 57:1067-1070.

Menges, R.W., Habermann, R.T., Selby, L.A., Ellis, H.R., Behlow, R.F. and Smith, C.D. (1963). A review and recent findings on histoplasmosis in animals. *Vet. Med.*, 58:331-338, 366.

Menges, R.W., Furcolow, M.L., Habermann, R.T. and Weeks, R.J. (1967). Epidemiologic studies on histoplasmosis in wildlife. *Environ. Res.*, 1:129-144.

Olson, B.J., Bell, J.A. and Emmons, C.W. (1947). Studies on histoplasmosis in a rural county. *Amer. J. Public Health*, 37:441-449.

Randall, C.C., Orr, M.F. and Schell, F.G. (1951). Detection by tissue culture of an organism resembling *Histoplasma capsulatum* in an apparently healthy horse. *Proc. Soc. Exp. Biol. Med.*, 78:447-450.

Richman, H. (1948). Histoplasmosis in a colt. *N. Amer. Vet.*, 29:710.

Rowley, D.A., Habermann, R.T. and Emmons, C.W. (1954). Histoplasmosis. Pathologic studies of fifty cats and fifty dogs from Loudoun County, Virginia. *J. Infect. Dis.*, 95:98-108.

Skulski, G. and Symmers, W.St.C. (1954). Actinomycosis and torulosis in the ferret (*Mustela furo L.*). *J. Comp. Path.*, 64:306-311.

Taylor, R.L. and Shacklette, M.H. (1962). Naturally acquired histoplasmosis in the mammals of the Panama Canal Zone. *Amer. J. Trop. Med.*, 11:796-799.

Walker, J. and Spooner, E.T. (1960). Natural infection of the African baboon (*Papio papio*) with the large-cell form of *Histoplasma*. *J. Path. Bact.*, 80:436-438.

Chapter 21

Serology in Animal Histoplasmosis

DAVID S. BAUMAN

ABSTRACT

The results of studies concerning histoplasmosis in animals are presented. An immunodiffusion test was used to detect antibodies against *Histoplasma capsulatum*.

Sera from 472 animals were tested and antibodies against *H. capsulatum* were detected in 25 (5%). The animals found positive included 17 dogs, 1 cat, and 6 cattle.

The data presented were comparable to the human skin test reactor rates for the same area.

DEMONBREUN (1939) opened a "Pandora's Box" with his original report of histoplasmosis in the dog. Since that time numerous investigators have tried to implicate dogs and other animals as the natural or intermediate hosts responsible for human infections (Emmons, 1950; Furcolow and Menges, 1952; Cole, 1953; Menges, Furcolow and Hinton, 1953; Menges, 1954; Menges, McClellan and Ausherman, 1954; Emmons, Rowley, Olson, Mattern, Bell, Powell and Marcey, 1955; Fattal, Schwarz and Straub, 1961).

Since *Histoplasma capsulatum* is known to grow saprophytically in the soil (Emmons, 1949; Ziedberg, Ajello, Dillon and Runyon, 1952), it is now felt that man and animals are infected similarly by inhaling spore-laden dust (Straub, Schwarz and Fattal, 1961; Menges, Habermann, Selby, Ellis, Behlow and Smith, 1963; Menges, Furcolow, Selby, Ellis and Habermann, 1964; Porter, Comfort, Menges, Habermann and Smith, 1965; Menges, Furcolow, Habermann and Weeks, 1967; Selby, Menges and Habermann, 1967; Turner, Furcolow and Smith, 1968). Dogs have been the most commonly reported animals with histoplasmosis, and the trend is evolving to use the dog as an epidemiologic tool for detecting *H. capsulatum* in endemic areas. The dog with its "nose to the ground" would seem to be the most logical choice as a tool.

This publication deals primarily with a serologic survey for histoplasmosis in animals performed at West Virginia University Medical Center. An attempt has been made to correlate the results from animals with those expected with humans.

170

Materials and Methods

Animals

From August, 1968, to July, 1969, a group of dogs obtained from Monongalia County, West Virginia, were bled and tested serologically for histoplasmosis. The dogs were from two sources: (1) 204 from the West Virginia University Medical Center dog pound (stray animals collected by the County Dogcatcher), and (2) 156 from the local veterinarians.

In addition, the local veterinarians submitted the following serum samples: 16 from cats, 79 from cattle, 1 from a horse and 16 from swine.

Preservation of Serum

Sera were divided into 0.5 ml aliquotes and stored at 70°C. The vials of serum were rapid thawed and mixed before use.

Antigen

Undiluted histoplasmin (HKC-43, obtained from M. L. Furcolow) was concentrated to one-tenth its original volume by adding dry Sephadex G-25 (Pharmacia Fine Chemicals, Inc.). The concentrated antigen was then filter sterilized and stored at 4°C until use.

Serologic Method

The sera were tested for antibody activity by a double-diffusion, immunodiffusion test. The method was modified from that described by Busey and Hinton (1965). A plastic matrix (John S. Chapman, L. L. Pellet, Co., Dallas, Texas) was employed which consisted of seventeen series of immunodiffusion wells. Each series was one machined hole surrounded by six equally spaced holes.

The agar medium contained 0.5 M glycine, 0.15 M NaCl, 0.5% sodium azide and 0.5% agarose. After dissolving, the agar medium was divided into 11 ml aliquotes and stored at 4°C until use.

To prepare an immunodiffusion plate for use, one tube of agar medium was melted in a boiling water bath, cooled to 50°C and 6.5 ml of agar was spread over the bottom of a 100 mm plastic petri dish and allowed to solidify. Then 3.5 ml of agar was pipetted over the first layer and the plastic matrix was placed in the agar before solidification, eliminating all air bubbles. The petri dish was refrigerated for 15 minutes and the excess agar was removed from the wells by suction.

Serum was added to the peripheral wells of each series and the plate was preincubated for one hour at 25°C before adding antigen to the central well of each series. One or more precipitin bands was accepted as a positive reaction. All positive sera were retested against dilutions of antigen in a macroimmunodiffusion test consisting of the same diffusion medium with wells (2 mm diameter) cut into the agar and an interwell distance of 4 mm. All tests were incubated at 25°C in a humidity chamber and read at 48 and 72 hours. Only those sera which reacted in both tests were considered to be positive.

Results and Discussion

The immunodiffusion test results for histoplasmosis in animals from northern West Virginia are shown in Table 21-I. The 204 dog pound dogs ranged in age from small pups to ten or twelve years of age and had been confined in closed kennels for an average of three months each (1 month's to 8 months' range). These animals showed a slightly lower reaction rate (4.4%) than the dog samples submitted by the veterinarians (5.1%), which might be accounted for by this period of confinement. Another possible explanation may be the fact that the pound dogs were almost exclusively captured within the city limits and most of the samples submitted by the veterinarians were from animals which were symptomatic in some way (selection was not made for animals with possible mycotic symptoms).

The 6.2 percent reaction rate for cats was not considered significant, since the sample size (16) was so small. However, the 7.5 percent reaction rate in cattle was rather surprising, especially so when the fact that four of the six reactions came from a single "closed" dairy herd of fifty cattle in which none of the animals had ever been off the same farm is considered. These animals were also skin tested, and only one of the four immunodiffusion reactors had a positive skin test with histoplasmin (HKC-43, 1:10).

The rate for animals with positive serologic tests was much lower than the rate of humans with positive histoplasmin skin tests for the same area. In a skin test survey in Monogalia County, West Virginia, Chick (1969) found that school children had an average positive skin test rate of 6 percent. Adults in the same area had a rate of between 30 and 40 percent.

Heiner (1958), Schubert, Lynch and Ajello (1961) and Turner, Furcolow

TABLE 21-I

Immunodiffusion Reactions for Histoplasmosis

Animals	No. Tested	No. Positive	% Positive
Dogs (dog pound)	204	9	4.4
Dogs (veterinarians')	156	8	5.1
Cats	16	1	6.2
Cattle	79	6	7.5
Swine	16	0	0
Horse	1	0	0

and Smith (1968) have shown that immunodiffusion is not as sensitive a method of detecting *Histoplasma* infection as other methods in both humans and animals. A positive immunodiffusion test was interpreted to indicate current or recent infection, and perhaps this would explain the reaction rate being much lower than the skin test reaction rate for humans.

As an epidemiologic tool, the immunodiffusion test, by detecting only current or recent infections but not old healed infections, has definite advantages over the skin test which would have to be repeated at intervals to detect "new" infections.

Furcolow and Menges (1952) found comparable skin test reaction rates in children (80%) and horses (73%) in Missouri. However, the reaction rate in cattle (13%) was much lower.

Menges, Furcolow and Hinton (1954) found 90 percent culturally positive and 25 percent serologically (complement fixation) positive for histoplasmosis in dogs from a Kansas highly endemic area. Thirty percent (30%) of the cats from the same area were culturally positive (cat sera do not react well in the complement fixation test).

In view of this work done in other geographic areas, the immunodiffusion results seem to be a reasonable measure of the infection rate occurring in northern West Virginia. And in view of the fact that it is usually much easier to obtain specimens from a random animal population than it is from a comparable human population, this author feels that animal surveys will prove to be a very valuable epidemiologic tool.

References

Busey, J.F. and Hinton, P.F. (1965). Precipitins in histoplasmosis. *Amer. Rev. Resp. Dis.*, 92:637-639.

Chick, E.W. (1969). Personal communication.

Cole, C.R. (1953). Histoplasmosis in Animals. *J. Amer. Vet. Med. Assoc.*, 22:471-473.

DeMonbreun, W.A. (1939). Dog as Natural Host for *Histoplasma Capsulatum*. *Amer. J. Trop. Med.*, 19:565-587.

Emmons, C.W. (1949). Isolation of *Histoplasma capsulatum* from soil. *Public Health Rep.* 64:892-896.

Emmons, C. W. (1950). Histoplasmosis: Animal reservoirs and other sources in nature of the pathogenic fungus, *Histoplasma*. *Amer. J. Public Health.* 40:436-440.

Emmons, C.W., Rowley, D.A., Olson, B.J., Mattern, C.F., Bell, J.A., Powell, E. and Marcey, E.A. (1955). Histoplasmosis: Proved Occurrence of inapparent infection in dogs, cats, and other animals. *Amer. J. Hyg.*, 61:40-44.

Fattal, A.R., Schwarz, J. and Straub, M. (1961). Isolation of *Histoplasma capsulatum* from lymph nodes of spontaneously infected dogs. *Amer. J. Clin. Path.*, 36:119-124.

Furcolow, M.L. and Menges, R.W. (1952). Comparison of histoplasmin sensitivity rates among human beings and animals in Boone County, Missouri. *Amer. J. Public Health.*, 42:926-929.

Heiner, D.C. (1958). Diagnosis of histoplasmosis using precipitin reactions in agar gel. *Pediatrics,* 22:616-627.

Klite, P.D. (1965). Interpretation of agar-gel precipitin reactions in histoplasmosis. *J. Lab. Clin. Med.,* 66:770-787.

Menges, R.W. (1951). Canine histoplasmosis. *J. Amer. Vet. Med. Assoc.,* 199:411-415.

Menges, R.W., Furcolow, M.L. and Hinton, A. (1953). The role of animals in the epidemiology of histoplasmosis. *Amer. J. Hyg.,* 59:113-118.

Menges, R.W. (1954). Histoplasmin sensitivity in animals. *Cornell Vet.,* 42:21.

Menges, R.W., McClellan, J.T. and Ausherman, R.J. (1954). Canine histoplasmosis and blastomycosis in Lexington, Kentucky. *Amer. J. Vet. Med. Assoc.,* 124:235-241.

Menges, R.W., Habermann, R.T., Selby, L.A., Ellis, H.R., Behlow, R.F. and Smith, C.D. (1963). A review and recent findings on histoplasmosis in animals. *Vet. Med.,* 58:331-338.

Menges, R.W., Furcolow, M.L., Habermann, R.T. and Weeks, R.J. (1967). Epidemiologic studies on histoplasmosis in wildlife. *Environ. Res.,* 1:129-144.

McMillin, S. and Devrae, S. (1963). Specific precipitin bands in the serology of histoplasmosis. *Amer. Rev. Resp. Dis.,* 87:438.

Porter, B.M., Comfort, B.K., Menges, R.W., Habermann, R.T. and Smith, C.D. (1965). Correlation of fluorescent antibody, histology, and culture on tissue from 372 animals examined for histoplasmosis and blastomycosis. *J. Bact.* 89:748-751.

Rowley, D.A., Habermann, R.T. and Emmons, C.W. (1954). Histoplasmosis: pathologic studies of 50 cats and 50 dogs from Loudoun County, Virginia. *J. Infect. Dis.,* 95:98-108.

Schubert, J.H., Lynch, H.J. and Ajello, L. (1961). Evaluation of the agar plate precipitin test for histoplasmosis. *Amer. Rev. Resp. Dis.,* 84:845.

Selby, L.A., Menges, R.W. and Habermann, R.T. (1967). Survey for blastomycosis and histoplasmosis among stray dogs, in Arkansas. *Amer. J. Vet. Res.* 28:345-349.

Straub, M., Schwarz, J. and Fattal, A.R. (1961). Spontaneous canine histoplasmosis. *Arch. Path.,* 71:685-692.

Turner, C., Furcolow, M.L. and Smith, C.D. (1968). Specificity and sensitivity of an agar gel precipitin test for *Histoplasma capsulatum* and *Blastomyces dermatitids* in dogs. *Bact. Proc.,* 68:82.

Wiggins, G.L. and Schubert, J.H. (1965). Relationship of histoplasmin agar gel bands and complement fixation titers in histoplasmosis. *J. Bact.,* 89:589.

Ziedberg, L.D., Ajello, L., Dillon, A. and Runyon, L.C. (1952). Isolation of *Histoplasma capsulatum* from the soil. *Amer. J. Public Health,* 42:930-935.

Chapter 22

Isolation of *Histoplasma capsulatum* from Mongrel Dogs in Central Kentucky

CLENON TURNER, COY D. SMITH AND MICHAEL L. FURCOLOW

ABSTRACT

The most sensitive method found in this experiment for isolating *H. capsulatum* from dog tissue is by direct culture. The mouse technique is less effective and requires more time and expense.

H. capsulatum was isolated from 47.7% of the mongrel dogs in central Kentucky. The fungus is relatively easy to isolate without a great deal of contamination if the tissues are macerated and diluted in normal saline prior to culturing on plates instead of tubes. Using tissues for culture, more isolations were obtained on modified Sabouraud's or Smith's yeast extract media than on blood medium. These two media appear about equal.

Therefore, *H. capsulatum* is quite prevalent in mongrel dogs in central Kentucky and presents a problem for the veterinarians in that area, as well as potentially interfering with the experimental use of dogs in research.

THIS study was performed in order to determine the prevalence of active histoplasmosis in the mongrel dog population in central Kentucky and to evaluate serologic and culture techniques in these dogs.

The most sensitive method previously reported (Rowley, Habermann and Emmons, 1954) (Emmons and Rowley, 1955) for isolating *Histoplasma capsulatum* from canines was by injecting portions of tissue into mice. The fungus could then be grown from the infected mouse tissue. This technique was more efficient than direct culture, since often the dog tissue was contaminated with bacteria or saphrophytic fungi that overgrew the cultures.

Since there are no reports in the literature of the precipitin test as a screen for selecting infected dogs, it was decided to include this in the study.

Materials and Methods

Selection of Dogs for Precipitin Studies

A group of 442 mongrel dogs which were randomly selected were bled and tested serologically for histoplasmosis by the agar-gel plate precipitin test employing Busey's modification of Crowle's method (Busey and Hinton,

1965). For this part of the study only the dogs positive to the test were autopsied and cultured.

Random Selection of Dogs

Mongrel dogs were obtained from dog wardens in central Kentucky. The animals were randomly selected with no regard to age, sex, or state of health. The dogs were euthanized and necropsied on the same day they were obtained.

Cultures

Three different media were used for comparison in the study. These were brain heart infusion agar containing 5% (outdated) citrated human blood, modified Sabouraud's dextrose agar (Emmons, Binford and Utz, 1963), and yeast extract agar medium (Smith, 1964). All media contained 2% agar, 20 units of penicillin, 40 mg of streptomycin, 5 µg of polymixin B sulfate, and 0.5 mg of cycloheximide per ml. The media was dispensed in 15×100 mm petri dishes.

Tissue Preparation and Cultures

Portions of lung, spleen, and caudal mediastinal lymph node tissue were cultured separately from each animal. Pieces of lung and spleen (approximately 2×2 cm) (lesions excised when present) and the entire lymph node, except when enlarged beyond 2×2 cm, were selected. These were macerated in a mortar, using a pestle with the aid of sterile sea sand, then diluted approximately 1:5 using sterile physiological saline. Of this suspension 0.5 ml. was cultured on four plates each of the above media from thirty-one animals. These plates were incubated at room temperature and examined at weekly intervals for four weeks before being discarded.

Indirect Mouse Isolation Compared to Direct Culture

Tissue suspensions were made as described above from the mediastinal lymph nodes of seventy-four dogs. A portion of the suspension was drawn into a 10 cc syringe using a 20-gauge needle. Of this 0.5 ml was cultured on yeast extract medium and 0.5 ml was injected intraperitoneally into each of six white Swiss Webster albino mice (approximately 20 gm). Three of the mice were maintained at room environment ($22°$-$25°$C) and the other three at 5°C. The mice were killed and necropsied after four weeks and the liver and spleen removed for culture. A piece of the liver (2-3 gm) and the entire spleen was macerated in a mortar using a pestle and a small amount of sea sand and diluted approximately 1:5. Of this suspension 0.5 ml was cultured on one plate containing yeast extract medium with penicillin and streptomycin in the concentrations described above. The plates were held at room temperature for four weeks before the final readout. Identification of

TABLE 22-I

Comparison of Efficiency of Three Different Media For Isolation of *Histoplasma Capsulatum* From Canine Tissues

Blood Agar	Sabouraud's	Yeast Extract		Total
		+	−	
+	+	15	0	15
+	−	0	0	0
−	+	2	1	3
−	−	1	12	13
Total		18	13	31

H. capsulatum was based on the microscopic morphology of typical micro and tuberculated macroconidia.

Results

Selected by Precipitin Test

Of the 442 dogs tested by the precipitin test, 104, or 23.8 percent, were positive. Among these 104 dogs, 50 isolates of *H. capsulatum* were obtained, or 48.1 percent. Thus, although only one fourth of the random dogs showed positive serology, one half of those positive were positive by culture.

Comparison of Culture Media

The comparison of three different media used for the isolation of *H. capsulatum* from tissues is shown in Table 22-I. A total of 19 isolations were obtained using the three media of which 18 were on both yeast extract and Sabouraud's media, but only 15 on the blood agar. There was 1 additional isolation obtained on the yeast extract that was missed on the Sabouraud's medium. Also, 1 isolation was obtained using Sabouraud's medium that was missed on yeast extract. While 3 additional isolations were obtained on yeast extract and Sabouraud's medium compared to blood agar, no isolations were obtained in this medium that was missed by the other two.

The results comparing direct culture to mouse inoculation for isolating *H.*

TABLE 22-II

Comparison of Direct Culture on Yeast Extract Medium Versus Mice for Isolation of *H. capsulatum* From Caudal Mediastinal Nodes of Seventy-four Mongrel Dogs

Method	*H. capsulatum*		
	+	−	*% Positive*
Direct culture	33	41	41.9
Mice at 25°	18	56	32.1
Mice at 4°C	10	64	13.5

TABLE 22-III

Comparison of Tissues Yielding Isolations of *H. capsulatum* by Direct Culture
From Seventy-seven Mongrel Dogs

Tissue	Number of Tissue Cultured	Number Positive	% Positive
Lung	77	11	14.3
Spleen	77	21	27.3
Caudal Mediastinal Nodes	77	68	88.3

capsulatum from tissue are shown in Table 22-II. The highest percentage of isolations (42%) was obtained by direct culture compared to 32.1% from mice at 25°C and only 13.5% from the mice kept at 4°C.

The results of comparing cultures of lung, spleen, and lymph node tissues are shown in Table 22-III. The caudal mediastinal nodes yielded 88.3% positive isolations of *H. capsulatum*, compared to spleens which were second best with 27.3%, and the lungs with only 14.3% isolations.

Frequency of Isolation From Randomly Selected Dogs

In Table 22-IV is shown the frequency of *H. capsulatum* isolated from mongrel dogs in central Kentucky. Almost half the animals (47.7%) from counties other than Fayette County were found positive for the fungus as shown by culture. These dogs were obtained at random from various counties surrounding the city of Lexington. The thirty-seven animals, however, obtained from Fayette County, which is chiefly a suburban area around the city of Lexington, yielded only 10.8% positive isolations.

Figure 22-1 shows the distribution and percent of positive dogs obtained in the central Kentucky. The percent positive ranges from a high of 60 percent in Madison County, which borders Fayette, to a low in Fayette County of 10.8 percent.

TABLE 22-IV

Frequency of Isolation of *H. capsulatum* From Mongrel Dogs in Central Kentucky

Dogs	Number of Dogs	Number Positive by Culture	% Positive
Central Kentucky except Fayette Co.	153	73	47.7
Fayette County (Lexington suburbia)	37	4	10.8
Total	190	77	40.5

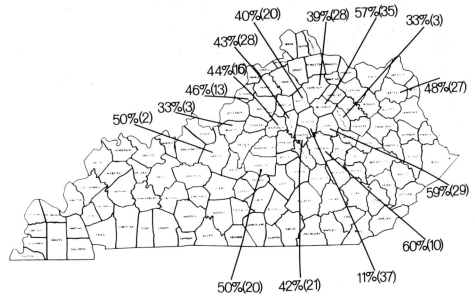

FIGURE 22-1. Frequency of isolation of *Histoplasma capsulatum* from mongrel dogs from various counties in central Kentucky. The number sampled for each county is given in parenthesis.

Discussion

These data show that the most efficient method of isolating *H. capsulatum* from canine tissue is by direct culture. This result is in contrast to that of Emmons (Emmons *et al.*, 1955a), who found mouse inoculation best. Sabouraud's and yeast extract media appeared to serve equally as well for use as a culture media. We believe that better results were obtained in this study using direct culture because petri plates were used and the tissue ground and diluted for culture, whereas Emmons, Rowley, Olson, Mattern, Bell, Powell and Marcey (1955a) used media slants in tubes and cultured the tissue by placing pieces directly on the media.

Yeast extract medium was used subsequently to the media comparison tests, since it is a simple, inexpensive medium to prepare and sporulation of the fungus was obtained faster. The more rapid sporulation enabled us to identify the fungus more readily. Perhaps the reason animals obtained from counties surrounding Fayette were considerably higher (47.7%) in active disease than Fayette (10.8%) is because they were collected chiefly from rural communities instead of a suburban region.

References

Busey, J.F. and Hinton, P.F. (1965). Precipitins in histoplasmosis. *Amer. Rev. Resp. Dis.*, 92:(4) 637-639.

Emmons, C.W., Binford, C.H. and Utz, J.P. (1963). *Medical Mycology*. Philadelphia, Lea and Febiger, p.347.

Emmons, C. W. and Rowley, D.A. (1955). Isolation of *Histoplasmosis capsulatum* from fresh and deep frozen peribronchial lymph nodes of dogs by mouse inoculation. *J. Lab. Clin. Med.*, 45:303-307.

Emmons, C.W., Rowley, D.A., Olson, B.J., Mattern, C.F.T., Bell, J.A., Powell, E. and Marcey, E.A. (1955a). Histoplasmosis: proved occurrence of inapparent infection in dogs, cats, and other animals. *Amer. J. Hyg.*, 61:40-44.

Rowley, D.A., Habermann, R.J. and Emmons, C.W. (1954). Histoplasmosis: pathologic studies of fifty cats and fifty dogs from Loudoun County, Virginia. *J. Infect. Dis.*, 95:98-108.

Smith, C.D. (1964). II. Evidence of the presence in yeast extract of substances which stimulate the growth of *Histoplasma capsulatum* and *Blastomyces dermatitidis* similarly to that found in starling manure. *Mycopathologia*, 22:99-105.

Chapter 23

The Efficacy of Amphotericin B as a Means of Reducing Histoplasmosis in Mongrel Dogs in Central Kentucky

MARTIN B. MARX, CHARLES E. EASTIN, CLENON TURNER, COY D. SMITH, IRENE ROECKEL, AND MICHAEL L. FURCOLOW

ABSTRACT

The efficacy of the treatment of mongrel dogs with amphotericin B as a means of reducing the proportion of animals infected with *H. capsulatum* determined by culture of lymph nodes was examined by means of an experimental study. Each of fifty-one randomly assigned dogs received a total of 1.85 mg/lb body weight of amphotericin B stock solution. Fifty dogs in the matched control group received no treatment. Thirty days following the last of ten intravenous injections, given 48 hours apart, all dogs were autopsied and the lung, spleen, and mediastinal nodes were examined by culture and histologically. The dogs not receiving amphotericin B had significantly more *H. capsulatum* infection than those animals receiving the drug.

HISTOPLASMOSIS has been diagnosed with increasing frequency in recent years among humans and dogs residing in the endemic area of central Kentucky (Robinson and Kotcher, 1951; Grayson and Furcolow, 1953; Menges, McClellan and Ausherman, 1954; Furcolow, Balows, Menges, Pickar, McClellan and Saliba, 1966; Balows, Ausherman and Hopper, 1966). At least one survey of counties surrounding Lexington has indicated a prevalence rate of infection among mongrel dogs, determined by culture of lymph nodes, as high as 60 percent (Turner, Smith and Furcolow, 1969).

To test the efficacy of amphotericin B[*] as a means of reducing fungus infection in dogs, an experimental study was carried out utilizing mongrel dogs obtained from those counties where high rates of infection had been previously reported.

Methods

A randomly assigned group of fifty-one mongrel dogs received 1.85 mg of amphotericin B per pound of body weight over a nineteen-day period. The

NOTE: This study was supported in part by the General Research Support Grant, University of Kentucky College of Medicine, No. FR 05-374-07.

[*] Amphotericin B used was furnished as *Fungizone Intravenous* through the courtesy of The Squibb Institute for Medical Research, New Brunswick, New Jersey.

181

regimen followed consisted of ten intravenous injections from a stock solution containing 0.2 mg/cc amphotericin B. The first injection was at the dosage of 0.1 mg/lb; the second at the dosage of 0.15 mg/lb; and the third through the tenth injections at the dosage of 0.2 mg/lb. All injections were given at 48-hour intervals. This regimen is the one suggested by Balows *et al.* (1966).

Thirty days following treatment the results of culture examination for *Histoplasma capsulatum* of the lymph nodes from the treated dogs were compared with similar cultures from a matched sample of fifty dogs who received no treatment. All laboratory examinations were performed without knowledge of the group assignment of the animal providing the specimen.

Results

Prior to the initiation of treatment the two groups were examined and found to be comparable on the basis of several potentially relevant characteristics. These included sex, initial body weight, initial blood urea nitrogen (BUN) values, age and the results of a histoplasmin skin test.

Among the 97 animals completing the study, *H. capsulatum* was isolated by culture from 12 of 50 untreated dogs (24%) and from 1 of 47 treated dogs (2%). Using the proportion of positives in the control group as the best estimate of the true proportion, the difference between the infection rates in the two groups was tested using the student's t test, $t = 2.52$, $P <$ .01 (Table 23-I).

TABLE 23-I

H. capsulatum Isolations Thirty Days Post-treatment

Group	Culture Results		
	No. & % Positive	No. & % Negative	Total
Study	1 (2)	46 (98)	47*
Control	12 (24)	38 (76)	50
Total	13 (13)	84 (87)	97

$t = 2.52$, P less than .01; proportion positive in control group taken as best estimate of true rate.
* Four dogs died prior to autopsy date.

Four animals in the treatment group died during the study. Although they were negative on culture for histoplasmosis and blastomycosis at the time of their death, they must be considered unfavorable outcomes, since they failed to complete the study, and it is possible that their deaths were associated with toxicity of the drug. If these animals are included in the analysis, the difference in the proportion of unfavorable outcomes in the two groups (24% versus 10%) is significant, $t = 1.67$, $P < .05$, (Table 23-II).

TABLE 23-II

Group Status* Thirty Days Posttreatment

Group	No. & % With Unfavorable (a) Outcome	No. & % With Favorable (b) Outcome	Total
Study	5† (10)	46 (90)	51
Control	12 (24)	38 (76)	50
Total	17 (17)	84 (83)	101

* Status = (a) Unfavorable outcome: Positive for *H. capsulatum* or dead prior to autopsy date.

(b) Favorable outcome: Alive on autopsy date and negative for *H. capsulatum* on culture.

† Includes: one animal with positive culture for *H. capsulatum* and four animals with premature deaths. These four were negative for *H. capsulatum*.

$t = 1.67$, P less than .05; proportion unfavorable in control group taken as best estimate of true rate.

Conclusions

Based on the differences observed between the treated and untreated groups in their proportions of animals infected with *H. capsulatum*, treatment of mongrel dogs with the described regimen of amphotericin B is effective in reducing the infection rate. In this study a reduction in the expected number of cases of at least 58 percent was attained.

★   ★   ★

The authors wish to express their gratitude for the consultation offered by Drs. R. J. Ausherman and C. S. Steiner, Lexington, and L. S. Shirrell, Frankfort, in connection with this study.

References

Balows, A., Ausherman, R.J. and Hopper, Joan M. (1966). Practical diagnosis and therapy of canine histoplasmosis and blastomycosis. *J. Amer. Vet. Med. Assoc.,* 148:678-684.

Furcolow, M.L., Balows, A., Menges, R.W., Pickar, D., McClellan, J.T. and Saliba, A. (1966). Blastomycosis—an important medical problem in the central United States. *J.A.M.A.,* 198:529-532.

Grayston, J.T. and Furcolow, M.L. (1953). The occurrence of histoplasmosis in epidemics—epidemiological studies. *Amer. J. Public Health,* 43:665-674.

Menges, R.W., McClellan, J.T. and Ausherman, R.J. (1954). Canine histoplasmosis and blastomycosis in Lexington, Kentucky. *J. Amer. Vet. Med. Assoc.,* 124:202-207.

Robinson, J.E. and Kotcher, E. (1951). Histoplasmosis survey of dogs in Louisville, Kentucky. *Public Health Rep.,* 66:1533-1537.

Turner, C., Smith, C.D. and Furcolow, M.L. (1969). Comparison of two methods of isolating *Histoplasma capsulatum* from caudal mediastinal lymph nodes of mongrel dogs. American Society for Microbiology, Bacteriological Proceedings, Abstracts of the 69th Annual Meeting, Miami Beach, Florida, p.112.

Chapter 24

Control of Epidemic Foci
of *Histoplasma capsulatum*

ROBERT J. WEEKS AND FRED E. TOSH

ABSTRACT

A review of the various chemicals and procedures for controlling *Histoplasma capsulatum* in the soil was made. Additional results were presented on attempts to control the organism at an epidemic site in Mason City, Iowa. At Mexico, Missouri, the surface of a 7.5-acre positive site was treated with 333,000 gallons of 3% formalin solution. The treatment appears to have successfully eliminated the organism from the site.

OUTBREAKS of histoplasmosis that are due to point sources in urban areas have dictated a need to control the foci of infection (D'Alessio, Heeren, Hendricks, Ogilvie and Furcolow, 1965; Furcolow, Tosh, Larsh, Lynch and Shaw, 1961). The occurrence of a second epidemic from the same site in an urban area further emphasized the need to eliminate *Histoplasma capsulatum* from these sites (Tosh, Doto, D'Alessio, Medeiros, Hendricks and Chin, 1966). There is also a need to eliminate the fungus from smaller foci such as chicken houses. Cases of histoplasmosis have occurred among three different families who occupied a farm in Iowa over a period of several years (Weeks, Hendricks and Tosh, 1969). The most direct method to prevent infection is to eliminate or reduce the number of infectious particles of *H. capsulatum* contained in the site. This approach has been attempted by several investigators using physical changes, biological changes, and fungicidal chemicals on the site.

Materials and Methods

The use of formalin to kill *H. capsulatum* in an epidemic site in Mason City, Iowa, in 1964 has been reported (Tosh, Weeks, Pfeiffer, Hendricks, Greer and Chin, 1967). The length of follow-up from the time of application of the chemical was approximately one year. Because *H. capsulatum* was occasionally recovered from depth samples from the site, the area was treated with formalin again in May 1966. Prior to this application, the surface of the area was scored, using a road grader. Where positive samples had been obtained, 31,500 gallons of 3% formalin were applied to the general area. In June, 1967, an additional 1,000 gallons of 3% formalin were applied to eight areas of the site where *H. capsulatum* had been recovered from depth samples. An area of 100 square feet around each point where a positive isolation had been made was measured. Holes approximately 6 inches deep were punched throughout these areas. The 3% formalin was then applied to each square and permitted to soak into the soil. Samples were collected at monthly intervals for three months and again six months after this application. In January, 1968, a bridge was constructed across the creek which borders the north side of the epidemic site. It was necessary to excavate part of the treated site for the foundation of the bridge. During the excavation, twenty-seven composite soil samples were collected from material removed from a depth of approximately five feet below the surface. These samples were processed as described previously for the presence of *H. capsulatum* (Tosh *et al.*, 1967).

In March, 1966, 3% formalin was applied to the 7.5-acre positive site in Mexico, Missouri, which had been responsible for an outbreak of histoplasmosis (Furcolow *et al.*, 1961). The chemical was applied as described in a previous publication (Tosh *et al.*, 1967). The site was sampled monthly for four months and then yearly for three years after application of the 3% formalin.

Results

The data relating to control of *H. capsulatum* in the epidemic site in Mason City are shown in Table 24-I. After the initial application of formalin, all but one of the surface samples were negative for the fungus, but depth sam-

TABLE 24-I

Isolation of *Histoplasma capsulatum* From Epidemic Site, Mason City, Iowa 1962–1968

Years Sampled	Surface Samples			Depth Samples		
	Total	Positive		Total	Positive	
		Number	Percent		Number	Percent
1962–1964	434	273	62	—	—	—
October 1964—233,000 gallons 3% formalin applied.						
1964	195	1	0.5	—	—	—
1965	367	0	0	78	9	12
1966	30	0	0	30	6	20
May, 1966—31,500 gallons 3% formalin applied to area of positive depth samples.						
1966	120	3	3	120	7	6
1967	30	0	0	30	1	3
June, 1967—1,000 gallons 3% formalin applied to area of positive depth samples.						
1967	72	0	0	72	0	0
1968*	7	0	0	27	2	7
1968†	10	0	0	—	—	—

* Isolations made from soil excavated for bridge foundation.
† Surface samples from along side completed bridge and road.

ples continued to be positive. Following the application of 31,500 gallons of 3% formalin in May, 1966, three surface and seven depth samples were found to be positive during the remainder of that year. The three positive surface samples were from areas in which depth samples were positive on earlier collections. In the early part of 1967, samples from the surface were negative, and one positive depth sample was obtained. Following the third application of 1,000 gallons of formalin to the positive foci on the site in June, 1967, all surface and depth samples remained negative for the remainder of that year. During excavation for the bridge foundation in January, 1968, two of twenty-seven soil specimens were positive for *H. capsulatum*. Surface samples collected after completion of the bridge were negative for the fungus.

The results of decontamination of the 7.5-acre site at Mexico, Missouri, are shown in Table 24-II. A total of 333,000 gallons of 3% formalin were applied to the area, and this was sufficient to thoroughly saturate the soil. The soil samples collected prior to decontamination revealed the presence of the fungus, but surface and depth samples collected since the application of the chemical have been negative for *H. capsulatum*.

Discussion

A summary of the various chemicals and procedures reported in the literature for controlling *H. capsulatum* in the soil is shown in Table 24-III. Emmons and Piggott (1963) attempted control by using sulfur as a soil conditioner, hoping that it would change the pH of the soil or act as a fungistatic agent, but this attempt was unsuccessful. They also studied the effect of an overlay with negative soil, a maneuver which did eliminate the organism from that part of the site during the period studied. In addition, biological control methods have been attempted. One method consisted of seeding the positive area with several strains of *Streptomyces* which had produced zones

TABLE 24-II

Isolation of *Histoplasma capsulatum* From Epidemic Site, Mexico, Missouri 1959–1969

Years Sampled	Surface Samples			Depth Samples		
	Total	Positive		Total	Positive	
		Number	Percent		Number	Percent
1959–1966	831	467	56	149	53	36
April 1966, 333,000 gallons 3% formalin applied.						
1966	103	0	0	29	0	0
1967	41	0	0	12	0	0
1968	20	0	0	4	0	0
1969	20	0	0	4	0	0

of inhibition against *H. capsulatum in vitro.* A second approach was an attempt to alter the microflora of the sites by the addition of chitin in an effort to increase the prevalence of chitinolytic fungi, on the theory that their presence might be antagonistic to *H. capsulatum.* They had partial success in establishing the *Streptomyces,* but neither this nor the addition of chitin to the soil had any effect on *H. capsulatum.* They did successfully eradicate *H. capsulatum* from a site by using pentachlorophenol in fuel oil.

TABLE 24-III

Chemicals and Procedures Tested for the Control of *Histoplasma capsulatum* in soil

Investigators	Chemical or Procedure	Where Tested
Emmons and Piggott (1963)	Physical changes Biological control *Streptomyces* Chitin Chemical Pentachlorophenol Sulfur	Epidemic site
Smith, Furcolow and Tosh (1964)	Physical changes Chemicals Orthocide D-D SD345 Beta-propiolactone	Epidemic site (bird roost).
Tosh, Weeks, Pfeiffer, Hendricks and Chin (1966)	Chemicals Cresol compound Formalin	Laboratory and epidemic site (bird roost).
Tosh, Weeks, Pfeiffer, Hendricks, Greer and Chin (1967)	Chemical Formalin	Epidemic Site (bird roost)

Smith, Furcolow and Tosh (1964) attempted control by utilizing physical changes in the environment and the application of liquid fungicidal agents to the surface of the positive site. The physical changes consisted of clearing the area of brush and large trees, allowing the sunlight to penetrate to the soil surface, and planting grass to help reduce the dust arising from the site and to create biological competition unfavorable to the fungus. Four different chemicals were applied to the surface of designated plots within the site. Three of the fungicides were sprayed onto the surface and were followed by applications of water to increase penetration. The fourth chemical was applied and the area covered with plastic sheets to enhance its action.

Their attempts to control *H. capsulatum* by physical changes in the site and the application of fungicidal chemicals were not effective. They were able to reduce the number of isolates of *H. capsulatum* by an overlay of positive soil with negative soil, but this effect was only temporary.

Tosh, Weeks, Pfeiffer, Hendricks and Chin (1966) reported laboratory and limited field trials using various solutions of formalin or cresol compound for the control of *H. capsulatum.* In the laboratory, 1%, 3%, and 5%

concentrations of the chemicals were applied to soils seeded with *H. capsu-latum*, to soil in which the organism was growing, and to naturally infected soil from a positive site. Field experiments consisted of a study of eight plots, measuring 5 × 5 feet square, situated in a large epidemic site. Under laboratory conditions, they found that a 3 or 5 percent solution of the chemicals would destroy the organism when applied to the soil in which it was growing or into which it had been inoculated. In field tests, applications of these chemicals reduced significantly the frequency with which the fungus could be isolated from the positive site.

Tosh *et al.* (1967) later reported attempts to control *H. capsulatum* in a 5-acre site using a 3% formalin solution. Although the surface became negative for *H. capsulatum*, soil samples taken at a depth of six inches were occasionally positive. Since then studies on the site have continued, and two other applications of 3% formalin have been made to the site. Following the last application, all surface and depth samples were negative until the construction of a bridge and road across the site. At that time, composite soil samples taken from material excavated down to a depth of five feet did reveal the presence of the fungus. This probably represented detection of viable spores that had been buried during the leveling of the site during initial treatment.

The application of 3% formalin to the 7.5-acre positive site in Mexico, Missouri, appears to have successfully eliminated the fungus from the site. The ease of decontamination of this site as compared to that in Mason City was probably due to the physical characteristics of the site. The site in Mexico, Missouri, consisted of fertile soil covered with grass and effective penetration of the chemical seemed to occur. In Mason City, the site was filled with an extensive amount of debris consisting of pieces of concrete and rock which prevented uniform penetration of the chemical.

The agents which have resulted in effective control of *H. capsulatum* in epidemic foci include pentachlorophenol in fuel oil, cresol, and formalin. As has been stated by Smith *et al.* (1964), the ideal agent for control is one that destroys the organism, is relatively nontoxic to animals, humans, and vegetation, and is relatively inexpensive and easy to apply. The relative importance of these factors depends upon the area in which control is to be attempted. In some areas, such as chicken houses, barns, and silos, where growth of vegetation after treatment is not a factor, solutions of pentachlorophenol in fuel oil or 3% cresol solution would be indicated, since both would be effective in controlling the organism and the nature of the chemicals would provide prolonged residual action. Pentachlorophenol is the least desirable, since it is suspended in a flammable base. In the treatment of larger areas, and of those in which the quick return of vegetation is desired, the use of 3% formalin would be indicated. This chemical solution comes close to meeting the requirements for the ideal agent. Formalin is relatively inexpensive in large quantities, it is an effective contact fungicide, and it is relatively nontoxic to the individuals applying it.

References

D'Alessio, D.J., Heeren, R.H., Hendricks, S.L., Ogilvie, P. and Furcolow, M.L. (1965). A starling roost as the source of urban epidemic histoplasmosis in an area of low incidence. *Amer. Rev. Resp. Dis.,* 92:725-731.

Emmons, C.W. and Piggott, W.R. (1963). Eradication of *Histoplasma capsulatum* from soil. *Mycologia,* 55:521-527.

Furcolow, M.L., Tosh, F.E., Larsh, H.W., Lynch, H.J., Jr. and Shaw, G. (1961). The emerging pattern of urban histoplasmosis: Studies on an epidemic in Mexico, Missouri. *New Eng. J. Med.,* 264:1226-1230.

Smith, C.D., Furcolow, M.L. and Tosh, F.E. (1964). Attempts to eliminate *Histoplasma capsulatum* from soil. *Amer. J. Hyg.,* 79:170-180.

Tosh, F.E., Doto, I.L., D'Alessio, D.J., Medeiros, A.A., Hendricks, S.L. and Chin, T.D.Y. (1966). The second of two epidemics of histoplasmosis resulting from work on the same starling roost. *Amer. Rev. Resp. Dis.,* 94:406-413.

Tosh, F.E., Weeks, R.J., Pfeiffer, F.R., Hendricks, S.L. and Chin, T.D.Y. (1966a). Chemical decontamination of soil containing *Histoplasma capsulatum. Amer. J. Epidem.,* 83:262-270.

Tosh, F.E., Weeks, R.J., Pfeiffer, F.R., Hendricks, S.L., Greer, D.L. and Chin, T.D.Y. (1967). The use of formalin to kill *Histoplasma capsulatum* at an epidemic site. *Amer. J. Epidem.,* 85:259-265.

Weeks, R.J., Hendricks, S.L. and Tosh, F.E. (1969). Unpublished data.

Part IV
Clinical and Pathological Aspects

Chapter 25

Pulmonary Histoplasmosis

N. ALEXANDER SALIBA

ABSTRACT

The principal types of pulmonary histoplasmosis, that is, acute, disseminated, and chronic, are briefly outlined. The differential diagnosis includes many other types of pulmonary infections, particularly tuberculosis, but also fungal disease, sarcoidosis, carcinoma, pneumonia, occupational diseases, and so on. It is pointed out that the diagnosis of chronic pulmonary histoplasmosis is being increasingly made, that screening procedures with skin tests and serologic studies are very useful, and that a high index of suspicion is essential.

Histoplasmosis may coexist with tuberculosis, making the diagnosis somewhat more difficult. The need for diagnostic efforts in the chronic pulmonary and disseminated types is emphasized because of the relatively poor prognosis without specific treatment.

HISTOPLASMOSIS is now recognized in many countries, but it has been increasingly diagnosed in its various forms in the United States since the 1950's (Furcolow, 1958). Chronic pulmonary histoplasmosis was described by Bunnell and Furcolow in 1948, and by 1953 only eleven cases of cavitary pulmonary histoplasmosis were collected from the literature (Sutliff, Hughes, Ulrich and Burkett, 1953). It is evident that in endemic areas the higher the index of suspicion on the part of physicians, the more frequently is the diagnosis made.

We have been interested in the systemic mycoses during the past eleven years because Kentucky is well within the endemic area of histoplasmosis and blastomycosis in the United States. We have participated in a United States Public Health Service Mycoses Cooperative Study, and in over nine hundred cases of histoplasmosis in the study the predominant type has been chronic cavitary, (Table 25-I). All our inpatients and many outpatients are screened with skin-testing and complement fixation examinations. In our hospital we have diagnosed approximately 130 cases of histoplasmosis, proved either by sputum culture or tissue studies; and here again, most of them were of the chronic pulmonary cavitary type. There was a second group of some thirty-six patients who were also considered highly suspicious for histoplasmosis. These were patients with no other confirmed diagnosis, tuberculosis was ruled out, they had high complement fixation titers, and usually either exacerbation of symptoms, or deterioration by chest x-ray over a period of follow-up. An example of this type of patient is seen in Figure 25-1.

TABLE 25-I

Mycotic Diseases
Cases on Record at Kansas City Field Station
(Cooperative Study)

Disease	Total to 8–31–67	New Cases Since 8–31–67	Total to 8–31–68
Histoplasmosis	851	53	904
Blastomycosis	88	7	95
Coccidioicomycosis	99	10	109
Cryptococcosis	65	7	72
Sporotrichosis	23	5	28
Aspergillosis	33	23	56
Other	20	4	24
Total	1179	109	1288

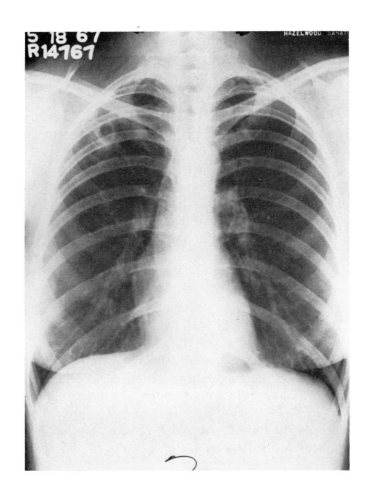

Clinical Notes

The principal types of pulmonary histoplasmosis are as follows.

Acute Pulmonary Form

This often presents as an upper respiratory infection and may be described as a "prolonged cold," an influenza-like illness that may progress to actual pneumonitis. Radiologically the primary infection may present with hilar adenopathy, as in the case of tuberculosis, or by multiple pulmonary lesions scattered through both lung fields. (Figs. 25-2, 25-3).

Disseminated Variety

The disease process may be slowly progressive following dissemination by the blood stream and spread to various organs, or it may be fulminating with rapid clinical deterioration resulting in death (Saliba and Anderson, 1967). Many of these cases may be indistinguishable from miliary tuberculosis, and the condition is characterized by fever and hepatosplenamegaly. We had a young man who had at least four episodes of hematogenous dissemination of histoplasmosis since 1962. He responded rapidly to amphotericin B treatment on each occasion.

Chronic Cavitary Pulmonary Histoplasmosis

The disease process may be the result of the initial pulmonary infection that has not been arrested but has become progressive with increased involvement of lung parenchyma over a period of months or years. However, more frequently, this type probably represents a reinfection type of histoplasmosis as in the case of tuberculosis. Cavitation may involve a segment, a lobe, or practically an entire lung (Fig. 25-4). The disease is frequently bilateral (Fig. 25-5) and besides cavitation may present with extensive infiltration, fibrosis, and calcification. Complicating bronchiectasis may also be encountered. Extensive fibrotic and calcific changes in the mediastinum are

---

←◀◀◀

FIGURE 25-1. This twenty-nine-year-old white female (a packer and weigher) was admitted 3-16-67 with moderate disease. Complement fixation was positive for histoplasmosis: H 1, 1:16; H 2, 1:32. Her sputum cultures for AFB, and fungi were reported negative. In the next few weeks the cavitation increased in size in spite of an initial trial of antituberculous drugs. She was then given 480 mg I.V. amphotericin B over a four-week period. She is doing well, symptom free, with persisting evidence of cavity closure. In October, 1968, her CF was 1:8, H 1; 1:8, H 2.

sometimes the result of chronic pulmonary histoplasmosis and may have undesirable sequelae.

Another variety of chronic pulmonary histoplasmosis is the coin lesion or
histoplasmoma, which at best can only be suspected because of the difficulty
of differentiating it from a carcinoma or some other type of granuloma. The

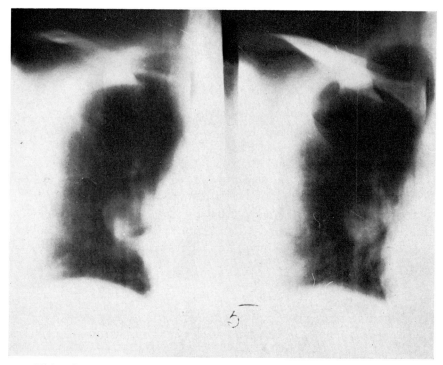

FIGURE 25-2. This twenty-three-year-old white female, an employee of our hospital,
complained of a "protracted cold," with cough and occasional right-sided pleurisy in
September, 1959. There was no other relevant history. On chest x-ray and tomograms
right hilar adenopathy was found. Her purified protein derivitive (PPD) and histoplasmin skin tests were strongly positive at this time; but there was a question as to whether
the tuberculin skin test had also been positive a few years previously. Complement
fixation was positive for histoplasmosis, 1:16 antigen one; 1:128, antigen two. A thoracotomy was advised by the surgeon who removed a mass of caseonecrotic glands from
the hilar area. Tissue stains were negative for mycobacteria but positive for *H. capsulatum*. She is doing well and the last CF about one year ago was negative.

FIGURE 25-3. This nineteen-year-old white female, a student nurse, had a history of
mild recurring upper respiratory infections in April, 1963. Her PPD was negative,
histoplasmin 20 mm. Complement fixation was positive for histoplasmosis: H 2, 1:16,
B 1, 1:8. Chest x-ray showed five nodules scattered in both lungs, but more so on the
right. On follow-up till 1965 these became progressively more calcified, and she had
become symptom free. In 1965 her CF was H 1, 1:8; H 2, 1:16; Blasto 1, 1:8. (In December, 1963, the readings were H 1, 1:16; H 2, 1:32; Blasto 1, 1:8.)

diagnosis is therefore usually made following resection, and those patients having exploratory surgery or biopsy without a known diagnosis should have tissue cultures for fungi and special stains, particularly the methenamine silver stain.

Not infrequently histoplasmosis may be associated with tuberculosis and occasionally with other fungal infections or carcinoma. When histoplasmosis is associated with tuberculosis, these infections may run concurrently, or one of these diseases may precede or follow the other, as reported by Goodwin, Snell, Hubbard and Terry (1967), and Beatty and Saliba (1963). When both diseases run concurrently, multiple positive cultures can usually be isolated. On the other hand, one disease entity, the primary active process, may cause the shedding of a few organisms of the secondary process through the breakdown of a dormant focus without fully reactivating the disease. Eighteen cases of histoplasmosis associated with tuberculosis have been documented at District Two Hospital as seen in Table 25-II. There were seventeen males and one female, and all but two had far advanced pathology.

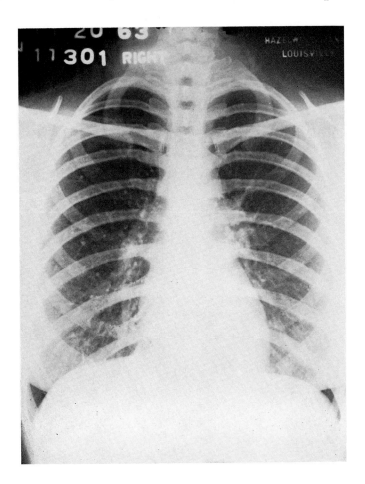

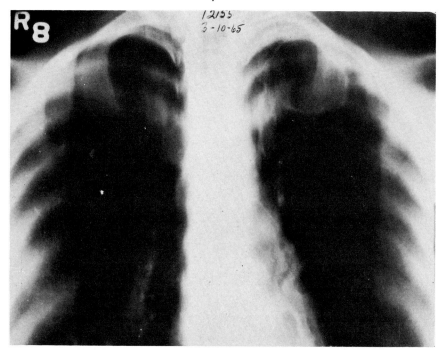

FIGURE 25-4. This seventeen-year-old white female, a student, was admitted 11-17-64 with complaints of a persisting cough and weight loss. Her chest x-ray showed cavitary disease in the left upper lobe. Her PPD and histoplasmin skin tests were positive; compliment fixation on 12-11-64 was H 1, 1:32; H 2, 1:64. She received a trial of antituberculous chemotherapy, but the cultures for AFB and fungi returned negative. Resection of the apicoposterior segment of left upper lung was therefore carried out under coverage of amphotericin B treatment. The tissue stains and culture were positive for *H. capsulatum*. When last seen December, 1968, she was doing well, and her chest x-ray showed no recurrence.

When histoplasmosis is associated with tuberculosis, there is a danger that histoplasmosis may be missed because the diagnosis of tuberculosis is more easily made by sputum smears and cultural studies (Fig. 25-6). Therefore,

TABLE 25-II

Histoplasmosis Associated With Tuberculosis
(Hazelwood Hospital)

	No. of Cases	Age	Sex		Extent of Disease		Dead Since Diagnosis
			M	F	MA	FA	
Concurrent							
Histoplasmosis and TB	6	34–72	6	0	1	5	3
Histoplasmosis preceded TB	4	36–68	4	0	0	4	1
TB preceded Histoplasmosis	8	44–69	7	1	1	7	1
Total	18		17	1	2	16	5

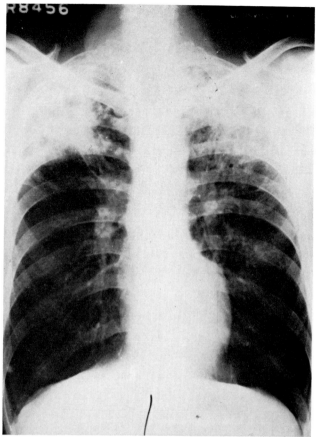

FIGURE 25-5. This forty-three-year-old white male (truck driver) was first admitted 7-13-60 with bilateral infiltrative and fibrocavitary disease on chest x-ray. This was confirmed to be histoplasmosis by several sputum cultures. He received 2700 mg amphotericin B with overall clinical and radiological improvement. He relapsed with symptomatic and x-ray deterioration in 1964 and 1965, and received approximately 2 gm and 1 gm amphotericin B, respectively. There was again overall improvement, although sputum cultures had remained negative. Between 1965 to 1967 he received three additional courses amphotericin B, 0.5 gm each. He has remained clinically and radiologically stable when last seen 8-18-69.

the importance of fungal serologic studies cannot be overemphasized, as these could alert the physician to the possibility of a second pathologic process.

Discussion

Chronic pulmonary histoplasmosis is more predominant in the older age white male. The presenting signs and symptoms are indistinguishable from

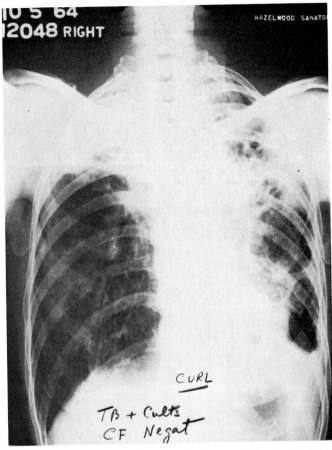

FIGURE 25-6. A sixty-nine-year-old white female (housewife) admitted 10-5-64 with far advanced pulmonary tuberculosis and positive sputum smears and cultures for AFB. She improved clinically on antituberculous chemotherapy, the sputum converting in December, 1964. She was readmitted in October, 1966, and was then found to have active histoplasmosis with positive sputa. Tuberculosis status remained negative. She continued antituberculosis drugs and received 1,490 mg amphotericin B. She improved. She died in another hospital in April, 1968, apparently of "hepatic abscess and old fibrocaseous tuberculosis."

those of other chronic pulmonary infections, and the differential diagnosis includes, besides tuberculosis, other mycoses, sarcoidosis, carcinoma, certain occupational diseases, and others. Chronic cavitary histoplasmosis mimics tuberculosis extremely well, and in the past was quite often misdiagnosed for tuberculosis in the absence of bacteriologic confirmation (Saliba and Beatty, 1960; Furcolow, Brasher, 1956). Chick (1962) has reemphasized the presenting clinical aspects of some of these fungal infections in a series of cases that were initially mistaken for other more common diseases.

Chronic pulmonary histoplasmosis usually pursues a progressive course with partial remissions, and over a period of years there is increasing disability and death in many cases (Rubin, Furcolow, Yates and Brasher, 1959). In the United States Public Health Service Mycoses Cooperative Study (Furcolow, 1963), a group of such patients was treated with amphotericin B and followed for a number of years. These patients had an overall better prognosis than a second group who had received no specific treatment, either because they refused treatment or because they were diagnosed prior to amphotericin B.

Of the three principal types of pulmonary histoplasmosis, that is, acute pulmonary, chronic pulmonary, and disseminated, the chronic pulmonary and disseminated forms carry the worst prognosis with regard to progressive disability or mortality. Therefore, specific medical and surgical treatment is often indicated. In the disseminated form there can be a 70 to 80 percent mortality without treatment. The acute pulmonary form is usually benign and frequently exhibits spontaneous remission, but in cases of prolonged illness treatment may also be indicated.

The relapse rate among patients with chronic pulmonary histoplasmosis is estimated at approximately 5 percent per year, most of these occurring during the first five years. The predisposing factors for such relapses have not yet been defined, and there is much to be learned from the pursuit of research on histoplasmosis in all its aspects.

References

Beatty, O.A. and Saliba, N.A. (1963). Co-existing pulmonary fungus infection and tuberculosis at District Two State Hospital. *Kentucky Med. J.*, *61*:502.

Bunnell, I.L. and Furcolow, M.L. (1948). A report of ten proven cases of histoplasmosis. *Public Health Rep.*, *63*:299.

Chick, E.W. (1962). Pulmonary fungal infections simulating and misdiagnosed as other diseases. *Amer. Rev. Resp. Dis.*, *85*:702.

Furcolow, M.L. (1958). Histoplasmosis. *G.P.*, *18*:117.

Furcolow, M.L. (1963). U. S. Public Health Service Cooperative Mycoses Study, comparison of treated and untreated severe histoplasmosis, *J.A.M.A.*, *183*:823.

Furcolow, M.L. and Brasher, C.A. (1956). Chronic progressive (cavitary) histoplasmosis as a problem in tuberculosis sanatoriums, *Amer. Rev. Tuberc.*, *73*:609.

Goodwin, R.A., Snell, J.D., Hubbard, W.W. and Terry, R.T. (1967). Relationships in combined pulmonary infections with *Histoplasma capsulatum* and *Mycobacterium tuberculosis*. *Amer. Rev. Resp. Dis.*, *96*:990.

Rubin, H., Furcolow, M.L., Yates, J.L. and Brasher, C.A. (1959). The course and prognosis of histoplasmosis. *Amer. J. Med.*, *27*:278.

Saliba, N.A. and Anderson, W.H. (1967). Acute disseminated histoplasmosis. *Amer. Rev. Resp. Dis.*, *95*:94.

Saliba, N.A. and Beatty, O.A. (1960). Pulmonary histoplasmosis. *J.A.M.A.*, *173*:902.

Sutliff, W.D., Hughes, F., Ulrich, E. and Burkett, L.L. (1953). Active chronic pulmonary histoplasmosis. *Arch. Intern. Med.*, *92*:571.

Chapter 26

Progressive Disseminated Histoplasmosis

PRATHAPCHANDRA A. REDDY

ABSTRACT

This study of twenty-five adult patients illustrates the diverse manifestations of progressive disseminated histoplasmosis and the diagnostic dilemma the disease may produce. The progressive nature and serious prognostic import are revealed by the followup of untreated patients with 100 percent mortality. Amphotericin B therapy, when instituted early, is highly efficacious in reducing the mortality.

U SUALLY considered a pulmonary infection, histoplasmosis can involve every organ in the body, causing a wide disease spectrum similar to that of tuberculosis. There is no single, generally accepted, clinical classification of *Histoplasma capsulatum* infection. Furcolow (1960) offered a broad classification and Reddy, Gorelick, Brasher and Larsh (1969) modified classification in order to include the various clinical forms. From the several published reports of Furcolow and Brasher (1956), Baum and Schwarz (1958) and Cooperative Mycoses Study (1961), it is quite clear that the course is progressive and carries a serious prognosis in disseminated and cavitary forms of histoplasmosis.

The purpose of this presentation is to describe the clinical and pathological manifestations of progressive disseminated histoplasmosis along with emphasis on recognition and prognosis in the treated and untreated groups of patients. We prefer to apply the term *progressive disseminated histoplasmosis*, which is more descriptive than the designations *chronic disseminated* and *extrapulmonary*, as various organs in addition to pulmonary tissue are involved.

Material and Methods

At the Missouri State Sanatorium, a center for chest diseases, 530 patients were diagnosed as having active histoplasmosis from January, 1955, to December, 1968. Among these, 25 were found to have progressive disseminated histoplasmosis. This study includes adults aged sixteen to seventy-five, with an average range of fifty three years. Males predominate with a ratio of 12:1. Sixty percent (60%) of the group were farmers or lived on farms for many years. Table 26-I summarizes the various organ involvement in twenty-five patients. Demonstration of *H. capsulatum* in extrapulmonary organs was a prerequisite for inclusion in this study.

TABLE 26-I

Organ Involvement in Twenty-five Patients with
Progressive Disseminated Histoplasmosis

Organ	No. Patients	Presenting Area
Oral cavity	5	Tongue, soft palate, glottis, epiglottis, left false cord, ventricle
Gastrointestinal tract	5	Stomach, ileum, jejunum, cecum, colon, mesenteric glands, peritoneum
Liver	3	
Spleen	6	
Genitourinary tract	6	Urine, kidney, bladder, prostate
Heart and great vessels	2	Pericardial effusion
Blood and bone marrow	19	Anemia, leukopenia, thrombocytopenia
Adrenal glands	8	
Lymph nodes	15	Mesenteric, inguinal, cervical and sub-mandibular glands
Skin	1	Subcutaneous abscess

Clinical Manifestations

The common presenting symptoms were mild fever, cough, dyspnea, fatigue, weakness, anorexia and weight loss. Other features were related to the involved organ system.

Five patients with lesions of the oral cavity presented painful ulceration, pain on swallowing, difficulty in speech and hoarseness. All the five patients were later proven to have disseminated form of the disease.

Gastrointestinal involvement was seen in five patients. Anorexia, nausea, and abdominal pain were the common symptoms. Severe hematemesis and melena were present in one patient with gastric histoplasmosis. Two patients had signs of an acute abdomen. At laparotomy, one of them had a tumorlike mass of the cecum; the other, a constricting lesion of the small bowel. One patient developed signs of peritonitis and died shortly after admission. At time of necropsy, the infection had invaded peritoneum, mesenteric glands, liver, spleen, and adrenal glands.

Adrenal involvement in disseminated histoplasmosis is reported to be frequent. Eight out of nine autopsied cases in this series had adrenal lesions. Clinical features include fatigue, hyponatremia, hypotension, hyperpigmentation, decreased excretion of twenty-four-hour urinary 17-hydroxy and ketogenic steroids and poor response to intravenous adrenocorticotropic hormone (ACTH) test.

Hepatic involvement with histoplasmosis is reported to be frequent and Silverman *et al.* (1955) recommended liver biopsy as a useful diagnostic aid. Although hepatosplenomegaly were present in eleven cases, only three patients had involvement of liver as shown at necropsy. Splenic involvement was demonstrated in six cases.

Renal histoplasmosis developed in only one patient, although *Histoplasma* organisms were isolated from urine cultures in six cases. One patient had vesical and prostatic involvement.

Anemia of less than 10 gms of hemoglobin occurred in ten patients. One patient had severe leukopenia; another patient with thrombocytopenia had symptomatic purpura. Bone marrow cultures for *H. capsulatum* were positive in fifteen cases.

In one patient, multiple subcutaneous abscesses were distributed over the scalp, shoulders, chest wall and right hand. *H. capsulatum* was cultured from the material of the abscess wall, drainage fluid, blood, and bone marrow.

Pathogenesis

Most investigators believe that the natural route of infection is through the respiratory tract by inhalation of spores. Ritter (1954) and Gordon (1952), however, suggest that the spores may gain entry to the gastrointestinal tract from drinking contaminated water. This theory is substantiated in one of our patients who had dissemination to bone marrow, peritonium, mesenteric glands, liver, spleen, and adrenals. Meticulous examination of the lungs at necropsy disclosed no lesions to suggest active or healed *Histoplasma* infection. Whichever the portal of infection, when the local host resistance is overcome, hematogenous dissemination may occur. No accurate incidence of this event is available. The role of predisposing factors in development of opportunistic fungus infections is well established. Furcolow (1962) has discussed the term *opportunism* as applied to the pathogenic fungi, which takes on a different significance when applied to the nonpathogenic fungi. He has also stressed that such predisposing factors in the very young and very old may modify a mild or asymptomatic infection to a severe and serious form of the disease. Frenkel (1962) has shown in animal experiments that corticosteroids may convert a benign fungus infection into a severe, fatal form. Nineteen of our patients with disseminated histoplasmosis had recognizable predisposing factors.

Treatment and Prognosis

The outcome of this serious form of disease is directly related to therapy. Amphotericin B is currently the preferred drug in treatment of histoplasmosis. Our trials and failures with several antifungal agents have been reviewed by Yates, Atay, Langeluttig, Brasher and Furcolow (1960).

Mode of therapy and the follow-up on twenty-five patients in this series are listed in Table 26-II. The grave prognosis of progressive disseminated histoplasmosis is demonstrated by the uniformly fatal outcome in Group IV patients who received no therapy and Group III patients whose therapy was incomplete.

TABLE 26-II

Analysis of Outcome in Twenty-Five Patients with Progressive Disseminated Histoplasmosis

Amphotericin B	No. of Cases	Improved	Average Follow-up (months)	Dead No. (%)	Histoplasmosis-Dead No. (%)
Adequate therapy (Group I)	14	12 (85%)	54	4 (29)	1 (7)
Inadequate therapy (Group II)	5	2 (40%)	16	3 (60)	2 (40)
Incomplete therapy (Group III)	3	None	0	3 (100)	Histoplasmosis 1 Problem 1 (100)
No amphotericin B therapy (Group IV)	3	0	0–2	3 (100)	3 (100)

The efficacy of amphotericin is borne out by the follow-up on fourteen patients who received adequate dosage of the drug. Only one patient in this group died as a result of histoplasmosis. There was a striking reduction in mortality rate to 7 percent in this almost universally fatal disease when therapy was instituted early.

References

Baum, G.L. and Schwarz, J. (1958). Pulmonary histoplasmosis. *New Eng. J. Med., 258:* 677-684.

Cooperative Mycosis Study (1961). Course and prognosis of untreated histoplasmosis. *J.A.M.A., 177:*292-296.

Gordon, M.A., Ajello, L., Georg, L.K. and Zeidberg, L.D. (1952). *Microsporum gypseum* and *Histoplasma capsulatum* spores in soil and water. *Science, 116:*208-213.

Frenkel, J.K. (1962). Role of corticosteroids as predisposing factors in fungal diseases. *Lab. Invest., 11:*1192-1208.

Furcolow, M.L. and Brasher, C.A. (1956). Chronic progressive (cavitary) histoplasmosis as a problem in tuberculosis sanatoria. *Amer. Rev. Tuberc. Pulmon. Dise., 73:*609-619.

Furcolow, M.L. (1960). Clinical types of histoplasmosis. In Sweany, H.C. (Ed). *Histoplasmosis,* Springfield, Thomas, pp.382-404.

Furcolow, M.D. (1962). Opportunism in histoplasmosis. *Lab. Invest., 11:*1134-1139.

Reddy, P.A., Gorelick, D.F., Brasher, C.A. and Larsh, H. (1970). Progressive disseminated histoplasmosis as seen in adults. *Amer. J. Med.* 48:629-635.

Ritter, C. (1954). Studies of the viability of *Histoplasma capsulatum* in tap water. *Amer. J. Public Health,* 44:1299-1304.

Silverman, F.N., Schwarz, J., Lahey, M.E. and Carson, R.P. (1955). *Amer. J. Med.,* 19:410-459.

Yates, J.L., Atay, M.N., Langeluttig, H.V., Brasher, C.A. and Furcolow, M.L. (1960). Experience with amphotericin in the therapy of histoplasmosis. *Dis. Chest,* 37:144-159.

Chapter 27

Presumed Histoplasmic Choroiditis:
A Possible Late Manifestation of
Benign Disease

DAN B. JONES

ABSTRACT

In 1960, Woods and Wahlen first proposed *Histoplasma capsulatum* as the probable etiological agent for a characteristic form of posterior uveitis in man. This now consists of a normal anterior segment, clear vitreous, multiple discrete peripheral and posterior choroidal lesions, peripapillary scarring, and a hemorrhagic disciform macular lesion in patients with some suggestion, usually histoplasmin hypersensitivity, of previous histoplasmosis. Although there is a large body of clinical, epidemiological, pathological, and experimental evidence supporting the hypothesis that *H. capsulatum* produces this entity, the fungus has never been identified in a human eye with presumed histoplasmic choroiditis.

PRESUMED histoplasmic choroiditis is a collection of ophthalmoscopically similar fundus lesions in patients with some suggestion, usually histoplasmin hypersensitivity, of previous infection with *Histoplasma capsulatum*. During the past ten years it has become generally accepted among ophthalmologists as a distinct entity and has served as a useful category for posterior uveal tract disease. Despite the large body of circumstantial evidence linking this ocular lesion complex with histoplasmosis, *H. capsulatum* has never been identified in a human eye with the entity. My purpose is to review the clinical, epidemiological, pathological, and experimental evidence in support of the hypothesis that histoplasmosis produces a specific form of uveitis.

Background

In 1942, Reid, Scherer, Herbut and Irving (1942) described "small, white irregular areas surrounded by hemorrhages . . . not unlike tubercles" in a fatal case of disseminated histoplasmosis. Unfortunately the eyes were not examined histopathologically. In 1949, Day (1949) suggested that some cases of granulomatous uveitis might be due to ocular infection with *H. cap-*

NOTE. Supported in part by a U.S. Public Health Service grant NB-06959 from the National Institute of Neurological Diseases and Blindness, National Institutes of Health, Bethesda, Maryland, and in part by an unrestricted grant from Research to Prevent Blindness.

sulatum because of its ability to produce a mild, subclinical granulomatous disease. He found a higher percentage of histoplasmin reactors among a small number of unselected cases of uveitis than among other hospitalized eye patients, and he produced a progressive granulomatous uveitis in rabbits with the mycelial phase of the organism. In 1951, Krause and Hopkins (1951) described a focal nodular fundus lesion in a young housewife with histoplasmin reactivity, positive complement fixation test, tuberculin anergy, and discrete pulmonary calcifications. The appearance of fresh macular hemorrhages and a drop in visual acuity following the histoplasmin skin test were offered as definite evidence of *H. capsulatum* causing the choroiditis.

In 1960, Woods and Wahlen (1960) produced the first definitive study proposing this fungus as the agent of a distinct ocular entity. On the basis of these earlier reports and the observation of a peculiar choroidal lesion in a patient with a severe histoplasmin reaction, they began to include histoplasmin skin testing in the survey of uveitis patients at the Wilmer Institute in 1951. The rapid succession of three clinically similar cases with positive histoplasmin tests, pulmonary calcifications, and tuberculin anergy in 1958 prompted them to analyze their previous data. They found 62 histoplasmin reactors among 186 patients (33%) with granulomatous uveitis as compared to 16 positive reactors among 107 patients (15%) with nongranulomatous uveitis. More striking was the similarity of the ophthalmoscopic findings in all nine patients in a group categorized by histoplasmin reactivity, tuberculin anergy, and pulmonary calcifications. The ocular lesions consisted of peripheral discrete spots of atrophic choroiditis and macular subretinal cysts surrounded by serous exudate with occasional hemorrhage. One patient developed a fresh macular hemorrhage and reactivation of a nasal choroidal lesion twenty-four hours after skin testing. Ten of the remaining 53 skin test reactors in the granulomatous group shared the same clinical picture with less convincing other evidence of previous histoplasmosis.

Woods and Wahlen theorized that small choroidal granulomas were formed during the generalized parasitemia of the initial phase of benign histoplasmosis. The lesions healed and became atrophic with either death or encapsulation of the spores. They thought that the macular lesions were caused by late, atypical granulomatous lesions or hypersensitivity reactions. The stimulus for these reactions might be the exacerbation of peripheral choroidal lesions or remote, nonocular foci.

Additional Studies

The most extensive epidemiological test of the hypothesis that *H. capsulatum* produces a characteristic uveitis was reported by Van Metre and Maumenee in 1964 (1964). They classified 251 consecutive cases of uveitis at the Johns Hopkins Hospital into ten groups on the basis of the morphology of

TABLE 27-I

Incidence of Additional Factors in Patients With and Without the
Hypothetical Histoplasmosis Ocular Lesion

Factor	Hypothetical Histoplasmosis Ocular Lesion		Other Forms of Uveitis	
	Number	Percent	Number	Percent
Histoplasmin skin-test positive	57/61	93	48/190	25
Histoplasmosis complement fixation test positive	9/56	16	5/151	3
Residence for 6 months or longer in Illinois, Ohio, Indiana, Kentucky, Tennessee, or Misourri	27/61	44	33/182	18
Fibrocalcific lesions in chest x-ray	47/52	90	90/166	54

From Van Metre and Maumenee, 1964.

the ocular lesions. Following the clinical features which had been outlined by Woods and Wahlen (1960), they collected sixty-one patients with the "hypothetical histoplasmosis lesion" and compared this group to the others on the basis of histoplasmin reaction, positive complement fixation test, residence for six months or longer in a histoplasmosis endemic state (Missouri, Illinois, Indiana, Ohio, Kentucky, and Tennessee), and fibrocalcific lesions in chest roentgenograms. There was a statistically significantly higher incidence of these factors in the patients with the hypothetical ocular lesion of histoplasmosis than in those with other lesions (Table 27-I).

Others have added to the circumstantial evidence. The incidence of positive histoplasmin skin tests in reported series of presumed histoplasmic choroiditis has varied from 89 percent (Schlaegel, Weber, Helveston and Kenney, 1967) to 100 percent (Suie, Rheins and Makley, 1965) (Table 27-II). Suie *et al.* (1965) found 100 percent (79/79) histoplasmin reactors and 68 percent (23/34) positive complement fixation tests among patients with the typical ocular lesions, as compared to 36 percent (39/109) and 38 percent

TABLE 27-II

Results of Histoplasmin Skin Tests and Complement Fixation Tests in
Reported Series of Presumed Histoplasmic Choroiditis

Source	Positive Histoplasmin Skin Test		Positive Histoplasmic Complement Fixation Test	
	Number	Percent	Number	Percent
Van Metre and Maumenee (1964)	57/61	93	9/56	16
Suie *et al.* (1965)	79/79	100	23/34	68
Schlaegel *et al.* (1967)	50/56	89	—	—
Krill *et al.* (1969)	38/42	90	11/33	33

(30/78), respectively, in other uveitis cases. Presumed histoplasmic choroiditis accounted for 30 percent and 22 percent of consecutively studied uveitis cases in clinics serving histoplasmosis endemic areas in Columbus, Ohio (Suie *et al.*, 1965), and Indianapolis (Schlaegel *et al.*, 1967), whereas ophthalmologists in the low incidence areas in New York, San Francisco, and Seattle have identified the entity infrequently (Schlaegel *et al.*, 1967). It has not been recognized in uveitis clinics in England (Perkins, 1968) or Switzerland (Witmer, 1968) where pulmonary histoplasmosis is virtually nonexistent.

Clinical Picture

The characteristic clinical picture of presumed histoplasmic choroiditis consists of a normal anterior segment, clear vitreous, multiple discrete choroidal lesions, peripapillary scarring, and serous or hemorrhagic detachment

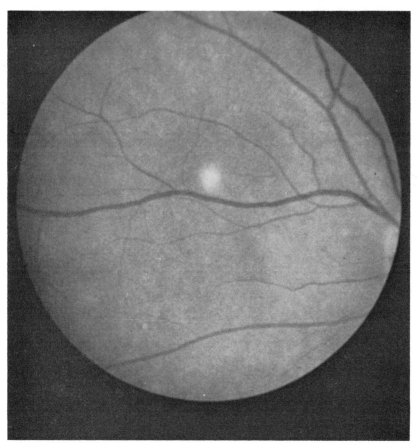

FIGURE 27-1. Peripheral choroidal nodule of presumed histoplasmic choroiditis. Note the indistinct borders.

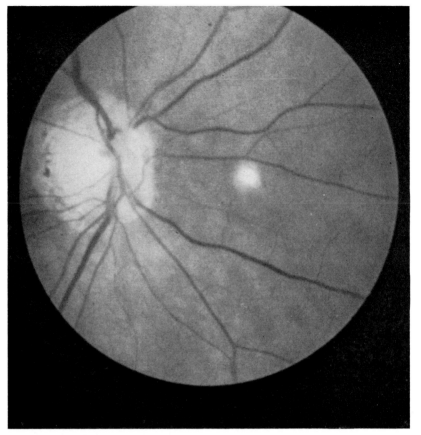

FIGURE 27-2. Inactive, punched-out lesion with sharp demarcation from normal pigment epithelium and choroid. Note the absence of pigment.

of the macular region. The disseminated choroidal lesions or "histo spots" (Asbury, 1966) are usually 0.1 to 0.5 disc diameter in size and are located anywhere in the fundus. In the acute phase, they appear as round, yellow-white, slightly elevated nodules with indistinct borders (Fig. 27-1) (Krill *et al.*, 1969), occasionally accompanied by haze in the overlying retina (Walma and Schlaegel, 1964). They are usually noted in the late stages when they represent focal areas of choroidal and pigment epithelial atrophy. The sharp border of normal pigment epithelium then gives them a "punched-out" appearance (Figs. 27-2, 27-3) (Gass, 1967).

The peripapillary scarring represents degeneration of the choroid and pigment epithelium adjacent to the nerve head following choroidal infiltration (Fig. 27-4). Active stages may produce symptoms by spread of subretinal blood or serous exudate (Schlaegel and Kenney, 1966; Gass, 1967). Eighty-five percent (85%) of cases in one series (Schlaegel and Kenney, 1966) had peripapillary lesions in one or both eyes.

Macular involvement produces the first symptoms in most patients, usually a sudden blurring of vision and metamorphopsia, and is the complication which often leads to severe permanent visual loss. The initial change is a focal, yellowish white or gray choroidal infiltrate in the macular region (Gass, 1967). As the lesion progresses, the overlying pigment epithelium develops a dark greenish doughnut-shaped nodule approximately one-fourth to one-half disc diameter in size (Fig. 27-5). This is usually accompanied by a serous detachment of the overlying retina. Bleeding into the subretinal space probably occurs because of altered permeability of the choriocapillaris and the rich arterial blood supply in these areas (Fig. 27-6) (Gass, 1967). Organization of the blood subsequently produces a fibrous scar (Fig. 27-7).

Several observers (Gass, 1967; Krill *et al.*, 1969) have suggested that the basic lesion in this ocular complex is a focal choroidal nodule. If located in the peripheral fundus, it produces a small discrete lesion which progresses to an atrophic scar and, because it does not cause symptoms, usually goes

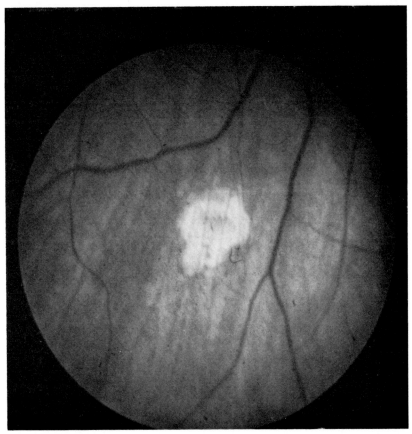

FIGURE 27-3. Large, irregular atrophic lesion of pigment epithelium and choroid.

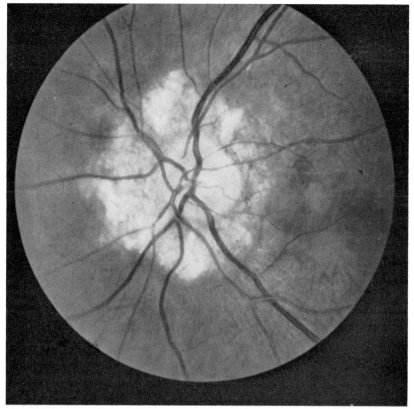

FIGURE 27-4. Peripapillary scarring in presumed histoplasmic choroiditis. Note the sub-retinal hemorrhage which has spread toward the macula.

undetected in the active stages. If located in the macular region, the nodule produces serous or hemorrhagic detachment of the retina because of a unique anatomic predisposition of the submacular choroid.

Recurrent macular hemorrhages may occur over a varying period after the initial episode. Involvement of the second macula has been noted from one month to twenty-eight years (Schlaegel *et al.*, 1967) and has been estimated to occur in from 10 percent (Schlaegel *et al.*, 1967) to 50 percent (Maumenee, 1965) of patients. Fifty-six percent (56%) of patients in one series with macular lesions developed 20/200 vision or less and only 16 percent retained or recovered 20/20 vision (Schlaegel *et al.*, 1967).

The entity occurs more frequently in males and during the fourth decade. Patients are typically in excellent health. It is apparently rare in the Negro (Schlaegel *et al.*, 1967; Gass, 1967; Krill *et al.*, 1969).

If we accept the "histo theory," the appearance of the typical fundus lesions in patients with negative histoplasmin skin tests can be excused on the basis that all patients with benign pulmonary histoplasmosis do not retain histoplasmin reactivity. Furcolow (1962) found 83 percent positive skin tests among 108 cases of untreated histoplasmosis. Zeidberg and Dillon (1951) found 15.8 percent negative reversions among 506 initially positive histoplasmin reactions after an average retest interval of twenty-five months. Reversion was highest in the forty years and over age group. The other possibility is that this ocular complex represents a nonspecific choroidal response to a variety of etiologic agents (Gass, 1967). The following patient seen by me at Moorfields Eye Hospital in London supports this latter concept.

A forty-two-year old Caucasian housewife was referred to Professor Barrie R. Jones with an eleven week history of "spots" in the central vision of the left eye, metamorphopsia, and micropsia. When examined at Moorfields Eye Hospital on October 3, 1967, vision in the right eye was 6/6 and the left eye 6/9. Slit-lamp examination was normal in both eyes. Ophthalmoscopy in the right eye was normal. In the left eye, there was a dark green, doughnut-shaped lesion with a white center approximately ¼ disc diameter, located superior and temporal to the macula. This was surrounded by a serous detachment of the retina which involved the macula. Superior to the disc were several discrete, "punched-out" areas of

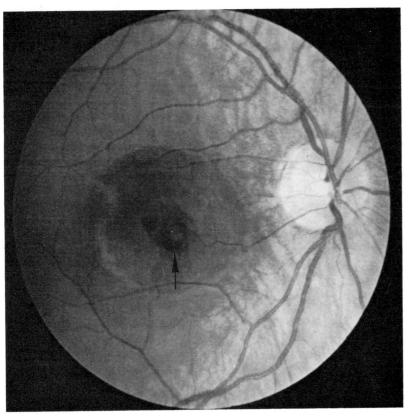

FIGURE 27-5. Doughnut-shaped submacular nodule (arrow) with serous detachment of the retina.

choroidal and pigment epithelial atrophy. The peripapillary area was normal and the vitreous was clear.

The patient had been a lifetime resident of the British Isles and had never visited abroad. At age two she was apparently treated for an empyema of unknown etiology. In 1946, she developed a nodule in the neck which was reported to her as tuberculous after a needle biopsy. Excisional biopsy was subsequently done. Unfortunately, the full clinical report and pathological sections were no longer available.

Chest x-ray revealed scarring of the right apex with a small anterior cyst. A 1:10.000 skin test on October 3, 1967, was strongly positive. A histoplasmin skin test on October 18, 1967, was negative. One sputum culture yielded *Mycobacterium xenopei*.

The patient was treated with daily systemic steroids, INH, and PAS for ten weeks with no change in vision or the ophthalmoscopic appearance of the left eye. On April 22, 1969, she returned with vision reduced to 6/60 in the left eye and fresh subretinal hemorrhage and fluid beneath the macula.

The ophthalmoscopic findings and clinical course in this patient resembled those of presumed histoplasmic choroiditis, yet the past history sug-

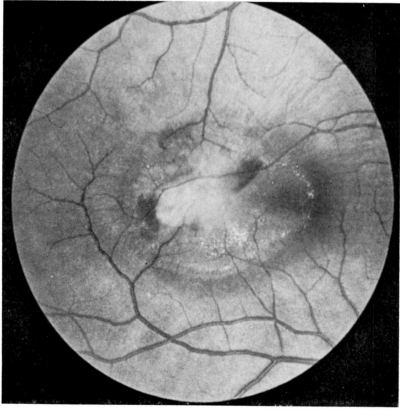

FIGURE 27-6. Hemorrhagic disciform detachment of the macula. The hemorrhages are surrounded by serous detachment of the retina.

gested another more likely cause for the focal choroiditis. Further circumstantial evidence against histoplasmosis in this patient is the extreme rarity of the disease in England. Only sixteen cases of histoplasmosis have been reported there, and only one unequivocally acquired his infection in the British Isles (Knight, 1968).

Pathological Studies

H. capsulatum has never been cultured from or identified histopathologically in an eye with presumed histoplasmic choroiditis. Adequate pathological material is lacking, as it is not possible to biopsy choroidal tissue from an eye with active inflammation, and the basic process does not warrant enucleation. Maumenee (1968) failed to find microorganisms in three or four eyes seen clinically with the typical lesions, although all had inflammatory cells in the choroid and one contained peripheral granulomatous lesions. Gass (1967) noted focal submacular choroiditis, hemorrhagic retinal detachment, and focal peripheral choroiditis in an eye removed from a forty-

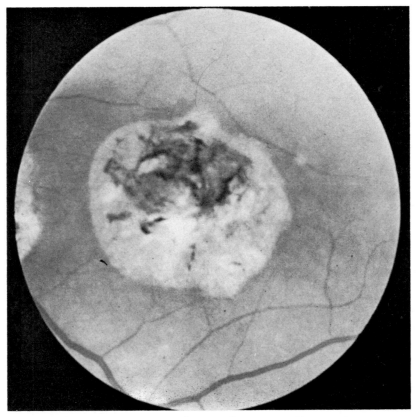

Figure 27-7. Diffuse, late scarring of the macular region following absorption of blood and serous exudate.

two-year-old Caucasian male thought to have malignant melanoma. He suggested that the ophthalmoscopic picture might have resembled the typical findings of ocular histoplasmosis. Stains for fungi and bacteria were negative. One year following enucleation of the right eye, the patient returned with a perimacular hemorrhagic lesion and was found to have a positive histoplasmin skin test and multiple pulmonary calcifications.

In 1967, Hoefnagels and Pijpers (1967) identified oval bodies resembling the yeast phase of *H. capsulatum* in the anterior and posterior chambers, vitreous, conjunctiva, iris, ciliary body, and retina of an eye with severe panophthalmitis removed from a sixty-three-year-old male in the Netherlands. *H. capsulatum* had been cultured from a gingival biopsy prior to enucleation. Cultures of aqueous and vitreous were negative. Although this report is good evidence that the fungus can invade the human eye, the clinical and pathological findings were not in any way similar to the accepted picture of presumed histoplasmic choroiditis.

The absence of stainable *H. capsulatum* in sections from eyes seen clinically with the typical picture is not totally incompatible with this fungus causing uveitis, particularly if we accept the hypersensitivity theory of pathogenesis. Even following primary infection, viable or structurally intact organisms are usually not present in old pulmonary lesions. Day (1949) was also unable to fund yeast cells in the late stages of experimentally produced ocular histoplasmosis in rabbits.

Experimental Studies

Day (1949) first produced experimental ocular histoplasmosis in rabbits and followed the natural course of the disease in this animal. A number of investigators have since produced intraocular granulomatous uveitis and focal mononuclear inflammation by several routes in birds, subprimates, and primates (Table 27-III). Although these studies have demonstrated that *H. capsulatum* can produce progressive ocular infection, none has reproduced the exact clinical picture of presumed histoplasmic choroiditis.

Two investigations merit further mention. Smith and Singer (1964b) inoculated 9,400 *H. capsulatum* yeast cells into the vitreous of an owl monkey. One week later, they noted an active focal choroidal nodule in the periphery of one eye. Two weeks following inoculation, there were multiple discrete choroidal lesions resembling typical "histo spots." The macular region remained uninvolved. The animal was sacrificed on day 18. Pathological sections revealed the cornea, anterior chamber, iris, and retina to be normal. There were several focal choroidal nodules which contained dense infiltration of mononuclear inflammatory cells and were loaded with *H. capsulatum* organisms by Grocott stain. This represents the only experimental eye in which lesions resembling a portion of the ocular complex in man have

TABLE 27-III

Summary of Experimental Ocular Histoplasmosis in Animals

I. Nonsensitized Animals
  A. Mycelial phase live organism.
    1. Anterior chamber inoculation in rabbits (Day, 1949).
    2. Intravitreal inoculation in rabbits (Day, 1949).
  B. Yeast phase live organisms.
    1. Anterior chamber inoculation.
      a. Pigeon (Smith and Jones, 1962; Sethi and Schwarz, 1966).
      b. Rabbit (Smith and Singer, 1964; Sethi and Schwarz, 1966a).
      c. Rat (Okudaira and Schwarz, 1962).
      d. Squirrel monkey (Smith, Singer, Goldwyn, Kulvin and Pinnas, 1964).
      e. Owl monkey (Smith and Singer 1964a).
    2. Intravitreal inoculation.
      a. Rabbit
      b. Owl monkey (Smith and Singer, 1964b).
    3. Intravenous inoculation in dogs (Salfelder, Schwarz and Akbarian, 1965).
    4. Corneal inoculation in rabbits (Smith and Singer, 1964c).
  C. Histoplasmin (yeast and mycelial phase).
    Intravitreal and suprachoroidal inoculation in rabbits (Schlaegel, Swinton, Weber, and Moorman, 1965).
II. Sensitized Animals
  A. Following inoculation of live mycelial phase organisms in the other eye.
    Anterior chamber inoculation in rabbits (Day, 1949).
  B. Following intraperitoneal inoculation of live and killed yeast phase organisms.
    Anterior chamber inoculation of live and killed yeast phase organisms and mycelial phase histoplasmin in rats (Okudaira and Schwarz, 1962).
  C. Following intraperitoneal inoculation of mycelial phase histoplasmin.
    Anterior chamber inoculation of live yeast phase organisms in rats (Okudaira and Schwarz, 1962).
  D. Following intradermal yeast and mycelial phase histoplasmin.
    Intravitreal and suprachoroidal inoculation of yeast and mycelial phase histoplasmin in rabbits (Schlaegel *et al.*, 1965).

been seen ophthalmoscopically and photographed. The absence of pathological changes in the retina overlying the focal choroidal nodules is also consistent with ophthalmoscopic observations of the typical lesions in man.

Okudaira and Schwarz (1962) were able to produce iridocyclitis, retinitis, and mononuclear choroiditis by injecting killed yeast phase organisms or mycelial phase histoplasmin into the anterior chambers of rats which had been previously sensitized with live or killed organisms by intraperitioneal route. This production of focal inflammation without the use of viable organisms partially supports the theory of Woods and Wahlen (1960) and others (Makley, Wong, Suie, and Stephan, 1965; Asbury, 1966) that the ocular lesions may be hypersensitivity phenomena.

Treatment

The multiple modes of treatment proposed by a number of investigators (Table 27-IV) are testament to the ineffectiveness of any given one. Similarly, no support is found for the hypothesis that *H. capsulatum* is responsible for this ocular entity or that the presumed lesions represent active, pro-

TABLE 27-IV

Suggested Methods of Treatment in Presumed Histoplasmic Choroiditis

1. Moving out of the endemic area.
2. Systemic amphotericin B (Falls and Giles, 1960; Giles and Falls, 1961; Jarvis and McCullough, 1963; Giles and Falls, 1968).
3. Histoplasmin desensitization (Makley *et al.*, 1965; Schlaegel *el al.*, 1968; Van Metre, 1968).
4. Systemic steroids (Schlaegel *et al.*, 1968; Van Metre, 1968).
5. Local steroids (Schlaegel *et al.*, 1968).
6. Antihistamines (Schlaegel *et al.*, 1968).
7. 6 Mercaptopurine (Schlaegel *et al.*, 1968).
8. Photocoagulation (Maumenee, 1966; Gass, 1967; Schlaegel *et al.*, 1968; Maumenee, 1968).

liferating organisms or hypersensitivity phenomena. Although Falls and Giles (1960) first proposed the use of amphotericin B in this form of uveitis in 1960, they have recently retracted this recommendation on the basis of their disappointing results in twenty patients when weighed against the serious risks associated with this drug (Giles and Falls, 1968). Others (Schlaegel, Cofield, Clark and Weber, 1968) have joined the abandonment of this regimen. The use of systemic and local steroids has failed to lessen significantly the active stages of the uveitis, a point of disappointment to those who favor the hypersensitivity theory of pathogenesis. There has been some degree of recent encouragement with the use of photocoagulation (Schlaegel *et al.*, 1968; Maumenee, 1968; Maumenee, 1968a). This is intended to reduce the serous and hemorrhagic subretinal exudate responsible for disciform macular scarring by sealing the area of leakage in the choriocapillaires. The use of fluorescein angiography has significantly aided this procedure (Gass, 1967).

★   ★   ★

Professor Barrie R. Jones kindly gave permission to include the case from Moorfields Eye Hospital, London. Mrs. Reva Hurtes, Bascom Palmer Eye Institute, Miami, Florida, assisted in the preparation of the bibliography.

References

Asbury, T. (1966). The status of presumed ocular histoplasmosis: including a report of a survey. *Trans. Amer. Ophthal. Soc.*, 65:371-400.

Day, R. (1949). Experimental ocular histoplasmosis. *Amer. J. Ophthal.*, 32:1317-1330.

Falls, H.F. and Giles, C.L. (1960). The use of amphotericin B in selected cases of chorioretinitis. *Amer. J. Ophthal.*, 49:1288-1298.

Furcolow, M.L. (1962). Immunology in histoplasmosis. *Excerpta Medica International Congress Serices No. 55*, Washington, pp. 515-522.

Gass, J.D.M. (1967). Pathogenesis of disciform detachment of the neuroepithelium. V. Disciform macular degeneration secondary to focal choroiditis. *Amer. J. Ophthal.*, 63:661-687.

Giles, C.L. and Falls, H.F. (1961). Further evaluation of amphotericin B therapy in presumptive histoplasmosis choroiditis. *Amer. J. Ophthal.* 51:588-598.

Giles, C.L. and Falls, H.F. (1968). Amphotericin B therapy in the treatment of presumed histoplasma chorioretinitis. A further appraisal. *Amer. J. Ophthal.* 66:101-104.

Hoefnagles, K.L.J. and Pijpers, P.M. (1967). *Histoplasma capsulatum* in a human eye. *Amer. J. Ophthal.*, 63:715-723.

Jarvis, G.J. and McCulloch, C. (1963). Ocular histoplasmosis. *Canad. Med. Assoc. J.*, 89:1270-1273.

Knight, R.K. (1968). Histoplasmosis; Why not in Britain? *Guy. Hosp. Rep.*, 117:309-317.

Krause, A.C. and Hopkins, W.G. (1951). Ocular manifestations of histoplasmosis. *Amer. J. Ophthal.*, 34:564-566.

Krill, A.E., Chishti, M.I., Klien, B.A., Newell, F.W. and Potts, A.M. (1969). Multifocal inner choroiditis. *Trans. Amer. Acad. Ophthal. Otolaryng.* 73:222-242.

Makley, T.A., Jr., Wong, J.W., Suie, T. and Stephan, J.D. (1965). Presumed histoplasmic chorioretinitis with special emphasis on the present modes of therapy. *Trans. Amer. Acad. Ophthal. Otolaryng.*, 69:443-457.

Maumanee, A.T. (1965). Clinical manifestations. In Symposium: Macular diseases. *Trans. Amer. Acad. Ophthal. Otolaryng.*, 69:605-613.

Maumanee, A.E. (1966). Serous and Hemorrhagic Chorioretinopathy. In *Retinal Diseases. Symposium on Differential Diagnostic Problems in Posterior Uveitis.* Philadelphia,, Lea and Febiger, pp. 244-256.

Maumanee, A.E. (1968). An Approach to the Study of Uveitis. In *Clinical Methods in Uveitis.* St. Louis, C. V. Mosby, pp. 21-40.

Maumanee, A.E. (1968a). Discussion of Schlaegel, Cofield, Clark, and Weber. *Trans. Amer. Acad. Ophthal. Otolaryng.*, 72:374-376.

Okudaira, M. and Schwarz, J. (1962). Experimental ocular histoplasmosis in rats; A histopathological study of immunogenic and hypersensitive ophthalmitis produced in rats by *Histoplasma capsulatum* and histoplasmin. *Amer. J. Ophthal.*, 54:427-44.

Perkins, E.S. (1968). Quoted by Maumanee, A.E. In *Clinical Methods in Uveitis.* St. Louis, C. V. Mosby, p.33.

Reid, J.D., Scherer, J.H., Herbut, P.A. and Irving, H. (1942). Systemic histoplasmosis diagnosed before death and produced experimentally in guinea pigs. *J. Lab. Clin. Med.*, 27:419-434.

Salfelder, K., Schwarz, J. and Akbarian, M. (1965). Experimental ocular histoplasmosis in dogs. *Amer. J. Ophthal.*, 59:290-299.

Schlaegel, T.F., Jr., Swinton, S., Weber, J.C. and Moorman, R.S., Jr. (1965). A comparison of the intraocular reactions of rabbits to yeast-phase and mycelial-phase histoplasmin. *Exp. Eye Res.*, 4:162-167.

Schlaegel, T.F., Jr. and Kenney, D. (1966). Changes around the optic nerve head in presumed ocular histoplasmosis. *Amer. J. Ophthal.*, 62:454-458.

Schlaegel, T.F., Jr., Weber, J.C., Helveston, F. and Kenney, D. (1967). Presumed histoplasmic choroiditis. *Amer. J. Ophthal.*, 63:919-925.

Schlaegel, T.F., Jr., Cofield, D.D., Clark, G. and Weber, J.C. (1968). Photocoagulation and other therapy for histoplasmic choroiditis. *Trans. Amer. Acad. Ophthal. Otolaryng.*, 72:355-363.

Sethi, K.K. and Schwarz, J. (1966). Experimental ocular histoplasmosis in pigeons. *Amer. J. Ophthal.*, 61:538-543.

Sethi, K.K. and Schwarz, J. (1966a). Amphotericin B in ocular histoplasmosis of rabbits, *Arch. Ophthal.*, 75:818-825.

Smith, J.L. and Jones, D.B. (1962). Experimental avian ocular histoplasmosis. *Arch. Ophthal.*, 67:349-356.

Smith, J.L. and Singer, J.A. (1964). Experimental ocular histoplasmosis. I. The natural course of primary infection in the rabbit eye. *Amer. J. Ophthal.*, 58:3-6.

Smith, J.L., Singer, J.A., Goldwyn, R.H., Kulvin, S.M. and Pinnas, G. (1964). Experimental ocular histoplasmosis. II. Primary infection in the primate eye. *Amer. J. Ophthal.*, 58:226-230.

Smith, J.L. and Singer, J.A. (1964a). Experimental ocular histoplasmosis. III. Experimentally produced retinal and choroidal lesions. *Amer. J. Ophthal.*, 58:413-423.

Smith, J.L. and Singer, J.A. (1964b). Experimental ocular histoplasmosis. IV. Fluorescein photographs of choroiditis in the primate. *Amer. J. Ophthal.*, 58:1021-1026.

Smith, J.L. and Singer, J.A. (1964c). Experimental corneal histoplasmosis. *Brit. J. Ophthal.* 48:293-297.

Suie, T., Rheins, M.S. and Makley, T.A., Jr. (1965). Serologic studies of presumed histoplasmic choroiditis. *Amer. J. Ophthal.*, 60:1059-1061.

Van Metre, T.E. and Maumenee, A.E. (1964). Specific ocular uveal lesions in patients with evidence of histoplasmosis. *Arch. Ophthal.*, 71:314-324.

Van Metre, T.E. (1968). In *Clinical Methods in Uveitis*. St. Louis, C. V. Mosby, p.103.

Walma, D., Jr. and Schlaegel, T.F., Jr. (1964). Presumed histoplasmic choroiditis: A clinical analysis of 43 cases. *Amer. J. Ophthal.*, 57:107-110.

Witmer, R. (1968). In *Clinical Methods in Uveitis*. St. Louis, C. V. Mosby, p.91.

Woods, A.C. and Wahlen, H.E. (1960). The probable role of benign histoplasmosis in the etiology of granulomatous uveitis. *Amer. J. Ophthal.*, 49:205-220.

Zeidberg, L.D. and Dillon, A. (1951). Some factors in the epidemiology of histoplasmin sensitivity in Williamson County, Tennessee. *Amer. J. Public Health*, 41:80-89.

Chapter 28

Presumed Histoplasma Uveitis: Continuing Doubts as to Its Actual Cause

GEORGE LINK SPAETH

ABSTRACT

Histoplasma capsulatum apparently can rarely cause an intensely inflammatory uveitis. Whether the organism is also responsible for the clinical entity consisting of punched-out chorioretinal lesions, macular hemorrhage, and a clear vitreous is less definite. Complete reevaluation of the literature dealing with "presumed *Histoplasma* uveitis" suggests that the etiology of this condition is still undetermined. Certainly therapy with toxic agents such as amphotericin B is no longer justified.

A review of the history of the diagnosis and therapy of the many varieties of uveitis indicates that diagnostic criteria have not been sufficiently strict. This criticism may also be applied to the question of the relationship between histoplasmosis and uveitis.

Future investigation should include prospective studies to determine if individuals converting from histoplasmin negative to positive develop chorioretinitis, complete ocular examination by an ophthalmologist of patients with known histoplasmosis, and more thorough study of patients with "presumed histoplasma uveitis."

THAT histoplasmosis causes a particular type of uveitis is a contention now generally accepted as established fact. In an excellent review recently surveying the subject, the sole dissenting report, like the irascible and acid-tongued old aunt you wish you had not invited but just could not gracefully omit, though listed in the references, was not mentioned in the text (Leinfelder, 1967). The purpose of this presentation is to determine, in light of accumulated evidence, if such a contention is justified.

Materials and Methods

Hospital records of patients at the National Institutes of Health (NIH) and the Walter Reed Army Medical Center (WRAMC) were reviewed. Cases were selected in which the diagnosis of histoplasmosis had been established with certainty by cultural or histopathologic techniques. Those in which the clinical and laboratory findings were so highly characteristic of histoplasmosis that the patients had been actively treated with specific medication, even though cultural diagnosis was not made, were considered "suspects" and are considered separately. If specific mention of ophthalmo-scopic examination was not included in the record (such as "fundi nega-tive," or "eyegrounds normal") the case involved was discarded. The follow-ing data were compiled for all cases: age, sex, race, presence of ocular symp-toms, description of eye examination, interpretation of chest, roentgenogra-phy, outcome of skin testing with histoplasmin, treatment given, clinical course, method of diagnosis, and clinical diagnosis; autopsy findings were included in those cases which came to postmortem examination.

Results

Eighty-eight patients at the NIH and 196 at the WRAMC had diagnoses of clinical histoplasmosis. Of these 284 cases 196 were cases of unquestion-able histoplasmosis; 62 were discarded, however, because of inadequate de-scription of the ocular fundi. The basis for this study thus consisted mainly of 134 cases: these included 113 cases of pulmonary histoplasmosis (95 of which had their diagnosis verified by surgical resection of involved lung, the remainder having been diagnosed by culture), 17 cases of disseminated dis-ease (diagnosed by biopsy or autopsy), 2 cases in which the organisms were found only in the central nervous system, 1 case in which the disease was apparently limited to the liver, and 1 in which only the tongue was involved. An additional 88 cases were considered highly suspicious; in 77 of these the ocular examination was adequate to allow inclusion into the study as a sepa-rate group.

The patients' ages ranged from 3 months to 77 years; by far the greatest number were between 20 and 50 years of age. Males were represented six times as frequently as females (115:19). This was not just a function of the Army selection of patients because the distribution in the smaller NIH pop-ulation was also strongly weighted towards males (32:7). Almost all cases were white (11 Negroes). Autopsies were performed in fourteen cases.

No patients had ocular symptoms when first examined. One developed ocular disease during the course of treatment of his illness. This was a sixty-two-year-old white man with histoplasmosis affecting primarily the central nervous system. Cultures of blood, bone marrow, and spinal fluid were positive when the patient was first seen; later bone marrow, blood, urine, and lymph nodes were negative, whereas spinal fluid consistently contained organisms. Chest x-ray, histoplasmin skin test, and complement fixation tests were re-peatedly negative. While being treated with amphotericin B the patient de-veloped an acute, granulomatous panuveitis associated with severe inflam-mation. Efforts to culture organisms from material obtained by paracentesis of the vitreous and the aqueous of the involved eye failed; histological ex-amination of the material was similarly negative. In an attempt to lessen the extreme inflammation of the eye, the patient was treated with systemic corticosteroids; this was associated with worsening of the patient's general condition and eventual death; no autopsy was able to be performed.

Abnormal ocular findings of interest were seen in three other cases. Small white exudates resembling "cytoid bodies" were described on one occasion in a fifty-one-year-old man with disseminated disease; no other abnormalities were noted in the fundi, and a repeat examination later was negative. An eighteen-year-old boy with recurrent pulmonary disease showed optic atrophy of his right optic disc associated with a strabismus; the rest of the ocular examination was normal. A seventy-seven-year-old man with acute pulmonary histoplasmosis and diabetes mellitus had two "punched-out lesions" inferiorly in his right eye; the maculas of both eyes were normal; vascular changes compatible with diabetes were seen in the left eye. No ocular abnormalities of interest were seen in the seventy-seven suspect cases.

Histoplasmin skin tests were negative in 10 of the 134 cases with proven active histoplasmosis (7%). Complement fixation tests were negative, even when various different techniques were used, in 25 of the 134 cases (19%)

In sum, none of the patients with documented histoplasmosis had the clinical entity which is presently being called "*Histoplasma uveitis.*"

Comment

Histoplasmosis was reported as a possible cause of uveitis in 1951 (Krause and Hopkins, 1951), though Reid *et al.* in 1942 described "small, white, irregular areas" in the fundi of a patient with severe systemic disease. Falls, Giles, Schlaegel, van Metre, Maumenee, and others have clearly defined what appears to be a clinical entity consisting of small, punched-out chorioretinal lesions associated with macular hemorrhage, clear vitreous, and positive histoplasmin skin test; juxtapapillary choroiditis, positive complement fixation test, and x-ray evidence of old pulmonary disease complete the picture (Falls and Giles, 1959; Woods and Wahlen, 1960; Giles and Falls, 1961; McCulloch, 1963; Mann, 1963; van Metre and Maumenee, 1964; Walma and Schlaegel, 1964; Suie, Rheins and Makley, 1965; Makley *et al.*, 1965; Schlaegel and Kenney, 1966; Schlaegel *et al.*, 1967; Giles and Falls, 1967). "A presumptive diagnosis of histoplasmosis can be based on the typical clinical picture (as described) plus a positive skin test or a positive complement fixation test" (Leinfelder, 1967). Failure to find any "cause other than histoplasmosis to which the uveitis might be attributed" has been considered supporting evidence (Leinfelder, 1967), and in the period when the entity was first being outlined, Woods included anergy to tuberculin as a diagnostic criterion (Woods and Wahlen, 1960).

The most convincing evidence that *H. capsulatum* actually is the etiologic agent responsible for this particular type of uveitis is the high percentage of clinically involved individuals who react positively to histoplasmin skin tests.

For example, in sixty cases with the ophthalmic signs previously described, van Metre and Maumenee found skin tests positive in 93 percent, whereas they were positive in only 25 percent of 190 cases of uveitis not having the characteristic ophthalmoscopic changes (van Metre and Maumenee). Similarly, Walma and Schlaegel (1964) found 85 percent of 68 cases with disseminated choroiditis to be histoplasmin positive, while only 58 percent of 95 cases with focal lesions reacted positively to histoplasmin skin testing.

Another indication that *H. capsulatum* is the cause of this type of uveitis is the concentration of cases in the Ohio Valley, the same area in which histoplasmosis is known to be endemic.

Other evidence considered to support the contention that *Histoplasma* organisms cause the characteristic chorioretinal lesions in the presence of a clear vitreous includes worsening of the ocular condition associated with the development of a positive skin test, presence of anti-*Histoplasma* antibodies, increased incidence of fibrocalcific abnormalities in the lungs, and favorable response to amphotericin B therapy.

Hoefnagels and Pijpers (1967) have demonstrated the presence of *Histoplasma capsulatum* in the enucleated eye of a patient with proven gingival histoplasmosis, and uveitis due to this fungus has been produced experimentally in various animals (Okudaira and Schwarz, 1962; Smith and Jones, 1962; Smith and Singer, 1964; Salfelder, Schwarz and Akbarian, 1965; Sethi and Schwarz, 1966), seemingly satisfying most of the required criteria for diagnosis.

However, as several authors have noted, none of these arguments is conclusive proof. For example, Asbury found the histoplasmin skin test positive in 53 percent of 1,395 Ohio residents with no evidence of "presumed *Histoplasma* uveitis." This is only a slightly lower incidence than the 64 percent positive skin tests he observed in twenty-two cases with the typical ophthalmoscopic findings examined in the same prospective study (Asbury, 1966). Histoplasmosis is such an extremely focal disease geographically that the response of two populations to histoplasmin skin testing can only be validly compared if the two populations are selected from the same town or county, as Asbury's apparently were. Thus patients selected from a uveitis center to which they have been referred from a broad area comprise a population which is too heterogeneous to allow valid conclusions unless specific matching of patients has been made.

Flare-up of disease coincidental with skin testing has been reported too infrequently to warrant serious consideration. Furthermore, the presence in the patient's blood of antibodies to *H. capsulatum* in a titer of 1:8 does not constitute proof of disease. These antibodies have been found quite prevalently in populations presumably not afflicted with histoplasmosis (Campbell, 1960). Moreover, it is important to realize that skin testing itself can provoke the presence of *H. capsulatum* antibodies (Campbell, *et al.,* 1961 and McDearman and Young, 1960). Since it is usual for a patient with uveitis to have histoplasmin skin testing done as one of the first diagnostic procedures, it is to be expected that a significant percent will later have detectable anti-*H. capsulatum* antibodies. Suie *et al.* reported that only 6 percent of thirty-four patients with suspected histoplasmic chorioretinitis had yeast phase and histoplasmin complement fixation tests positive in a titer of 1:32 or higher. Furthermore, the *H. capsulatum* collodion agglutination test was positive in only 1 percent of thirty-nine cases with presumed *H. capsulatum* uveitis (Suie *et al.*, 1965).

Regarding the pulmonary findings, it is difficult to be certain that fibrocalcific lesions in chest roentgenographs are actually caused by histoplasmosis; furthermore, unless the radiologist reads the films "blind," it is hard to avoid seeing lesions in cases where histoplasmosis is strongly suspected.

When amphotericin B was introduced as therapy for histoplasmosis, it appeared to be effective in healing the choroiditis, though the reserve with which Falls and Giles (1959) reported their results is so admirable that it demands citing. They stated that their paper had "not established . . . that histoplasmosis affects the eye. . . . Suffice it to say that an agent, successful elsewhere in treating systemic histoplasmosis has been employed in the therapeusis of certain cases of chorioretinitis. It appears, with and without the use of steroids, to effect quiescence of the chorioretinitis." However, most investigators, including Giles and Falls, now believe that the natural history of the ocular disease is not favorably influenced by the administration of this notoriously toxic agent (Giles and Falls, 1967). This ineffectiveness is in striking contrast to the well-established efficacy of amphotericin B in systemic and experimental histoplasmosis (Sethi and Schwarz, 1966).

Some authors have observed moderate benefit from corticosteroids (Makley, *et al.*, 1965; Spaeth, 1967), though not all agree (Giles and Falls, 1967). Nevertheless, there are no reports in the ophthalmic literature stating that steroids are contraindicated or that they have triggered a relapse of generalized histoplasmosis. Such an occurrence could be expected if viable *H. capsulatum* organisms were present, because of the adverse effect corticosteroids have on the clinical course of systemic histoplasmosis.

The type of destructive, conspicuously inflammatory uveitis that led to the enucleation of a globe in which *H. capsulatum* organisms were demonstrated is at the opposite pole from the quiet, noninflammatory process presently designated "presumed *Histoplasma* uveitis." Hoefnagels' case resembled the striking panuveitis seen in the sixty-two-year-old man described earlier in this report. And it seems entirely justified to assign histoplasmosis as the cause of this uveitis, which was made worse by the administration of steroids (Tynes, Crutcher and Utz, 1963; Paton, 1959). The existence of this clinical entity in no way substantiates the hypothesis that *H. capsulatum* is responsible for the other, noninflammatory variety.

On the other hand, the absence of disseminated, punched-out lesions or macular disease in patients with proven, active histoplasmosis does not indicate that this type of uveitis is unrelated to infection with *H. capsulatum*. Failure of the eyes to be involved in active disease does not, of course, mean that they may not be affected by a different mechanism. One of the most characteristic features of systemic histoplasmosis is the relative benignity of the condition in almost all individuals it attacks. Only rarely does the organism spread virulently to produce pulmonary disease or disease of the reticuloendothelial tissues. It is entirely possible that the macular disseminated choroiditis type of uveitis described previously may be related to a hypersensitivity type of response of the choroid to a product formed during the brief subclinical attacks of histoplasmosis that are so common in the midwestern United States.

Factors suggesting that *H. capsulatum* is not the cause of the chorioretinal lesions, presently termed *presumed Histoplasma uveitis*, are listed in Table 28-I. In evaluating the validity of these factors, it should be remembered that the conclusion that chorioretinal lesions are absent in patients with known disease has been based on a retrospective study in which charts, not patients, were examined. Despite this limitation the accumulated evidence regarding the etiology of this distinctive variety of uveitis cannot be deemed conclusive. It does seem highly unlikely that viable *H. capsulatum* organisms in the eye or elsewhere in the body are causative of the entity. Consequently, there is no justification for therapy with specific antifungal agents such as amphotericin B.

Loss of sight is such a tragic affliction that physicians are easily pushed into treating more vigorously than may actually be indicated. As therapy must be directed at something definite, diagnostic significance tends to be assigned to any positive findings. Perhaps nowhere is this more graphically illustrated than in the diagnosis and treatment of uveitis. Uveitis, being common, destructive of vision, and productive of keratopathy, cataract and glaucoma, is a particularly troublesome disease for the ophthalmologist.

It is not necessary to reach far back into the history of medicine to find diversities of opinion regarding the etiology of uveitis. Indeed, valid imputa-

TABLE 28-I

Factors Suggesting that Histoplasmosis is Not the Cause of "Presumed *Histoplasma* Uveitis"

1. Absence of chorioretinitis in patients with known histoplasmosis (Spaeth).
2. Approximately the same distribution of histoplasmin skin test reactors among patients with and without the typical chorioretinitis (Asbury).
3. Possible improvement of the condition in response to corticosteroids and failure of improvement with amphotericin B (Makley; Giles and Falls).
4. Noninflammatory nature of "presumed *Histoplasma* uveitis" in contrast to conspicuously inflammatory aspect of uveitis proved due to *H. capsulatum* (Hoefnagels and Pijpers).
5. Inconclusive character of evidence presently considered indicative of *H. capsulatum* as the agent responsible for the typical clinical picture of "presumed *Histoplasma* uveitis."

tions could not be expected until techniques of accurately determining cause-effect relationships were clarified and became the basis of all types of investigation. In the nineteenth century among the diseases commanding the most attention were tuberculosis and syphilis, and it is natural that uveitis should have been considered an expression of these apparently prevalent illnesses. The wide disagreements regarding relative frequency do not seem to represent changes in actual incidence of particular disease, however, so much as they mirror the psychological set of the physicians making the diagnosis. The reported incidence of syphilis as a cause of uveitis is instructive in this regard. In Table 28-II is listed the frequency with which syphilis has been considered responsible for uveitis in central Europe (mainly Germany). The figures do not appear to express the actual incidence of syphilis in the population at those dates, but rather other considerations. For example, serological testing was introduced in the first decade of the twentieth century, and it seems reasonable to ascribe the tremendous decrease in reported incidence of syphilitic uveitis about the same time to more accurate diagnosis. That is, after the Wasserman test became widely known, fewer cases were improperly diagnosed as syphilis; there is no reason to believe that there was a real decrease in patients actually affected with syphilis at that time. In recent years syphilis has been less often reported as a cause of uveitis, despite information suggesting that the incidence of the disease is not declining.

Table 28-III even more graphically illustrates the contention that the diagnosis of uveitis has not truly reflected the real causes of the disease. The data on which this table is based were accumulated almost wholly by one observer in one geographic area. It is unlikely that tuberculosis so remarkably declined in the thirteen years between 1941 and 1954. Similarly, it is clear that toxoplasmosis did not suddenly leap into existence during the same interval. What did change were the techniques and the criteria for diagnosis.

The etiology of sixteen cases of uveitis in Yugoslav children and sixteen American children is listed in Table 28-IV. The patients of Giles were stud-

TABLE 28-II

Syphilis as a Cause of Uveitis

	Year	%
De Wecker	1876	65
Baum	1902	30
Leber	1909	17
Hessberg	1910	12
Kahoun	1930	6
Müller	1949	5
Kumstat	1967	1

Note. Modified from Duke-Elder and Perkins, 1966, and Kumstat and Anton, 1967.

TABLE 28-III

Etiology of Granulomatous Uveitis

Etiologic Factor	Guyton and Woods, 1941 134 cases %	Woods, et al. 1954 191 cases %	Woods 1960 134 cases %
Tuberculosis	80	23	20*
Syphilis	17	7	2
Sarcoidosis	1	6	3
Brucellosis	0.7	7	2
Toxoplasmosis	0	25	36*
Histoplasmosis	0	0	13
Miscellaneous	1.3	13	2
Undetermined	0	19	1

Note. Modified from Kumstat and Anton, 1967, and Woods, 1960.
* In an additional 21 per cent of cases, a diagnosis of "*either* tuberculosis or toxoplasmosis" was made.

ied at the National Institutes of Health in the most complete manner possible, utilizing extensive immunological, microbiological, biochemical, and pathological techniques over a five and one-half year period, yet in 81 percent of the cases no etiologic diagnosis could be made. The contrast between these two studies is conspicuous and is better explained as an expression of different diagnostic criteria than actual incidence of disease.

Clearly treatment must be based on something, and therefore positive findings are considered by the conscientious ophthalmologist as signals to direct therapy. Assuredly this is justified. It is unfair to the patient to withhold treatment because a diagnosis has not been made with absolute certainty. In fact, the great majority of patients today are well treated without ever having had their illness conclusively delineated. However, the history of uveitis has been a startling recitation of the conservative, the unscientific, and the faddish nature of physicians, specifically ophthalmologists. Undeniably well-meaning though motives have been, the uncritical willingness to embrace specific diagnostic labels has hindered rather than furthered the advance of knowledge, which advance is nourished only by meticulous and

TABLE 28-IV

Etiology of Uveitis in Children

Ljubibratic, 1967		Giles, 1969	
Tuberculosis	3	Sarcoidosis	2
Staphylococcus	1	Tuberculosis or	
Streptococcus	1	Herpes zoster	1
Leptospirosis	1	Unknown	13
Sarcoidosis	1		
Brucellosis	1		
Toxocara canis	1		
Unknown	2		

innovative disentanglement of the spurious and specious from the real and actual cause of a specific effect.

The relationship between histoplasmosis and *presumed Histoplasma uveitis* demands further definition. There must be (1) a complete ocular examination by an ophthalmologist of every patient with known histoplasmosis; (2) more thorough clinical, microbiological, and immunological study of patients with the entity presently called *presumed Histoplasma uveitis;* that is, more active interchange between the laboratory and the clinic; (3) a prospective, long-term investigation monitoring the fundi of individuals converting from histoplasmin negativity to positivity; specifically, Asbury should reexamine the histoplasmin negative cases in his study to determine whether those becoming positive also develop chorioretinitis; (4) a more realistic, more humble estimation of the limitations of our present knowledge, with an awareness that many diagnoses that we make are tentative and all are incomplete; (5) a flexibility and a willingness on the part both of those in clinical practice and those in basic research to readjust their thinking and working in response to what is hopefully a constantly more correct interpretation of reality.

References

Asbury, T. (1966). The status of presumed ocular histoplasmosis: including a report of a survey. *Trans. Amer. Ophthal. Soc., 64*:371-400.

Campbell, C.C. (1960). The accuracy of serologic methods of diagnosis. *Ann. N. Y. Acad. Sci., 89*:163-177.

Campbell, C.C., Nolte, L.B. and Hill, G.B. (1961). Serologic effects of histoplasmin skin testing. *Amer. Rev. Resp. Dis., 83*:276-279.

Duke-Elder, S. and Perkins, E.S. (1966). *Systems of Ophthalmology, Diseases of the Uveal Tract.* St. Louis, C. V. Mosby, vol. 9, pp.39-41.

Falls, H.F. and Giles, C.L. (1959). The use of amphotericin B in selected cases of chorioretinitis. *Trans. Amer. Ophthal. Soc., 57*:344-363.

Giles, C.L. (1963). Anterior uveitis in children. A report of 16 cases including long-term follow-up. *Arch. Ophthal., 70*:779-785.

Giles, C.L. and Falls, H.F. (1961). Further evaluation of amphotericin B therapy in presumptive histoplasmosis chorioretinitis. *Amer. J. Ophthal., 51*:588-598.

Giles, C.L. and Falls, H.F. (1967). Amphotericin B therapy in the treatment of presumed *Histoplasma* chorioretinitis: a further appraisal. *Trans. Amer. Ophthal. Soc., 65*:136-145.

Hoefnagels, K.L.J. and Pijpers, P.M. (1967). *Histoplasma capsulatum* in a human eye. *Amer. J. Ophthal., 63*:715-723.

Krause, A.C. and Hopkins, W.G. (1951). Ocular manifestation of histoplasmosis. *Amer. J. Ophthal., 34*:564-566.

Kumstat, Z. and Anton, M. (1967). Lues a Iridocyclitis. *Cs. Oftal. 23*:103-108 (#2) 1967. Abstract in *Excerpta Medica Ophthal., 21*:281.

Leinfelder, J.T. (1967). Ocular histoplasmosis (a survey). *Survey Ophthal., 12*:103-111.

Ljubibratic, D. (1967). Znacenje kvantitativno seroloskih pretraga kod uveitisa u djecjoj dobi (Significance of quantitative serological examinations in uveitis of childhood).

An. Bolnice 'Dr. M. Stojanovic,' 6:467-476. Abstract in *Excerpta Medica Ophthal.*, 22:275 (Aug.) 1968.

Makley, T.A. Jr., Long, J.W., Suie, T. and Stephan, J.D. (1965). Presumed histoplasmic chorioretinitis with special emphasis on the present modes of therapy. *Trans. Amer. Acad. Ophthal. Otolaryng.*, 69:443-457.

Mann, W.H. (1963). Chorioretinitis due to histoplasmosis. *Amer. J. Ophthal.*, 55:999-1006.

McCulloch, C. (1963). Histoplasmosis. *Trans. Canad. Ophthal. Soc.*, 26:107-125.

McDearman, S.C. and Young, J.M. (1960). The development of positive serologic tests with *Histoplasma capsulatum* antigens following single histoplasmin skin tests. *Amer. J. Clin. Path.*, 34:434.

van Metre, T.E., Jr. and Maumenee, A.E. (1964). Specific ocular uveal lesions in patients with evidence of histoplasmosis. *Arch. Ophthal.*, 71:314-324.

Okudaira, M. and Schwarz, J. (1962). Experimental ocular histoplasmosis in rats. A histopathologic study of immunogenic and hypersensitive ophthalmitis produced in rats by *Histoplasma capsulatum* and histoplasmin. *Amer. J. Ophthal.*, 54:427-444.

Paton, D. (in discussion), Falls, H.F. and Giles, C.L. (1959). The use of amphotericin B in selected cases of chorioretinitis. *Trans. Amer. Ophthal. Soc.*, 57:361-362.

Reid, J.D., Scherer, J.H., Herbut, P.A. and Irving, H. (1942). Systemic histoplasmoses: diagnosed before death and produced experimentally in guinea pigs. *J. Lab. Clin. Med.*, 27:419-434.

Salfelder, K., Schwarz, J. and Akbarian, M. (1965). Experimental ocular histoplasmosis in dogs. *Amer. J. Ophthal.*, 59:290-299.

Schlaegel, T.F., Jr. and Kenney, D. (1966). Changes around the optic nervehead. *Amer. J. Ophthal.*, 62:454-458.

Schlaegel, T.F., Jr., Weber, J.C., Helveston, E. and Kenney, D. (1967). Presumed histoplasmic choroiditis. *Amer. J. Ophthal.*, 63:919-925.

Sethi, K.K. and Schwarz, J. (1966). Amphotericin B in ocular histoplasmosis of rabbits. *Arch. Ophthal.*, 75:818-825.

Smith, J.L. and Jones, D.B. (1962). Experimental avian ocular histoplasmosis. *Arch. Ophthal.*, 67:103-110.

Smith, J.L. and Singer, J.A. (1964). Experimental ocular histoplasmosis. I. The natural course of primary infection in the rabbit eye. *Amer. J. Ophthal.*, 58:3-6.

Smith, J.L. and Singer, J.A. (1964). Experimental ocular histoplasmosis. IV. Fluorescein fundus photographs of choroiditis in the primate. *Amer. J. Ophthal.*, 58:1021-1026.

Spaeth, G.L. (1967). Absence of so-called *Histoplasma* uveitis in 134 cases of proven histoplasmosis. *Arch. Ophthal.*, 77:41-44.

Suie, T., Rheins, M.S. and Makley, T.A., Jr. (1965). Serologic studies of presumed histoplasmic choroiditis. *Amer. J. Ophthal.*, 60:1059-1061.

Tynes, B., Crutcher, J.C. and Utz, J.P. (1963). *Histoplasma* meningitis. *Ann. Intern. Med.*, 59:615-621.

Walma, D., Jr. and Schlaegel, T.F., Jr. (1964). Presumed histoplasmic choroiditis. A clinical analysis of 43 cases. *Amer. J. Ophthal.*, 57:107-110.

Woods, A.C. (1960). Modern concepts of the etiology of uveitis. *Amer. J. Ophthal.*, 50:1170-1187.

Woods, A.C. and Wahlen, H.E. (1960). The probable role of benign histoplasmosis in the etiology of granulomatous uveitis. *Amer. J. Ophthal.*, 49:205-220.

Chapter 29

Cardiac Involvement

ROBERT J. MARSHALL

ABSTRACT

Cardiac involvement is an uncommon but serious complication of infection with *Histoplasma capsulatum*. Sixteen cases of endocarditis, verified by a complete autopsy, have been recorded in the literature. In only one adequately documented case did the patient recover following treatment with amphotericin B. The clinical features of *Histoplasma* endocarditis resemble those of bacterial endocarditis, but since the vegetations are unusually large and friable, large arteries may be blocked by emboli. The incidence of *Histoplasma* pericarditis is difficult to determine, unless fluid or tissues are available for culture in the acute stage of the disease, or unless there is clear evidence of a serum antibody response. In chronic pericarditis the histological changes are nonspecific, and the presence of a positive skin test is insufficient to warrant the diagnosis. Myocarditis is rare. *Histoplasma* mediastinitis occasionally obstructs or occludes great vessels, such as pulmonary arteries, pulmonary veins, or the superior vena cava.

CARDIAC involvement is an uncommon but serious complication of infection with *Histoplasma capsulatum*. The most fully documented lesions are endocarditis and pericarditis; myocarditis has been described in a few cases. The heart may also be indirectly involved as a result of either chronic pulmonary fibrosis secondary to histoplasmosis, or stenosis or occlusion of great veins or arteries secondary to mediastinal fibrosis.

Endocarditis

The original case was reported by Riehl (1925), and the first from the United States by Broders, Dochat, Herrell and Vaughn (1943). To date, a total of sixteen cases have been verified by complete necropsy (Weaver, Batsakis and Nishiyama, 1968). In a further case, necropsy was limited to examination of the heart (Moore, 1955). In only one adequately documented instance did the patient recover, following therapy with amphotericin B (Derby, Coolidge and Rogers 1962).

The clinical features of *Histoplasma* endocarditis resemble those of bacterial endocarditis. Signs and symptoms in the seventeen cases with necropsy verification are summarized in Table 29-I.

Some of these clinical features are also typical for disseminated histoplasmosis. The findings that should arouse particular suspicion of endocarditis are a cardiac murmur (especially when its characteristics change in the course of the disease), petechiae, Osler's nodes, and arterial emboli.

TABLE 29-I

Clinical Findings in Seventeen Cases of *Histoplasma* Endocarditis

Signs or Symptoms	Number of Cases
Fever	17
Heart Murmurs	14
Leukocytopenia	12
Anemia	10
Splenomegaly	9
Hepatomegaly	8
Petechiae	6
Major arterial emboli	5

The aortic valve was most commonly the site of the mycotic infection (11 cases). The mitral valve was involved in three cases, the mitral and aortic valves together in one case, and the tricuspid valve in two cases. In nine of the seventeen cases there was pathological evidence of valve damage preceding the infection with *Histoplasma* (Weaver *et al.*, 1968). The vegetations were often large and friable, as they are also in infections with other fungi such as *Candida albicans;* this accounts for the fact that the emboli arising from the valvar vegetations may be large and block major arteries (Merchant, Louria, Geisler, Edgcomb and Utz, 1958; Palmer, Geraci and Thomas, 1962; Derby *et al.*, 1962).

In the case reported by Palmer *et al.* (1962), the endocarditis developed within three months after an apparently uncomplicated closed operation for mitral valvotomy. The first of two cases reported by Weaver *et al.* (1968) demonstrated the infection around a Teflon® prosthesis that had been inserted for the relief of aortic valve regurgitation. These are the only instances in which *Histoplasma* endocarditis has occurred as a consequence of cardiac surgery. This situation contrasts with the increasing incidence of *Candida* endocarditis in patients who have had prosthetic valves inserted together with prolonged antibiotic therapy.

The diagnosis of *Histoplasma* endocarditis is difficult. Usually it was not made prior to necropsy. In some cases, it was not considered, while in others blood cultures were negative. Skin tests are of little help. A negative histoplasmin skin test may be explained by anergy secondary to the severity of the infection, while in endemic areas positive skin tests are so common as to be of no value. A rising *Histoplasma* complement fixation titer may support the diagnosis of active infection, although it will not help to differentiate between disseminated histoplasmosis and *Histoplasma* endocarditis. Even when the diagnosis is suspected in life, confirmation may be difficult. Blood cultures may be negative even when special media are used. Therefore, cultures should be obtained from the throat, skin and urine, and if necessary from lymph nodes (Merchant *et al.*, 1958).

Published experience with the treatment of *Histoplasma* endocarditis is limited to four cases. Merchant *et al.* (1958) gave their patient a total of 2.4

gm amphotericin B over a period of six months; there was definite clinical improvement, but eventually sudden death occurred. At necropsy a large friable vegetation was found on the aortic valve, and *H. capsulatum* was cultured from it. Derby *et al.* (1962) gave 4.2 gm amphotericin B over eighty-seven days to a patient with endocarditis in whom the diagnosis was made by culturing *H. capsulatum* from a large femoral embolus; twenty months after the end of treatment, there was no evidence of recurrence. Because of severe renal failure, the patient of Palmer *et al.* (1962) could not be given adequate doses of amphotericin B; at necropsy, *H. capsulatum* was recovered from vegetations on the mitral valve. The patient reported by Hartley *et al.* (1967) received 1.7 gm amphotericin B over eighty-seven days, but despite clinical improvement, he died suddenly; cultures obtained at necropsy were negative, but budding organisms were seen in vegetations on the mitral valve.

These cases illustrate the problems inherent in therapy. In endocarditis, regardless of the nature of the responsible agent, the infection can be consistently eradicated only if bactericidal agents are given over sufficiently long periods. Amphotericin B is far from ideal, since its action is generally suppressive rather than bactericidal, and since systemic reactions as well as the chance of progressive impairment of renal function make prolonged therapy difficult. An additional factor is the luxuriant growth of the vegetation, which means that deeper organisms are not accessible to the drug.

Pericarditis

In their comprehensive review of histoplasmosis, Silverman, Schwarz, Lahey and Carson (1955) found no recorded cases of pericarditis to be due to histoplasmosis. In the same year, Billings and Couch described two patients with pericardial calcification, positive histoplasmin skin tests, and negative tuberculin skin tests. Their presumptive diagnosis was chronic calcific pericarditis secondary to histoplasmosis. However, these findings alone are insufficient to make the diagnosis, since calcification of the pericardium may result from diseases other than tuberculosis and histoplasmosis. For confirmation, either the organism should be isolated from pericardial fluid or tissue, or there should be definite evidence of serum antibody response, assessed by complement fixation or agar-gel diffusion techniques.

A survey of the literature reveals eighteen cases in which there was good evidence for *H. capsulatum* as the cause of the pericarditis (Riegel and Schriever, 1967). In 2, the organism was cultured from pericardial fluid; in 7 it was demonstrated in pericardial tissue in biopsy specimens or at necropsy; in 9 there was serological evidence. In none of the patients was there evidence of associated endocarditis.

The pericarditis may be acute, subacute, or chronic. Acute pericarditis is associated with the sudden onset of substernal pain that may be made worse by breathing, and by shaking chills and fever. There is a polymorphonuclear leukocytosis. The electrocardiogram shows elevation of the ST segment and inversion of the T wave in many leads. Serial x-ray films of the chest may show an increasing cardiac silhouette as a result of the accumulation of pericardial fluid. Coexistent infiltrates or effusions may be noted in the lung fields.

The condition may gradually resolve, with apparent cure, or may enter a prolonged subacute or relapsing phase as in the case of Riegel and Schriever (1967), who eventually died of the disease.

At least two cases have proceeded to the development of constrictive pericarditis. Heiner (1958) described a thirteen-year-old boy with acute pericarditis that became constrictive within two months. Serological tests provided definite evidence of histoplasmosis. Subsequently the pericardium was resected, but microscopic examination showed only chronic inflammation and fibrosis. Wooley and Hosier (1961) described an eleven-year-old girl who had acute pericarditis and pleuritis, and three years later was seen in severe congestive heart failure. X-ray films of the chest showed calcification in the pericardium and both lungs, the histoplasmin complement fixation test was strongly positive, and cardiac catheterization provided supportive evidence for constriction. Pericardial tissue obtained at corrective surgery was found to contain *H. capsulatum*.

In view of the clinical and pathological resemblance to tuberculosis, and of the relatively frequent involvement of the mediastinum (Slyer, Harrison, Winn and Taylor, 1959; Marshall, Edmundowicz and Andrews, 1964), it is surprising that histoplasmosis does not more frequently involve the pericardium. It may be that in endemic areas some of the cases of acute or chronic pericarditis for which no etiology can be established are due to histoplasmosis.

Other Forms of Cardiac Involvement

Histoplasmosis occasionally causes myocarditis (Humphrey, 1940; Kuzma, 1947). Crawford, Crook, Harrison and Somervill (1961) reported acute myocarditis and pericarditis in two siblings with fever, symptoms of respiratory tract infections, and positive complement fixation tests for histoplasmosis. In one of the children there was persistent flattening and inversion of the T waves of the electrocardiogram together with persistent tachycardia and cardiomegaly.

Goldin and Saliba (1967) surveyed thirty-five patients with chronic pulmonary histoplasmosis. Using clinical, radiological and electrocardiographic criteria, they found evidence of cor pulmonale in seven (20%).

Finally, there have been a few reports of obstruction of the pulmonary veins (Bindelglass and Trubowitz, 1958; Haché, Woolner and Bernatz, 1962) and arteries (Söderberg, 1945; Marshall *et al.*, 1964) by chronic mediastinal fibrosis.

References

Billings, F.T., Jr. and Couch, O.A., Jr. (1955). Pericardial calcification and histoplasmin sensitivity. *Ann. Intern. Med., 42*:654-658.

Bindelglass, I.L. and Trubowitz, S. (1958). Pulmonary vein obstruction: An uncommon sequel to chronic fibrous mediastinitis. *Ann. Intern. Med., 48*:876-890.

Broders, A.C., Dochat, G.R., Herrell, W.E. and Vaughn, L.D. (1943). Histoplasmosis producing vegetative endocarditis. *J.A.M.A., 122*:489-492.

Crawford, S.T., Crook, W.G., Harrison, W.W. and Somervill, B. (1961). Histoplasmosis as a cause of acute myocarditis and pericarditis: report of occurrent in siblings and a review of the literature. *Pediatrics, 28*:92-95.

Derby, B.M., Coolidge, K. and Rogers, D.E. (1962). *Histoplasma capsulatum endocarditis* with major arterial embolism. *Arch. Intern. Med., 110*:63-69.

Goldin, A.G. and Saliba, N.A. (1967). The heart in chronic pulmonary histoplasmosis. *Southern Med. J., 60*:638-642.

Haché, L., Woolner, L.B. and Bernatz, P.E. (1962). Idiopathic fibrous mediastinitis. *Dis. Chest, 41*:9-25.

Heiner, D.C. (1958). Diagnosis of histoplasmosis using precipitin reactions in agar gel. *Pediatrics, 22*:616-627.

Humphrey, A.A. (1940). Reticuloendothelial cytomycosis (histoplasmosis of Darling). *Arch. Intern. Med., 62*:902-918.

Kuzma, J.F. (1947). Histoplasmosis: the pathologic and clinical findings. *Dis. Chest, 13*:338-344.

Marshall, R.J., Edmundowicz, A.C. and Andrews, C.E. (1964). Chronic obstruction of the superior vena cava due to histoplasmosis. A hemodynamic and angiographic correlation. *Circulation, 29*:604-609.

Merchant, R.K., Louria, D.B., Geisler, P.H., Edgcomb, J.H. and Utz, J.P. (1958). Fungal endocarditis: review of literature and report of 3 cases. *Ann. Intern. Med., 48*:242-266.

Moore, M. (1955). Morphologic variation in tissue of organisms of the blastomycoses and of histoplasmosis. *Amer. J. Path., 31*:1049-1063.

Palmer, R.L., Geraci, J.E. and Thomas, B.J. (1962). *Histoplasma* endocarditis. *Arch. Intern. Med., 110*:359-365.

Riegel, N. and Schriever, H.G. (1967). Fatal pericarditis due to histoplasmosis. Report of a case. *Amer. Rev. Resp. Dis., 95*:99-102.

Riehl, G. (1925). Durch pathogene Sprosspilze bedingte Granulome. *Arch. Derm. Syph., 148*:392-398.

Silverman, F.N., Schwarz, J., Lahey, M.E. and Carson, R.P. (1955). Histoplasmosis. *Amer. J. Med., 19*:410-459.

Slyer, J.M., Harrison, H.N., Winn, D.F. and Taylor, R.R. (1959). Chronic fibrous mediastinitis and superior vena caval obstruction due to histoplasmosis. *Dis. Chest, 35*:364-377.

Söderberg, G. (1945). Om striktur av arteria pulmonalis genom skrupnande mediastinit. *Nord. Med., 28*:2051-2056.

Weaver, D.K., Batsakis, J.G. and Nishiyama, R.H. (1968). *Histoplasma* endocarditis. *Arch. Surg., 96*:158-162.

Wooley, C.F. and Hosier, D.M. (1961). Constrictive pericarditis due to *Histoplasma capsulatum*. *New Eng. J. Med. 264*:1230-1232.

Chapter 30

Patterns of Histoplasmosis Among Children

WARREN E. WHEELER

ABSTRACT

Children show a great range of patterns of infection by *Histoplasma capsulatum*. Local and skin lesions are rare; serious life-threatening infections are uncommon and are concentrated in the very young. On the other end of the frequency spectrum, relatively asymptomatic infection with skin test conversion may be occurring in 5 percent of children at any time in areas of high incidence, as in Central Kentucky. The use of steroids and immunosuppresive drugs may elevate asymptomatic histoplasmosis to clinical significance. The occurrence of R-E (reticuloendothelial) blockade and disseminated intravascular clotting in patients with severe disseminated histoplasmosis are possible.

IN the "*Histoplasma* belt" of the United States, infection of children with *H. capsulatum* is almost universal. Disease in these children recognized by the physician, on the other hand, is quite uncommon. Most childhood histoplasmosis is never brought to the attention of the physician. One reason for failure of physicians to recognize the disease is the tendency of this fungus to mimic self-limited trivial respiratory illness. When it does occasionally impress the physician because of its severity, histoplasmosis mimics a variety of other illnesses including tuberculosis, leukemia, and other granulomatous diseases. Correct diagnosis depends on an awareness of its manifold patterns of presentation plus the availability of skin-testing material and a repertory of laboratory tests including culture, biopsy, and serologic methods. The present report makes no attempt to be encyclopedic but represents the recent experience of one small pediatric service situated in the *Histoplasma* belt.

Patterns of Histoplasmosis Among Children

Table 30-I portrays children with positively diagnosed histoplasmosis since the opening of the children's service at the University of Kentucky in 1962. These children were diagnosed by a pediatric staff acutely aware of histoplasmosis, using histoplasmin skin test freely, and having available to it in its own laboratories agar-gel precipitins, and at the State Department of Health Laboratories complement fixation tests, and in the central clinical laboratories and the laboratories of the Department of Community Medicine competent cultural methods. The case material of the University of

Kentucky Medical Center comes about equally from the *Histoplasma* belt, where over 80 percent of young adults are histoplasmin positive, and the Cumberland plateau, where only 10 to 20 percent are positive. Table 30-I does not include children who have positive histoplasmin skin tests but no clinical evidence of histoplasmosis. We must admit we have not routinely retested with skin tests "in follow-up" all our children with nonspecific pneumonia. During this time there were 7,200 inpatient admissions to the children's service. Although our total case material is relatively small, we must conclude that compared to the prevalence of histoplasmosis in children in our area, serious disease is remarkably uncommon. Rather than variations in virulence of the organism, this encourages us to suspect innate or temporary aberrations in defense in these few children.

Among this small number of patients the following patterns of infection can be recognized:

1. Asymptomatic infection with skin test conversion.
2. Self-limited pulmonary infiltrate with skin test conversion.
3. Disseminated histoplasmosis.
4. *Histoplasma* meningitis.
5. Local surface lesions.

TABLE 30-I

Some Characteristics of Patients With Childhood Histoplasmosis

Patient	Age (years)	Type of Infection*	Disseminated	Local	Skin Test	Low WBC	Low Platlet	Amphotericin
Pr	2/12	3	+		−	+	+	+
Bo	3/12	3	+		+	−	−	+
Bi	3/12	3	+		−	+	+	+
Mo	3/12	3	+		N.D.	N.D.	+	−
Th	5/12	3	+		−	+	+	+
Ri	6/12	3	+		−	+	+	+
Su	6/12	3	+		−	−	+	+
Ma	1 1/2	3	+		+	+	+	+
Sp	2	2		+	+			
Co	3	3–5	+		N.D.	(+)	(+)	+
Ri	5	2		+	+	+		
Fo	5	6		+	+			
Cr	5	2		+	+			
Fi	6	2		+	+			
St	6	2		+	+			
Wi	6	2		+	+			
Pd	7	1		+	+			
Ta	8	6		+	+			
Sr	8	4		+	+			+
Je	9	7		+	+	+		
Ca	10	7		+	+			+
Ga	11	7		+	+			

* Numbers refer to table of patterns of infection in text.
N.D. = Not Done

6. Chronic active pulmonary infiltrate.

7. Lymphadenitis

With two exceptions all the cases of disseminated histoplasmosis were under one year of age. In one instance the disease disseminated in a patient under the influence of steroids and immunosuppressive agents. There was one instance of meningitis, an eight-year-old boy who was thought initially to have aseptic meningitis and who carried cells in his spinal fluid for two years before chronic increase in intracranial pressure led the neurosurgeons to introduce a ventriculojugular shunt. Shortly after this foreign body was placed, cultures of the fluid obtained from the shunt valve yielded *Histoplasma*. An attempt was made to treat this child with amphotericin B systemically, but the cultures remained positive until the shunt was removed. The evidences of meningitis cleared rapidly following shunt removal, and the child has remained well for at least a year subsequently.

It will be noticed that negative skin tests were the rule in the infants with disseminated histoplasmosis under a year. Most of these children had normal or elevated gamma globulins, none were studied for phagocytic dysfunction, nor were any studied for paralysis of delayed hypersensitivity reactions. At least three of the older children had moved into our area within one year. Peripheral white counts less than 5,000 usually accompanied serious illness; all of those with this degree of leukopenia were treated. It is possible that this may be accounted for partly by the fact that a low white count has been one of our indications for treatment.

Table 30-II, again listing patients according to increasing age, shows the patients' status on admission. It is clearly evident that the clinical picture of disseminated disease was well established at admission in all the infants under six months, regardless of their presenting complaint. Indeed, the presenting complaint was associated with the respiratory tract in four of these infants. In general, the preschool and early school-age children presented with pulmonary symptoms, and the routine application of skin tests and resort to serologic confirmation led to the diagnosis of histoplasmosis. Glandular involvement as a major problem occurred in older children. All the patients survived, except for two who were moribund on admission.

Mode of Transmission

If, as has been suggested, histoplasmosis is transmitted by inhalation of spore-laden dust, it is understandable how active older children might become infected. But how about tiny infants who spend most of their time inside their homes, relatively protected from the outside environment? We have only a few observations on this point, although we are fascinated by the problem. With the aid of residents and fellows of the Department of

TABLE 30–II

Status of Patients on Admission

Patient	Age (years)	Anemia	Big Liver, Spleen	Positive Skin Test Serology*	Cough Fever	Big Glands	Other
Pr	2/12	+	+				1 jaundice
Bo	3/12		+		1		
Bi	3/12	+	+		1		
Mo	3/12	+	+		1		died
Th	5/12	+	+		1		
Ri	6/12	+	+		+		1 malabsorption
Su	6/12	1	+				died
Ma	1½	+	+		1		
Sp	2				1		
Co	3	(+)	(+)	1 (bone marrow)		(+)	relapse of leukemia
Ri	5				1		
Fo	5				1		
Cr	5				1		
Fi	6			1	+		nephrosis
St	6				1		
Wi	6				1		
Pd	7			1			pericarditis
Ta	8			1			rheumatic fever
Sr	8			1 (culture)			aseptic meningitis
Je	9		+		+	1	
Ca	10					1	
Ga	11					1	

1 = Presenting complaint due to histoplasmosis.
+ = Incidental finding on admission.
* = Finding organism or + skin test or + serology lead to diagnosis.

Community Medicine, visits have been made to the homes of several of our infant patients. In one instance, a family with a newborn baby moved to a new home on the outskirts of Lexington. The previous owners of the one-room dwelling kept chickens in a coop outside the door. The patient's family did not want to raise chickens but saw in the old chicken coop an ideal coal bin. Inside the shack the coal stove, the coal bucket, and the baby's crib were arranged in sequence along one wall. We never isolated *H. capsulatum* from the coal dust, but we did grow the fungus from the soil from the floor of the coal bin. The dust-borne route of transmission seems obvious. This baby had his first symptoms at two and one-half months of age.

Another family with an affected three-month-old infant lived in a shack on a rural hillside. The shack stood on stilts four feet above the bare ground, chickens had roosted under the house four or five years ago; the family dogs lived there now. There were wide cracks in the wooden floor which allowed a lively up-draft from the prevailing wind into the shack. The up-draft was understandably dusty when the dogs were active. Of numerous soil samples taken about the premises, only the soil under the house yielded *H. capsu-*

latum. Such instances do not prove the mode of transmission, but they point the way to further investigation. We are encouraged to consider dust inhalation as the most likely avenue of infection even in small infants.

Intravascular Clotting

As have others, we have been impressed by the tendency of infants with disseminated histoplasmosis to have hemolytic anemia, leukopenia, and thrombopenia in the acute phase of their infection (Holland and Holland, 1966). In the past we have attributed this to "hypersplenism" and have considered it to be analogous to similar hematologic consequences of miliary tuberculosis in the infant.

That this may not be the entire explanation is illustrated by the findings in several children we have observed. Recently, since we became aware of the association of disseminated intravascular clotting (consumption coagulopathy) and sepsis, we have observed a three-month-infant dying of histoplasmosis. The infant was referred to us because of pneumonia, anemia, and an enlarged spleen. He had been ill two weeks. He was moribund on admission and died within an hour. Diagnosis of disseminated histoplasmosis was made by observing large numbers of phagocytized *H. capsulatum* in the peripheral smear. The platelets in the smear were nearly absent. Autopsy was performed within a few hours of death. No postmortem blood clot was found. While no determinations of fibrinogen or individual clotting factors were performed, it seems evident that disseminated intravascular clotting had occurred.

This patient recalled another six-month-old, jaundiced infant referred to the medical center because of severe anemia and petechiae (case 4, Holland and Holland, 1966). He had been ill two weeks and was also moribund. *Histoplasma* organisms were seen in his peripheral smear. Despite treatment with amphotericin B, he died on the fourth hospital day. Platelets were 52,000 on entry but fell to 5,000 before death. His peripheral blood smear showed severe red cell fragmentation, anisocytosis, target cells, nucleated red cells, and marked polychromatophilia. This is identical to the hematologic findings in the hemolytic-uremic syndrome of infancy (Gianantonio *et al.,* 1964). Indeed, postmortem examination showed a number of thrombi in small blood vessels in the lungs.

The occurence of disseminated intravascular clotting in the hemolytic-uremic syndrome has been attributed to the intravascular liberation of thromboplastic substances from the hemolyzed red cells (Rodriguez-Erdmann, 1965). The severe anemia, jaundice, and absence of serum haptoglobin in this case indicate a hemolytic anemia which might lead to disseminated intravascular clotting. On the other hand, similar, if not identical, red cell morphology has been observed in disseminated intravascular clotting as a result of sepsis (Rosner and Rubenberg, 1969). We have, ourselves, observed fragmented red cells in instances of proven disseminated intravascular clotting in patients with meningococcemia and Rocky Mountain spotted fever. Could sepsis that is due to disseminated histoplasmosis cause disseminated intravascular clotting by the same mechanisms as in gram-negative bacillus sepsis?

Still another observation of the postmortem examination mentioned above seems relevant. The cells of the entire reticuloendothelial system were chock-full of *H. capsulatum*. It is now recognized that R-E blockade is essential for the full manifestations of the syndrome of disseminated intravascular clotting. It seems likely that reticuloendothelial system so busy coping with *H. capsulatum* would be unable to eliminate efficiently circulating fibrin and other generators of intravascular clotting. We mention these observations in the hope that others will amplify them. We would suggest that in the future, examination of individual clotting factor levels be made in any instance of thrombopenia in disseminated histoplasmosis. In our opinion, histoplasmosis must be added to the list of infections capable of causing disseminated intravascular clotting.

Spread by Steroids

One three-year-old child was followed in our clinic for acute lymphoblastic leukemia. She had been treated with prednisone and 6-mercaptopurine for a period of about three months and had enjoyed a satisfactory hematologic remission. Then she developed a sore on the tip of her tongue, her liver and spleen increased in size, her anemia returned, and her platelets fell. It was thought that she had a relapse of her leukemia, and a bone marrow examination was performed to document this relapse. Instead, *H. capsulatum* were found in mononuclear cells in her bone marrow smear, and *Histoplasma* were later cultured from this material. The steroids and 6-mercaptopurine were stopped immediately, and she was treated for ten days with amphotericin B and tranfusions. The organisms disappeared quickly from her bone marrow; the lesion on her tongue, from which *H. capsulatum* was recovered, healed, and she made a very satisfactory recovery from her disseminated histoplasmosis, only to die at a later date of her leukemia. There were no signs of active histoplasmosis following her antifungal treatment, nor were there any at autopsy.

Since steroids and the use of immunosuppressive agents have been shown to increase the chances of dissemination of tuberculosis, it is not surprising to find similar dissemination of histoplasmosis with the use of these agents. Presumably, the impairment of delayed hypersensitivity reaction, the inhibition of phagocytosis, and the stabilization of lysosomal membranes which may result from corticosteroid administration can reduce the host's ability to localize and contain the infection. In a slow-moving disease such as convalescent pulmonary histoplasmosis, dissemination may not be observed and documented because steroids may have to be administered in high dosage over a prolonged interval to spread the disease. On the other hand, in areas of high prevalence of histoplasmosis, the problem frequently arises that one wishes to treat with steroids a child who is undergoing his initial *Histoplasma* infection at that time. For instance, in Pulaski County in Kentucky, a survey of six-year-old children examined for the Head-start program showed that one child out of every twenty had active pulmonary histoplasmosis at the time of examination, even though the symptoms were so mild that the children were not under medical care. Presumably steroid administration might be harmful instead of helpful in one out of every twenty, six-year-old nephrotics, rheumatics, or leukemics in Pulaski County.

Since serologic tests can give information leading one to assume activity or quiesence of infection, it would seem wise, when considering the use of steroid or immunosuppressive agents, to skin test children for histoplasmosis as well as tuberculosis.

We have had several instances where such decisions had to be made. One little girl had childhood nephrosis and was discovered to have a positive skin test. A complement fixation titer of 1:32 (yeast phase) and a positive pulmonary infiltrate and hilar nodes by chest radiograph indicated active histoplasmosis. In her case the nephrosis was treated symptomatically for two years, and steroids and Cytoxan® were withheld, since she was doing pretty well without them. Another girl of eight years developed acute rheumatic fever and rheumatic carditis. In addition she had a right lower lobe infiltrate and a story of chronic cough, and it was felt she also had bronchiectasis. Hr histoplasmin skin test was positive and her serum showed strongly positive H and M precipitin bands. Her complement fixation test (yeast phase) was 1:32. Her rheumatic carditis and her heart failure were treated without the use of steroids. At a later date a right lower lobectomy was performed for her bronchiectasis and a mitral valvuloplasty was also performed. It is interesting that two years after her lobectomy which possibly removed her main area of *histoplasmosis*, her skin test was negative. This was unexpected, so a repeat test was performed four days later. A positive reaction occurred in forty-eight hours at the site of both the first and the second intradermal injections of histoplasmin.

Another boy of seven years developed acute pericarditis within a year after moving to Lexington from India. His disease was compatable with acute rheumatic fever, but he also had a positive histoplasmin skin test, strongly positive H and M precipitin bands, and a white blood count of only 6,000. In cases of acute rheumatic pericarditis of this severity, steroids are usually indicated. In his case, however, the pericarditis was treated symptomatically because we could not be sure that it was not due to histoplasmosis. He recovered without ill effects.

In another instance a ten-year-old boy who had dyspnea owing to tracheal compression as a result of peritracheal adenitis was noted to have a positive histoplasmin skin test at admission. *H. capsulatum* was never recovered from bone marrow, blood, or gastric aspirates, but he had strongly positive H and M precipitin bands and a complement fixation titer of 1:128 (yeast phase). His airway was precarious. X-ray treatment for the severe tracheal obstruction was considered dangerous; tracheotomy, too difficult. Had the adenopathy been due to lymphoma, steroids would have been indicated. The patient was given amphotericin B for twenty-two days, concurrent steroids, for one month. There was slight shrinkage of the glands at the end of one week and considerable shrinkage at the end of one month. Clearing progressed and was complete at six months. No dissemination was detected.

These anecdotes illustrate the reasons behind our recommendation that in the areas of high rates of histoplasmin conversion whenever steroid administration is considered in children, 1) a skin test with histoplasmin should be performed and serum should be drawn at the same time for complement fixation tests or precipitins 2) a positive skin test and serologic evidence of active histoplasmosis should make one reconsider the necessity of the steroids, and 3) if steroids are essential, then concurrent amphotericin treatment should be administered unless it, in turn, is otherwise contraindicated.

References

Holland, P. and Holland N. (1966). Histoplasmosis in early infancy. *Amer. J. Dis. Child.*, 112:412.

Gianantonio, C., *et al.* (1964). Hemolytic-uremic syndrome. *J. Pediat.*, 64:478.

Rodriguez-Erdmann, F. (1965). Bleeding due to increased intravascular blood coagulation. *New Eng. J. Med.*, 273:1370.

Rosner, F. and Rubenberg, M.K. (1969). Erythrocyte fragmentation in consumption coagulopathy. *New Eng. J. Med.*, 280:219.

Chapter 31

The Pathogenesis of Histoplasmosis

JAN SCHWARZ

ABSTRACT

The respiratory portal of entry and pulmonary primary complex of African and American histoplasmosis are stressed. The infantile type in classic histoplasmosis with hepatosplenomegaly and lymphadenomegaly is rare to exceptional, the self-limited or even subclinical disease being the rule. Hematogenous (self-limited) dissemination is common during primary infection, as evidenced especially by splenic "metastases." The morphologic response to *Histoplasma duboisii* is so radically different from the pathology seen in infection with *H. capsulatum* that a considerable case for species difference can be made.

THE pathogenesis of histoplasmosis now seems an open book: *Histoplasma capsulatum* enters the lungs by inhalation of spore-containing dust; a pulmonary inflammation results, then becomes localized, the necrosis in the lung becomes encapsulated—to calcify subsequently. At the same time the regional lymph nodes become inflamed and reflect, as in tuberculosis, the disease process in the lungs. This phenomenon is rightly called Parrot's law.*

Often the lymph node component of the primary complex is larger than the primary pulmonary focus proper. When we compare the size of the primary calcified focus with the Ghon lesion of tuberculosis, we find many more large foci with histoplasmosis than with tuberculosis. Or, putting it differently, whenever we find a calcified focus larger than 1 cm in diameter, chances are excellent that we shall find *H. capsulatum* in its center and no *Mycobacterium tuberculosis*. (Table 31-I)

In addition, the histoplasmic lesions are frequently characterized by multiple discrete calcific foci, in contradistinction to most other granulomatous diseases, which exhibit one, single, uniformly calcified focus after healing. The primary complex may be described as classic in histoplasmosis as compared to the primary infection in blastomycosis and coccidioidomycosis; in coccidioidomycosis, pulmonary foci are always demonstrable, but not necessarily the lymph node component, and we conclude (Straub and Schwarz, 1962) that in coccidioidomycosis the involvement of lymph nodes actually represents the first stage of dissemination. While primary foci are seen in blastomycosis, there is not enough well-studied material available to make

---

* . . . lymph nodes reflect like a mirror the pathology of the parenchyma . . . (Parrot, 1876.).

TABLE 31-I

Comparison of Size of Components of Primary Complexes in
Histoplasmosis and Tuberculosis

	Total Number	1–4 mm	5–10 mm	10 mm or More
Primary Focus Lung				
Histoplasmosis	67	34%	62%	3%
Tuberculosis	34	79%	20%	
Lymph Nodes of the Primary Complex				
Histoplasmosis	70		68%	32%
Tuberculosis	24		88%	12%

Modified from Straub, M. and Schwarz, J., 1962.

sweeping statements about the regularity of a "classic" primary complex.
(Table 31-II)

During the primary infection in histoplasmosis, hematogenous dissemination is very common, if not the rule. We can demonstrate this dissemination by occasional positive blood cultures in minimal clinical disease and, more frequently in the form of granulomas in spleen and liver (Schwarz *et al.*, 1955; Okudaira *et al.*, 1961; Salfelder and Schwarz, 1967). We have found such granulomas in all stages of activity in incidental splenectomies, undertaken for other reasons, and at autopsy. Interestingly enough, we have recently seen one acute such dissemination in an afebrile patient who was prepared for renal transplant (unpublished data). In the first stage her kidneys and spleen were removed; the astute surgeon, noticing the innumerable nodules in the spleen, also took a liver biopsy and stopped right there without attempting to implant the new kidney. After the diagnosis of disseminated active histoplasmosis, the patient was given intense amphotericin therapy, and her complement fixation titer dropped from 128 to 4 while on the dialyzer, without a kidney; in this way the damage to the new (future) kidney was, hopefully, avoided and the dissemination checked. We will undoubtedly learn more in the future about the influence of therapy on the pathogenesis of the disease.

We were able to demonstrate splenic calcifications in almost half of our

TABLE 31-II

X-ray Measurement of Intrathoracic Calcific Foci

	5 mm or Less	6 mm or More	"Stippled"
Positive histoplasmin negative tuberculin	1	30	75
H. capsulatum demonstrated in focus	2	22	67

Modified from Serviansky and Schwarz, 1957.

random autopsy material and to recognize them *in vivo* on x-ray (Servian-sky and Schwarz, 1956). When there were concentric rings in the calcific shadows, or if there were five or more foci, *Histoplasma* could always be demonstrated on microscopic examination in the lesions. Young *et al.* (1957), who first had difficulty in confirming our findings, are now convinced (Mashburn *et al.*, 1961) that splenic calcifications—if multiple—are a sure sign of healed primary self-limited benign dissemination of *H. capsulatum*. (Table 31-III)

No such dissemination seems to occur during primary infection with any of the other deep fungi, or if it does, it would seem to heal without leaving traces or certainly without resulting in multiple calcifications. Whether tuberculosis can produce multiple calcifications in the spleen is somewhat doubtful; if it occurs at all, it must be exceptional. Certainly the calcifications in the spleen (when multiple) are not phleboliths, as has been commonly held, since we can demonstrate *H. capsulatum* with the Grocott stain quite convincingly.

In addition to the classic solitary primary focus, we find cases with multiple to numerous primary foci. Two to ten simultaneous foci of equal size are distinctly more common in dogs than in man, but dozens to hundreds are in turn more often seen in man and represent the result of massive exposure to heavily infected dust (Schwarz *et al.*, 1960). In such episodes, numerous foci of inflammation develop quickly in the lung and seldom reach large sizes. After years, when the lesions are calcified, they measure just a few millimeters and can be recognized by their uniform appearance as to size, calcific quality, and frequently by the presence of a bony rim commonly with a bone marrow cavity.

In spite of the great number of pulmonary foci, the draining lymph nodes are not more numerous or larger than in primary infection with one single pulmonary focus. The x-ray sequence of the development of multiple calcifications after heavy exposure to contaminated soil is uniform also, but with a certain degree of variation in the speed with which calcification becomes demonstrable. Hazy multiple foci are first seen on x-rays a few days to two weeks after exposure, but calcification can take many months to develop or, in some cases, may fail to develop at all; one wonders whether this conceivably could be the case in patients who had partial protection through previ-

TABLE 31-III

Frequency of Splenic Calcifications of Histoplasmic Origin in Consecutive Autopsy Cases in Three Cities

	Total Number	"Typical" round foci	%
Cincinnati	120	53	44
New York	108	3	3
Rotterdam	102	2	2

ous primary infection but who have insufficient immunity to prevent reinfection after massive exposure. We have reported several such instances, the
most dramatic connected with the Eden Park water tower epidemic in Cincinnati, Ohio (Schwarz and Baum, 1963). Autopsies on persons with multiple calcified lesions sometimes show thousands of foci, uniform in size and
age, generally 4 to 5 mm in diameter, within a bony rim and with central
calcification.

The microscopic picture of reaction to *H. capsulatum* varies considerably
and differs greatly, depending on immunologic factors, but also on age, dose
of inoculum, concurrent therapy, and so on. In early age—and only exceptionally in later life—the tissue reaction is characteristically histiocytic, with
innumerable large phagocytic cells comprising the normal structure of the
organ. This is most outstanding in the organs such as spleen, lymph nodes,
bone marrow and liver, endowed normally with numerous histiocytic elements.

In discussing pathogenesis, a clear understanding is necessary on the portal of entry of *H. capsulatum* into the animal body and on which lesions
should rightly be called "primary."

That the lung is almost without exception the portal of entry is attested
by the following reasons: (1) epidemiologic evidence—the exposure to cultures in the laboratory, the inhalation of spore-containing dust, and the so-
called epidemic cases arising after particularly heavy exposure; (2) this can
often be verified by x-ray; (3) this in turn can be found in the acute form at
autopsy or at surgery. Fortunately, acute cases are few and far between, and
relatively few autopsies with florid acute pulmonary complexes occur, but
they have been described exquisitely by Schulz and have been seen by
many others, including ourselves. In view of the relatively benign nature of
the infection, the primary lesion almost always becomes arrested; and in
view of the ensuing necrosis, the lesion subsequently calcifies, and the
healed primary complex is a constant classic, and irrevocable sequela of pulmonary primary infection. (Table 31-IV)

Upon scrutiny of the three points, it becomes obvious that the respiratory
tract, open as it is to contact with the outer world, offers easy entry to the
airborne spores or mycelial fragments of *H. capsulatum*. Common experi-

TABLE 31-IV

Presence of Healed Histoplasmic Lesions in Unselected Consecutive Autopsies in Cincinnati
in Patients Dying of Diseases Other Than Histoplasmosis

Total number of autopsies	Histoplasmosis demonstrated	%
105	70	66.6
55	47	85.4*

* X-ray examination of lungs after removal from thoracic cavity.

ence indicates that other parts of the respiratory system (nose, pharynx, trachea) rarely become the site of a primary granulomatous infection; on the contrary, it can be stated safely that laryngeal granulomas are for all practical purposes secondary to pulmonary lesions, either in "contact" infection— sputum from the deep bronchial channels lodging on the laryngeal mucosa— or by way of blood-borne "metastases." Exceptional intranasal syphilitic chancres have been observed, but to claim that this is frequent would be a grave mistake. Similarly, the possibility of an intranasal chancre in histoplasmosis is conceivable, but if it occurs, it must be the exceptional case, where some experimental injection fluid loaded with organisms has hit the nasal mucosa rather than its intended target; such accidental primary intraocular infection in the conjunctiva is fairly well documented in one case (Spicknall *et al.*, 1956).

Ordinarily the morphologist would religiously avoid offering an opinion on taxonomic problems and would shun the responsibility of entering into this area of controversy, but in view of the contribution that morphology can make in the distinction between *H. capsulatum* and *H. duboisii*, it would be a distinct disservice on my part to skip the issue. The pros and cons, whether *H. duboisii* is a separate species, have been discussed *in extenso* (Ajello, 1968; Pine *et al.*, 1964), but it may suffice to say that while all observers agree that *H. duboisii* is different in the yeast form from the run-of-the-mill strain of *H. capsulatum*, there is no agreement on whether the morphologic and biologic behavior of the strains justify a separate species or whether some less definite separation and classification will suffice (Vanbreuseghem, 1964).

The tissue response in spontaneous and experimental disease is so markedly different from the pathology observed in classic histoplasmosis that one cannot help but feel that we are dealing with a different organism. If a culture of *H. duboisii* in the yeast form is injected into animals, it will contain a fair number (frequently a majority) of "*capsulatum* forms," or small yeasts of about 5µ tops, and few large round or slightly oval "*duboisii* forms." After passage of time (several days to about 2-6 weeks), the number of "*capsulatum* forms" decreases to a point where they have to be hunted for, and the field is taken over completely by the "*duboisii* forms."

Equally, the response of the invaded human or lower animal body does not consist of the classic histiocytic proliferation which we see with regularity in classic histoplasmosis; in *duboisii* infection, spectacular syncytial giant cells are formed, some more than 200µ in diameter, and in the giant cells we find, neatly stacked, the large round-to-ovoid duboisii forms.

In human disease of African histoplasmosis little material has been worked up to my satisfaction, and I am skeptical of statements that the respiratory tract is bypassed as the portal of entrance. Not only empiric and theoretic reasons would suggest the lung as the logical locus for the primary infection, but we are also steered in this direction by some other rather pointed information. One patient of Basset *et al.*, (1962), for instance, acquired his infection after "sweeping duty" in a bat-infested school! Further, three cases with positive sputa are on record (Dubois *et al.*, 1952; Jarniou *et al.*, 1958; Vandepitte *et al.*, 1957). Radiologic evidence of pulmonary disease was mentioned by Jarniou *et al.*, 1958, and Lanceley *et al.*, 1961. Somewhat surprisingly, Vandepitte *et al.*, 1957, interpreted lung lesions found at autopsy to contain yeast cells of *H. duboisii* as mycobacteria. Clark and Greenwood, 1968, tabulate ten cases of African histoplasmosis with pulmonary involvement and concur with the concept of the pulmonary origin of African histoplasmosis so thoroughly documented for the classic "American" histoplasmosis, for coccidioidomycosis, N.A. blastomycosis, and so on. Only a half dozen cases were brought to autopsy, and performing an autopsy, unfortunately, is not synonymous with a searching, conclusive, and competent laboratory investigation.

To underline the possible neglect of demonstration of lesions in the lung during autopsy, we quote two sentences from a manuscript presently in press: "Good evidence exists that pulmonary lesions can be found in African histoplasmosis if searched for properly. Few dilettante performers of autopsies can possibly be trusted to rule out small primary lesions in the lung; even the most experienced (and specialized) pathologists prefer the help of x-rays of lungs removed from the body in order to locate small calcified foci" (Schwarz).

In addition to the distinctly different microscopic reaction to *H. duboisii*, there is also an organ involvement and distribution of lesions which is radically different from the one seen in classic histoplasmosis. In the first place, there is a marked tendency to involvement of flat bones, particularly of the skull, scapula, and jaw, frequently with overlying abscesses. Multiple skin lesions are also seen, often connected with subcutaneous abscesses, which in turn are frequently secondary to osteomyelitis and osteitis.

Certain reluctance should exist in accepting this apparent tropism of *H. duboisii* in skin and bone, since the initial claim of Darling that the disease was characterized by hepatosplenomegaly and was always fatal certainly would not be acceptable today when we have established that the overwhelming majority of "American" cases are asymptomatic and subclinical. The small number of observations of African histoplasmosis may not be representative of the natural history of the disease. Lymphadenopathy also appears very prominent in African histoplasmosis, to judge from published illustrations.

In summary, we can say that everything points toward the lungs as the portal of entrance in natural infection with both *H. capsulatum* and *H. duboisii*. A self-limited benign, frequently asymptomatic, reaction leads subsequently to establishment of a calcified primary complex that is larger and, therefore, easier to spot on x-ray, at surgery, or at autopsy. Multiple splenic calcifications are visible proof of hematogenous spread during primary infection.

Figure 31-1 should facilitate the derivation of complications and pathogenetic development in the comparatively few symptomatic cases of the disease. The very different morphology in reactions to *H. duboisii* and to the lesions encountered in classic histoplasmosis gives further evidence to a recognition of their separate nature.

References

Ajello, L. (1968). Comparative morphology and immunology of members of the genus *Histoplasma. Mykosen, 11*:507-514.

Basset, A., Quenum, C., Hocquet, P., Camain, R. and Basset, M. (1962). Histoplasmose a forme cutaneo-osseuse. *Bull. Soc. Med. Afr. Noire, 7*:69-70.

Clark, B.M. and Greenwood, B.M. (1968). Pulmonary lesions in African histoplasmosis. *P. Trop. Med. Hyg., 71*:4-10.

Dubois, A., Janssens, P.G., Brutsaert, P. & Vanbreusegham, R. (1952). Un cas d'histoplasmose africaine. Avec une note mycologique sur *H. duboisii* n. sp. *Ann. Soc. Belg. Med. Trop., 32*:569-583.

Jarniou, A.P., Kerbrat, G., Moreau, A. and Duval. (1958). Etude mycologique: Drouhet,

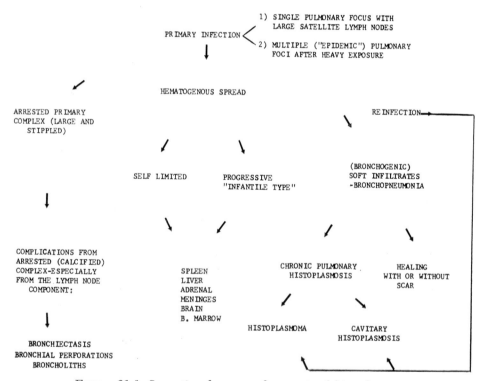

FIGURE 31-1. Synoptic scheme: pathogenesis of histoplasmosis.

E. Histoplasmose pulmonaire africaine avec suppuration diffuse apparue apres une annee d'evolution. *Bull. Mem. Soc. Med. Hopitaux Paris, 74:*32-33.

Lanceley, J.L., Lunn, H.F. and Wilson, A.M.M. (1961). Histoplasmosis in an African child. *J. Pediat., 49:*756-764.

Mashburn, J.D., Dawson, D.F. and Young, J.M. (1961). Pulmonary calcifications and histoplasmosis. *Amer. Rev. Resp. Dis., 84:*208-216.

Okudaira, M., Straub, M. and Schwarz, J. (1961). The etiology of discrete splenic and hepatic calcifications in an endemic area of histoplasmosis. *Amer. J. Path., 39:* 599-611.

Parrot, L.M.J. (1876). *C. R. Soc. Biol., 28:*308-309.

Pine, L., Drouhet, E. and Reynolds, G. (1964). A comparative morphological study of the yeast phases of *Histoplasma capsulatum* and *Histoplasma duboisii. Sabouraudia,* 3:211-224.

Salfelder, K. and Schwarz, J. (1967). Histoplasmotische Kalkherde in der Milz. *Dtsch. Med. Wchschr., 92:*1468-1470.

Schulz, D.M. (1950). A partially healed primary lesion in a case of generalized histoplasmosis. *Arch. Path., 50:*457-463.

Schwarz, J. (in press). Histoplasmosis in Henke-Lubarsch, Spez. *Pathol. Anat.*

Schwarz, J. (1960). The primary lesion in histoplasmosis. In Sweany, H.C. (Ed.). *Histoplasmosis.* Springfield, Thomas, pp.292-310.

Schwarz, J., Baum, G.L. and Floyd, H. (1960). The pathogenesis of "epidemic" histoplasmosis. *Ann. N.Y. Acad. Sci., 89:*47-58.

Schwarz, J. and Baum, G.L. (1963). Reinfection in histoplasmosis. *Arch. Path., 75:* 475-479.

Serviansky, B. and Schwarz, J. (1956). The incidence of splenic calcifications in positive reactions to histoplasmin and tuberculin. *Amer. J. Roentgen., 76:*53-59.

Serviansky, G. and Schwarz, J. (1957). Calcified intrathoracic lesions caused by histoplasmosis and tuberculosis. *Amer. J. Roentgen., 77:*1034-1041.

Spicknall, C.G., Ryan, R.W. and Cain, A. (1956). Laboratory-acquired histoplasmosis. *New Eng. J. Med., 254:*210-214.

Straub, M. and Schwarz, J. (1962). Histoplasmosis, coccidioidomycosis and tuberculosis: A comparative pathological study. *Path. Microbiol., 25:*421-477.

Vanbreuseghem, R. (1964). Les manifestations cutanees de l'histoplasmose africaine. *Ann. Soc. Belg. Med. Trop., 44:*1037-1056.

Vandepitte, J., Lamote, J., Thys, A. and Vanbreuseghem, R. (1957). Deuxieme cas congolais e'histoplasmose par *Histoplasma duboisii* Vanbreuseghem 1952. *Ann. Soc. Belg. Med. Trop., 37:*515-528.

Young, J.M., Bills, R.J. and Ulrich, E. (1957). Discrete splenic calcification in necropsy material. *Amer. J. Path., 33:*189-197.

Chapter 32

Reinfection Histoplasmosis

JOHN J. PROCKNOW

ABSTRACT

It has been impossible to produce either new pulmonary lesions or reactivation or cavitation of old lesions in dogs by multiple experimental attempts at exogenous reinfection with airborne mycelial elements or catheter-placed spores and yeast cells. Primary immunity achieved by active infection and subsequently boosted by reinfection appears to provide almost absolute protection against exogenous reinfection disease. Although these conclusions constitute a minority report, I should like to propose that chronic or cavitary histoplasmosis is an endogenous reinfection or continuous primary infection in man and dogs, having little or no relationship to environmental reexposures to *Histoplasma capsulatum* within an endemic area. Quiescent or attenuated foci of infection may reside for prolonged periods in organs of the reticuloendothelial system, including the lung, to serve as niduses for exacerbation or spread of infection when and if immunity becomes suppressed or host-organism relationship is unfavorably altered to the disadvantage of the host.

THE controversy concerning the actual pathogenesis of reinfection or chronic histoplasmosis merits our attention today, rather than the well-documented clinical and roentgenographic expression, diagnosis, prognosis and treatment of this interesting form of the disease. It still remains vague whether chronic histoplasmosis is the result of single or multiple exogenous reexposures to an endemic source of *H. capsulatum*, an endogenous reinfection, a reactivation, or merely a primary focal infection which progresses to chronicity. In the short time allotted me, I should simply like to present evidence from studies of experimental histoplasmosis in dogs which stresses the role of acquired immunity in preventing reinfection with *H. capsulatum* and seriously challenges the majority concept that exogenous reinfection produces chronic pulmonary histoplasmosis.

A simple closed device for inhalation exposure of dogs to airborne mycelial elements of *H. capsulatum* has been used successfully in our laboratory for many years to simulate naturally acquired infection. The ease of achieving an active primary histoplasmal infection by this means is substantiated by the fact that only four out of forty-one animals failed to develop clinical or laboratory confirmation of acute infection after experimental exposure. Chest roentgenograms showed a variety of lesions from single pneumonic

NOTE. This work was supported in part by Research Grant AI-00283 from the National Institute of Allergy and Infectious Diseases, United States Public Health Service.

infiltrates to diffuse granulomatous involvement, simulating the spectrum of human primary pulmonary histoplasmosis. Further evidence of the success of this method in producing primary infection, the acute dissemination of the infection, and the remarkable tendency for healing is derived from an evaluation of twelve of the dogs which expired or were sacrificed from three days to nine years after infection (Table 32-I). In the seven dogs necropsied within a two-week period following infection, cultures of tissues showed the immediate presence of *H. capsulatum* in the lungs. Lymphogenous spread to hilar lymph nodes occurred within one week, and hematogenous spread to other reticuloendothelial organs, namely, the liver, spleen and adrenals, during the second week. The death of a single animal of disseminated histoplasmosis at six weeks after infection, proved by positive cultures for *H. capsulatum* in enormous numbers from multiple tissues sampled, exemplifies the exceptional infection which overwhelms all natural and acquired defenses of the host. An animal necropsied at nineteen weeks after infection culturally revealed the residual presence of *H. capsulatum* in the hilar lymph nodes. The containment and subsequent healing, being the usual clinical course in histoplasmal infection, is substantiated by the remaining dogs examined four to nine years following infection. All tissues, including hilar lymph nodes, cultured from these animals were negative for *H. capsulatum*.

Following primary infection with airborne mycelial elements in the total complement of dogs, dermal hypersensitivity to histoplasmin developed in 90 percent of the animals, usually during the second or third week following infection. Complement-fixing antibodies to whole yeast antigen of *H. capsulatum* developed in serum titers ranging from 1:16 to 1:1024. A maximum

TABLE 32-I

Tissue Dissemination after Primary Infection with Airborne Mycelial Elements of *H. capsulatum*

Dog	Time Between Infection & Necropsy	Cultures					
		Lung	Hilar Nodes	Liver	Spleen	Adrenal	Bone Marrow
38	3D	+	0	0	0	0	ND
74	6D	ND	+	0	0	0	0
52	7D	+	+	0	0	ND	0
39	7D	+	+	+	0	0	0
73	13D	ND	+	+	+	0	0
44	14D	+	+	+	+	0	0
29	14D	+	+	+	+	+	0
1	6W	+	+	+	+	+	+
28	19W	C	+	0	0	0	ND
32	4Y	0	0	0	0	0	0
35	6Y	ND	0	0	0	0	0
8	9Y	0	0	0	0	0	0

ND = not done.
C = contaminated.

titer of 1:64 or over occurred in 84 percent of the dogs. These complement-fixing antibodies appeared during the second week following infection, reached a peak during the third week, sustained this level for a few weeks, and gradually declined thereafter over months to several years. To histoplasmin antigen, complement-fixing antibodies developed in a serum titer range of 1:2 to 1:128, with maximum titers of 1:8 or over observed in 85 percent of the animals. These complement-fixing antibodies to histoplasmin appeared during the third week following infection, lagging behind the appearance of antibodies to whole yeast antigen. They reached an abrupt peak by the end of the third week, sustained this level through the seventh week, rapidly declined thereafter, and totally disappeared by five months after infection. Precipitating antibodies to histoplasmin, utilizing either the tube or agar-gel diffusion method, were detected in 91 percent of the dogs and closely paralleled the presence and disappearance of complement-fixing antibodies to histoplasmin antigen.

In fourteen dogs having acquired a primary infection, reinfection with airborne mycelial elements was attempted on one to thirty-three occasions at time intervals varying from one day to three years following the previous infection challenge. All but one dog received six or less such infections. Serologically, those animals having minimal titers of complement-fixing antibodies or prompt decreases in titer following primary infection developed significantly higher titers promptly following a reinfection challenge. Reinfection served to boost low antibody titers, probably by the presence of additional antigen; however, if complement-fixing antibodies were present at substantial titer, little or no rise in titer resulted. Clinical symptoms or roentgenographic evidence of reinfection did not accompany an antibody rise.

The characteristic serologic responses to multiple reinfection challenges with airborne mycelial elements of *H. capsulatum* is shown in Figure 32-1. The reinfection attempts totaled from forty-seven to eighty-two for the various time intervals through the fifteenth postinfection week, as noted at the bottom of the graph. The booster effect on the complement-fixing antibodies to whole yeast and histoplasmin antigens occurred during the second and third weeks following a reinfection challenge. The geometric mean titer rise was only a twofold serum dilution for both complement-fixing antibodies, but usually the antibodies to histoplasmin reappeared at a 1:2 titer for about four weeks and then disappeared. The reappearance of precipitating antibodies, as titers of complement-fixing antibodies elevated, probably indicates the response to the renewed presence of live antigen, while the prolonged plateauing of complement-fixing antibodies to whole yeast antigen probably denotes the response to the persistence of inactivated antigen. The more frequent the reinfection challenges, the more stable became the titer of complement-fixing antibodies to whole yeast antigen. In the course of eighty of the reinfection challenges given the fourteen dogs, only a single positive

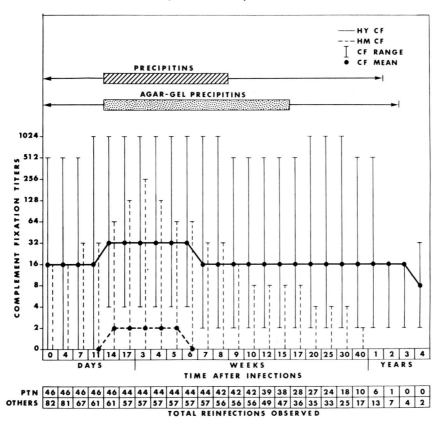

FIGURE 32.1. Serologic patterns in reinfections of dogs with airborne spores of *H. capsulatum.*

culture for *H. capsulatum* was obtained from 593 venous blood specimens cultured during the first to tenth week after infection.

All fourteen dogs have been necropsied, making possible the cultural and microscopic examination of the lungs and other organs of the reticuloendothelial system (Table 32-II). Of these fourteen dogs, the results in five must be excluded because of the administration of corticosteroids or immunosuppressants during the course of infection. Although multiple small nodular pulmonary lesions with caseation have frequently been present, cultures of lung tissue have been negative for *H. capsulatum*. Foci of residual active infection, if present, were confined to lymph nodes draining pulmonary tissue and the liver. In dog 7, diffuse pulmonary infiltrates developed roentgenographically, and the animal experienced a prolonged illness following primary infection. After expiring of unknown causes seven week after the second reinfection attempt, all tissues acquired at necropsy were culturally negative for *H. capsulatum*. In dogs 15 and 16, both of which were sacrificed only two weeks after the third reinfection challenge, a few scattered pulmonary nodules were present, although chest roentgenograms appeared

TABLE 32-II

Necropsy Findings in Dogs Receiving Multiple Reinfection Challenges

Dog	Total Infections (Including Primary)	Total Time Observed (Months)	Time Between Last Infection & Necropsy	Gross Pulmonary Findings (Nodules)	Tissues Positive by Culture
7	3	36	7 weeks	Multiple	0
15	4	24	2 weeks	Few	0
16	4	24	2 weeks	Few	Hilar lymph nodes; liver
9	4	18	10 weeks	Multiple	Hilar lymph nodes
10	4	54	26 weeks	Multiple	Hilar lymph nodes; liver
45	6	66	30 months	Few	0
26	6	93	51 months	None	Prescapular lymph node
6	7	90	18 months	Multiple	Hilar lymph nodes
17	34	105	7 weeks	Multiple	0

normal. All tissues of dog 15 were negative by culture for *H. capsulatum,* but dog 16 harbored a few organisms within the hilar lymph nodes and liver. Dog 9, which died under anesthesia ten weeks after the third reinfection challenge, had multiple pulmonary lesions, but cultures of all tissues were negative except for a few colonies of *H. capsulatum* cultured from the hilar nodes. Dog 10, sacrificed twenty-six weeks after the third reinfection challenge, developed multiple pulmonary granulomas which were culturally negative for *H. capsulatum;* however, the hilar lymph nodes and liver still contained a few viable organisms. Dog 45, sacrificed two and one-half years after the fifth reinfection attempt, had scattered pulmonary lesions, but all tissues were negative for *H. capsulatum* by culture. Dog 26, sacrificed four and one-fourth years following the fifth reinfection attempt, showed no significant pulmonary lesions, but a few colonies of *H. capsulatum* were cultured from a prescapular lymph node. Dog 6, sacrificed one and one-half years after the sixth reinfection challenge with innumerable pulmonary nodules which were negative by culture, had a few colonies of *H. capsulatum* culturable from the hilar lymph nodes.

The most pointed evidence that actively acquired immunity from primary histoplasmal infection protects against exogenous reinfection and the development of chronic pulmonary disease is exemplified by dog 17. The situation concerning this animal might be considered comparable to a person living in a highly endemic area for histoplasmosis and experiencing repeated infection-producing exposures to airborne mycelial elements of *H. capsulatum* from a point source. A series of thirty-three reinfection challenges was administered to this animal over a period of slightly more than eight years, beginning six months following a successful primary infection. The inflammatory reaction to the primary infection was evident from the elevations in temperature, sedimentation rate, and white blood count. The histoplasmin skin test converted to positive during the third week. Complement-fixing antibodies to whole yeast and histoplasmin antigens reached maximum titers of 1:512 and 1:128, respectively, by the end of the third week, and precipitating antibodies promptly appeared. Diffuse pulmonary infiltrates developed by the third week and persisted throughout the life span of the animal.

The first six reinfections were given to this particular dog from eleven to thirty-seven weeks after the previous infection. The last of this series was observed for thirty-seven months, until complement-fixing antibodies to histoplasmin and precipitins were negative, and complement-fixing antibodies to whole yeast antigen had long persisted at a titer of 1:16 (Table 32-III). Approximately five years after the primary infection, nine additional reinfection challenges at two- to seven-day intervals caused no apparent illness, roentgenographic changes, or significant elevation in antibody titers regardless of the additive doses of fungal antigen. Four additional reinfection challenges, now totaling twenty, were given after more prolonged observation periods, the longest being sixteen months. Approximately seven and one-half years after the primary infection and sixteen months after the previous infection, another series of eight reinfection challenges were spaced

TABLE 32-III

Complement-fixing Antibody Titers in Dog Seventeen During Multiple Reinfection Challenges

Infection	Time Observed Before Next Infection	CF (HY)		CF (HM)	
		Maximum Titer	Titer Before Next Infection	Maximum Titer	Titer Before Next Infection
1	25W	512	64	128	8
2	37W	64	16	16	4
3	17W	16	16	4	4
4	11W	32	16	4	4
5	15W	32	32	4	2
6	16W	64	32	4	4
7	37M	32	16	4	N
8–15	3–4D (4W)	32	32	2	2
16	1W	32	16	2	2
17	13W	16	8	2	N
18	2W	16	8	N	N
19	27W	32	16	N	N
20	16M	64	8	2	N
21–27	3–4D (3W)	16	8	N	N
28	46W	8	4	N	N
29–31	7–8D (3W)	16	16	2	2
32	13D	16	8	2	N
33	7D	16	8	N	N
34	6W	8	8	N	N
Total	8Y 10M				

at intervals of three to four days. After a forty-six-week observation period, the final series of six challenges was given at intervals of one to two weeks.

Complement-fixing antibodies to whole yeast antigen tended to decline and persist at titers of 1:4 to 1:32, usually with twofold increases in titer occurring after a reinfection challenge, if the interval between reinfections was prolonged. Complement-fixing antibodies to histoplasmin antigen recurred at titers of 1:2 infrequently, and precipitating antibodies never reappeared after the sixth reinfection challenge. Multiple venous blood specimens obtained for culture after each reinfection attempt remained negative for *H. capsulatum*. Frequent chest roentgenograms revealed no new infiltrates after any of the reinfection attempts but merely demonstrated the fibrosing and calcifying of those lesions produced by the primary infection. Necropsy grossly revealed multiple firm small raised nodules throughout both lungs. Microscopic section showed these lesions to be thick-walled and partially calcified with necrotic or hyalinized centers devoid of yeast cells by special fungal staining. All other tissues were unremarkable. Direct culture and mouse inoculation technique applied to macerated tissue samplings from the lungs, liver, spleen, adrenals, kidney, hilar lymph nodes, bone marrow, and spinal fluid were all negative for *H. capsulatum*.

To even more emphatically demonstrate that exogenous reinfection and focalized hypersensitivity is not responsible for chronic or cavitary forms of pulmonary histoplasmosis, the technique of repeated catheter placement of viable histoplasmal spores or yeast suspensions by bronchoscopic direction into the right lower lobe of dogs was also utilized. It is readily conceded that this experimental technique does not simulate the natural mode of infection with *H. capsulatum,* as does the inhalation of airborne spores, but more specifically explores the role of localized tissue hypersensitivity and immunity. A total of twelve dogs were challenged from two to nine times with a saline suspension of 500 thousand to 14 million spores or 30 to 500 million yeast cells by bronchoscopic placement at intervals of eight weeks to one and one-half years following a primary or previous infection. The singular roentgenographic evidence of pulmonary disease arising from such reinfection attempts was a fleeting manifestation of tissue hypersensitivity. A pneumonic infiltrate usually appeared in the infected lobe within one to three days after the reinfection challenge and resolved by the second week. Although no residual or chronic lesions, necrosis, or cavitations resulted, new acute local infiltrates developed following each reinfection challenge in some of the animals. Such an exudative phenomena, occurring so promptly following the catheter placement of living spores or yeast cells of *H. capsulatum,* occurred identically in response to placement of killed yeast cells or histoplasmin. This pulmonary reaction seems comparable to the delayed hypersensitivity reaction demonstrated by a positive histoplasmin skin test. The patterns of antibody response to this method of infection were very similar to the airborne method but with more elevated titers in evidence. Of 554 blood cultures obtained at frequent intervals following reinfection challenges with such large numbers of spores or yeast cells placed directly into the lung, not a single specimen was positive for *H. capsulatum*.

All twelve dogs were necropsied, but two animals receiving corticosteroid treatment during their last reinfections will be excluded from the comments. Culturally, broad tissue sampling of the lungs, lymph nodes, and other organs of the reticuloendothelial system produced negative results for *H. capsulatum* except for a positive hilar lymph node in one animal and a single colony of *H. capsulatum* from the liver of another. It is indeed remarkable that all tissue samplings from the lung areas which had been so heavily and repeatedly infected with *H. capsulatum* were culturally negative for the fungal organism and were microscopically free of any granulomatous involvement, caseation, or cavitation.

Chapter 33

Reinfection Histoplasmosis

FRED E. TOSH

ABSTRACT

Several reports have indicated that reinfection may occur in histoplasmosis. Several epidemics of acute pulmonary histoplasmosis have occurred in the endemic area where many of the individuals involved should have had previous exposure to *Histoplasma capsulatum*. In some instances, the incubation period was only a few days, suggesting an early response by hypersensitive individuals. The incubation periods for sixty-four cases of acute pulmonary histoplasmosis having a known date of exposure were examined. Lifetime residents eighteen years of age or older in the endemic area tended to have shorter incubation periods than lifetime residents less than eighteen years of age. Nonlifetime residents of the endemic area tended to have longer incubation periods. However, the incubation period for a histoplasmin skin test positive individual who developed acute pulmonary histoplasmosis after entering a cave was thirty days.

The occurrence of eight cases of chronic pulmonary histoplasmosis during the second outbreak of histoplasmosis in the same community suggested exogenous reinfection. Anatomical studies of chronic pulmonary histoplasmosis have also suggested exogenous reinfection. Although epidemiological and anatomical data suggest exogenous reinfection in chronic pulmonary histoplasmosis, definite proof is lacking.

SEVERAL investigators have reported that reinfection may occur in histoplasmosis. At the previous conference on histoplasmosis, Furcolow (1952) suggested that reinfection does occur in histoplasmosis, especially in the chronic pulmonary (cavitary) type. Several years later, the authors (Baum and Schwarz, 1962) of a paper on chronic pulmonary histoplasmosis stated that this disease is most likely due to exogenous reinfection.

In the report of an outbreak of acute pulmonary histoplasmosis among school children in Arkansas, the authors Chin, Ney, Saltzman, Paxton, Rakich, Ware, Whitmore and Furcolow (1956) suggested that reinfection may have occurred in some of the children. A report on reinfection in histoplasmosis by Schwarz and Baum (1963) presented epidemiological and anatomical data suggesting that acute pulmonary (epidemic) histoplasmosis and chronic pulmonary (cavitary) histoplasmosis can be a result of exogenous reinfection. A documented case of acute pulmonary histoplasmosis which was due to exogenous reinfection was reported in 1967 (Hasenclever, Shacklette, Young and Gelderman). This report will review some of the data supporting reinfection and present data on observations made at the Kansas City Laboratories.

Materials and Methods

Reinfection as used in this report refers to the development of active disease some time after the primary infection and its associated hypersensitivity. Reinfection is considered to occur after the primary infection has become quiescent or apparently healed and the clinical picture of reinfection may be that of acute pulmonary, disseminated, or chronic pulmonary histoplasmosis. Endogenous reinfection is new disease produced by organisms already present in the host but released by breakdown of the primary focus or secondary lesions and may occur years after the primary infection. Exogenous reinfection is new disease resulting from exposure of the host to the organism as it exists in the environment.

For many years individuals at the Kansas City Laboratories have been interested in histoplasmosis and have investigated numerous outbreaks and individual cases. Through careful case histories and investigations of the sources of infection, it has been possible to document the date of exposure and incubation in sixty-four cases of acute pulmonary histoplasmosis. All subjects had a clinical illness and the diagnosis was established on the basis of histoplasmin skin test conversion to positive in a few cases, isolation of the organism from clinical materials in a few cases, and positive skin tests, serological tests, and compatible x-ray findings in the remainder.

The occurrence of two large outbreaks of histoplasmosis (D'Alessio, Heeren, Hendricks, Ogilvie and Furcolow, 1965; Tosh, Doto, D'Alessio, Medeiros, Hendricks and Chin, 1966) in a community located outside the endemic area for histoplasmosis provided an opportunity to make some observations on the possible occurrence of reinfection histoplasmosis. A group of children found to have a positive histoplasmin skin test after the first epidemic were again studied during the investigation of the second outbreak. A history was obtained on each child, a serum obtained for serological tests, and a 14 × 17 inch chest film was taken. Each child had a sample of serum and a chest x-ray on file from the first epidemic. The complement fixation test employing the yeast phase antigen was performed on the paired sera from each child simultaneously. The two chest x-ray films from each child were compared to detect any changes.

Results

The incubation period of 64 histoplasmosis cases having known date of exposure are shown in Figure 33-1. Fifty of these individuals were involved in outbreaks where two or more persons were infected at a common source. Of the 14 not involved in epidemics, 7 were employees of the Kansas City Laboratories, 6 of whom were known to be skin test negative and were ex-

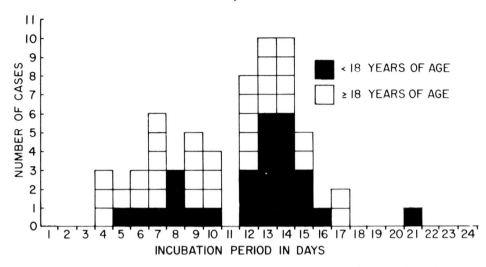

FIGURE 33-1. Incubation periods of sixty-four cases of acute pulmonary histoplasmosis having known dates of exposure.

posed at sites positive for *Histoplasma capsulatum.* The incubation period for the sixty-four cases ranged from four to twenty-one days, with a mean incubation period of eleven days. The curve appears bimodal, with a group of individuals having a short incubation period and a group having a long incubation period. Slightly more than two thirds of the individuals under eighteen years of age had the longer incubation period, while individuals eighteen years of age or older were equally distributed between long and short incubation periods.

In Figure 33-2, the group of cases is divided by lifetime and nonlifetime residence in the endemic area for histoplasmosis. Among the lifetime residents, about half the group had an incubation period of ten days or less and the other half had an incubation period greater than this. The majority of individuals having the longer incubation period were less than eighteen years of age, while those having a shorter incubation period were eighteen or over. The incubation period for twenty-three nonlifetime residents ranged from five to seventeen days, but is more like the normal distribution curve.

Data from the study of reinfection among fifty-seven children living in a community experiencing two outbreaks of histoplasmosis are shown in Table 33-I. Most children had no change or a decrease in the serologic titer between 1963 and 1964. One child showed a two-tube rise in titer but denied any sort of febrile illness during the 1964 epidemic. Most children had a negative chest x-ray in 1963 and in 1964, while one showed no change and four improved during this period. Two children developed new x-ray lesions between 1963 and 1964. One of these had developed a solitary nodule and had a positive serology with no change in titer between 1963 and 1964. The

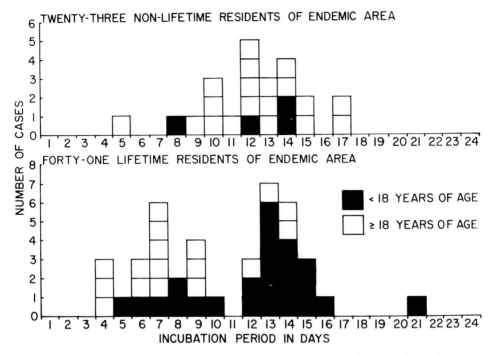

FIGURE 33-2. Incubation periods of sixty-four cases of acute pulmonary histoplasmosis.

other child developed three nodules; this was the student who had a two-tube increase in titer in the complement fixation test between 1963 and 1964. Neither of the children developing new x-ray lesions had a febrile illness during the epidemic in 1964.

During the investigation of the second outbreak of histoplasmosis in this community, nine individuals were found to have severe pulmonary involvement with a type of disease that we classified as chronic pulmonary histoplasmosis. Data on these individuals are given in Table 33-II. One individ-

TABLE 33-I

Findings in Fifty-seven Children Examined for Evidence of
Reinfection With *Histoplasma capsulatum*, 1964

Complement Fixation Results, 1963 and 1964	Number Tested	Chest x-ray results				Febrile Illness, 1964
		Neg. 1963-1964	No Change 1963-1964	Improved 1964	New Lesion 1964	
Neg. 1963—Neg. 1964	10	10				1
Positive—no change between 1963 and 1964	15	12	1	1	1	3
Decreased titer in 1964	27	24		3		5
Increased titer in 1964						
1 tube	4	4				
2 tube	1				1	
Totals	57	50	1	4	2	9

TABLE 33-II

Data on Chronic Pulmonary Histoplasmosis Cases Seen During Epidemic in 1964

Case	Age	Date Onset	Skin Test	Serology	H. capsulatum demonstrated
C.N.	37	1–26–63	–	+	pathology
R.B.	42	2–13–64	+	+	no
D.D.	40	2–28–64	–	–	culture
H.S.	65	3–2–64	+	+	pathology
W.S.	42	4–5–64	+	+	culture
P.N.	57	4–4–64	+	+	no
W.R.	41	4–9–64	+	+	pathology
H.M.	41	?	+	+	no
E.W.	65	4–29–64	+	+	culture

ual had onset of his illness in January, 1963, approximately four months after the first outbreak and one year before the second outbreak. This is the only individual known to have developed this type of disease following the first outbreak. Seven of the remaining cases had onset of their illness during the epidemic, while the date of onset of one case is not known.

The chest x-rays often revealed unilateral involvement with extensive infiltration, honeycombing or definite cavitation involving upper lobes. Pulmonary biopsies or resections in several cases revealed a granulomatous reaction, with some granulomas having central caseation and yeast organisms compatible with *H. capsulatum.* The individuals were white males and all were forty years of age or older except one who was thirty-seven. All had resided in Mason City during the first and second outbreaks, and five worked in the downtown area. Chest films made prior to the onset of their histoplasmosis were available in eight of the nine individuals. In only two of these individuals were the earlier films interpreted as completely normal. Two had changes suggestive of emphysema, one had a solitary nodule which cleared, two had a granular appearance of the lung parenchyma, and one had cystic changes at the base of the left lung. None of these cases had a previous histoplasmin skin test, but all had negative tuberculin skin tests at the time of their illness.

Discussion

Individuals who contract histoplasmosis show an immune response evidenced by the development of circulating antibodies. If upon reexposure some of these individuals respond with a hyperergic reaction, then perhaps the incubation period would be shorter. The observations on forty-one lifetime residents of the endemic area (Fig. 33-2) who had acute pulmonary histoplasmosis revealed that many of them indeed had short incubation periods. It is also interesting to note that the individuals in this group less than eighteen years of age had longer incubation periods and may have been having their first experience with *H. capsulatum*, while individuals over eighteen years of age had shorter incubation periods and are more likely to have had previous contact with the organism. Among twenty-three nonlifetime residents of the endemic area, most tended to have longer incubation periods. In the report of an outbreak of histoplasmosis in Arkansas (Chin *et al.*, 1956), the authors stated that many children in the school may have responded to exposure with an immediate illness because the school is located in an endemic area for histoplasmosis where many of the children would have been expected to have had previous exposure to the organism. Those children having the usual incubation period represented those without a previous exposure to the organism. (Also see Chap. 57, p. 457.)

In another outbreak of histoplasmosis in Arkansas (Washburn, Tuohy and Davis, 1948) involving mostly children, the incubation was four to thirteen days, with a mean incubation of seven days. In a group of employees having a negative histoplasmin skin test and with a known date of exposure while working at the Kansas City Laboratories, the incubation period ranged from twelve to seventeen days. Therefore, the epidemiologic data suggest that individuals may become reinfected and have a clinical illness compatible with acute pulmonary histoplasmosis with an incubation period of four to seven days, while a true primary infection may have an incubation of eleven to seventeen days.

An exception to the hypothesis of a short incubation period is the case of reinfection histoplasmosis reported in 1967 (Hasenclever *et al.*). An individual known to have a positive histoplasmin skin test entered a cave from which *H. capsulatum* was recovered. Thirty days later he developed chills and fever and his chest x-ray film revealed diffuse nodular pulmonary infiltrates. He also developed antibodies to histoplasmin in the complement fixation test. The incubation period in this case was unusually long even for a primary infection, but no other exposure could be recalled.

The attempt to determine if reinfection occurred among a small sample of fifty-seven children during the second outbreak of histoplasmosis in a community in 1964 did not provide evidence supporting reinfection. Most of the children had no change or a decrease in their serologic titer for histoplasmosis; if reinfection occurred the titer should have risen. One child did show a two-tube increase in his titer and also developed a new pulmonary lesion by x-ray during the 1964 epidemic. The new x-ray lesion in this child and the lesion in one other child may not have been a truly new lesion but merely changes in an old lesion making it visible by x-ray. The number of children studied was small and it is possible they were not reexposed; however, the investigation revealed the organism was widely disseminated throughout the community.

The similarity of the clinical picture of chronic pulmonary histoplasmosis to adult-type pulmonary tuberculosis suggests that the pathogenesis may be the same. However, a report (Schwarz and Baum, 1963) describing anatomical findings in cases of chronic pulmonary histoplasmosis reveals that most patients had healed primary lesions probably acquired many years before because of the complete calcification and encapsulation of the lesions. Organisms assumed to be dead were demonstrated in the healed lesions, and cultures of the lesions were negative. The authors believed that reinfection foci or cavitary lesions developed from breakdown of acute necrotizing pneumonitis, which probably represented hyperergic reaction of a sensitized person whose immunity was deficient. They concluded that exogenous rather than endogenous reinfection occurs in histoplasmosis.

The development of cavitary cases during the second outbreak of histoplasmosis in one community suggests exogenous reinfection. All were living in the city during both outbreaks, and five were employed in the downtown area, near the epidemic site. Following the first outbreak in 1962, a sample of individuals employed in the downtown area or residing within one or two blocks of the epidemic site were tested with histoplasmin and 73 percent were positive. After the second outbreak, another group of employees of the downtown area not included in the first sample were tested, and 95 percent had a positive histoplasmin skin test. These findings indicate that individuals working or living near the downtown area had a very good chance of being infected during the first outbreak and an even greater chance of reexposure during the second outbreak. Unfortunately, none of the individuals developing chronic pulmonary histoplasmosis had had a histoplasmin skin test prior to the second epidemic. There is the possibility that these cases do not represent reinfection but a progression of a primary infection in individuals who did not have completely normal lung parenchyma. The concept of endogenous reinfection in these individuals is untenable. That eight individuals in a community of this size would develop chronic pulmonary histoplasmosis as a result of breakdown during the period of an acute epidemic of histoplasmosis is beyond the realm of chance.

If chronic pulmonary histoplasmosis is due to exogenous reinfection, one wonders why no cases have been described in the outbreaks of histoplasmosis occurring in the endemic area where most adults have had a prior experience with the organism. Perhaps it is a rare individual who will develop chronic cavitary histoplasmosis, even though he is exposed repeatedly. The individual may have to be over forty years of age and have had some previous insult to his lungs or have some immunologic deficit. If this is the case, then a large number of individuals must be exposed in order for only one case of cavitary histoplasmosis to develop. Epidemiological data indicate that during the second outbreak in the same community, thousands of people were exposed, and the development of eight cases of cavitary histoplasmosis might be expected. In the smaller outbreaks of histoplasmosis in the endemic area, the number of individuals exposed may have been too small to expect cavitary cases to develop.

Undoubtedly, endogenous reinfection or reactivation can occur in both disseminated histoplasmosis and chronic pulmonary histoplasmosis. It is not uncommon for some individuals having disseminated histoplasmosis to be treated and become asymptomatic for as long as a year or more before developing disseminated disease again without any evidence of a new pulmonary lesion. In some patients relapses have occurred as many as two or three times. In such cases, one must assume that there is endogenous reinfection or reactivation of their disease after long periods of quiescence. Similar observations have been made in chronic pulmonary histoplasmosis where patients are treated with a good response and may go for a year or longer before again developing active disease with a positive sputum (Communicable Disease Center Cooperative Mycoses Study, 1963). Although exogenous reinfection is a possibility in these cases, it seems much less likely than endogenous reinfection.

Although there are epidemiological data suggesting that exogenous reinfection may occur in acute pulmonary histoplasmosis, there is only one documented case of reinfection reported. There is both epidemiological and anatomical evidence suggesting that chronic pulmonary histoplasmosis is due to exogenous reinfection, but definite proof is lacking.

References

Baum, G.L. and Schwarz, J. (1962). Chronic pulmonary histoplasmosis. *Amer. J. Med.*, 33:873-879.

Chin, T.D.Y., Ney, P.E., Saltzman, B.N., Paxton, G.B., Rakich, J.H., Ware, M., Whitmore, M. and Furcolow M.L. (1956). An epidemic of histoplasmosis among school children in Arkansas. *Southern Med. J.*, 49:785-792.

Communicable Disease Center Cooperative Mycoses Study (1963). Comparison of treated and untreated severe histoplasmosis. *J.A.M.A.*, 183:823-829.

D'Alessio, D.J., Heeren, R.H., Hendricks, S.L., Ogilvie, P. and Furcolow, M.L. (1965). A starling roost as the source of urban epidemic histoplasmosis in an area of low incidence. *Amer. Rev. Resp. Dis.*, 92:725-731.

Furcolow, M.L. (1956). Clinical diagnosis of histoplasmosis. Proceedings of the Conference on Histoplasmosis, 1952. *Public Health Monogr.*, 39:3-7.

Hasenclever, H.F., Shacklette, M.H., Young, R.V., and Gelderman, G.A. (1967). The natural occurrence of *Histoplasma capsulatum* in a cave. *Amer. J. Epidem.*, 86: 238-245.

Schwarz, J. and Baum, G.L. (1963). Reinfection in histoplasmosis. *Arch. Path.*, 75: 475-479.

Tosh, F.E., Doto, I.L., D'Alessio, D.J., Medeiros, A.A., Hendricks, S.L. and Chin, T.D.Y. (1966). The second of two epidemics of histoplasmosis resulting from work on the same starling roost. *Amer. Rev. Resp. Dis.*, 94:406-413.

Washburn, A.M., Tuohy, J.H. and Davis, E.L. (1948). Cave sickness: A new disease entity? *Amer. J. Public Health*, 38:1521-1526.

Part V
Diagnostic and Immunologic Methods

Chapter 34

Isolation and Identification of
Histoplasma capsulatum

HOWARD W. LARSH

ABSTRACT

Isolation of *Histoplasma capsulatum* from human clinical specimens was not always successful on artificial media in this study. Animal inoculation was necessary, especially when the specimens were highly contaminated by other organisms. Here, too, universal success was not obtained because of bacteremia or candidiasis in the experimental species. However, blood agar base with the addition of human blood and antibiotics proved to be the most efficient agar medium. Growth on the blood agar was either luxuriant with cottony, fluffy mycelium or flat with little or no aerial mycelium. When it was in the former state, it was comparable to growth that has been observed on Sabouraud's dextrose agar. Sporulation was evident in microscopical preparations of typical isolates of the fungus in that microconidia and tuberculated macroconidia occurred. The pathogen was isolated very infrequently on Sabouraud's dextrose medium without antibiotics because of the rapid overgrowth of contaminating organisms. On many occasions, from the same clinical specimen, *H. capsulatum* was isolated on the blood medium but not on the Sabouraud's dextrose media. The most common or frequent yeast isolated on all types of media was *Candida albicans*. In some cases because of the rapid and confluent growth of this yeast, *H. capsulatum* was not recovered from the specimen. When this occurred, biotin-free medium and animal inoculation were used with some degree of success in recovering the fungus.

Identification of *H. capsulatum* after the organism had been isolated and grown in pure culture was not usually difficult. Many of the described, modern techniques were utilized to establish definitive identification. It was not uncommon for lacto-phenol blue preparations to suffice for specific identification of the mycelial phase. Incubation of many of the isolates at 37°C on brain heart infusion agar or blood agar resulted in conversion to the yeast form. However, many isolates obtained from chronic pulmonary cases of histoplasmosis proved to be atypical microscopically and macroscopically. No sporulation was the rule in many cultures, and failure to convert to the yeast form at 37°C was fairly common. These isolates were eventually converted to the yeast form either by serial transfers on artificial media over a long period or, more easily, by the mammalian tissue culture technique. They were proved also by histopathology, using the selective fungus stain. The animals inoculated were Swiss white mice and the golden hamster.

Throughout these investigations all clinical specimens were grown on three types of artificial media for isolation attempts. Typical and atypical isolates were converted to the yeast form and inoculated into experimental animals for histopathological studies. All three criteria were fulfilled before the isolate was given the definitive identification of *H. capsulatum*.

271

D E MONBREUN (1934) successfully isolated and characterized the growth of *Histoplasma capsulatum* from man. Since that date numerous new techniques and modification of old procedures have resulted in rather routine isolations of the fungus from nature, man, and other animals. During the past two decades sophisticated microscopy, histological procedures, and cultural methodology have assisted in delineating the epidemiology of histoplasmosis.

Papers published in the *Proceedings of the Histoplasmosis Conference* in 1952 as well as those in the text, *Histoplasmosis*, edited by Sweaney (1960) adequately cover the techniques of isolation and identification of *H. capsulatum*. There have been suggested improvements in isolation media and identification procedures in recent years; however, the basic principles remain essentially the same. Newer antibiotics have been incorporated in media for the inhibition or retardation of contaminating organisms. New staining procedures to accentuate selected morphological structures of the organism have been added to the histological procedures. Improvement in microscopy has played a major role in better understanding the changes and location of tissue reactions to the pathogen. All of these innovations and improvements in laboratory procedures have aided in the study of pathogenic fungi; nevertheless, problems still exist in the fields of isolation and identification of fungi in human clinical specimens.

Isolation of *H. capsulatum* from humans can be and is difficult, depending on the clinical specimen, type, and severity of the infection. In acute pulmonary histoplasmosis (Furcolow, 1960) the number of positive isolations of the fungus, in our experience, has been small. When multiple involvement of the lungs occurred, as seen in severe or epidemic types of the disease, isolations were made more frequently. However, even in these patients in which miliary calcifications developed, the percent of positive isolations was low.

In patients at the Missouri State Sanatorium, chronic pulmonary histoplasmosis has been the predominant type of the disease syndrome. Extensive cavitary disease was apparent in most of these individuals. Isolations of *H. capsulatum* were more successful from these patients as compared to all other types of pulmonary histoplasmosis. In many of the cases successful isolation of the fungus was not obtained until multiple and consecutive specimens were processed. In addition to various media, experimental animal inoculations had to be used to isolate the fungus from contaminated specimens.

The more serious acute and chronic disseminated cases of histoplasmosis have yielded a higher percentage of positive isolations of the fungus. Even in patients with disseminated histoplasmosis success has not always been the ultimate result of cultural attempts.

In this discussion the experience we have had in isolation and identification of *H. capsulatum* at the Missouri State Sanatorium will be presented.

Materials and Methods

The methodology used in our fungus laboratory has been consistent over the years. New techniques have been incorporated with our procedures for evaluation. In many instances dual studies have been followed for several months. The number of patients admitted to the hospital each month allows considerable flexibility in our overall mycotic studies. In our experience with the types of clinical disease presented by our patients, sputum has proved the most fruitful specimen for cultural isolation of pathogenic fungi; nevertheless, the clinician submits many other clinical specimens for study. These include gastric washings, bronchial lavage, urine, biopsies, and necropsy tissues. All of these, and other types of specimens, received special attention by our mycology technicians.

Sputum specimens were requested in all cases where it was possible to obtain this clinical specimen. Early morning sputum was obtained, and in nearly all cases the collection was completed prior to 8:00 AM. The specimen was collected in a sterile, screw cap jar immediately after the patient completed his oral hygiene procedures. The patient was encouraged to raise sputum from the lungs and trachea and not merely expectorate saliva. The amount and consistency of the sample were recorded. An attempt was made to collect 2 to 10 ml of sputum from each patient. Six specimens were collected from each patient over a two-week period.

Gastric washings were requested only when it was impossible to obtain sputum. In many cases gastric washings were received on patients in addition to sputum specimens. All gastric washings received were processed. They were centrifuged and only the sediment was used.

All clinical specimens were processed as soon as they reached the laboratory. Antibiotics were added to all contaminated specimens such as sputum, gastrics, bronchial lavages, and urine. If the history of the collection and handling of tissue specimens was not clearly known, they were treated with antibiotics. Penicillin and streptomycin, usually 10,000 units per milliliter of specimen, were used. Very thick, mucoid specimens were further diluted with sterile, cysteine saline. Fluid specimens were placed on a shaker for thirty minutes or longer prior to inoculation of the routine media. Tissues were ground, using sterile equipment, and cysteine saline then inoculated onto routine cultural media. Only petri plates were used and incubation was for at least four weeks at room temperature ($22°$-$25°C$).

The routine media consisted of Sabouraud's dextrose agar with and without antibiotics and blood agar base plus 8% to 10% human blood. Antibiotics used were penicillin, 10 units, and streptomycin, 20 units per milliliter of medium. In addition, cycloheximide, 0.5 mg/ml of medium, was added to Sabouraud's dextrose agar with penicillin and streptomycin.

The plain Sabouraud's dextrose agar plate was included for each specimen in view of certain pathogens' sensitivity to antibiotics.

Specimens inoculated into experimental animals were treated with penicillin. Animals were sacrificed after three to four weeks. The spleen and liver of each animal were removed using sterile equipment. The tissue was ground in sterile, cysteine saline and 1 ml plated on routine media and incubated at room temperature for three to four weeks.

Our policy was to examine the inoculated plates frequently and any suspicious growth was transferred to tubes of Sabouraud's and blood agar. In this manner isolations were made from plates containing contaminants prior to overgrowth by these organisms.

Results and Discussion

Isolation

Blood agar base medium enriched with 8% to 10% human blood proved to be the most efficient for the isolation of *H. capsulatum* from human, clinical specimens. In most instances excellent growth was evident on this medium and the pathogen could be isolated in pure culture directly from the plate. Very often the companion Sabouraud's plates of the specimen showed no growth of *H. capsulatum*. In other cases growth could be detected on Sabouraud's dextrose agar plates with antibiotics, but isolation of *H. capsulatum* proved difficult or impossible because of contaminating yeasts. *Candida albicans* was the most consistent contaminating yeast when sputum was the specimen under study. Kapica, Shaw and Bartlett (1968) also showed the inhibition of *H. capsulatum* by *C. albicans* and other yeasts on Sabouraud's agar media. Occasionally one could detect *H. capsulatum* growing through or around the colonies of *C. albicans*. The plain Sabouraud's plates supported saprophytic fungi and bacteria to the extent that *H. capsulatum* was only infrequently observed and recovery from this medium proved impossible.

Growth on blood agar may be cottony and luxuriant or it may be relatively free of aerial mycelium. It is usually possible to find definitive microconidia and macroconidia on blood agar, providing that the isolate is a typical one.

In a series of 762 gastric washings over a period of three years, six isolations of *H. capsulatum* were observed. All six of these isolations were from one patient. Her sputum specimens were positive to the fungus prior to processing the gastrics. During this three-year period *H. capsulatum* was isolated from sixty-six patients in the sanatorium. The positive isolations were from sputum specimens, many of which were from patients included in the gastric series.

Over a period of two years a series of 556 bronchial lavages were sent to the mycology laboratory for fungus study. Two of these specimens were positive for pathogenic fungi: one isolation of *Blastomyces dermatitidis* and the other *H. capsulatum*. During this same period forty isolations of *H. capsulatum* were made from sputum samples of patients in the sanatorium. Many of these patients had bronchial washings processed for fungi.

Urine from patients with disseminated histoplasmosis may yield the fungus on culture. We have had two cases in which the organism was isolated without any difficulty. In each instance the growth was nearly a pure culture of *H. capsulatum* from the cultured sediment.

Tissues collected and processed under aseptic conditions usually do not present any serious problems. It has been our policy to make a 1:10 dilution of the tissue in sterile, cysteine saline. Under these conditions we have found the results of isolation superior to inoculating concentrated tissue. Tissue should be processed immediately, as the pathogen will not withstand storage in tissue even at 4°C for long periods.

Identification

It is in this area of histoplasmosis studies that difficulty has existed and has not been recognized by many students of mycology. The definitive diagnosis of *H. capsulatum* is often described as the tuberculated macroconidium or chlamydospore. This may be true in "classical" or "typical" histoplasmosis seen in many types of the disease. However, in chronic pulmonary histoplasmosis it is frequent that no "characteristic" spores are observed. Also, macroscopical morphology of the colony may not coincide with the descriptions in textbooks. Therefore, I am concerned with the possible number of isolates of *H. capsulatum* that must be discarded each year. There is no doubt in my mind that in our earlier work at the Missouri State Sanatorium, isolates of the organism were discarded because they did not reveal typical microscopical and macroscopical morphology. In addition, conversion to the yeast form was not readily accomplished with all isolates.

Identification procedures must be inclusive, including all of the described techniques prior to discarding an isolate from a clinical syndrome of histoplasmosis as negative. As stated earlier, modern approaches have been well documented in several publications. Recent modifications have been projected, and these should be included in the overall identification of *H. capsulatum*.

Unequivocal identification requires that the organism be isolated from the disease process. This requires that media containing antibiotics must be used to isolate *H. capsulatum* from contaminated specimens. Antibiotics which will suppress the growth of bacteria and retard the growth of saprophytic fungi must be used. Seldom is it possible to make positive isolations without these special media. To date we have not been highly successful in controlling the growth of *C. albicans*, which is present in many clinical specimens. The biotin-free medium is of some help, but it is not the solution to the problem (Burns and Larsh, 1962).

It may not be necessary to convert the mycelial form to the yeast form in every case; however, in those isolates where definitive identification cannot be made from colony and microscopical observation, conversion should be done. In many isolates conversion can be accomplished on artificial media without difficulty. In isolates that do not convert readily on artificial media, the tissue culture technique has proved efficient. Our tissue culture technique has been modified as follows:

Suspect cultures of *H. capsulatum* obtained by primary isolation are sent to the tissue culture laboratory. A suspension of the organism, approximately 5×10^5 mycelial fragments per millimeter, is inoculated into HeLa cells maintained in monolayers. A special conversion medium made up of minimal essential medium (MEM) supplemented with glutamine (2mm/100ml) is used to bathe the cells. Twenty-four to forty-eight hours after inoculation mycelial fragments can be recognized and show various stages of becoming rounded up or segmenting into spherical shapes. After seventy-two hours a mixture of incomplete conversion is more readily seen, and shortly after this several converted forms can be observed. At this time the monolayer is removed from the Smith bottles and spread on the surface of a blood agar tube which also contains glutamine. A yeast form culture of the organism is usually obtained upon a single transfer of this material after two to three days.

Normally it is difficult to observe the stages of conversion as it occurs in the tissue culture system; however, through the use of fluorescent antibody techniques one can follow most stages of conversion.

It becomes an academic question as to whether or not phagocytosis of the organism is required for conversion. Our studies indicate the major requirement to be the presence of glutamine for conversion and maintenance of yeast form cultures upon primary isolation.

It has been our policy to convert all of our *H. capsaulatum* isolates to the yeast form. This with other findings will usually satisfy the most critical opponents of the pathogenesis of the fungus.

References

Burns, J. and Larsh, H.W. (1962). Selective isolation of *Histoplasma capsulatum* in presence of *Candida* spp. *Bact. Proc. 66.*

De Monbreun, W.A. (1934). The cultivation and cultural characteristics of Darling's *Histoplasma capsulatum*. *Amer. J. Trop. Med., 14:*93-125.

Furcolow, M.L. (1960). Clinical Types of Histoplasmosis, In Sweany, H.C. (Ed.): *Histoplasmosis.* Springfield, Thomas, pp. 382-404.

Kapica, L., Shaw, C.E. and Bartlett, G.W. (1968). Inhibition of *Histoplasma capsulatum by Candida albicans* and other yeasts on Sabouraud's agar media. *J. Bact., 95:*2171-2176.

Sweany, H.C. (Ed.) (1960). *Histoplasmosis.* Springfield, Thomas.

Chapter 35

Isolation and Identification of
Histoplasma capsulatum from Soil

COY D. SMITH

ABSTRACT

A new modified oil flotation technique is described for the indirect isolation of *Histoplasma capsulatum* from soil. Results of testing soil samples collected extensively from a large starling roost using this method indicated that it may be a sensitive one. The isolations of *H. capsulatum* were general throughout the area, except where the birds did not roost, or in a flooded area.

This technique was compared to the flotation method of Emmons for the isolation of *H. capsulatum* from soil collected adjacent to the bird roost described above. From a total of forty-nine samples, seven isolates of *H. capsulatum* were obtained using the modified oil technique. No isolations were obtained using the flotation method.

Identification of *H. capsulatum* from soil obtained by the indirect mouse method is seldom a problem, since the typical microconidia and tuberculated macroconidia are usually present in primary soil isolates. If there is doubt about the identification, then conversion to the characteristic yeast phase is recommended.

EMMONS (1949) was the first to isolate *Histoplasma capsulatum* from a natural reservoir in nature. Two techniques evolved from early studies have been responsible for the frequent isolation of the fungus at the present time. The first one was the use of laboratory animals, primarily the mouse, as an indirect method of isolating the fungus from soil; the second technique, the employment of soils from chicken houses where the fungus is often found (Zeidberg, Ajello, Dillon, and Runyon, 1952). Subsequently it has been shown that the fungus is associated with soil from other species of birds (Sabin, 1951; Ajello, 1960; Ajello, Briceño-Maaz, Campins and Moore, 1960b; Furcolow, Tosh, Larsh, Lynch and Shaw, 1961), as well as soil contaminated with bat droppings (Emmons, 1958).

The technique used by Emmons (1949) was similar to the flotation method described (Stewart and Meyer, 1932) to isolate *Coccidioides immitis* from soil. The efficiency of this method was questioned by Larsh, Hinton and Furcolow (1952), and it was demonstrated that the majority of viable particles of *H. capsulatum* did not float but would settle rapidly out of a soil suspension. They introduced a dilution method which appeared to be more sensitive. This method briefly is to make a soil dilution in saline (1:10) and inject a small portion of it directly into mice without allowing time for settling to occur. Hinton, Larsh and Silberg (1957) described another method of exposing mice to suspect soils placed in their cage and later moving them to clean cages. Smith and Furcolow (1964) described an oil flotation method for the isolation of *H. capsulatum* from soil. They did a study comparing the efficiency of this method to the soil dilution and soil exposure methods. The results obtained were only slightly better than the other two methods, which appeared about equal in sensitivity. At the present time not any one of the above methods are used universally by all investigators. However, all investigators do appear to still use the indirect mouse method instead of direct culture. The organism has been recovered from soil by direct culture as shown by Furcolow and Larsh (1952) and Smith and Weeks (1964). This method has never been sensitive enough to use as a reliable test.

We have been using for the past four years a new modification of the oil flotation method. Recently a study was completed comparing this method to the one described by Emmons (1949), which is still being used by many at the present time.

Materials and Methods

It has been shown previously that mineral oil will float the majority of viable particles from a sterilized soil inoculated with *H. capsulatum* when blended with an aqueous suspension (Smith and Furcolow, 1964). Subsequent studies have shown that centrifugation even at speeds as high as 10,000 rpm will not pull the fungus particles from an oil suspension back into an aqueous solution. Instead they seem to stick at the oilwater interface. This interface was investigated as a method to isolate *H. capsulatum* from soil by injection 0.2 ml intraperitioneally into mice. This method did not prove very desirable as the mice received such uneven doses because the inoculum was a heterogenic mixture of oil and water. Also if a soil contained high numbers of infective particles, part of the mice would die in ten to eighteen days. It was difficult to isolate *H. capsulatum* from the mouse tissues of these animals, since they had not eliminated in such a short period all the other nonpathogeniu bacteria and fungi normally found in soil.

The original oil flotation technique (Smith and Furcolow, 1964) recommends the following: approximately 100 cc of soil is blended in a Waring blender with 200 cc of physiologic saline and 15 ml of liquid petrolatum (U.S.P. heavy). The oil is drawn off the surface and placed into a 50 ml centrifuge tube with 10 ml of saline and centrifuged for at least 10 minutes at 2,000 rpm. The supernatent oil is pippetted off and discarded while the interface and sediment is injected into mice. We know at the present time that the sediment contains very few particles of *H. capsulatum*.

The following modification in the method has been developed to improve the technique.

Approximately 25 cc of the soil sample to be tested are placed in a 250 ml flask, and 100 ml of sterile physiologic saline added. Penicillin, 20 units, streptomycin, 40 µg and polymixin B, 10µg/ml, are added to the suspension. The flask is shaken vigorously by hand and strained through two layers of cheese cloth into a sterile Waring blender and blended for one-half minute. The suspension is poured into a clean sterile 250 ml flask (without allowing the sediment to settle) and 10 ml of liquid petrolatum (N.F. light) is added. The suspension is shaken for 15 minutes on an Eberbach reciprocating shaker; then saline is added to bring the suspension with the oil on the surface up to the neck of the flask. This suspension is allowed to stand at room temperature for 20 minutes, after which the oil is removed with a 20-gauge needle adapted to a 10 ml syringe. Of this suspension (the oil) 0.5 ml is injected intraperitoneally into each of five white Swiss mice. All mice that die during the first week after inoculation are discarded, but those dying thereafter are necropsied and cultured as follows:

At least three mice must survive for four weeks. The mice cages are checked daily the first week and additional mice if required are inoculated with one-half the original dosage of the suspension. If death continues to occur, additional mice are injected with one-fourth of the original suspension.

After four weeks the mice are killed; liver and spleen are combined and macerated in a mortar and diluted by adding approximately 20 ml of sterile physiologic saline. Of this suspension 0.5 ml is plated on two yeast extract agar plates containing penicillin and streptomycin. After two to three weeks' incubation at room temperatures, *H. capsulatum* usually can be identified if present. The cultures are discarded after four weeks' incubation at room temperature.

The yeast extract medium is modified from that which was first described by Smith (1964) and has the following composition:

Yeast extract (Difco)	1.0 gm
Phosphate buffer	2.0 ml
Bacto-agar	20.0 gm
Distilled water	1000.0 ml

The phosphate buffer is prepared as a concentrated stock solution by preparing $M/5$ KH_2PO_4 and $M/5$ Na_2HPO_4. Using 87.1 ml of the former mixed with 12.9 ml of the latter will result in a buffer with a pH of 6.0 which is the pH of the medium. The primary purpose of the phosphate, however, is that *H. capsulatum* grows better with this salt added to the medium. (Smith and Furcolow, 1969).

After sterilizing the medium by autoclaving, it is cooled to 45°C in a water bath and penicillin, 40 units, and streptomycin, 20µg/ml, are added.

Extensive soil sampling was recently done in an active starling roost and tested for *H. capsulatum* by the above method. The birds have not been identified as yet as all starlings; usually the population in such roosts consists of a mixture of blackbird species. The area contains approximately three acres located in central Kentucky. The area was divided into plots measuring approximately twenty-five square feet each, with wooden stakes placed at the corners as shown in Figure 35-1. A soil sample was collected from the center of each plot. Plots that are not shaded are those from which *H. capsulatum* was isolated, whereas the shaded plots were negative. The consistency of isolations indicate that either the test method was sensitive or this is a very highly infected area. After these results were obtained, a visit to the area revealed that in the negative plots there was an absence of trees and on the lower edge there was a stream which frequently floods this section and leaves water standing. These findings suggest that the fungus perhaps is sparse in the negative areas and the method is a sensitive one.

Modified Oil Flotation Test Compared to the Flotation Method

The modified oil flotation method as described above was compared to that described previously by Emmons (1949) for the isolation of *H. capsulatum* from this area. Beginning at the center and top edge of the area out from row A, plot 8 shown in Figure 35-1, a sample of soil was collected at one-foot increments. The samples were taken by going away from the edge

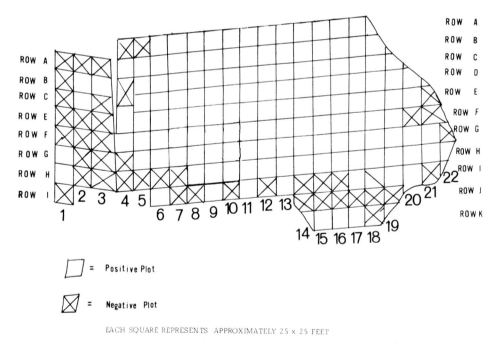

FIGURE 35-1. Results of testing a starling roost of 2.87 acres for *Histoplasma capsulatum* using the modified oil flotation method.

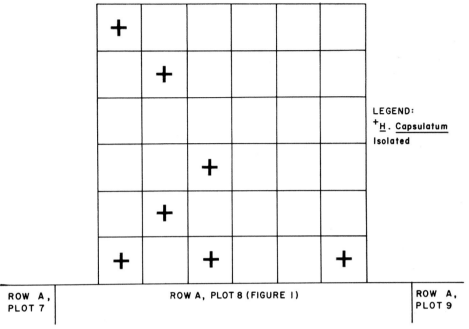

FIGURE 35-2. Comparison of the modified oil flotation technique to the flotation method for the isolation of *H. capsulatum* from soil. All thirty-six subplots were run by both methods. None were positive by the flotation method, seven were positive by the modified oil flotation method.

of the roost as shown in Figure 35-2. In other words a total of 49 samples were collected over an area of 36 square feet at each point on the grid where lines cross. Samples were collected in half-pint ice cream cartons, using a sterilized tongue blade for each. Soil for each test was taken from the same collection carton and processed on the same day. Five mice were used for each test, and after one month they were killed and necropsied with tissues cultured as described above. The seven positive signs represent the total number of isolations of *H. capsulatum*.

Results

All isolations were obtained by the use of the oil flotation method and none by the flotation method. These results indicate the oil method is probably a more sensitive one than the flotation method.

The inconsistency of the isolations shown in Figure 35-2 is a common occurrence when on the fringe area of a natural soil reservoir. This was the case in a roost located in Mexico, Missouri, described first by Furcolow, Tosh, Larsh, Lynch and Shaw (1961) and later tested extensively by Smith, Furcolow and Tosh (1964). *H. capsulatum* was found in a spotty distribution on the back side of the area, and two years later after the starlings left, the fungus could not be isolated from soil along the back side. Similar results are generally found a short distance away on the outside of a positive chicken house. The fungus appears well defined in point foci as has often been shown with *Coccidioides immitis.*

Identification of *H. capsulatum* from Soil

H. capsulatum in most cases is isolated from soil indirectly by the use of animals, primarily mice. Seldom are other fungi isolated from the mouse tissues one month after inoculation. In most cases the fungus is typical when isolated from soil, a fact which is not always true of human clinical isolates. The occurrence of both typical microconidia and macro-tuberculated conidia is usually a safe guide for identification. While *Sepedonium* species are common in soil it is seldom that these fungi are recovered from the mouse. These fungi do not have microconidia but rather echinulated macroconidia usually small and more spiney than the tuberculated spores of *H. capsulatum.* The rate of growth is faster and usually appears within a week compared to 10-14 days for *H. capsulatum.*

The same holds true for soil isolates as with clinical ones, i.e. when there is any doubt or when peculiarities exist in the morphology, the fungus isolated should be converted to the yeast phase for confirmation.

While many variations or atypical isolates of the fungus are observed among clinical isolates, especially from humans, we have observed only one from soil. This isolate was obtained from soil while investigating a small epidemic that occurred seventeen miles southwest of Hobbs, New Mexico (Furcolow and Smith, 1963). The source of this isolate was in an old abandoned gold mine in which two families were involved. The fungus was isolated on two different occasions from several soil samples. This is the farthest west and the first time *H. capsulatum* has been obtained from soil in the state of New Mexico. The fungus on culture produced almost entirely microconidia with only rare echinulated macrospores. This was a permanent state of the mycelial phase, but the yeast phase was typically characteristic of *H. capsulatum.*

References

Ajello, L. (1960). *Histoplasma capsulatum* soil studies. *Mykosen,* 3:43-48.

Ajello, L., Briceño-Maaz, T., Campins, H. and Moore, J.C. (1960). Isolation of *Histoplasma capsulatum* from an oil bird (*Steatornis caripensis*) cave in Venezuela. *Mycopathologia,* 12:199-206.

Emmons, C.W. (1949). Isolation of *Histoplasma capsulatum* from soil. *Public Health Rep.,* 64:892-896.

Emmons, C.W. (1958). Association of bats with Histoplasmosis. *Public Health Rep.* 73:590-595.

Furcolow, M.L. and Larsh, H.W. (1952). Direct isolation of *Histoplasma capsulatum* from soil: Probably etiological relationship to camp Gruber pneumonitis. *Proc. Soc. Exp. Biol. Med.* 80:246-248.

Furcolow, M.L., Tosh, F.E., Larsh, H.W., Lynch, H.J. and Shaw, G. (1961). The emerging pattern of urban histoplasmosis. Studies on an epidemic in Mexico, Missouri. *New Eng. J. Med.* 264:1226-1230.

Furcolow, M.L. and Smith, C.D. (1963). Unpublished data.

Larsh, H.W., Hinton, A. and Furcolow, M.L. (1952). Efficiency of the flotation method in isolation of *Histoplasma capsulatum* from soil. Proceedings of the conference on Histoplasmosis, *Public Health Monogr.*, 39:74-80.

Hinton, A., Larsh, H.W. and Silberg, S.L. (1957). Direct exposure of mice to soils known to contain *Histoplasma capsulatum*. *Proc. Soc. Exp. Biol. Med.*, 94:176-179.

Sabin, A.B. (1951). Nontuberculous diseases of the chest and related matters. Miliary granulomatous pneumonitis in a group of men exposed to pigeon excreta. Trans, 47th annual meeting of the National Tuberculosis Association, 290-291.

Smith, C.D. (1964). Evidence of the presence in yeast extract of substances which stimulate growth of *Histoplasma capsulatum* and *Blastomyces dermatitidis* similarly to that found in starling manure extract. *Mycopathologia*, 22:99-105.

Smith, C.D. and Furcolow, M.L. (1964). Efficacy of three techniques for isolating *Histoplasma capsulatum* from soil, including a new flotation technique. *J. Lab. Clin. Med.* 64:342-348.

Smith, C.D. and Furcolow, M.L. (1969). Nutritional studies of substances required for the growth and sporulation of *Histoplasma capsulatum* Proceedings of the Second National Conference on Histoplasmosis.

Smith, C.D., Furcolow, M.L. and Tosh, F.E. (1964). Attempts to eliminate *Histoplasma capsulatum* from soil. *Amer. J. Hyg.*, 79:170-180.

Smith, C.D. and Weeks, R.W. (1964). Isolation of *Histoplasma capsulatum* from soil by direct culture methods. *Proc. Soc. Exp. Biol. Med.*, 115:549-551.

Stewart, R.A. and Meyer, K.F. (1932). Isolation of *Coccidioides immitis* (Stiles) from the soil. *Proc. Soc. Exp. Biol. Med.*, 29:937-938.

Zeidberg, L.D., Ajello, L., Dillon, A. and Runyon, L.C. (1952). Isolation of *Histoplasma capsulatum* from soil. *Amer. J. Public Health*, 42:930-935.

Chapter 36

Preparation and Standardization
of Histoplasmin

RONALD F. SPROUSE

ABSTRACT

These investigations resulted in purification of crude histoplasmin via dextran chromatography polyacrylamide electrophoresis. The principal skin test reactive components, d_{II} and d_{III}, occurred in histoplasmin HKC-43 at approximately 5 percent. Similar concentrations of components d_{II} and d_{III} were detected in histoplasmin purified derivative (HPD) from different histoplasmin lots. The concentration of HPD varied among different histoplasmin lots. Approximately $0.05\mu g$ of d_{II} and $0.06+\mu g$ of d_{III} elicited delayed hypersensitive reactions in guinea pigs infected with *Histoplasma capsulatum*. Disc electrophoresis at various hydrogen ion concentrations, spectral analysis, and density gradient ultracentrifugation indicated that d_{II} was homogenous. Quantitative chemistries, selective staining, acid and heat coagulation, and differential dextran chromatography at various hydrogen ion concentrations suggest protein and carbohydrate moieties, covalent bonded.

THE medical significance of histoplasmosis has become increasingly evident in the last two decades. Reported cases of this disease in human beings and lower animals have risen sharply since Darling's initial observation (1906) in 1905. Numerous epidemiologists have studied the geographic distribution of human histoplasmosis, utilizing roentgenography and detection of infection allergy. Christie and Peterson (1946) and Palmer (1946) pioneered such epidemiologic surveys in the early 1940's. The major difficulties in interpretation of these findings have been variability of skin test antigens and cross reactivity with other mycoses.

The antigens most often used for detection of infection allergy by these early investigators and used by most clinicians at the present time are crude mycelial growth filtrates of *Histoplasmin capsulatum*. The methods of histoplasmin production were as varied as the investigators themselves.

Emmons (1945) early recognized the necessity for standardization of histoplasmin. He used asparagine medium (Smith, 1943) for the production of histoplasmin H-3 and determined its skin test potency by intradermal inoculation of *H. capsulatum* sensitized guinea pigs.

By 1945, the United States Public Health Service had become aware of the need for large scale epidemiologic studies of histoplasmosis. Since a large quantity of standardized H-3 was not available, several relatively small lots of histoplasmin were prepared by Shaw, Howell and Weiss (1950) and later pooled to form the skin test product designated as H-15. It was standardized by comparison with H-3 histoplasmin using the methods of Emmons (1945). These methods later formed the basis for adoption as minimal standards for preparation and standardization of histoplasmin for skin testing by the Division of Biologic Standards, National Institutes of Health, United States Public Health Service.

When widespread use of H-15 was adopted in 1946, it was thought that a large enough quantity had been prepared to suffice for a number of years. However, the supply was so depleted by 1948 that a new product was needed. Accordingly, another relatively small pooled lot, designated H-40, was prepared for interim use until a more adequate supply could be provided. After testing several proposed lots, a new pooled product designated H-42 was selected. This is the product most widely used today. A few major pharmaceutical companies, in recent years, have begun to produce and distribute histoplasmin commercially.

Numerous investigators throughout this era attempted to fractionate crude histoplasmin or various yeast cell preparations of *H. capsulatum* by ethanolic precipitation (Cross and Howell, 1948; Dyson and Evans, 1955; Knight and Marcus, 1958; Salvin and Smith, 1959) or utilization of various cellulosic ion exchangers (Greene, DeLalla and Tompkins, 1960; Markowitz, 1964; Fadula and Larsh, 1967). The development in recent years of cross-linked dextran polymers by Porath and Flodin (1959) has allowed a new approach to fractionation procedures based on molecular size and this indirectly on molecular weight. Application of this basic premise was utilized by Sprouse (1967) in preparation of histoplasmin purified derivative (HPD).

Regardless of the fractionation procedure, the basic objective in most instances has been to increase specificity or sensitivity of the antigen or antigens involved in serologic and infectious allergic reactions. One also could reasonably assume that if the skin test active component of histoplasmin could be separated from extraneous substances, it could be dehydrated and thus lend itself to quantitation in terms of dry weight of active substance. Such standardization would be desirable, not only from the practical standpoint of processing, handling, and preservation, but also from the academic point of view. Partial purification of the skin test active component of histoplasmin would be a step in the direction of elucidation and comprehension of its antigenic complexity.

Thus the objective of these investigations was to separate, isolate, and chemically elucidate the principal skin test reactive component or components from crude histoplasmin. It also was anticipated that the dry weight or chemically quantitated "skin test dose" could be determined.

Materials and Methods

Histoplasmin M-2 was prepared by the author as described by Goodman, Sprouse and Larsh (1968). Histoplasmin H-42* and HKC-43 were obtained from the United States Public Health Service. Histoplasmin purified derivative was derived from crude histoplasmins by dextran chromatography and lyophilized as described by Sprouse, Goodman and Larsh (1969). The HPD d-fractions were extracted from polyacrylamide gel columns previously subjected to electrophoresis. The combined dextran chromatographic-polyacrylamide electrophoretic procedure and the system used for labeling of respective fractions is illustrated in Figure 36-1.

Crude histoplasmins and their respective fractions were assayed for skin test reactivity by intradermal inoculation of guinea pigs infected with *H. capsulatum* (Goodman *et al.*, 1968). Cutaneous reactions were expressed as induration (millimeter) 48 hour after inoculation.

Protein extracted from polyacrylamide gels was determined by the Schuster and Schrier (1967) modification of the Folin phenol technique (Lowry, Rosebrough, Farr and Randall, 1951). Direct application of the Folin phenol technique was used for crude histoplasmins and fractions free of phenol, tetramethylethylenediamine, and tris (hydroxymethyl)-aminomethane. Carbohydrate was determined with the anthrone reagent (Scott and Melvin, 1953) and by the phenol-sulfuric acid technique (Dubois, Gilles, Hamilton, Rebers and Smith, 1956), using d-glucose as standard. Reducing sugars were determined colorimetrically, using the arsenomolybdate and copper reagents of Somogyi (1945). The presence of nucleoprotein was based on the principle of Warburg and Christian (1941), and confirmed by a positive diphenylamine reaction (Morse and Carter, 1949).

Paper electrophoresis was performed using E-C pressure plate electrophoresis cell (E-C Apparatus Corp., Philadelphia, Pa.), Whatman No. 3 mm paper, and phosphate or veronal buffers. Paper strips were developed with ninhydrin (Hambraeus and Reio, 1965) and alkaline silver nitrate (Trevelyan, Proctor and Harrison, 1950).

Polyacrylamide disc electrophoresis was performed as described by Sprouse (1969). Protein was stained by Amado Schwartz 10B, Coomassie® blue R-250, or nigrosin. Carbohydrate and glycoprotein were stained by a modification of the periodic acid-Schiff reaction. Lipid and substituted triglycerides were detected with aqueous ethanol (60%) saturated with oil-red-0.

Results

The elution pattern for histoplasmin HKC-43 from the Sephadex G-25 column (2.5 × 40 cm) is illustrated in Figure 36-2. The ordinate axis repre-

---
* Courtesy of Tuberculosis Program, USPHS.

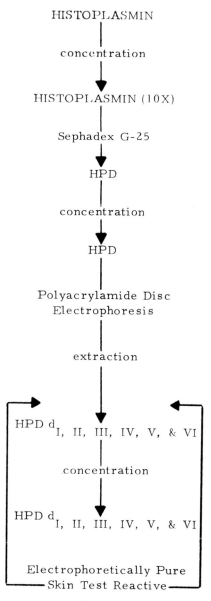

FIGURE 36-1. Schematic for fractionation-purification of histoplasmin.

sents protein, and the abscissa, the consecutive aliquots (5 ml) collected. Aliquots, in turn, were systematically pooled between the arrows and assayed for skin test reactivity, which occurred primarily in 9 through 13 (HPD, Fig. 36-2). This solution was lyophilized and subsequent retitration indicated that approximately 0.12µg protein would elicit a 10 mm reaction in guinea pigs infected with *H. capsulatum*. Examination of several other histoplasmin lots has demonstrated comparable skin test reactivity for HPD (Sprouse *et al.*, 1969).

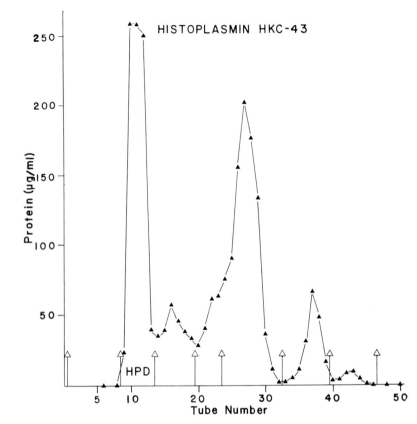

FIGURE 36-2. Elution pattern for histoplasmin HKC-43 from the Sephadex G-25 column.

Paper electrophoretic studies of HPD showed four to five bands sensitive to ninhydrin, one of which also was sensitive to alkaline silver nitrate. A strong protein band toward the anode and nearest the origin occurred in approximately the same position as the carbohydrate band. Polyacrylamide electrophoresis of HPD produced a similar distribution of proteinacious components, but with more distinct separation and elucidation of additional carbohydrate moeities. Figure 36-3 shows the Amido Schwartz 10B stained reference standard for HKC-43 HPD. Rf values expressed as a fraction of the mobility of the dye marker were determined for each demonstrable band. Other gels were sectioned, extracted, labeled as indicated. Distinct bands sensitive to nigrosin or Amado Schwartz 10B were demonstrable in HKC-43 HPD d_I, d_{II}, and d_{III}. HKC-43 HPD d_{IV} exhibited diffuse through definite sensitivity to the protein stains. Figure 36-4 shows a similar stained reference standard for M-2 HPD. Similar Rf values were noted for HKC-43 HPD d_{II} and M-2 HPD d_{II} and HKC-43 HPD, d_{III} and M-2 HPD d_{III} (Figs. 36-3, 36-4). HPD d_I, d_{II} and d_{III} reacted with basic leucofuchsin (PAS), thus suggesting free aldehyde groups from a carbohydrate or lipidal moiety.

Attempts were made to forgo the Sephadex chromatographic step and

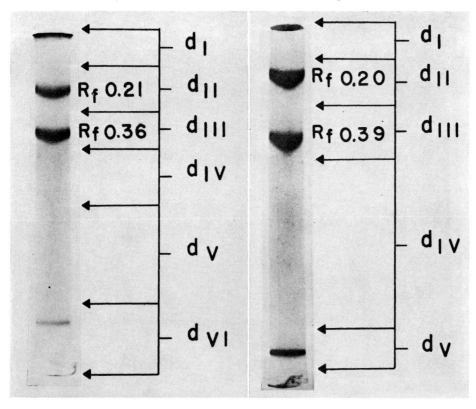

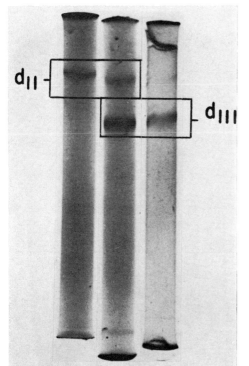

Figure 36-3. (Upper left) Polyacrylamide disc electrophoretic pattern for HKC-43 HPD, stained with Amino Schwartz 10B.

Figure 36-4. (Upper right) Polyacrylamide disc electrophoretic pattern for M-2 HPD, stained with Amino Schwartz 10B.

Figure 36-5. (Lower left) Polyacrylamide disc electrophoretic patterns for HKC-43 HPD and reelectrophoresed HKC-43 HPD d_{II} and HKC-43 HPD d_{III}, stained with 0.01 percent nigrosin.

directly electrophorese crude histoplasmin on the polyacrylamide columns. The effort proved futile in that subsequent extraction, reconcentration, and reelectrophoresis were required to obtain electrophoretically clean fractions (Fig. 36-5). Similar results were demonstrable for M-2 HPD d_{II} and M-2 HPD d_{III}.

The results of skin testing the HKC-43 HPD and the M-2 HPD d-fractions are shown in Table 36 I. Protein varied between 0.01μg-0.03μg/skin test dose. Fractions d_{II} and d_{III} were skin test reactive on guinea pigs infected with *H. capsulatum*. The M-2 HPD d-fractions were tested 18 weeks after the HKD-43 HPD d-fractions or twenty-seven weeks after initial infection of guinea pigs, and thus delayed hypersensitivity had waned. Analysis of average induration for the reference standard (H-42) tested in both instances also indicated reduction in delayed hypersensitivity.

In Fig. 36-6 are shown the results of testing various concentrations of HKC-43 HPD d_{II} and d_{III}. Approximately 0.05μg of d_{II} and 0.06+μg of d_{III} elicited delayed hypersensitive reactions on *H. capsulatum* infected animals.

Discussion

Several investigators have reported isolation of skin test reactive components from crude histoplasmin. However, in most cases the separation and isolation procedures were time consuming and complex, involving extremely harsh treatment of the biological product which was obtained in small yield. These investigations have demonstrated that several of the problems can

TABLE 36-I

Results of Skin Testing the HKC-43 HPD and M-2 d-Fractions

Antigens*	Protein (μg)	48-Hour Induration (mm)	
		Animals	
		H. capsulatum	Control
H-42(1:25)		11.7	2.4
HKC-43 HPD	0.123	11.2	0.9
HKC-43 HPD d_I	0.016	0	0
d_{II}	0.025	10.8	0
d_{III}	0.017	9.8	0
d_{IV}	0.026	0.8	0
d_V	0.015	0	0
d_{VI}	0.026	0	0
H-42(1:25)		8.0	0
M-2 HPD	0.15	9.0	0
M-2 HPD d_I	0.027	0	0
d_{II}	0.02+	3.9	0
d_{III}	0.02+	4.0	0
d_{IV}	0.02	0	0
d_V	0.02	0	0

* Dose volume for H-42(1:25) was 0.1 ml; for all other antigens it was 0.05 ml.

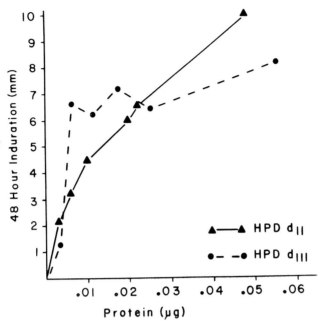

FIGURE 36-6. Detection of delayed hypersensitivity in guinea pigs infected with *Histoplasma capsulatum* with HKC-43 HPD d_{II} and HKC-43 HPD d_{III}.

be eliminated and large-scale isolation can be affected by nonionic dextran chromatography. Elution may be accomplished with physiological saline or distilled water, thus eliminating drastic pH changes or high salt concentrations required of ion exchange resins. The simplicity of eluting fluid eliminates the necessity for desalting by dialysis or other means. One major advantage is that little dilution of the desired compound or component occurs and in fact a concentration effect results. This is amply illustrated by fractionation of histoplasmin HKC-43 where 5 ml of a tenfold concentrate was applied to the column and HPD was collected in 25 ml (tube 9-13, Fig. 36-2).

In recent months HPD has been subjected to additional purification by electrophoresis. Densitometric analysis of the polyacrylamide columns after electrophoresis indicated that d_{II} comprised 11 to 15 percent and d_{III} 19 to 22 percent of HPD. As there was complete recovery of HPD, which comprised 32 percent of the total protein, from the Sephadex column, d_{II} and d_{III} therefore occur in crude histoplasmin HKD-43 at approximately 5 percent. Skin test assay of the extracted Sephadex disc electrophoretic components indicated additional purification with increased specificity.

Disc electrophoresis at various hydrogen ion concentrations, spectral analysis, and density gradient ultracentrifugation indicate that d_{II}, the principal reactive component of HPD, is homogenous. Quantitative chemistries, selective staining, acid and heat coagulation, and differential dextran chromatography at various hydrogen ion concentrations suggest protein and carbohydrate moieties, covalently bonded (Sprouse, manuscript in press). The polyacrylamide electrophoresis, exclusion gel chromatography, and density gradient ultracentrifugation data indicate that this antigenic glycoprotein compound, d_{II}, is less 300,000 molecular weight. This suggests a peptide or polypeptide, disregarding the carbohydrate moiety of less than 3,000 amino acid residues.

The preceeding discussion indicates that recent application of sophisticated biochemic technology has allowed large-scale isolation of the principal skin test reactive "compound" from crude histoplasmin. This is prerequisite to structural elucidation and comprehension of the mode of action of its antigenic determinate. Current immunologic investigations (Schlossman and Levine, 1967) suggest that an antigenic determinant active in detection of delayed hypersensitivity may consist of as few as seven amino acid residues. Thus, large-scale isolation and specifically structural or partial structural elucidation of HPD d_{II} could allow future large-scale synthetic production by (Merrifield, 1964) solid phase protein synthesis of an antigenic determinant reactive in detection of histoplasmosis. Such a defined antigenic determinant should preclude or at least allow comprehension of the cross reactivity currently exhibited in delayed hypersensitive reactions among the mycoses.

These investigations reemphasize the difficulty encountered in biochemical purification, the minute concentration of skin test reactive material and the antigenic heterogeneity of crude histoplasmin. These data, however, suggest that fraction d_{II} from HKC-43, M-2, and possibly any histoplasmin lot could provide the basic unit for dose-weight standardization. At any rate the skin test reactive compound can be dehydrated to a solid state which is easily redissolved in physiological saline or nonpyrogenic distilled water. Existence of solid antigens reduces the laborious task of processing, reduces chances of contamination, and enhances preservation.

References

Christie, A. and Peterson, J.C. (1946). Pulmonary calcification and sensitivity to histoplasmin, tuberculin and haplosporangin. *J. A. M. A., 131*:658-660.

Cross, F.W. and Howell, A. (1948). Studies of Fungus Antigens II. Preliminary reports on the isolation of an immunologically active polysaccharide from histoplasmin. *Public Health Rep., 63*:179-183.

Darling, S.T. (1906). A protozoan general infection producing pseudo-tuberculosis in the lungs, and focal necrosis in the liver, spleen and lymph nodes. *J. A. M. A., 46*:1283-1285.

Dubois, M., Gilles, K.A., Hamilton, J.K., Rebers, P.A. and Smith, F. (1956). Colorimetric method for determination of sugars and related substances. *Analyt. Chem., 28*:350-356.

Dyson, J.E. and Evans, E.E. (1955). Delayed hypersensitivity in experimental fungus infections. *J. Lab. Clin. Med., 45*:449-454.

Emmons, C.W., Olson, B.J. and Eldridge, W.W. (1945). Studies of the role of fungi in pulmonary disease: Cross reactions to histoplasmin. *Public Health Rep.*, 60: 1383-1394.

Fadula, S. and Larsh, H.W. (1967). Separation of specific antigens from two strains of *Histoplasma duboissi* by ion-exchange chromatography. *Bact. Proc.*, M-51, 69.

Goodman, N.L., Sprouse, R.F. and Larsh, H.W. (1968). Histoplasmin potency as affected by culture age. *Sabouraudia*, 6:273-284.

Greene, C.H., DeLalla, L.S. and Tompkins, V.N. (1960). Separation of specific antigens of *Histoplasma capsulatum* by ion-exchange chromatography. *Proc. Soc. Exp. Biol. Med.*, 105:140-141.

Hambraeus, L. and Reio, L. (1965). A study of the ninhydrin-positive components derived from cystine during the Cyanide-Nitroprusside Test. *Acta Chem. Scand.*, 19:2243-2245.

Knight, R.A. and Marcus, S. (1958). Polysaccharide skin test antigens derived from *Histoplasma capsulatum* and *Blastomyces dermatitidis*. *Am. Rev. Tuberc. Pulm. Dis.*, 77:983-989.

Lowry, O.H., Rosebrough, A.L., Farr, A.L. and Randall, R.J. (1951). Protein measurement with the Folin-Phenol reagent. *J. Biol. Chem.*, 193:265-275.

Markowitz, H. (1964). Polysaccharide antigens from *Histoplasma capsulatum*. *Proc. Soc. Exp. Biol. Med.*, 115:697-701.

Merrifield, R.B. (1964). Solid phase peptide synthesis. III. Improved synthesis of bradykinin. *Biochem.*, 3:1385-1390.

Morse, M.L. and Carter, C.E. (1949). The synthesis of nucleic acids in a culture of *Eschericha coli;* Strain B and B/R. *J. Bact.*, 58:317-326.

Palmer, C.E. (1946). Geographic difference in sensitivity to histoplasmin among student nurses. *Public Health Rep.*, 61:475-487.

Porath, F. and Flodin, P. (1959). Gel filtration: a method for desalting and group separation. *Nature, Lond.*, 183:1657-1659.

Salvin, S.B. and Smith, R.F. (1959). Antigens from the yeast phase of *Histoplasma capsulatum*. III. Isolation, properties, and activity of a protein-carbohydrate complex. *J. Infect. Dis.*, 105:45-53.

Schlossman, S.F. and Levine, H. (1967). Desensitization to delayed hypersensitivity reactions. *J. Immunol.*, 99:111-114.

Schuster, L. and Schrier, B.K. (1967). Acrylamide gel-sucrose gradient electrophoresis. *Anal. Biochem.* 19:280-293.

Scott, T.A. and Melvin, E.H. (1953). Determination of dextran with anthrone. *Anal. Chem.*, 25:1656-1661.

Shaw, L.W., Howell, A. and Weiss, E.S. (1950). Biological assay of lots of histoplasmin and the selection of a new working lot. *Public Health Rep.*, 65:583-610.

Smith, C.E. (1943). Coccidioidomycosis. *Med. Clin. N. Amer.*, 27:790-807.

Somogyi, M. (1945). A new reagent for the determination of sugars. *J. Biol. Chem.*, 150:61-68.

Sprouse, R.F. (1967). Chromatographic Separation and Isolation of Skin Test Active Components of Histoplasmin. Ph.D. dissertation. The University of Oklahoma, Norman.

Sprouse, R.F. (1969). Purification of histoplasmin purified derivative. *Amer. Rev. Resp. Dis.* 99:685-690.

Sprouse, R.F., Goodman, N.L. and Larsh, H.W. (1969). Fractionation, isolation and chemical characterization of skin test active components of histoplasmin. *Sabouraudia*, 7:1-11.

Trevelyan, W.E., Proctor, D.P. and Harrison, J.S. (1950). Detection of sugars and alditols on chromatograms with alkaline silver nitrate. *Nature*, 166:444-445.

Warburg, O. and Christian, W. (1941). Isolierung und Kristallisation des Garunsferments Enolase. *Biochem. Z.*, 310:384-421.

Chapter 37

The Histoplasmin Tine Test

MICHAEL L. FURCOLOW

ABSTRACT

History and progress in the development of the tine histoplasmin test are recorded along with some of the difficulties involved.

AS most of you know, an entire afternoon of the 1952 Conference was devoted to the histoplasmin skin test. Interestingly enough, there have been very few developments in this test except for new methods of application such as tine and jet, which you will hear about later. A few new lots of histoplasmin have appeared and have been standarized by comparative tests on humans, and NIH now has more stringent requirements for standardization. In addition, the most controversial development is the question of the influence of the skin test on the serologic tests. I am sure you will hear about this later.

Since Dr. Chick delved into history, I thought you might permit me to tell you a bit about the development of the tine test. This story begins in 1945, when I was first transferred to Kansas City for the specific purpose of studying the importance of histoplasmosis to human health and the means of differentiating this disease from tuberculosis, if indeed it caused much disease. About the time we set up in Kansas City, in the course of a widespread skin-testing program in Kansas City Schools, patch testing was done for the purpose of seeing how useful this tool was on a wide-spread basis. Unfortunately, it turned out that about one fourth of the total number of children reacted to the patch test. We then tried to determine what had caused this large number of false positives, and in doing so, I contacted Lederle Company, since they made the patch, and tried to find out what they had done recently to change their method of manufacture, since the patch test had never shown such poor results before. We found out that they had developed a different method of concentrating the Old Tuberculin, using, instead of boiling, vacuum distillation which did not require such high temperatures. In doing so, they failed to denature some of the tubercule bacillus proteins which were in the tuberculin in its original state. I suggested that they revert back to the old method of concentration, and this was done, and the trouble disappeared. This was the beginning of our working with the Lederle Company. We then did extensive testing in Kansas City and thereabouts, comparing the Mantoux test with the patch test, and we got some pretty sorry results,

TABLE 37-I

Comparisons of Various Patch Tests and Intradermal PPD

Type of Patch Test	Number Tested	Percent Missed	Percent False Positives
Commercial Old Tuberculin			
Children	2339	27.7	2.6
Adults	2008	18.8	9.6
Sanitarium patients	816	25.3	13.1
Commercial Old Tuberculin+			
20% glycerine	565	13.6	15.1
PPD+6% glycerine	1001	25.1	7.13
PPD+20% glycerine	564	25.5	11.4

as you can see from Table 37-I. These tests showed conclusively the patch test was not a good enough test for widespread clinical use. It missed a considerable number of people who were positive to the standard Mantoux and also picked up some false positives who were negative to the Mantoux test. Our first thought was that if we should try PPD (purified protein derivative) or increase the concentration of tuberculin or make it penetrate the skin by some means, we might be able to improve the performance. We, therefore, incorporated more glycerin in the patch, we abrased the skin in various manners, and changed the patch test to include a sort of aluminium material sort of like sandpaper, with the results seen in Table 37-II. None of these changes seemed to do very much about improving the efficacy of the tests. We then thought perhaps it was necessary for us to actually abrade the skin with some instrument with the tuberculin on it or rub the tuberculin into the skin in order to achieve a satisfactory test. Indeed, when the first tests were done, we secured some old tin graters which had been originally used in abrading inertubes to patch old-fashioned tires. Maybe most of you are too young to know what I am talking about. These showed very suggestive results, and in 1957 we used these disks in wet and dry tests, which showed relatively satisfactory results (Table 37-III). We also experimented

TABLE 37-II

Comparisons of Various Patch Tests and Intradermal PPD

Type of Patch Test	Number Tested	Percent Missed	Percent False Positives
.0167 cc Old Tuberculin alundum patch			
Normal adults	331	16.8	6.1
Sanitarium patients	170	4.9	
.0334 cc Old Tuberculin Alundum			
Normal adults	331	14.9	10.4
Sanitarium patients	170	3.1	50.0
Commercial Old Tuberculin patch applied after abrasion			
Sanitarium patients	816	4.6	63.1
Commercial Old Tuberculin patch with disk			
Normal adults	542	28.0	1.7

TABLE 37-III

Comparisons of Various Patch Tests and Intradermal PPD

Type of Patch Test	Number Tested	Percent Missed	Percent False Positives
Undiluted Old Tuberculin wet patch	281	6.5	18.8
⅓ Diluted Old Tuberculin wet patch	292	14.1	3.9
		2 or More Papules—Positive	
Disk dipped in 4×Old Tuberculin	840	4.6	14.8
		3 or More Papules—Positive	
Disk dipped in 4×Old Tuberculin	840	7.7	9.8
		4 or More Papules	
Disk dipped in 4×Old Tuberculin	840	13.1	6.4

with methods of reading. In 1958, we then received our first shipment of what we called wet and dry disks, and by 1960, as seen in Table 37-IV, we began to get some satisfactory results. The wet and dry disks were so called because we had the disks incorporated in a bag of Old Tuberculin as the so-called wet disk. The dry disk was the same sort of disk with the Old Tuberculin dried on the tines of the disk. We found what we called a wet disk did not work well because when the disk was pushed through the tuberculin bag, the bag ruptured and splattered the tuberculin all over the room, getting into our eyes, and so on. However, the test worked reasonably well. It was at this time that Dr. Virgil Place of the Lederle Company suggested that we first employ the use of measurement of the tine reactions, which we

TABLE 37-IV

Comparison of Wet and Dry Disks With PPD Intermediate Dose Intracutaneous Test
Percentages Employing Three or More Papules as Positive

Wet

Results on PPD Intermediate	Total	Wet Disc Number		Wet Disc Percent	
		Negative	Positive	Negative	Positive
Negative (0–4 mm)	229	211	18	92	8
Positive (5 mm)	266	54	212	20	80

Percentages Employing Three or More Papules as Positive

Dry

PPD Intermediate	Total	Dry Disc Number		Dry Disc Percent	
		Negative	Positive	Negative	Positive
Negative (0–4 mm)	273	248	25	91	9
Positive (5 mm)	208	30	178	14	86

TABLE 37-V

Comparison of Tine Test With Intradermal PPD
(Topeka State Hospital, January, 1960)

Intradermal PPD (mm)	Tine 4×STD Dipped Twice	
	<2 mm	>2 mm
0–4	251 (91.9%)	22 (8.1%)
5+	18 (8.7%)	189 (91.3%)

had previously not done, relying on counting and description of papules. As you can see, the application of Place's measurement and the 2 mm limit gave us some relatively satisfactory results. Table 37-V prepared in 1960, shows that the tine test dipped twice in four times the concentrated standard Old Tuberculin gave a reasonable satisfactory result. That is about 9 percent false positive and 8 percent false negative. It was, at this time, that the Lederle people decided to move toward commercial production. However, you must remember that all this material was related to the tuberculin tine and not the histoplasmin.

Coming to histoplasmin tine, it was natural for us to begin to experiment with different concentrations of histoplasmin on the tine tests. Table 37-VI shows the results of tests performed on University of Kentucky students in 1964 employing 12 X and 18 X histoplasmin. It is evident that the results were not too bad. Indeed they were perhaps better than we should have expected. Tests performed in Bell County in 1964 with 10 X and 18 X histoplasmin are shown in Table 37-VII, and again the results appeared quite satisfactory. The next table (37-VIII) shows further tests performed in 1967 with the standard test, which was then being produced and is 15 X concentration of histoplasmin. Again, as you can see, the results are within a permissible range of error; that is, about 9 percent and 2½ percent. Also in

TABLE 37-VI

Lexington College Students, 1964

		12×Tine			
		+	−	Total	
Mantoux	+	81	6	87	6.9%
	−	0	72	72	0%
	Total	81	78	159	
		18×Tine			
		+	−	Total	
Mantoux	+	80	6	86	7.0%
	−	0	67	67	0%
	Total	80	73	153	

TABLE 37-VII

Bell County, Kentucky, Children, 1965
Two Concentrations of Histoplasmin on Tines

		10×Tine			
		+	−	*Total*	
Mantoux	+	25	1	26	*3.8%*
	−	3	347	350	*0.8%*
	Total	28	348	376	

		18×Tine			
		+	−	*Total*	
Mantoux	+	25	1	26	*3.8%*
	−	0	311	311	*0.0%*
	Total	25	312	337	

TABLE 37-VIII

University of Kentucky Students, 1967

		Tine			
		+	−	*Total*	
Mantoux	+	174	17	191	(8.9%)
	−	14	548	562	(2.5%)
	Total	188	565	753	

TABLE 37-IX

False Positive and Negative Reactions To Histoplasmin Tine Tests,
Four Independent Studies, 1965–1966

Study	*No. Tested*		*Ages*	*False Positive*	*False Negative*
A	496	Negro children	12–18	6.0	6.6
B	278	Male mental patients	18–92	14.0	1.2
C+	179	College students	20–25	0.0 R_1†	5.5 R_1†
				7.6 R_2*	3.0 R_2†
Present Study	414	Mental patients	19–59	1.8	8.0

Reproduced with the permission of the *Archives Environmental Health*, from Jarvis, Chick and Sehwerha, 1967. Intradermal method used as reference standard.

* Studies A, B, and C, personal communication, Lederle Laboratories.

† R_1 = reader one; R_2 = reader two.

TABLE 37-X

Danville, Kentucky, 1967

		Tine 48 Hours			
		+	−	*Total*	
Mantoux	+	292	156	448	*34.8%*
	−	17	183	200	*8.5%*
	Total	309	339	648	

		Tine 72 Hours			
		+	−	*Total*	
Mantoux	+	238	73	311	*23.5%*
	−	10	139	149	*6.7%*
	Total	248	212	460	

1967, Jarvis, Chick and Schwerha reported three studies from the literature and one of their own in West Virginia, showing again quite satisfactory results within the probable range of error, although one study did indicate a fairly large proportion of false positive reactors (Table 37-IX). Most of the above studies were used in securing NIH clearance for the sale of the tine test.

This was the status of affairs in 1967. It is interesting to note that the same lot of histoplasmin tines used in Table 37-VIII was used about a week later in another study in Danville, Kentucky, as seen in Table 37-X. It is thought that the tines had been kept for the preceding week in the trunk of a car which was very hot, since it was summer. At any rate, in Danville the results were much different than those shown in the Table 37-VIII. Thus, the false negatives had risen from 9 to 35 percent and false positive from 2.5 and 8.5 percent. Another interesting thing became evident in Danville—there appeared to be a decrease in both the false positive and the false negative reactors at 72 hours as compared to 48 hours. Similar results have been reported by Chase, Kadull and Reynolds (1968) and seen in Table 37-XI.

This more or less brings us to the present. We have a test made with the

TABLE 37-XI

Fredrick, Maryland, 1968

		Tine			
		+	−	*Total*	
Mantoux	+	632	246	878	*28%*
	−	19	444	463	*4%*
	Total	651	690	1341	

From Chase, Kadull, and Reynolds, 1968.

same lot histoplasmin in the same manner over the years which had performed very satisfactory, as shown by its acceptance by the National Institutes of Health. It now tends to show an excessive number of false negatives or misses of positive histoplasmin skin reactions. The obvious inference is that the antigen has in some way lost some potency, for at the same time the false negative has risen, the false positive rate has actually fallen. In addition to this, the improvement in the results at 72 hours suggests that the antigen might be there but in a somewhat weakened state. This has led the Lederle Company to investigate the matter extensively. One of the theories on the loss of potency of the antigen was the creeping of the antigen up the tine toward the base because of the presence of large amounts of glycerin in the material. While only 10 cc of glycerin per 1,000 cc are used in the preparation of the original media, this liter has decreased to about 800 cc by the time of completion of the growth of the histoplasmin because of evaporation. Since the tines are used at 15 X, this would mean that the 800 cc would then be concentrated to about 50 cc. Since it is presumed that the glycerin is not concentrated, it would, therefore, be about 20 percent of the histoplasmin which was put on the tines. It is very easy to see why the glycerin might have played a part in the migration of the material away from the points.

This matter has been attempted to be remedied by the preparation of glycerin-free histoplasmin which Mr. Smith has prepared during the past year. He has found that the presence of glycerin is not necessary for adequate growth of *H. capsulatum* and the production of histoplasmin. The material appears fully potent when prepared without glycerin. It has been applied to tines and is presently undergoing field tests.

References

Chase, H.V., Kadull, P.J. and Reynolds, R.C. (1968). Comparison of histoplasmin tine test with the histoplasmin Mantoux test. *Amer. Rev. Resp. Dis.*, 98:1058-1059.
Jarvis, M.A., Chick, E.W. and Schwerha, J.E. (1967). Usefulness of the histoplasmin tine test for screening. *Arch. Environ. Health*, 14:668-670

The Relationships Between Methods of Skin Testing and Results Obtained in Histoplasmosis

ERNEST W. CHICK

ABSTRACT

Currently two, and potentially three or more, methods are available for skin testing in histoplasmosis. Properly administered, these tests do provide a means to determine delayed hypersensitivity related to histoplasmosis in individuals or in population groups, with reasonable accuracy. There is a need, however, for further study on the nature of the antigen to be used, on variations in individual host response to the antigen, and on methodology which would remove human error and various mechanical and traumatic factors to insure reproducible localization and deposition of the antigen.

THE procedure of skin testing may be considered the introduction of a test material into the skin to determine if it will produce a reaction of that particular recipient's skin. Even with this broad and general definition some variables are immediately apparent.

First to be considered is the test material to be introduced into the skin. This may be a simple or complex chemical, or it may be a biological. The material may be a chemically defined substance, or it may be a complex mixture of substances of unknown chemical composition. The nature of the material may profoundly influence the results obtained.

Second is the method by which the material is introduced into the skin. This may be by topical application on the unbroken skin surface, which may or may not produce absorption into the deeper skin layers. To inject intracutaneously (i.e. beneath the stratum corneum to epidermis, or dermis) necessitates a break in the integrity of the tissue. Obviously this implies a degree of trauma which may vary from mild to severe. Since the body will react to trauma, whatever its nature or intent, this reaction to trauma may mask, alter, or influence the nature of possible reaction produced by the test material.

Third, is the recognition and interpretation of the reaction produced by the material, if indeed a reaction is produced. The reaction may be an immediate one. Immediate reactions may be produced by simple physical or chemical irritation or damage to the surrounding cells, such as would be produced by the injection of acid intracutaneously. Immediate reactions may also be produced by antigen-antibody reactions, usually relating to antigens acting as allergins or anaphylaxins. Or the reaction may be of the delayed hypersensitivity type, usually seen with histoplasmin, tuberculin, and others. Recognition of these reactions is usually based on the production of an area of induration and sometimes on the accompanying erythema. Unfortunately, induration may be variable, and one has the question as to what degree of induration means what? Variations in induration may relate to the nature of the antigen, the dilution of the antigen initially, the amount of antigen actually deposited in the skin, or it may relate to variations in individual host response.

These considerations may be applied to skin testing for histoplasmosis. The test material is a biological derived from the fungus *Histoplasma capsulatum*. However, the test material may be derived from the mycelial or the yeast phase of the fungus. It may be crude filtrate of an aged culture, such as histoplasmin, or it may be specific fraction of the organism, either protein or polysaccharide in nature. Previous papers in this conference by Kobayashi, Bauman, Bartells, and others, have discussed the status of these potential test materials. Whatever the nature of the antigen used, it should be standardized with an accepted reference antigen.

The reaction produced by the test materials derived from *H. capsulatum* is a manifestation of hypersensitivity resulting in a focal area of induration often accompanied by erythema. The chapter by Furcolow discusses recognition and interpretation of these reactions.

Currently much consideration is being given to the most appropriate way to test intracutaneously for histoplasmosis. Ideally such a method should be simple, inexpensive, and suitable for epidemiologic field studies as well as for office or hospital diagnostic use. The method should be one that insures technical reproducibility in placement of the test material at the same depth intracutaneously from patient to patient. Equally important the method should insure the deposition of a constant amount of the test material from patient to patient. Ideally the method would be one that would minimize the influence of human error by the tester.

A review of the methods which have been used historically to introduce a biological material into the skin is both enlightening and entertaining. The rubbing of salves or ointments onto the suface of the skin probably began with perhistoric man and has continued to the present. Modifications of this method to test for delayed hypersensitivity are exemplified in the Vollmer and Moro patch tests for tuberculosis. This method has not been used in histoplasmosis except for rare sporadic research endeavors.

Most of the tests for delayed hypersensitivity have utilized some method of intracutaneous penetration. Figure 38-I shows a device of 1862 used to introduce biologicals into the skin. The hollow wooden body contained the fluid; leakage was prevented by a piece of buckskin. When the device was placed on the patient's skin, pressure on the central cylinder forced the nee-

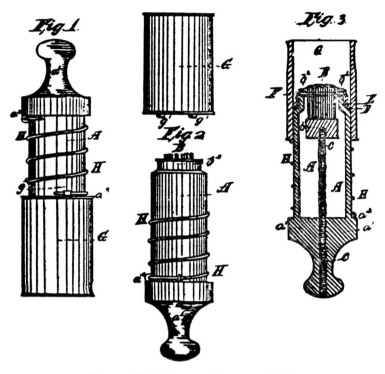

FIGURE 38-1. Firmenich patent, 1862.

dles through the buckskin into the patient's skin. The biological was carried along with the needles in their passage.

Figure 38-2 is a device from 1867, again composed of a hollow wooden body with a central needle-bearing cylinder. The wooden base protected the needles and held the biological about the needles. In use the base was removed, the device placed against the patient's skin, and the needles driven into the skin. The liquid was carried into the skin with the needles. This method was said to "supersede, to a great extent, the use of blisters, irritating plasters, and the other usual medical counterirritants, lineaments, and so on, as well as the merely mechanical means, such as scarifying, cupping, puncturing, leeches, setons, etc."

Figure 38-3 illustrates a sharpened quill of 1882. The dried biological was carried on the point into the patient's skin. Figure 38-4 shows a glass device from 1903. The pointed glass applicator rested in a hollow glass tube containing the biological and carried the material into the patient's skin. Presumably these devices could be used by scarification or by puncture.

Figure 38-5 illustrates a 1952 metal disk with multiple sharp prongs. The biological was applied to the patient's skin, then the device placed over this area. Pressure forced the prongs intracutaneously, carrying the biological along with them.

Figures 38-6, 38-7, and 38-8 illustrate devices of 1951, 1959, and 1964, respectively. All have in common a mechanism of holding a liquid biological,

FIGURE 38-3. Dickson patent, 1882.

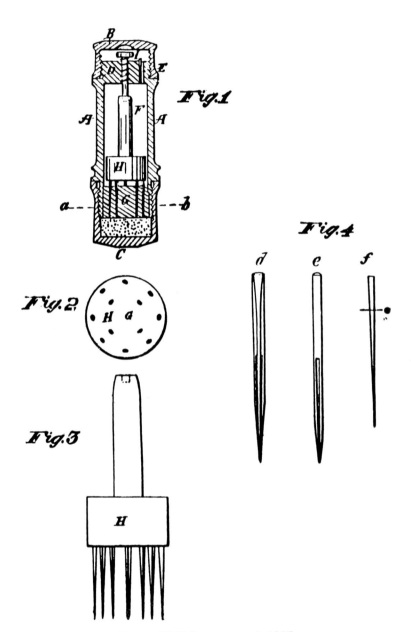

FIGURE 38-2. Brown patent, 1867.

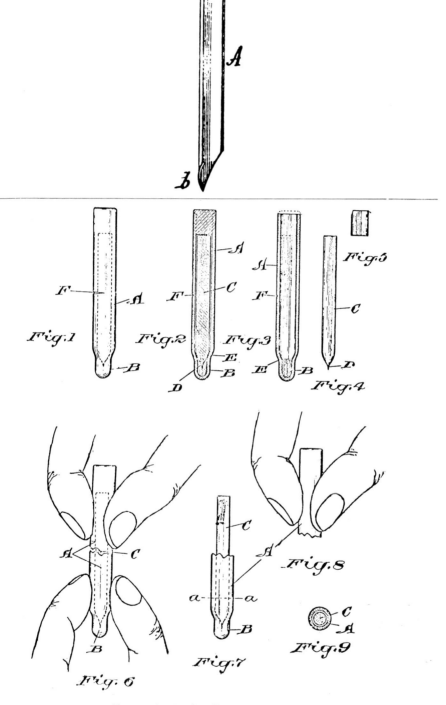

FIGURE 38-4. Chandler patent, 1903.

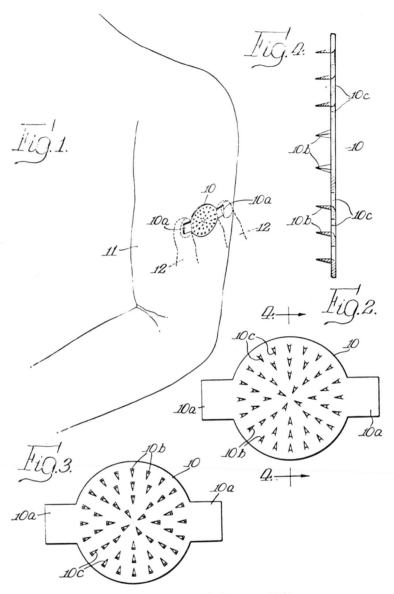

FIGURE 38-5. Rosenthal patent, 1952.

a plastic bubble or bag, and a method of puncturing the bubble or bag and introducing the biological into the skin by multiple sharp prongs.

With the exception of the device in Figure 38-5, none of these are in current usage. However, some of the more recent methods used in skin testing are based on one or more of these concepts. The Pirquet Test and the Heaf Multiple-Puncture Test have been used in tuberculosis. In the Pirquet test the biological is applied to the skin and a single scratch of proper depth. This potential for human error has limited the use of this method, at least in this country. In the Heaf multiple-puncture test the biological is applied to the skin or the needles dipped in the biological; the apparatus is placed over the area and a spring released forcing the six needles into the skin to predetermined depths of 1 or 2 mm. The test is used by measurement of induration at seventy-two hours. Neither method has been used to any significant extent in histoplasmosis.

Historically, the standardized method of skin testing in histoplasmosis has been the use of the hollow needle and syringe, i.e. the Mantoux test. With well-trained testers who take particular care to do a proper test, this method has provided reproducible results. However, in routine practice this care is not always taken. Cognizance must be taken of the sources of human and of mechanical errors which may occur. The depth of needle placement may profoundly alter the result. Too shallow penetration of the epidermis allows antigen leakage to the surface; too deep penetration of the dermis allows subcutaneous tissue diffusion of the antigen. Either produces erratic and inconsistent results. The amount of antigen placed intracutaneously must be consistent. Unfortunately, besides the human error in syringe manipulation, some syringes, particularly some plastic varieties, may be improperly calibrated. The test is read by measurement of induration at the puncture site at forty-eight hours.

Because of these potential sources of error, and recognizing the need for an improved method which would offer simplicity and ease in method and

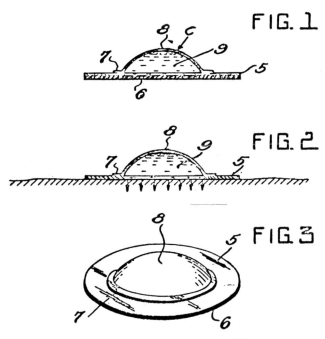

FIGURE 38-6. Prisk patent, 1951.

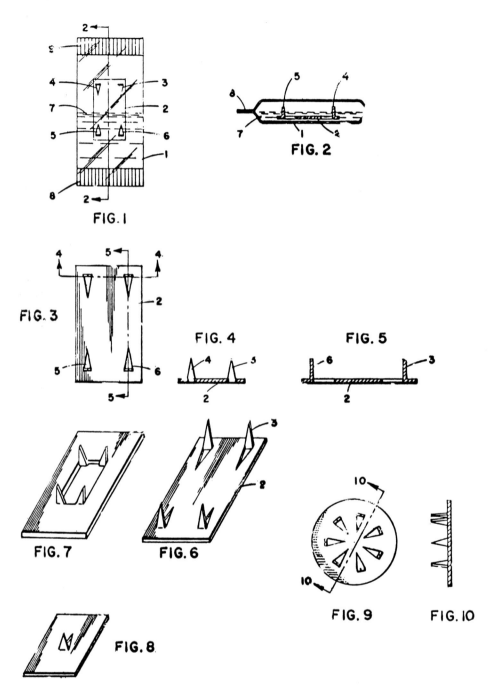

FIG. I

FIG. 2

FIG. 3

FIG. 4

FIG. 5

FIG. 7

FIG. 6

FIG. 9

FIG. 10

FIG. 8

FIGURE 38-7. Wagner patent, 1959.

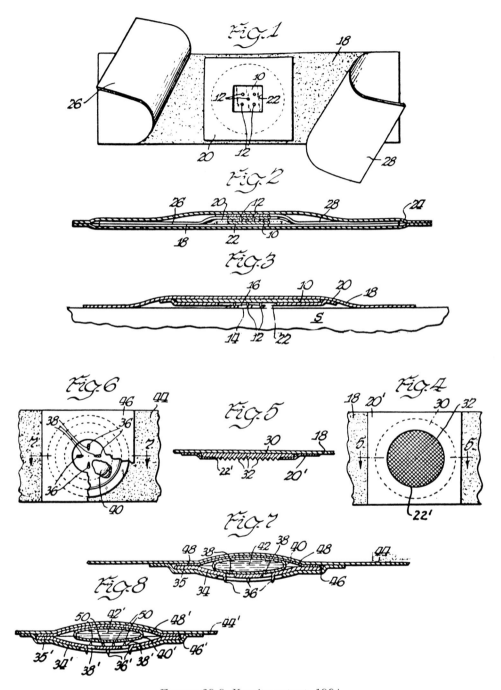

FIGURE 38-8. Kravitz patent, 1964.

reproducibility in antigen placement and deposition, alternative methods
have been studied in recent years. Lederle Laboratories has made the tine
test available commercially with tuberculin and histoplasmin. Lincoln Laboratories has available commercially the Mono-Vacc with tuberculin; potentially this could be used with histoplasmin. The Jet gun has been discussed
by Millar *et al.* (1969).

Figure 38-9 shows the tine test. This device consists of a plastic handle
which can be held between the fingers. Four metal tines or prongs are located at the base of the handle. The length of the tines is estimated to penetrate the epidermis but not the dermis of patients with normal skin thickness. The antigen is dried on the tines. A plastic cap over the end maintains
sterility until use. The test is administered by pressing the device on the
patient's arm for one second. Properly done, on removal one should see mo-
mentarily the imprint of the circular base ring and the puncture sites of the
four tines. The test is read by measurement of induration at each puncture
site at forty-eight or seventy-two hours.

The Mono-Vacc test (Fig. 38-10) consists of a plastic ring which fits
around the distal portion of the thumb. Nine plastic points or prongs are located on the base. Again, the length of the points is estimated to penetrate
the epidermis but not the dermis of patients with normal skin thickness. A

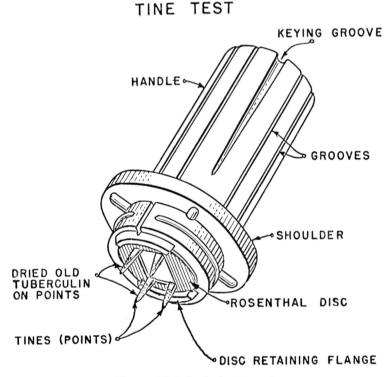

FIGURE 38-9. Lederle tine test.

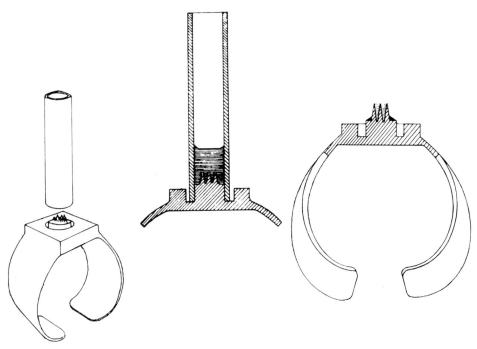

FIGURE 38-10. Lincoln Mono-Vacc test.

small plastic cylinder encloses the base and the points and contains the liquid antigen. The test is administered by removing the plastic cylinder and pressing the device on the patient's arm. Properly done, again one should see the momentary imprint of the base and the puncture sites. The test is read by measurement of induration at the puncture site at forty-eight or seventy-two hours.

In the tine test the dried antigen is deposited by a combination of a "wiping effect" of the tines against tissue cells and by solubilizing in extracellular fluid. In the Mono-Vacc and the Heaf multiple-puncture tests, the liquid antigen is carried with the points into the tissue and may flow from about the base along the puncture tracks. With these methods tissue trauma is minimal, but occasional bleeding is noted, and on rare ocassions the resultant hematoma may interfer with test interpretation. This may also occur with the Mantoux test.

In practice both the tine and Mono-Vacc tests have shown encouraging results as a rapid simple method which can be used epidemiologically in the field or clinically in office or hospital. These results are summarized in the chapter by Furcolow.

Academically, several questions are unanswered. How does the standardized length of the tines or points of the tine test, the Mono-Vacc test, and the Heaf multiple-puncture test compare with actual differences in skin thicknesses of different patients and of patients at varying ages? Individual and age differences in skin thicknesses do occur. Do these methods insure a precise deposition of a constant amount of antigen? It has long been recognized with the Mantoux test that varying amounts of antigen deposition may alter the resultant induration of a positive test. In studies of series of patients or population groups these methods appear relatively consistent. Yet, could the above factors be operative in the small percentage of false positives and false negatives observed when compared to the Mantoux test? (Ironically, one may also ask similar questions of the reference Mantoux test.) Furthermore, consideration must always be given to the nature of the antigen utilized and to the variations in individual host response which it may elicit.

Finally, a fresh look should be directed to current clerical and statistical methods used in data analysis of skin-testing procedures and surveys. Do the methods utilized insure adequate evaluation of the above variables? Such preciseness is always desirable, but becomes a necessity when dealing with data from areas of low reactor sensitivity rates, percentages of false positive or false negative reactions, and of cross reactions between antigens.

★   ★   ★

The author would like to express his appreciation to John C. Blair, Stamford, Connecticut, for making available the patents, from which most of the illustrations were taken.

Reference

Millar, J.D., Tosh, F., Ismach, A., Morris, L. and Sellers, T.F., Jr. (1969). Histoplasmin skin testing by intradermal jet injection. *Amer. Rev. Resp. Dis., 100*:542-549.

Chapter 39

Cross Reactivity in Histoplasmin Skin Testing

NORMAN L. GOODMAN

ABSTRACT

Studies with guinea pigs sensitized to standardized doses of mycelial particles of several fungi showed that histoplasmin will significantly cross react with *Blastomyces dermatitidis, Aspergillus terreus, Aspergillus fumigatus* and *Penicillium* sp. Cross reactions also occurred with *Sporothrix schenckii, Emmonsia crescens,* and *Beauveria* sp. to a lesser extent.

A reduction in cross reactivity was accomplished by using fractions of histoplasmin prepared with acrylamide gels.

The results of the studies presented suggest that a number of fungi besides the often mentioned *Blastomyces* and *Coccidioides* should be considered as possible causes of cross reactions to histoplasmin in naturally infected human and animal populations.

THE histoplasmin skin test has been in use for over twenty years as a tool in the clinical diagnosis of histoplasmosis and for epidemiological studies of histoplasmal infection (Emmons *et al.*, 1945). Accurate interpretations of the results of the test have been hampered by the knowledge that delayed type skin reactions to histoplasmin can be caused by infection with fungi other than *Histoplasma capsulatum*. Early experimental and clinical studies showed this with *Coccidioides immitis* and *Blastomyces dermatitidis* (Emmons *et al.*, 1945; Howell, 1947; Smith *et al.*, 1949).

There is increasing evidence that there are more fungi involved in cross reactivity to histoplasmin than *Coccidioides* and *Blastomyces* (Larsh *et al.*, 1964; Asgari and Conant, 1964). This evidence, together with the increasing incidence of infection in man with these fungi, makes the present histoplasmin skin-testing method suspect as an accurate epidemiological or diagnostic tool.

The object of this paper is to discuss some of the evidence of cross reactivity to various fungal infections and examine possible means for alleviating the problem. The first observations on cross reactivity was published by Emmons in 1945, when he showed cross reactivity between histoplasmin, blastomycin, coccidioidin, and haplosporangin. These findings have been confirmed and expanded upon repeatedly in various animals in the ensuing years. Howell, in 1947, showed that if histoplasmin is highly standardized, a quantitative assessment may be made regarding its cross reactivity to blasto-

313

mycin. Unfortunately, most histoplasmin is not subjected to critical titration, and there are fungi other than *Blastomyces* with which to be concerned. Also, there is a lack of blastomycin for simultaneous testing to measure cross reactivity to that infection, as proposed by some investigators. As a matter of fact, we have been using a multitude of antigens, prepared under various conditions, for epidemiological studies.

The problems in cross reactivity with *Blastomyces* and *Coccidioides* were evident and discussed thoroughly during the first conference on histoplasmosis in 1952. Subsequently, Palmer, Edwards and Allfather, in 1957, suggested the possibility of fungi other than *Blastomyces* and *Coccidioides* causing nonspecific sensitivity to histoplasmin. As a result of these studies, Palmer, Edwards and Larsh embarked on a program to test this hypothesis in laboratory animals.

Materials and Methods

Our studies were made by infecting guinea pigs with standardized doses of mycelial particles of several isolates of fungi. Most of the fungi used were isolated from clinical specimens. The number of animals inoculated with each fungus varied from eighteen to fifty-four. All animals were housed in randomly assigned cages.

Soon after infection each pig was tested simultaneously with histoplasmin H-42 (1:25), blastomycin B-7 (1:250), and coccidioidin C-59 (1:25). The animals were subsequently tested with other antigens. All animals were skin tested using the intradermal method with 0.1 ml of antigen being injected as superficially as possible. All reactions were read by measuring, in millimeters, the transverse diameter of erythema and induration. Forty-eight-hour readings were used for statistical purposes.

Results and Discussion

Results of testing animals of the various infection groups with the three antigens are summarized in Figure 39-1. This shows the percent of animals in each different infection group that reacts to histoplasmin, blastomycin, and coccidioidin. The length of the bars indicates graphically for each antigen the percent of pigs inoculated with the isolate to the right that had a reaction of any size.

The panel of bars to the right represents the specificity profile of histoplasmin. The three isolates at the top show the highest frequency of reactors to histoplasmin—more than 85 percent—and the differences among the three regimens are small. Two of the three isolates are from patients with histoplasmosis; the third isolate is from soil.

Now observe the profile to see which of the other fungi produce sensitivity to histoplasmin. The results are somewhat surprising. Infection with *As-*

SPECIFICITY   PROFILES
(based on percent reacting)

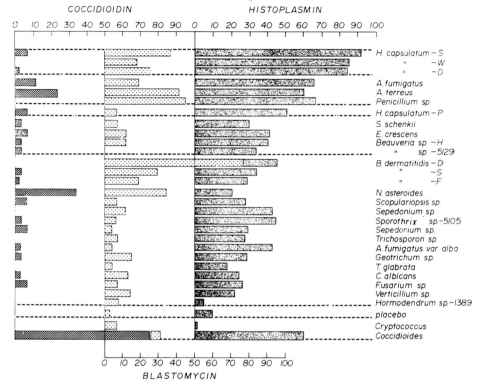

FIGURE 39-1. Specificity profiles of fungal skin test antigens on guinea pigs infected with homologous and heterologous fungi.

pergillus fumigatus, A. terreus, and *Penicillium* species produced as many cross reactions to histoplasmin as did infection with *C. immitis;* over 60 percent reacted. Only one other isolate, another *Histoplasma* isolate, this one isolated from a pillow, caused over 50 percent to react. Also, note here that there was a higher percentage of reactivity to the aspergilli and *Penicillium* species than to the pillow isolate of *H. capsulatum* and *B. dermatitidis,* which is classically known to cross react with histoplasmin.

Also, almost all of the different isolates produced some sensitivity.

The results from the blastomycin testing showed that at the two- and four-week testing, only one of the three isolates of *Blastomyces* caused a high frequency of reactions to blastomycin. It is important to note that in two regimens of animals infected with *Blastomyces,* a higher percent of the animals reacted to histoplasmin than to blastomycin. It is evident, from these studies, that there are fewer cross reactions to blastomycin than to histoplasmin.

It is clear, from the results obtained, that coccidioidin is a more specific antigen than either histoplasmin or blastomycin. In spite of critical illness in many of the pigs infected with *Coccidioides,* 74 percent reacted to coccidioidin. Only three other fungi caused more than 10 percent to react; *Nocar-dia asteroides, A. terreus,* and *A. fumigatus.*

Figure 39-2 shows the percentage of animals reacting to histoplasmin at different times. The animals infected with *Coccidioides* and *Cryptococcus* were not included because too many died. For this illustration, regimens were grouped by the percent with reactions out of the total number of tests done during the study. The top line shows the percent reacting among animals infected with three isolates of *H. capsulatum* (Scritchfield, Ward and District). The next line shows the percent reacting among those infected with *A. fumigatus, A. terreus,* and *Penicillium sp.* Note, the percentages are higher than for those animals infected with isolates of *B. dermatitidis* and the pillow isolate of *H. capsulatum.* However, this group showed a significant waning of sensitivity within thirty-four weeks of inoculation. Also note that the *S. schenckii, Emmonsia crescens,* and *Beauveria* group showed greater sensitivity than the *Blastomyces* group. The lower grouping of fungal isolates combines all those regimens with a lower total percent reacting than among the animals infected with the isolate of *Blastomyces* with the lowest percent reacting.

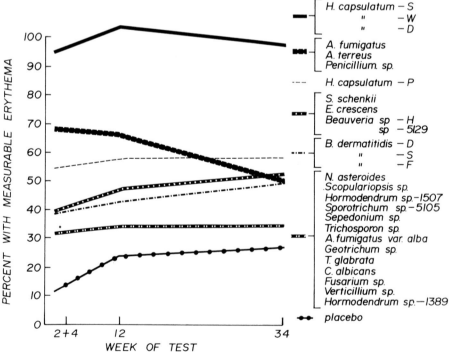

FIGURE 39-2. Skin test reactions of histoplasmin (H-42) on guinea pigs inoculated with different fungi. Histoplasmin H-42 (1:25).

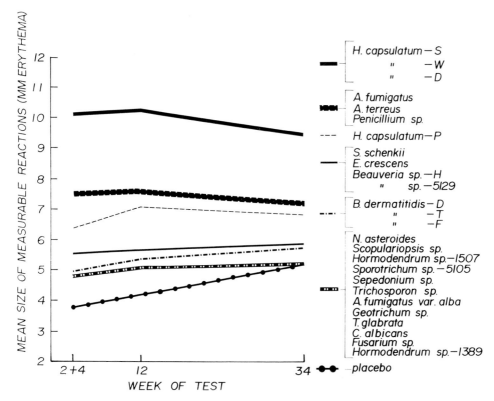

FIGURE 39-3. Mean size of skin test reactions to histoplasmin (H-42) by week of test: guinea pigs inoculated with different fungi.

Figure 39-3 shows the average sizes of reactions for the same groups as in Figure 39-2. As shown, some fungi produce relatively large reactions, others small ones. This fact, as well as the percentage of cross reactions, may be of value in determining which organisms may be causing cross reactions in different animal and human populations. Note, in Figure 39-3 that the lines depicting the mean size reactions fall into the same pattern as those in Figure 39-2.

The above results were obtained with the histoplasmin antigen H-42. To investigate the possibility that other comparably titered histoplasmins might not cause such a high frequency of cross reactions, guinea pigs were tested with six other histoplasmins. The results of this study are shown in Figure 39-4. As can be seen here, most of the seven histoplasmins used on Scritchfield, Ward, and District infected pigs showed minor variations in mean skin test size; however, some of the differences are as much as 4 mm (NCDC 267 on Scritchfield- and Ward-infected pigs). Note that all antigens tested gave small reactions on animals infected with *H. capsulatum*, pillow isolate, generally smaller, in fact, than on animals infected with *Aspergillus* and *Penicillium* isolates. This is especially true of the two commercial antigens tested. These results point up the fact that there is variability in skin sensitivity re-

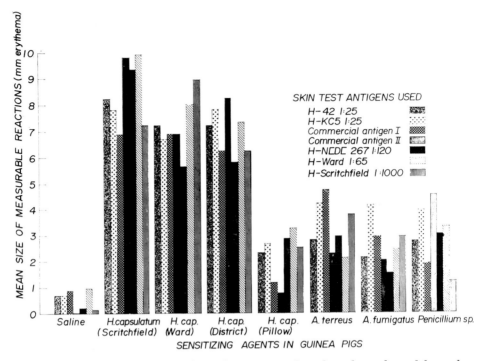

FIGURE 39-4. Variation in seven histoplasmins tested on homologously and heterologously sensitized guinea pigs.

actions among the various isolates of *H. capsulatum,* and the cross reactions from other fungal infections may give larger reactions than the less sensitive histoplasmin reactions. This would be especially important in epidemiological studies involving small reactors.

It is a well-accepted fact that histoplasmin will cross react with animals and humans infected with *B. dermatitidis* and *C. immitis.* Other fungal infections by *Haplosporangium* and *Chrysosporium* (Asgari and Conant, 1964) have also been incriminated as causing histoplasmin sensitivity. Now there is evidence of an even greater array of fungi which will cross react with histoplasmin. This raises the question of the accuracy of previous epidemiological interpretations, especially regarding marginal reactions. If, indeed, there are numerous organisms that will cause cross reactivity to histoplasmin, what, if anything, can be done to correct the situation?

There is evidence indicating that increased culture age is associated with increased cross reactivity to histoplasmin (Goodman, Sprouse and Larsh, 1968). Histoplasmin from one- to three-month-old cultures does not show as many fractions of protein as older cultures when the filtrates are studied electrophoretically (Goodman, Taha and Larsh, 1968; Taha, 1969). Presumably, these late-appearing protein fractions are associated with more complete lysis and degradation of the mycelium, thus releasing proteins common to many fungi. Current work tends to corroborate these findings.

TABLE 39-I

Percent Guinea Pig Reactors to Crude and Fractionated Histoplasmin

Skin Test Antigen	Animals Sensitized To				
	H. capsulatum Scritchfield	*H. capsulatum District*	*Histoplasma duboisii*	*Blastomyces dermatitidis*	*Sporothrix schenckii*
H-42 (1:25)	80	75	50	40	25
H-42 (Dialyzed)	80	66	28	44	25
H-42 A-2	75	58	21	33	0
H-42 S-2	83	83	29	25	8
Histoplasma "duboisii"	88	83	95	88	42
Physiological Saline	0	0	0	0	0

Positive reaction, ≥ 5 mm induration.

Table 39-I shows results of studies by Bartels and Larsh *et al.*, (1969). Guinea pigs infected with two isolates of *H. capsulatum, H. duboisii, B. dermatitidis*, and *Sporothrix schenckii* were skin tested with: histoplasmin H-42 (1:25), dialyzed histoplasmin H-42 (1:25), a fraction collected from analytical acrylamide gel (H-42, A-2), a fraction collected from separatory acrylamide gel (H-42, S-2), histoplasmin duboisii (1:25), and 0.85% saline.

The point to be made from this study is the reduction in the percentage of cross reactions when fractions of histoplasmin are used instead of the crude material. Note the percent reactors in *B. dermatitidis*-infected animals dropped from 44 percent when using crude histoplasmin to 25 percent when using a purified fraction. The cross reactivity to *S. schenckii* was also greatly reduced by using purified fractions.

Similar work has been reported by Sprouse (1969) using fractions of HKC-43 (Table 39-II). The HKC-43 was separated into six fractions on

TABLE 39-II

Results of Skin Testing with Histoplasmin Fractions

Skin Test Antigen	Mean Skin Reactions, 48 hour (mm Induration)		
	Infected Animals		Control Animals
	Histoplasma capsulatum	*Blastomyces dermatitidis*	
H-42 (1:25)	11.7	6.3	2.4
HKC-43	11.2	3.7	0.9
HKC-43 HPD$_I$	0.0	0.0	0.0
HKC-43 HPD$_{II}$	10.8	0.0	0.0
HKC-43 HPD$_{III}$	9.8	7.5	0.0
HKC-43 HPD$_{IV}$	0.8	0.0	0.0
HKC-43 HPD$_V$	0.0	0.0	0.0
HKC-43 HPD$_{VI}$	0.0	0.0	0.0

Sprouse, 1969.

acrylamide gel. Crude histoplasmin and the above fractions of the histoplasmin HKC-43 were used to skin test animals infected with *H. capsulatum* and *B. dermatitidis.* The crude antigen give cross reactions to *Blastomyces*-infected animals. Two fractions of the antigen gave reactions to *Histoplasma*-infected animals, while only one of the two fractions showed cross reactivity on *Blastomyces*-infected animals. Thus, it appears that by fractionating and selecting the proper fractions, cross reactivity can be reduced, or eliminated, at least for certain fungi.

In summary, these studies suggest generally that a number of fungi besides the often mentioned *Blastomyces* and *Coccidioides* should be considered as possible causes of cross reactions to histoplasmin in naturally infected human and animal populations. Such fungi as *A. fumigatus, A. terreus, S. schenckii, E. crescens* and *Beauveria* species caused as many or more cross reactions as *Blastomyces* in experimental animals.

Accumulating experimental evidence indicates that these cross reaction problems may be alleviated by more controlled ageing of cultures and subsequent fractionation, providing a more purified material with which to skin test.

References

Asgari, M. and Conant, N.F. (1964). A preliminary note on inter-reaction of skin test sensitivity between histoplasmin and chrysosporin in experimental animals. Mycopath. 23:321-327.

Bartels, P. (1969). Personal communication.

Emmons, C.W., Olson, B.J. and Eldridge, W.W. (1945). Studies of the role of fungi in pulmonary disease. I. Cross reactions of histoplasmin. *Public Health Rep.,* 60 (47):1383-1394.

Goodman, N.L., Sprouse, R.F. and Larsh, H.W. (1968). Histoplasmin potency as affected by culture age. *Sabouraudia,* 6(4):273-284.

Goodman, N.L., Taha, B. and Larsh, H.W. (1968). Characterization and skin test reactivity to histoplasmins. *Proc. Amer. Soc. Microbiol.,* 81.

Howell, A. (1947). Studies of fungus antigens. I. Quantitative studies of cross-reactions between histoplasmin and blastomycin in guinea pigs. *Public Health Rep.,* 62(18):631-651.

Larsh, H.W., Goodman, N.L., Palmer, C.E. and Collins, S. (1964). Histoplasmin sensitivity in guinea pigs produced by fungi isolated from sputum. *Proc. Amer. Soc. Microbiol.,* 70.

Palmer, C.E., Edwards, P.Q. and Allfather. (1957). Characteristics of skin reactions to coccidioidin and histoplasmin, with evidence of an unidentified source of sensitization. *Amer. J. Hyg.,* 66(2):196-213.

Smith, C.E., Saito, M.T., Beard, R.R., Rosenberger, H.G. and Whiting, E.G. (1949). Histoplasmin sensitivity and coccidiodal infection. I. Occurrence of cross reaction. *Amer. J. Public Health,* 39:722-736.

Sprouse, R.F. (1969). Purification of histoplasmin purified derivative (HPD). I. Disc electrophoresis separation of skin test active components. *Amer. Rev. Resp. Dis.,* 100:685-690.

Chapter 40

Serological Tests for Histoplasmosis:
Their Use and Interpretation

LEO KAUFMAN

ABSTRACT

The use of immunological procedures for the diagnosis of histoplasmosis is discussed in terms of the antigen used, cross reactions, and diagnostic and prognostic values.

AN unequivocal diagnosis of histoplasmosis is based on the isolation of *Histoplasma capsulatum* from clinical materials. However, all too frequently efforts to isolate this fungus end in failure. The clinician is then perforce obliged to make a diagnosis on presumptive evidence. Such evidence may be rapidly obtained through the use of immunologic procedures. Immunologic tests often provide the first clue to the existence of a fungus infection and, in addition, provide information regarding the progression or regression of the disease and the effects of therapy. Perhaps of most importance, positive immunologic findings in many cases stimulate increased efforts to isolate the etiologic agent and establish a definitive diagnosis. The following discussion summarizes the current status of immunologic procedures in the diagnosis and follow-up of histoplasmosis, with particular emphasis on the experience of the Center For Disease Control's Fungus Immunology Unit.

The *H. capsulatum* cellular and metabolic products presently used in serology are crude and are composed of a variety of antigens, many of which are shared by fungi of different genera. Attempts to purify these preparations and to obtain specific fractions have been unsuccessful (Pine, Boone and McLaughlin, 1966). Cross reactions are frequently observed when heterologous sera are tested with these *H. capsulatum* antigens. Consequently, a prudent diagnosis is based upon the interpretation of tests with a battery of antigens, including those of antigenically related fungi. The diagnosis will be determined in part by the following: the pattern of antibody reactions, the level of antibody titers against various test antigens, changes in titer between serial serum specimens collected from the patient at the onset of illness and at various stages thereafter, information about acquired hypersensitivity obtained with a histoplasmin skin test, and the clinical state of the patient.

Individuals infected with *H. capsulatum* usually demonstrate a sensitivity

321

to histoplasmin skin test antigen within two weeks after exposure (Furcolow, 1963). In sensitized persons, an area of induration and erythema develops at the injection site. The test is read at forty-eight hours, and the largest diameter of induration is measured and recorded. An induration of 5 mm or more in diameter is generally considered a positive reaction.

The skin test is most useful in defining endemic areas of histoplasmosis. It has limited value as a diagnostic tool, since it does not distinguish between past or present infections. In general, a positive reaction is of diagnostic significance only if the skin test was negative before the onset of clinical symptoms. Except in infants, a positive reaction with no past history has little diagnostic value. A negative reaction may be of greater significance, since it shows definite absence of the disease except when the patient is in the very early stages of infection or suffering from severe disseminated disease.

The reactivity of clinically defined cases of histoplasmosis to skin tests with histoplasmin has been described by Furcolow (1963). Skin test sensitivity in acute pulmonary histoplasmosis approaches 100 percent. In chronic histoplasmosis the skin test appears to be positive in most cases, but in disseminated histoplasmosis or in patients who are severely ill with some other disease, the skin test is often negative. For example, only 55 percent of twenty-four disseminated cases of histoplasmosis showed positive skin tests.

The level of complement-fixing antibodies, precipitins, and agglutinins to *H. capsulatum* antigens may be significantly increased in histoplasmin-sensitized individuals after a single histoplasmin skin test (Bennett, 1966; Campbell and Hill, 1964; Kaufman, Terry, Schubert and McLaughlin, 1967). Unquestionably the laboratorian and physician should be familiar with any factor or factors other than the disease which may alter serologic findings. In a recent study of 114 histoplasmin-sensitized but clinically well subjects, less than 12 percent showed complement-fixing antibodies following a single skin test with H-42 histoplasmin. The majority of antibody responses detected by the CDC complement fixation (CF) test (PHS Publication, 1965) occurred in the 1:8 to 1:16 range; 1.7 percent of the subjects showed a maximum titer of 1:32 (Kaufman *et al.*, 1967). Of the same 114 hypersensitive individuals, 17 (15%) produced precipitins in response to a single skin test with the H-42 histoplasmin. For the most part these antibody responses were detected in serum specimens drawn fifteen days after skin testing. Preferably, blood should be drawn for serological studies before skin testing, but the patient can usually be bled within two or three days after the skin test without induced antibodies being detected in the serum. Furthermore, it is the serum reaction with histoplasmin antigen that is primarily affected, although effects on the yeast form antigen titer have also been reported (McDearman and Young, 1960). A single histoplasmin skin test produces no serological responses in nonsensitized individuals.

Ideally, a skin test antigen should detect hypersensitivity without stimulating humoral antibodies. Production of such a histoplasmin would reduce the false positive rate in the serodiagnosis of histoplasmosis. Recent studies conducted in our laboratory suggest that a histoplasmin purified to contain only the H component will detect hypersensitivity without inducing antibodies. Of thirty histoplasmin hypersensitive subjects skin tested with an experimental antigen deficient in the M component but containing the H component, only six showed induced serological responses. These six sera only showed weak precipitin reactions, none showed complement fixation titers. (Kaufman, McLaughlin and Terry, 1969).

Serologic evidence is often the prime factor responsible for the later definitive diagnosis of histoplasmosis. Such evidence is most often obtained through CF, immunodiffusion (ID), and latex agglutination (LA) tests, used either alone or in combination. Of these procedures, the most widely employed is the CF test. Properly performed either as a tube or microtitration procedure, it can yield information of diagnostic and prognostic value.

In general, the serologic tests tend to become positive within a month after infection and remain positive for varying intervals of time.

Two antigens are used in the CF test at the CDC (PHS Publication, 1965): yeast form antigen made up of a suspension of merthiolated intact yeast cells of *H. capsulatum* (Schubert and Ajello, 1957); and histoplasmin, which is a soluble mycelial filtrate. Adequate diagnostic coverage is not provided when only one of those antigens is used, since sera from culturally confirmed cases of histoplasmosis may react to only one of the antigens (Hill and Campbell, 1956; Kaufman, Schubert and Kaplan, 1962). In most instances both antigens may be positive. In a recent study of 220 serum specimens from proven human histoplasmosis cases, 182 (83%) were positive when the histoplasmin antigen was used alone, and 206 (94%) were positive when only the yeast form antigen was used. Of the sera, 212 (96%) were positive when both antigens were used.

Interpreting test results can be difficult since these antigens commonly cross react with sera from individuals suffering from other systemic mycotic infections. In addition, the antigens may react with sera from clinically normal individuals, from individuals who have had a mycotic infection but are presently well, or from individuals suffering from nonmycotic infections. In such instances, titers are usually 1:8 or 1:16 and are mainly noted with the yeast form antigen. Many sera from culturally proven cases of histoplasmosis, however, demonstrate titers of 1:8 and 1:16. Consequently, such titers with either antigen are considered presumptive evidence of histoplasmosis. Titers of 1:32 or greater are highly suggestive of *H. capsulatum* infection and are of more diagnostic significance than lower titers (Campbell, 1960); however, they cannot be relied upon as the sole means of diagnosis (Kaufman, 1966). For example, sera from patients suffering from carcinoma, uveitis, blastomycosis, coccidioidomycosis, and cryptococcosis have reacted with the *H. capsulatum* antigens with titers ranging from 1:32 to 1:128. Because a serologic reaction is not always indicative of active disease, CF titers must be interpreted in terms of the total clinical picture, including radiological findings. Changes in titer are often of great assistance in making a diagnosis; fourfold changes in titer in either direction are usually significant indications of disease progression or regression. Reactions with heterologous antigens may complicate interpretation of results obtained with a single serum specimen. Patients suffering from histoplasmosis may, for example, be immunologically responsive to all *H. capsulatum, Blastomyces dermatitidis,* and *Coccidioides immitis* antigens, to only some of them, or to none (Kaufman, 1966). In some histoplasmosis cases, the first serologic response noted has been with the *B. dermatitidis* antigen. The absence of specific immunological response does not exclude histoplasmosis, particularly when only a single specimen has been tested and when the clinical picture strongly suggests pulmonary mycotic disease. In such cases, we recommend that several successive specimens be tested for antibodies. In disseminated or terminal histoplasmosis a state of anergy frequently exists and immunologic responses are negative.

The ID test using concentrated histoplasmin may be used as a supplementary or screening procedure in the serological diagnosis of histoplasmosis. Two bands have diagnostic value (Heiner, 1958). One, designated H, is rarely influenced by skin testing. Antibody to H is found in patients having active and progressive histoplasmosis and may be detectable for one to two years after apparent clinical recovery. The second, designated M is found in sera of patients with acute and chronic histoplasmosis and may appear in sensitized normal individuals after skin testing with histoplasmin. Finding only M antibody in sera may be indicative of active infection, past infection, or recent skin testing.

Proper interpretation of the agar-gel reaction requires that the clinician know whether the patient was recently skin tested. The detection of an M band in the absence of a recent skin test may reveal early disease, since this band appears before the H band. The disappearance of the H band is of prognostic value. The M band will eventually disappear but more slowly than the H band.

The ID test results are frequently useful in interpreting cross reactions, which are so often encountered with the CF test, and in testing anticomplementary sera. In our laboratory, the combined use of the CF and ID tests permitted a presumptive diagnosis of histoplasmosis for 215 of the 220 (98%) proven case sera recently studied.

LA test reagents for histoplasmosis are commercially available (Hill and Campbell, 1962). This test is particularly useful with early case serum specimens and for testing anticomplementary sera. The test is not a substitute for the CF test, but merely an adjunct that is easy to perform. In our experience most LA positive sera are positive in the CF test (with both antigens). Occasionally an early case serum will be LA positive and CF negative. However, successive serum specimens from patients with such serum reactions soon demonstrates CF titers. Strong (3-4+) LA reactions at 1:16 dilutions or higher may reflect active or very recent disease. Such titers, however, may also be nonspecific. Latex agglutinins are transitory and tend to diminish and disappear rather rapidly.

Perhaps the greatest limitations of the immunologic procedures used in diagnosing histoplasmosis lie in the use of unpurified, intact yeast form and histoplasmin antigens. These antigens consist of multiple components, some specific and others shared with heterologous fungal pathogens. Isolation and characterization of the active specific *H. capsulatum* antigens would undoubtedly contribute to improved standardization of tests and less equivocation in interpreting test results. However, until that millennium arrives, we must continue to perform a battery of CF and ID tests with homologous and heterologous antigens. This entails the use of CF tests with four antigens: yeast form *B. dermatitidis* and *H. capsulatum*, as well as coccidioidin and histoplasmin. Antigens used in the ID tests are blastomycin (Kaufman, unpublished data), coccidioidin (Huppert and Bailey, 1965), and histoplasmin. A presumptive diagnosis of histoplasmosis is reported on those sera which exhibit only *H. capsulatum* reactions regardless of the test used and on those showing homologous and heterologous CF antibodies but no precipitins for blastomycin and coccidioidin.

We feel that using this battery of tests reduces the false positive rate and increases the accuracy of our serodiagnosis for histoplasmosis.

References

Bennett, D.E. (1966). Laboratory diagnosis of histoplasmosis: A review. *Southern Med. J.*, 59:922-926.

Campbell, C.C. (1960). The accuracy of serologic methods in diagnosis. *Ann. N.Y. Acad. Sci.*, 89:163-178.

Campbell, C.C. and Hill, G.B. (1964). Further studies on the development of complement-fixing antibodies and precipitins in healthy histoplasmin sensitive persons following a single histoplasmin skin test. *Amer. Rev. Resp. Dis.*, 90:927-934.

Furcolow, M.L. (1963). Tests of immunity in histoplasmosis. *New Eng. J. Med.*, 268: 357-361.

Heiner, D.C. (1958). Diagnosis of histoplasmosis using precipitin reactions in agar gel. *Pediatrics*, 22:616-627.

Hill, G.B. and Campbell, C.C. (1956). A further evaluation of histoplasmin and yeast phase antigens of *Histoplasma capsulatum* in the complement fixation test. *J. Lab. Clin. Med.*, 48:255-263.

Hill, G.B. and Campbell, C.C. (1962). Commercially available histoplasmin sensitized latex particles in an agglutination test for histoplasmosis. *Mycopathologia*, 18: 169-179.

Huppert, M. and Bailey, J.W. (1965). The use of immunodiffusion tests in coccidioidomycosis. I. The accuracy and reproducibility of the immunodiffusion test which correlates with complement fixation. *Amer. J. Clin. Path., 44:*364-368.

Kaufman, L. (1966). Serology of systemic fungus diseases. *Public Health Rep., 81:* 177-185.

Kaufman, L., McLaughlin, D. and Terry, R.T. (1969). Immunologic studies with an in deficient histoplasmin skin test antigen. *Appl. Microbiol., 18:*307-309.

Kaufman, L., Schubert, J.H. and Kaplan, W. (1962). Fluorescent antibody inhibition test for histoplasmosis. *J. Lab. Clin. Med., 58:*1033-1038.

Kaufman, L., Terry, R.T., Schubert, J.H. and McLaughlin, D. (1967). Effects of a single histoplasmin skin test on the serological diagnosis of histoplasmosis. *J. Bact., 94:*798-803.

McDearman, S.C. and Young, J.M. (1960). The development of positive serologic tests with *Histoplasma capsulatum* antigens following single histoplasmin skin tests. *Amer. J. Clin. Path., 34:*434-438.

Pine, L., Boone, C.F. and McLaughlin, D. (1966). Antigenic properties of the cell wall and other fractions of the yeast form of *Histoplasma capsulatum. J. Bact., 91:*2158-2168.

Standardized Diagnostic Complement Fixation Method and Adaptation to Micro Test. U.S. Public Health Service Publication No. 1228, 1965.

Schubert, J.H. and Ajello, L. (1957). Variation in complement fixation antigenicity of different yeast phase strains of *Histoplasma capsulatum. J. Lab. Clin. Med, 50:* 304-307.

Chapter 41

Application of the Fluorescent Antibody Technique to the Diagnosis and Study of Histoplasmosis

WILLIAM KAPLAN

ABSTRACT

The significant contributions made in the application of the fluorescent antibody (FA) technique to the diagnosis and study of histoplasmosis are reviewed. Much progress has been made in the development and use of FA reagents for the demonstration of the yeast form of *Histoplasma capsulatum* in cultures and in a diversity of clinical materials. All investigators stress the need for specific conjugates for performing accurate diagnostic work. Developmental work must be done before ideal conjugates are available. However, two products currently on hand can be profitably used. One, a conjugate prepared by the adsorption of fluorescein-labeled *H. capsulatum* antibodies with yeast cells of *Blastomyces dermatitidis*, enables specific identification of most strains of *H. capsulatum*. However, it fails to react with strains belonging to one serotype of this fungus. The second, a reagent prepared by adsorbing labeled *H. capsulatum* antiglobulins with *Candida* species cells, offers broader diagnostic coverage, since it reacts with all strains of *H. capsulatum* regardless of serotype. This conjugate still cross stains *B. dermatitidis* and *H. duboisii*. This sacrifice in specificity is of acceptable proportions. Less advanced are applications of immunofluorescence to the identification of the mycelial form of *H. capsulatum*. The FA reagents that have been developed only permit the differentiation of the mycelial form of *H. capsulatum* from morphologically similar tuberculate spore-bearing species of *Sepedonium* and *Chrysosporium*. Their diagnostic applications are therefore limited.

Progress made in the application of immunofluorescence to the demonstration of *H. capsulatum* antibodies in sera is also reviewed. The FA inhibition technique employing *H. capsulatum* yeast cells can be used for the rapid detection of antibodies against whole yeast cells of *H. capsulatum*. However, the test was not found to be effective for the detection of antibodies to histoplasmin. The indirect FA procedure, using soluble antigens from *H. capsulatum* in the yeast and the mycelial forms, has also been shown to be useful in demonstrating antibodies to this organism in sera.

This review also covers the use of immunofluorescence as a research tool in various studies. The FA technique has numerous potentialities and has been used to determine the antigenic relationships of *H. capsulatum* to other fungi and to study the pathogenesis of experimental histoplasmosis.

THE usefulness of the Coons fluorescent antibody (FA) technique as a diagnostic and research tool in microbiology has been firmly established. This procedure can be employed for the rapid detection and study of microorganisms, both viable and nonviable, in culture as well as in clinical and environmental specimens. With appropriate modification, immuno-fluorescence can also be used to detect and measure antibodies in various types of clinical samples. Attracted by the diagnostic and research potential-ities of this versatile technique, a number of investigators have explored the possibility of using FA in medical mycology. Immunofluorescence has been applied to most of the principal mycotic diseases. For the most part, investi-gators have emphasized practical diagnostic use; however, in some cases the applications of FA have been on the level of basic research. An objective review of what has been done clearly indicates that immunofluorescence is a reliable and practical tool with potentially wide application in the diagnosis and study of mycotic diseases.

There is no lack of techniques for the diagnosis and study of histoplasmo-sis. A number of good methods and media have been developed for the iso-lation and identification of *Histoplasma capsulatum*. Because of the fastidi-ous nature of this fungus, cultural procedures are time consuming and not infrequently unsuccessful. Animal inoculation techniques can be used to iso-late this organism, but they are time consuming. A variety of excellent histo-logical stains are available for the demonstration of *H. capsulatum* in tis-sues. However, occasional variations in morphology and morphological re-semblances to other fungi may make definite identification of this organism in tissues difficult. Several serologic tests have been developed to demon-strate antibodies to *H. capsulatum*. These tests are very helpful in the diag-nosis and study of histoplasmosis. However, depending upon the test used and the stage of the disease, antibodies may not be demonstrable (Kauf-man, 1966). Furthermore, the problem of cross reactions may limit the accu-racy of the serodiagnosis of histoplasmosis. These deficiencies in the avail-able conventional laboratory procedures have led a number of workers to explore the possibility of applying immunofluorescence to the diagnosis and study of this disease. Investigations have been carried out to develop FA reagents for the accurate detection and identification of the yeast form of *H. capsulatum* in culture and in clinical materials. Studies have also been car-ried out to develop FA reagents for the detection and identification of the mycelial form of *H. capsulatum* in culture and for its demonstration in soil samples. These studies have been extended to the application of immuno-fluorescence to the detection of antibodies to *H. capsulatum* in sera. In addi-tion, the FA technique has been used as a research tool to study certain phases of the pathogenesis of histoplasmosis and to investigate antigenic re-lationships among isolates of *H. capsulatum* and between *H. capsulatum* and other fungi. The significant accomplishments made in each of these ar-eas of investigation are reviewed in the present report.

Development of FA Reagents for the Yeast Form of *Histoplasma capsulatum* and Their Diagnostic Application

The earliest report on the application of the FA technique to histoplasmosis is that by Gordon (1959). This worker successfully stained yeast form cells of *H. capsulatum* with fluorescein-labeled globulins obtained from rabbits infected with *H. capsulatum*. The labeled antibodies also stained the small buds of *H. duboisii* and the buds of an aberrant strain of *H. capsulatum* that formed numerous large cells resembling those of *H. duboisii*. In addition, some isolates of *Blastomyces dermatitidis* tested with Gordon's conjugate showed variable fluorescence. Gordon attempted to remove the cross-reacting factors by adsorption of the conjugate with cells of *B. dermatitidis*. Such adsorption resulted in the reagent's losing staining reactivity for both the homologous and heterologous organisms. However, Gordon did find that dilution of the nonadsorbed conjugate (1:4) resulted in a reagent that still brightly stained *H. capsulatum* yeast cells, the buds of *H. duboisii* and *Paracoccidioides brasiliensis*, and the cell walls of some isolates of *B. dermatitidis*. However, the diluted conjugate did not react with cells of sixteen isolates of seven heterologous species representing six genera. Furthermore, the diluted reagent did not cross stain *Toxoplasma gondii* and *Leishmania donovani*. These two protozoan species can be confused with *H. capsulatum* in conventionally stained smears or tissue sections. This study showed that it is feasible to stain the yeast form of *H. capsulatum* by the FA procedure and also pointed to the value of this procedure for the rapid differentiation of this organism from morphologically similar organisms. Although the diluted reagent prepared by Gordon makes it possible to differentiate the yeast form of *H. capsulatum* from a number of heterologous fungi, a species-specific conjugate would be preferable.

After Gordon's report was published, Kaufman and Kaplan (1961) initiated studies to develop an FA reagent specific for the yeast form of *H. capsulatum*. They prepared conjugates from globulins of rabbits that had been immunized with formalin-killed *H. capsulatum* yeast form cells. Their labeled antiglobulins brightly stained six yeast form isolates of *H. capsulatum* but also cross stained ten yeast form isolates of *B. dermatitidis* and up to eighteen other heterologous fungal isolates representing seventeen species of ten genera. These cross reactions illustrate the widespread existence of common antigens among the various species of fungi. Kaufman and Kaplan found that adsorption of the labeled antiglobulins, either twice with formalin-killed yeast cells of *B. dermatitidis*, or twice with formalin-killed mycelial form cells of *Coccidioides immitis* and once with yeast form cells of *B. dermatiditis*, eliminated the cross reactions and resulted in a reagent specific for the yeast form of *H. capsulatum*. The adsorbed antiglobulins brightly stained yeast form cells of six isolates of *H. capsulatum* in culture and made possible the rapid detection of *H. capsulatum* in smears prepared from exudates and organs of experimentally infected mice. In an extensive investigation, Porter, Thomas, Furcolow and Varga (1963) examined eight hundred clinical specimens with a specific conjugate produced in accordance with the procedure of Kaufman and Kaplan (1961) and with a reagent produced by multiple adsorption with tissue and *Candida sp.* powders. They reported the former reagent to be effective, easy to prepare, and more specific than the latter product.

In a further evaluation of the adsorbed conjugate specific for the yeast form of *H. capsulatum,* several isolates of this fungus were encountered that failed to stain or stained weakly (Pine, Kaufman and Boone, 1964; Kaufman and Blumer, 1966). Most isolates, however, strongly reacted with the adsorbed antiglobulins. These findings suggested that antigenic variants of *H. capsulatum* might exist. Kaufman and Blumer (1966) carried out an investigation to ascertain whether serotypes existed among yeast form isolates of this fungus. Using reciprocal cross-staining and adsorption procedures with fluorescein-labeled antiglobulins to several yeast form isolates of *H. capsulatum,* they demonstrated four distinct antigenic factors, designated 1, 2, 3, 4. Depending upon the combination of factors present, at least five serotypes of this organism were found to exist. All serotypes were shown to share at least one (antigen 1) factor; therefore, unadsorbed fluorescein-labeled antiglobulins to any one of the serotypes stain the other serotypes. Furthermore, they showed that all five serotypes are related antigenically to the yeast forms of *B. dermatitidis* and *H. duboisii.* However, one, designated type 1:4, was found to be more closely related antigenically to these heterologous organisms than the others. The strains of *H. capsulatum* that failed to react with the specific FA reagent developed by Kaufman and Kaplan (1961) were of this type. Of epidemiologic interest are the findings that this serotype (1:4) is commonly encountered among *H. capsulatum* isolates originating in Latin America.

The failure of the specific conjugate developed by Kaufman and Kaplan (1961) to stain the 1:4 serotype limits its diagnostic usefulness. Hence, Kaufman and Blumer (1968) carried out a study to produce an FA reagent that would make it possible to specifically demonstrate *H. capsulatum* regardless of its antigenic make up. Their approach was to prepare labeled antiglobulins against the most complete serotype of *H. capsulatum,* one that contained the four distinct antigenic factors. This conjugate was adsorbed with cells of *Candida albicans*, an organism that contains only factor 1 in common with *H. capsulatum.* Such adsorption would, in effect, remove antibodies to this common antigen which all strains of *H. capsulatum* share with *C. albicans* and numerous other heterologous organisms. The adsorbed reagent would still contain antibodies to antigens 2, 3, and 4, which are required for the staining of all five serotypes of *H. capsulatum*. This *C. albicans*-adsorbed conjugate brightly stained all known serotyes of *H. capsulatum*, but it also cross stained the yeast forms of *B. dermatitidis* and *H. duboisii*. Cross reactions with other heterologous fungi were not observed. Attempts to eliminate the residual cross staining by adsorption with either *B. dermatitidis* or *H. duboisii* resulted in products with identical staining properties. Staining of *H. capsulatum* serotype 1:4 was lost along with that of *B. dermatitidis* and *H. duboisii*. In effect, the staining properties of the resulting products were identical to those of the specific reagent that Kaufman and Kaplan (1961) had developed earlier. Kaufman and Blumer concluded that despite the presence of the cross-reacting antibodies, the *C. albicans*-adsorbed conjugate can be used diagnostically. Usually *H. capsulatum* can be differentiated from *B. dermatitidis* on the basis of morphology. When required, these two organisms can be differentiated with FA by using a conjugate specific for the yeast form of *B. dermatitidis* (Kaplan and Kaufman, 1963). This reagent brightly stains *B. dermatitidis* but does not react with *H. capsulatum*. Differentiation of *H. capsulatum* from *H. duboisii* cannot be accomplished by using the *C. albicans*-adsorbed reagent. When required, such differentiation would have to be achieved by animal inoculation. With the exception of strains of *H. capsulatum* belonging to serotype 1:4, *H. capsulatum* can be differentiated from *H. duboisii* by using the specific FA reagent produced by Kaufman and Kaplan in 1961.

A number of workers have investigated the feasibility of using the FA procedure to demonstrate *H. capsulatum* in clinical materials. The types of specimens used in these studies have included sputum, impression smears of tissues and exudates, and sections of fixed tissues. A review of the significant accomplishments made in these investigations follows.

Several workers explored the possibility of using the direct FA procedure for the rapid detection of *H. capsulatum* in human sputum. In their studies Lynch and Plexico (1962) used fluorescein-labeled rabbit *H. capsulatum* antiglobulins that had been adsorbed with *Candida* yeast cells to eliminate cross reactivity for *Candida* species and other heterologous fungi. The adsorbed reagent still showed a low degree of cross staining with *B. dermatitidis* yeast cells. Eighty-four sputum specimens from twenty-eight patients with proven or suspected chronic (cavitary) pulmonary histoplasmosis were studied. Two pairs of smears were prepared from each specimen. One pair was made from the centrifuged sediment of trypsin-digested material. The other pair was made directly from untreated samples. Examination of smears prepared from the enzymatically digested samples showed fluorescent antibody-stained yeast cells in 22 (88%) of 25 specimens from which *H. capsulatum* was isolated by culture. Stained yeast cells were also observed in seven culturally negative specimens obtained from five patients with confirmed histoplasmosis who were receiving antifungal therapy at the time the specimens were collected. Examination of smears from the untreated materials showed stained yeast cells in 18 (72%) of the 25 culturally positive sputums. Stained yeast cells were also observed in eight culturally negative samples obtained from the five patients under therapy. On the basis of these findings, Lynch and Plexico (1962) were of the opinion that the FA technique can be used as a rapid screening procedure for the presence of *H. capsulatum* in sputum.

Carski, Cozad and Larsh (1962) also investigated the possibility of using the FA procedure to detect *H. capsulatum* in sputum. These workers prepared three lots of labeled rabbit anti-*H. capsulatum* globulins, one of which cross reacted strongly with *C. albicans*. This was eliminated by a single adsorption with cells of the latter organism. All three lots of reagents, however, cross stained yeast cells of *B. dermatitidis*. Adsorption with yeast cells of *B. dermatitidis* eliminated cross staining of some strains of this organism. On the basis of findings with sputum samples, these workers concluded that the direct FA procedure can be a valuable adjunct to cultural and clinical methods in the diagnosis of pulmonary histoplasmosis. Because of persistent cross reactions of their conjugates with some strains of *B. dermatitidis* and several possible false positive results, these investigators urged caution when attempting to use immunofluorescence as the sole method for diagnosis of this disease.

Porter, Comfort, Menges, Habermann and Smith (1965) evaluated the FA technique for the detection of *H. capsulatum* in tissue impression smears. The reagent used in this study was fluorescein-labeled rabbit *H. capsulatum* antiglobulins that had been adsorbed with *Candida sp.* yeast cells to remove common antibodies to *Candida sp.* and other heterologous organisms. Tissues from 372 animals representing sixteen species were examined by the FA procedure for the presence of *H. capsulatum*, and the results were correlated with those obtained by culture and histopathology. Of the 372 animals in the series, 300 were negative by all three diagnostic methods. Twenty-one were positive by culture and/or histopathology. Of these 21 cases, 15 (71%) were positive by FA, 16 (76%) by histopathology, and 14 (67%) by culture. Seventeen of the 372 animals were positive by FA and negative by histopathology and culture. Although Porter and her associates were unable to confirm by conventional methods that the tissues from these latter 17 animals were indeed infected with *H. capsulatum*, they nevertheless held that these FA results were not necessarily false positives. The findings in this series that histopathology failed to demonstrate *H. capsulatum* in 24 percent of the cases and culture in 33 percent of the cases support this opinion. In view of the high degree of correlation between the results of the FA and the other diagnostic procedures, the authors held that immunofluorescence is very useful in demonstrating *H. capsulatum* in impression smears of naturally infected animal tissue. However, it appeared that neither FA, histopathology, or culture alone was completely reliable for the diagnosis of such infections. They recommended that all three techniques should be used for maximum diagnostic coverage.

Procknow, Connelly and Ray (1962) used the FA technique as a research tool in a study concerned with the pathogenesis of experimental histoplasmosis in the mouse. In this research, fluorescein-labeled rabbit *H. capsulatum* antiglobulins were employed. By using the FA procedure Procknow, Connelly and Ray were able to study the conversion of inhaled tuberculate spores of *H. capsulatum* within the mouse lung to yeast form cells, and the subsequent dissemination of the yeast form cells throughout the reticuloendothelial system. Immunofluorescence was used to follow these organisms in the various tissues for several months. Frozen and picric acid-alcohol-formalin-fixed tissue sections were used and found to be equally satisfactory for demonstrating *H. capsulatum* by the FA procedure. In addition to obtaining basic information on a disease process, Procknow and his associates demonstrated the practicability of applying immunofluorescence to the detection of *H. capsulatum* in sections of fixed tissues.

Yamaguchi, Adriano and Braunstein (1963) applied the FA technique to the demonstration of *H. capsulatum* in sections of human lung and lymph node tissue that had been fixed in either 10% formalin or Bouin's fluid. The conjugate used had been prepared from serum obtained from a patient with active primary histoplasmosis. Paraffin blocks from twenty-four inactive pulmonary or lymph node lesions shown by the Grocott method to contain yeastlike cells consistent in morphology with *H. capsulatum* were studied. These tissues had been obtained at autopsy from patients who died from causes unrelated to histoplasmosis. At the time of collection five of the twenty-four tissues had been cultured for the presence of fungi, with negative results. Yamaguchi and his associates reported that by using the FA technique they were able to demonstrate stained yeast cells in deparaffinized sections of twenty-two of the twenty-four tissues. These workers felt that there was little doubt that the stained yeast cells were *H. capsulatum*, although cultural proof for this opinion could not be obtained.

Rezai and Haberman (1966) also investigated the possibility of using immunofluorescence to demonstrate *H. capsulatum* in paraffin sections of fixed human tissue. They used fluorescein-labeled rabbit *H. capsulatum* antiglobulins that had been adsorbed with *B. dermatitidis* cells to reduce cross reactivity with heterologous fungi. One part of lissamine-rhodamine RP-200 (LR) was added to 20 parts of the conjugate to eliminate innate tissue autofluorescence. Paraffin sections of nine tissue specimens considered on the basis of histopathology to be infected with *H. capsulatum* were deparaffinized and tested. Rezai and Haberman demonstrated, by immunofluorescence, yeast cells in five of these nine tissues.

Sell, Christie and Schweikert (1968) successfully used the FA technique to demonstrate *H. capsulatum* in routine paraffin sections of fixed biopsy tissues and in smears of fresh biopsy tissue. The conjugate used was fluorescein-labeled rabbit *H. capsulatum* antiglobulins that had been adsorbed with *B. dermatitidis*, *C. albicans*, and *C. immitis* to eliminate cross reactions. These workers consider the FA procedure a very useful tool for diagnosing histoplasmosis.

In our diagnostic and research activities at the Center for Disease Control we had a number of occasions to apply the FA technique to the detection and identification of *H. capsulatum* as well as other fungi in routine paraffin sections of formalin-fixed tissue. Our findings agreed with those reported by other workers. We have been able to stain by FA *H. capsulatum* and other pathogenic fungi in fixed tissues from patients as well as from experimentally infected animals. However, in many cases, the procedure generally used, that is, direct application of fluorescein-labeled antibodies to deparaffinized sections, leaves much to be desired. For us, the method has worked satisfactorily in cases where organisms were very numerous or located in tissue that was not dense. However, stained fungal cells were not readily seen or were not found at all when they were few in number or situated in dense tissue. We could not regularly overcome these difficulties by using thin tissue sections, that is, cut at a thickness of 4μ or less. We have felt that these unsatisfactory results might be largely due to the inability of the labeled antibodies to reach the organisms embedded in the fixed tissue. If this were the case, treatment of the deparaffinized sections with a digestant to remove the unwanted protein prior to application of FA reagent could result in improved staining of the fungi, thereby enhancing the efficacy of this diagnostic procedure. In a recent study (Kaplan and Kraft, 1969) we found that digestion of deparaffinized sections in 1% trypsin solution (pH 8.0) for 1 hour at 37° C before labeled antibodies were applied is a simple procedure that considerably enhances the FA staining of *H. capsulatum* and other fungi. During this study we also found that *H. capsulatum* and other fungi can be stained by the FA procedure in tissue sections that have been previously stained by the hematoxylin and eosin, the Brown and Brenn, and the Giemsa techniques. Neither *H. capsulatum* nor other fungi can be stained by the FA technique in sections previously stained by the Gomori methenamine-silver nitrate, the PAS, or the Gridley procedures. Apparently, the hydrolysis and oxidation of polysaccharides in the walls of these fungi by the periodic acid or the chromic acid alters the antigenicity of these organisms so that they no longer react with the labeled antibodies.

In a limited study to evaluate the efficacy of the enzymatic digestion technique, we found that in all cases it was possible to stain with both unadsorbed and *C. albicans*-adsorbed (Kaufman and Blumer, 1968) fluorescein-labeled *H. capsulatum* antiglobulins *H. capsulatum* cells in formalinized tissues from culturally confirmed histoplasmosis cases. We were unable to stain with these conjugates the organisms in sections of seven tissues considered solely on the basis of histopathology to be infected with *H. capsulatum*. Two of these seven tissues showed the organisms centered in active disease processes. Attempts to isolate *H. capsulatum* from these two tissue specimens had been unsuccessful. The other five tissues were old, inactive calcified lesions. To investigate the possibility that the organisms present in these seven tissues might not be *H. capsulatum*, sections were stained with unadsorbed fluorescein-labeled *C. albicans* antiglobulins. In all seven cases stained yeast cells were observed in sections treated with this conjugate. This reagent was then adsorbed four times with *H. capsulatum* cells to remove all cross-staining activity for *H. capsulatum*. The four-times adsorbed fluorescein-labeled *C. albicans* antiglobulins still brightly stained the yeast cells in sections of the two tissues that showed active disease processes. These findings indicate that the organisms present were not *H. capsulatum* and that the histological diagnoses were not correct. The four-times adsorbed conjugate did not stain the organisms in the sections of the old calcified lesions. Too few tissues were examined in this study to permit any valid conclusions to be drawn concerning the accuracy of histological identification of *H. capsulatum*. An expanded investigation is currently in progress to determine the efficacy and limitations of the FA procedure for the detection and identification of *H. capsulatum* in routine paraffin sections of formalinized tissues. This expanded study is being carried out in collaboration with Dr. Jan Schwarz, Jewish Hospital, Cincinnati, Ohio. It is premature to report any definite findings of this joint investigation. However, it appears that it is not possible to regularly stain with our fluorescein-labeled *H. capsulatum* antiglobulins yeast cells that are considered to be *H. capsulatum* in sections of fixed tissues from old, inactive, calcified lesions. In contrast, it is possible to regularly stain morphologically similar organisms in active lesions (Kaplan, Schwarz and Kraft, unpublished data).

Attempts to Develop FA Reagents for the Identification of the Mycelial Form of *Histoplasma capsulatum*

Although many investigators have attempted to develop useful FA reagents and procedures for the detection and identification of the yeast form of *H. capsulatum*, relatively little has been done to produce reliable conjugates for the mycelial form of this organism. Such conjugates would greatly facilitate the identification of *H. capsulatum* because they would eliminate the time-consuming task of converting mycelial form isolates to the yeast form. In addition, they would offer the attractive possibility of applying the FA procedure to the demonstration of *H. capsulatum* in environmental samples.

It has long been known that the yeast and mycelial forms of *H. capsulatum* share common antigens; therefore, it is not surprising that unadsorbed conjugates against one form will stain the other form. These facts suggest that adsorbed conjugates specific for the yeast form of *H. capsulatum* could also be used for the specific identification of the mycelial form of this organism. Kaufman and Kaplan (1963) investigated this possibility and found that their labeled antiglobulins specific for the yeast form did not react with the mycelial form. A study was undertaken to characterize by the FA procedure the antigenic relationships between the two forms of *H. capsulatum* (Kaufman and Kaplan, 1963). Yeast and mycelial cells of this dimorphic fungus were found to share at least two antigens, designated A and C, and the yeast cells to contain two additional factors, designated B and E, that are not present in mycelial form cells. Mycelial form cells were not found to contain any factors not present in yeast cells. Hence, the mycelial form apparently possesses a less complex cellular antigenic make up than the yeast form. The antigenic relationships between the two forms of *H. capsulatum* and the two forms of *B. dermatitidis* were also investigated. Mycelial cells of *B. dermatitidis* were found to share factor A with the yeast and mycelial forms of *H. capsulatum*. However, the mycelial cells of *B. dermatitidis* lack factor C and do not contain any distinct antigens. The absence of factor C made it possible to develop conjugates for differentiating the mycelial form of *H. capsulatum* from the mycelial form of *B. dermatitidis*.

In a follow-up study Kaufman and Brandt (1964) investigated the possibility of developing FA reagents for the differentiation of the mycelial form of *H. capsulatum* from several morphologically similar tuberculate spore-forming species of the genera *Chrysosporium* and *Sepedonium*. Cross staining and adsorption procedures demonstrated antigenic relationships among species of these three genera and other fungi. Their attempts to develop a useful specific FA reagent for the mycelial form of *H. capsulatum* were not successful. In the context of the study they did demonstrate an antibody specific for the mycelial form of *H. capsulatum* in their labeled antiglobulins to this organism. However, it was present at too low a level for practical diagnostic use. Kaufman and Brandt did report that they could differentiate *H. capsulatum* from the other tuberculate spore-bearing fungi by using two conjugates, designated H-S and S. Reagent H-S was produced by adsorbing fluorescein-labeled mycelial form *H. capsulatum* antiglobulins with cells of a *Chrysosporium sp.* Reagent S was produced by adsorbing fluorescein-labeled *S. chrysospermum* antiglobulins with cells of the *Chrysosporium sp.* Staining with the H-S reagent indicated that the organism that formed tuberculate spores was either a *H. capsulatum* or a *Sepedonium sp.* If this fungus reacted with the S conjugate, it was a *Sepedonium sp.;* if not, it was an *H. capsulatum*. The H-S conjugate did not stain the mycelial form of *H. duboisii*. Hence, this reagent could be used to differentiate the mycelial form of *H. capsulatum* from that of *H. duboisii*. Kaufman and Brandt attempted to use the H-S reagent to demonstrate elements of *H. capsulatum* in soil samples previously found by conventional procedures to contain this pathogen. Treatment of ten positive soils with this reagent revealed brightly stained hyphae, microconidia, and smooth-walled macroconidia morphologically consistent with those produced by *H. capsulatum* in culture. However, no tuberculate spores were observed. Since the H-S conjugate had been shown to cross react with various soil fungi that do not produce tuberculate spores, the stained elements could not be established as *H. capsulatum*.

Application of the FA Technique to the Demonstration of *H. capsulatum* Antibodies in Sera

Several workers have investigated the possibility of using the FA procedure to demonstrate *H. capsulatum* antibodies in sera. In the first of such studies, Kaufman, Schubert and Kaplan (1962) used a modification of Goldman's one-step FA inhibition test (Goldman, 1957). In order to improve the accuracy of the test, they used the specific conjugate that had been developed by Kaufman and Kaplan (1961). These workers examined by the FA inhibition procedure fifty-three sera from suspected and confirmed cases of histoplasmosis and compared the results with those obtained by complement fixation (CF) and immunodiffusion tests. *H. capsulatum* yeast form antigens were used in the FA and CF tests and histoplasmin in the CF and immunodiffusion tests. The CF test was used as the criterion for the presence of both histoplasmin and *H. capsulatum* yeast form antibodies. Kaufman, Schubert and Kaplan reported that the FA inhibition test was both simple and effective in demonstrating antibodies to yeast form cells of *H. capsulatum*. It was not effective, however, for the detection of antibodies to histoplasmin. In contrast, the immunodiffusion test was effective for demonstrating antibodies to histoplasmin but not for antibodies to yeast form cells of *H. capsulatum*. It was therefore evident that neither the FA inhibition method nor the immunodiffusion test alone could be used as a substitute for the CF test that employed both histoplasmin and *H. capsulatum* yeast cell antigens.

In a follow-up study Kaufman, Brandt and McLaughlin (1964) used the FA inhibition method in conjunction with the immunodiffusion procedure to qualitatively test 127 anticomplementary sera from dogs and humans for antibodies to *H. capsulatum*. When possible, these results were compared with those obtained by CF tests on corresponding repeat nonanticomplementary sera. The results of the FA inhibition and immunodiffusion tests showed 97 percent agreement with those obtained by the CF tests. Kaufman and his associates concluded that the FA test can be used in conjunction with the immunodiffusion procedure to provide a rapid serological diagnosis in cases where sera are anticomplementary and cannot be examined by the CF method.

Recently, Hook and Fife (1967) investigated the possibility of using soluble antigens to detect antibodies to *H. capsulatum* by immunofluorescence.

Soluble antigens from both the yeast and mycelial forms of *H. capsulatum* were purified by gel filtration, fixed onto paper discs, and used in an indirect FA procedure to detect antibodies in sera from patients with histoplasmosis. A preliminary evaluation of this soluble antigen fluorescent antibody (SAFA) technique for histoplasmosis suggested adequate sensitivity for serodiagnosis, and in some cases the procedure appeared to be more sensitive than conventional tests. However, sera from culturally confirmed cases of blastomycosis, coccidioidomycosis, cryptococcosis, and tuberculosis also reacted with the soluble antigens. Thus, in terms of specificity the SAFA technique offered no advantages over standard serological tests for histoplasmosis. In view of its rapidity and relative simplicity, however, Hook and Fife concluded that the SAFA procedure could be profitably used as a screening procedure for the serological diagnosis of histoplasmosis. Their experiences with more than one-thousand sera submitted for routine fungal serological tests support this conclusion.

Discussion

An appraisal of what has been accomplished indicates that the FA technique is a practical laboratory tool with potentially wide application in the diagnosis and study of histoplasmosis. Most of the studies have emphasized diagnostic applications. They have shown that with appropriate reagents the FA procedure can be used to rapidly demonstrate *H. capsulatum* in cultures and in all types of clinical materials including fixed tissues that have been stored for long periods of time. All workers who have used immunofluorescence for diagnosis have stressed the importance of employing conjugates of a high degree of specificity for accurate results. The attempts by the various investigators to produce completely reliable specific reagents for *H. capsulatum* have not been fully successful, and developmental work remains to be done. Nevertheless, the conjugates that have been developed can be used to great advantage in the diagnosis of histoplasmosis. In the identification of the yeast form of most strains of *H. capsulatum*, the specific conjugate produced by Kaufman and Kaplan (1961) is valuable. However, this reagent, made by adsorbing fluorescein-labeled *H. capsulatum* antiglobulins with yeast form cells of *B. dermatitidis*, fails to react with one of the five serotypes of *H. capsulatum*. Hence, negative results must be interpreted with caution. For broader diagnostic coverage, at some sacrifice in specificity, a reagent produced by adsorbing fluorescein-labeled *H. capsulatum* antiglobulins with *Candida* cells (Kaufman and Blumer, 1968) can be used. The sacrifice, however, is of acceptable proportions. Through use of this reagent, the FA technique can serve as an excellent screening device for the presence of *H. capsulatum* and in some cases for definite identification of this organism.

At present, the FA technique is of limited value for the identification of the mycelial form of *H. capsulatum*. The reagents that have been developed can only be used to differentiate this organism from morphologically similar tuberculate spore-bearing species of *Sepedonium* and *Chrysosporium*. Hence, the accomplishments are merely a promising first step in the application of the FA technique to the identification of the mycelial form of *H. capsulatum*. The potentialities, however, are evident, and their realization awaits further investigation.

The studies by Kaufman and his colleagues (Kaufman, Schubert, and Kaplan, 1962; Kaufman, Brandt and McLaughlin, 1964) and by Hook and Fife (1967) clearly indicate that with appropriate modifications the FA technique can be used for the rapid detection of *H. capsulatum* antibodies in sera. Although immunofluorescence is effective for this purpose, this fact does not necessarily mean that it should be used in lieu of the routinely employed serological tests. Instead, at the present stage of development, its proper role is that of a supplementary diagnostic tool for use in testing anticomplementary sera and in other situations where conventional serological tests are not suitable.

The usefulness of immunofluorescence transcends the purely diagnostic applications. The FA technique can be used as a research tool in a diversity of investigative studies. For example, Procknow, Connelly and Ray (1962) showed that immunofluorescence can be used to great advantage in studies on the pathogenesis of experimental histoplasmosis. Similarly, Kaufman and Kaplan (1963) and Kaufman and Brandt (1964) showed that the FA procedure can serve admirably to investigate antigenic relationships between *H. capsulatum* and other fungi. The possible use of immunofluorescence as a research tool in histoplasmosis are numerous and merely await application.

This review clearly shows that the FA technique has many uses in the diagnosis and study of histoplasmosis, but the technique has not received the widespread application it merits. This, in time, will undoubtedly come to pass.

References

Carski, T.R., Cozad, G.C. and Larsh, H.W. (1962). Detection of *Histoplasma capsulatum* in sputum by means of fluorescent antibody staining. *Amer. J. Clin. Path.*, 37: 465-469.

Goldman, M. (1957). Staining *Toxoplasma gondii* with fluorescein-labeled antibody. II. A new serologic test for antibodies to Toxoplasma based upon inhibition of specific staining. *J. Exp. Med.*, 105:557-573.

Gordon, M.A. (1959). Fluorescent staining of *Histoplasma capsulatum*. *J. Bact.*, 77: 678-681.

Hook, W.A. and Fife, E.A. (1967). Soluble antigens for immunofluorescence detection of *Histoplasma capsulatum* antibodies. *Appl. Microb.* 15:350-356.

Kaplan, W. and Kaufman, L. (1963). Specific fluorescent antiglobulins for the detection and identification of *Blastomyces dermatitidis* yeast phase cells. *Mycopathologia*, 19:173-180.

Kaplan, W. and Kraft, D.E. (1969). Demonstration of fungi in formalin-fixed tissues by immunofluorescence. *Amer. J. Clin. Path.*, 52:420-432.

Kaplan, W., Schwarz, J. and Kraft, D.E. Unpublished data.

Kaufman, L. (1966). Serology of systemic fungus diseases. *Public Health Rep.*, 81: 177-185.

Kaufman, L. and Blumer, S. (1966). Occurrence of serotypes among *Histoplasma capsulatum* strains. *J. Bact.* 91:1434-1439.

Kaufman, L. and Blumer, S. (1968). Development and use of a polyvalent conjugate to differentiate *Histoplasma capsulatum* and *Histoplasma duboisii* from other pathogens. *J. Bact.* 95:1243-1246.

Kaufman, L. and Brandt, B. (1964). Fluorescent-antibody studies of the mycelial form of *Histoplasma capsulatum* and morphologically similar fungi. *J. Bact.* 87:120-126.

Kaufman, L., Brandt, B. and McLaughlin, D. (1964). Evaluation of the fluorescent antibody and agar gel precipitin tests for detecting *Histoplasma* antibodies in anticomplementary sera. *Amer. J. Hyg.*, 79:181-185.

Kaufman, L. and Kaplan, W. (1961). Preparation of a fluorescent antibody specific for the yeast phase of *Histoplasma capsulatum*. *J. Bact.*, 82:729-735.

Kaufman, L. and Kaplan, W. (1963). Serological characterization of pathogenic fungi by means of fluorescent antibodies. I. Antigenic relationships between yeast and mycelial forms of *Histoplasma capsulatum* and *Blastomyces dermatitidis*. *J. Bact.* 85: 986-991.

Kaufman, L., Schubert, J.H. and Kaplan, W. (1962). Fluorescent antibody inhibition test for histoplasmosis. *J. Lab. Clin. Med.*, 59:1033-1038.

Lynch, H.J. and Plexico, K.L. (1962). A rapid method for screening sputums for *Histoplasma capsulatum* employing the fluorescent antibody technique. *New Eng. J. Med.*, 28:811-814.

Pine, L., Kaufman, L. and Boone, C.J. (1964). Comparative fluorescent antibody staining of *Histoplasma capsulatum* and *Histoplasma duboisii* with a specific anti-yeast phase *H. capsulatum* conjugate. *Mycopathologia*, 24:315-326.

Porter, B.M., Thomas, B.K., Furcolow, M.L. and Varga, D.T. (1963). Comparison of two *Histoplasma capsulatum* fluorescent antibody conjugates based on 800 clinical specimens. *Bact. Proc.*, 90.

Porter, B.M., Comfort, B.K., Menges, R.W., Habermann, R.T. and Smith, C.D. (1965.) Correlation of fluorescent antibody, histopathology, and culture on tissues from 372 animals examined for histoplasmosis and blastomycosis. *J. Bact.*, 89:748-751.

Procknow, J.J., Connelly, A.P. and Ray, C.G. (1962). Fluorescent antibody technique in histoplasmosis as applied to the pathogenesis of experimental infection in the mouse. *Arch. Path.*, 73:313-324.

Rezai, H.R. and Haberman, S. (1966). The use of immunofluorescence for identification of yeastlike fungi in human infections. *Amer. J. Clin. Path.*, 46:433-439.

Sell, S.H., Christie, A. and Schweikert, N.S. (1968). The use of immunofluorescent techniques in the diagnosis of clinical histoplasmosis. *Dis. Chest.*, 54:36-39.

Yamaguchi, B., Adriano, S. and Braunstein, L. (1963). *Histoplasma capsulatum* in the pulmonary primary complex: Immunohistochemical demonstration. *Amer. J. Path.*, 43:713-719.

Chapter 42

History of the Development of Serologic Tests for Histoplasmosis

CHARLOTTE C. CAMPBELL

ABSTRACT

This is a historical review of the development of serologic tests for the diagnosis and prognosis of histoplasmosis from the earliest trials in the rare case in 1945 until routine use of the tests in thousands of patients annually at the present time. Despite the many shortcomings of the tests, the contributions their availabilities has made to the epidemiologic as well as clinical concepts of the infection and disease are substantial. Many of the immunologic and serologic problems confronting some of the earliest investigators have yet to be solved and continue to command the attention of contemporary investigators employing the most sophisticated tools, techniques, and procedures.

F EW aspects of histoplasmosis have been discussed as exhaustively as the serologic or interpretation of results of the various types of tests. As it is now nearing a quarter of a century that the tests have been used on an increasingly routine basis, it seemed appropriate to review the history of their development and to assess the contributions their availability has made to expanding the epidemiologic as well as clinical concepts of the infection and disease. This history traverses the era from the time the entity produced by *Histoplasma capsulatum* was clinically recognized only as a rare, chronically debilitating, uniformly fatal disease (Parsons and Zarafonetis, 1945).

Early Studies (1941-1949)

Suffice it to say that it is impossible to divorce any type of study on histoplasmosis from 1945 onward from the revolutionary findings in coccidioidomycosis which preceded them by only a few years. In no area is this more true than in the development of antigens for both skin and serologic tests, despite the fact that the chronology of the published literature in this respect is a poor guide. A student fifty years hence having access only to the published reports might indeed deduce that the serologic studies on histoplasmosis preceded those on coccidioidomycosis. In reality, they were modelled in many ways after those in coccidioidomycosis. It was the latter that brought an end to the concept of mycoses as exotic medical curiosities and introduced them into the mainstream of infectious diseases to be dealt with daily in the differential diagnosis of acute as well as chronic pulmonary infections. However, the classic report on the use of coccidioidin (Smith, Whiting, Baker, Rosenberger, Beard and Saito, 1948) was not published until two to three years after the initial skin test surveys with histoplasmin (Palmer, 1945; Emmons, Olson and Eldridge, 1945; Christie and Peterson, 1946). Similarly, the even more classical report, "Serologic tests in the diagnosis and prognosis of coccidioidomycosis" (Smith, Saito, Beard, Kepp, Clark and Eddie, 1950), also appeared two to three years after a series of reports on the serologic diagnosis of histoplasmosis (Table 42-I). For the future generations there is one explanation for this seeming paradox—the influence, enthusiasm, farsightedness, and generosity of one happily peripatetic professor of infectious diseases who unreservedly shared his pioneering experiences in developing serologic tests and antigens for coccidioidomycosis prior to publication with early investigators of histoplasmosis throughout the United States. The indebtedness of each of us to this able, amicable investigator—the late C. E. Smith—was perhaps best expressed by Christie (1958). As an early colleague, he was the first to exploit the early findings in coccidioidomycosis, and in continuing Smith's views to present, the first to show evidence that the high percentage of pulmonary calcifications in healthy persons east as well as west of the Rocky Mountains was due to infection with another mycotic agent, *H. capsulatum*, and not *Mycobacterium tuberculosis*.

Despite the model of coccidioidomycosis, there were a number of basic differences in the development of serologic tests for histoplasmosis. Primarily these were the following:

TABLE 42-I

Significant Developments in the Serologic Diagnosis of Histoplasmosis, 1941–1949
(Human Sera)

Item	Date	Test(s)	Antigen(s)	Reference
1	1941	CF and TP	HYP and H	Van Pernis *et al.*
2	11/47	CF	HYP, BYP, C, H	Salvin, S.B.
3	12/47	CF	HYP and H	Miller *et al.*
4	2/48	CF	H and B	Furcolow *et al.*
5	9/48	CF	HYP	Zarafonetis, C.J.D.
6	9/48	CA	H and B	Saslaw, S.
7	9/48	CF	HYP and BYP	Campbell, C.C.
8	4/49	CA	H and B	Saslaw and Campbell
9	5/49	CF	HYP and BYP	Campbell and Saslaw
10	5/49	CF	HYP	Zarafonetis, C.J.D.

CF = complement fixation.
TP = tube precipitin.
CA = collodion agglutination.
HYP = yeast phase *H. capsulatum.*
 H = histoplasmin.
BYP = yeast phase *Blastomyces dermatitidis.*
 C = coccidioidin.
 B = blastomycin.

1. The development of serologic tests was undertaken literally simultaneously by a number of different investigators in different geographic areas who for the most part worked independently of each other.

2. It could only be assumed that primary histoplasmosis would be similar clinically to primary coccidioidomycosis, and that it would be acquired in the same way. *H. capsulatum* was not recovered from the soil by Emmons (1949) until nearly two years after the first ten serologic reports (Table 42-I). *Coccidioides immitis,* on the other hand, had long been known to be a resident of the soil (Stewart and Meyer, 1932) when serologic tests were successfully developed for coccidioidomycosis.

3. *H. capsulatum* could be relatively readily cultivated *in vitro* in its yeast phase (Conant, 1941; Campbell, 1947; Salvin, 1947), whereas *C. immitis* would not be routinely cultivated *in vitro* in its parasitic phase until Converse (1955) succeeded in doing so five years after the serologic patterns with coccidioidins were well known (Smith, *et al.,* 1950). Thus, while it was impossible even to consider antigens for serologic tests from the parasitic phase of *C. immitis,* yeast as well as filamentous phase antigens of *H. capsulatum* were investigated from the very outset of serologic and immunologic study of histoplasmosis. This included the very early studies of Van Pernis, Benson and Holinger (1941) and Zarafonetis and Lindberg (1941). It was, in fact, the latter who recommended the term "histoplasmin" for filtrate antigens of both growth phases of *H. capsulatum.*

4. By necessity nearly all of the early serologic tests for histoplasmosis were first developed in the sera of experimentally infected animals. The total number of cases of the then only recognized clinical form of the disease was approximated to be not more than 150 (Peterson, 1948). These had occurred in many different geographic areas of the world (Parsons and Zarafonetis, 1945) and with few exceptions had been fatal. Thus, sera from recognized human cases were virtually impossible to obtain even to test the antigens that proved successful in demonstrating antibody in infected animals.

5. Cross reactions with antigens of *Blastomyces dermatitidis* and *C. immitis* were also assessed from the outset. This was due principally to the skin test studies of Emmons, Olson and Eldridge (1945) which emphasized that blastomycin frequently reacted to the same degree as histoplasmin in the same persons. Smith, Saito, Beard, Rosenberger and Whiting (1949) had also shown that histoplasmin cross reacted in both skin and serologic tests in proved coccidioidal infection.

Items 1 to 10, Table 42-I, illustrate the earliest developments. Items 1 and 3 were each studies on one serum from a single case of the advanced disseminated type. The results were negative in item 1, and the report is significant only in that it records the first effort to demonstrate circulating antibody in human histoplasmosis. Although item 3 is basically a report on the pathology of eight additional mucocutaneous cases, the perhaps uncontrolled serologic studies in one were more successful. A higher CF titer was demonstrated with a yeast phase antigen made from the patient's isolate than the histoplasmin. Salvin's report (item 2) consisted almost wholly of CF reactions in experimentally infected rabbit sera with four antigens: histoplasmin, coccidioidin (from C. E. Smith) and yeast phase (YP) antigens of *H. capsulatum* and *B. dermatitidis*. However, almost parenthetically, results of reactions on sera from two culturally confirmed cases of undescribed symptomatology were included. Again CF titers were higher with the YP antigen, and cross reactions with the heterologous antigens much lower or absent. Salvin concluded from the reactions in both experimental and human sera that YP antigens were superior and more highly specific than histoplasmins.

Within three months of Salvin's (1947a) report, companion pieces by Tenenberg and Howell (1948) and Furcolow, Bunnell and Tenenberg (1948) describing CF reactions in experimentally infected guinea pigs and ten culturally confirmed cases, respectively, appeared in the same issue of Public Health Reports. The antigens used were histoplasmin and blastomycin. Although these studies were adequately controlled and included sera from normal guinea pigs, from skin test positive and negative healthy persons, and from clinically presumptive as well as the ten confirmed cases, the CF tests were not quantitative. Serial serum dilutions were carried out only as far as was necessary to diminish cross reactions with blastomycin, which rarely exceeded 1:16 even in the confirmed cases. Thus the significance of this first published report of the more extensive surveys rested mainly on the suggestion that certain lots of histoplasmin might also be effective CF antigens and the fact that these investigators had sera from the widely envied total of ten confirmed cases in which to evaluate their antigens and tests. The absence of quantitation was therefore especially disappointing, for there was no clue as to possible differences in the level of antibody in the several cases which were expected to recover and those who expired.

Items 5, 6 and 7, Table 42-I, are little known early serologic studies. They were presented at a seminar on histoplasmosis, convened by N. F. Conant, September 13, 1948, for the Bacteriology Study Section, Division of Research Grants and Fellowships, National Institutes of Health, Bethesda, Maryland (Table 42-II). As noted by the Chairman, ". . . the section has had for consideration several projects on histoplasmosis. Due to the fact that knowledge in this field has been accumulating so rapidly, there has not been time for this knowledge to be crystallized," (Dack, 1948). Although the proceedings of this seminar were published shortly thereafter and widely distributed, the serologic data presented were seldom referred to even by the participants. This was because they already had been accepted for publication in widely read journals, as represented by items 8, 9 and 10, Table 42-I. This was also true of two papers pertaining to cultivation of the yeast phase of *H. capsulatum*, testifying to the fact that while this organism could be grown *in vitro* in its parasitic phase, the regularity with which this actually was accomplished then as now was not without its vicissitudes, especially with certain strains. Perhaps there is no better illustration of just how rapidly our knowledge of histoplasmosis was expanding during the late 1940's than the report by Emmons (1948) on "Histoplasmosis in Animals." In September, 1948, Emmons simply did not know that it would be he himself who would report the first isolation of *H. capsulatum* from soil in July, 1949 (Emmons, 1949). Even the word "soil" was not mentioned in his September 1948 report.

In no area, however, was information accumulating more rapidly than in the serologic. In April 1948, after almost two years of searching and several months before publication of their results of studies in experimental animals (Saslaw and Campbell, 1948) Saslaw (1948) and Campbell (1948) found their first two cases of primary pulmonary histoplasmosis (Wheeler, Friedman and Saslaw, 1950) and followed the antibody response in both CF and collodion agglutination (CA) tests from shortly after onset to what in six months appeared to be complete recovery. One was a markedly and the other a moderately severe infection. CF titers were high during the acute stage—1:1280 and 1:160, respectively—but decreased progressively with clinical improvement. CA titers, although lower, followed the same pattern. Serologic tests were thus at hand not only to rapidly detect the primary pul-

monary case but also to differentiate this from clinically and radiologically
indistinguishable infections of nonmycotic etiology. This was the break-
through for which we all had been looking. Sera on which to further explore
and evaluate the specificity or efficacy of serologic tests or antigens never
again would be lacking. Within days after the appearance of items 8 and 9,
Table 42-I, the deluge of requests for serologic tests for histoplasmosis began from civilian as well as military physicians and continued unabated for
the following twelve years (Campbell, 1960). Nevertheless, it was in the
1948 seminar on histoplasmosis that serologic reactions in the primary pulmonary case were first described. Characteristically both histoplasmin (CA)
and YP (CF) antigens were employed, but characteristically also the antigens were not derived from the same strain. Our main objective then was
not to compare antigens, but to find the cases that produced so much dermal
hypersensitivity and pulmonary calcification while they were clinically active. Most of us stayed with the tools that worked in our hands for several
years without further modification.

At this seminar also, Zarafonetis (1948) as a prelude to his own extensive
serologic data comparing the reactivity of YP antigens from eight strains of
H. capsulatum in sera from infected rabbits, and in sera from 164 patients
representing a wide variety of clinical entities including one case of apparently recovered histoplasmosis, two of systemic blastomycosis, and one each
of actinomycosis and cryptococcosis, set out the criteria necessary for the
clinically meaningful serologic diagnosis of any infectious disease which is
unexcelled even today. Slaslaw and Campbell (1948a) introduced a simpler
type of quantitative test than the CF—the CA—which was the forerunner of
the only serologic antigen yet commercially available, histoplasmin sensitized latex particles.[*] It was designed for use in any hospital laboratory to
detect the primary pulmonary case especially and in this respect is quite adequate still. My own contributions (Campbell, 1948) which did not appear
in the more widely read version (Campbell and Saslaw, 1949a) because of
editorial deletions were three: (1) the importance of adopting the 50 percent
end point method of complement fixation in mycotic serology as in all other
serologic and biologic tests, (2) emphasis on the marked differences in the
concentration of antigen required for the fixation of complement in sera from
experimentally infected animals as opposed to human, and that for results to
be clinically valid antigens to be used in human cases must be titrated versus
sera from positive cases, and (3) possibly the understatement in mycotic
serology of the last two and one half decades:

> With the increasing number of cases of histoplasmosis being reported in the
> literature it has become necessary not only to devise and investigate new immu-
> nologic tools but even more important to develop our old stand-by procedures to
> such a point that they will offer results of very real diagnostic and prognostic

---

[*] Consolidated Laboratories, Chicago Heights, Illinois.

value. In the CF test alone, there are almost as many variations of technic as there are workers. Where such a test is applied to the detection of antibodies to organism(s) which have a dual personality to begin with the variation possibilities are innumerable.

The latter perhaps was the first of the pleas for standardization that two and one-half decades later still are being made. Perhaps, on the other hand, the lack of standardization in serologic tests has not worked to the disadvantage of the accumulating knowledge on histoplasmosis in the long run. Had the early serologic investigators of histoplasmosis earlier adopted some standardized antigen which could not be reproduced—or test—we would not know nearly as much as we do about histoplasmosis or its causative organism. Histoplasmosis, after all, was not coccidioidomycosis which is confined to a miniscule of the geographic area now known to be endemic for *H. capsulatum* (Ajello, 1967).

The Decade, 1950-1959

Although the first sizable conference on histoplasmosis was not convened until 1952 and its proceedings regrettably not published until 1956 (Public Health Monograph No. 39, 1956), knowledge of histoplasmosis had greatly expanded by this time. Principally through the availability of serologic tests (item 1, Table 42-III) Grayston, Loosli and Alexander (1951) identified *H. capsulatum* as the cause of an outbreak of respiratory infection in a farm family and traced the source of the outbreak to a silo which they had cleaned. Earlier outbreaks of pneumonitic infections whose etiology had not been resolved prior to the availability of serologic tests for histoplasmosis were also shown to be due to *H. capsulatum* when stored sera were retrospectively tested with histoplasma antigens (*Public Health Monogr.*, 39:20-47, 1956). Thus, in this way, the serologic tests began to contribute to the identification of microfoci in nature from which primary infections were acquired as well as rapid identification of cases. At the present time, of course, outbreaks which have been similarly identified are legion. During this period also, the serologic tests—especially the CF—were being carried out on a routine basis in at least some state health laboratories, e.g. New York (Hazen and Tahler, 1951). Despite these very real advancements, the controversy over which growth phase of *H. capsulatum* produced the better serologic antigen continued. A cooperative study to compare histoplasmin versus YP antigens in the sera of culturally verified and clinically and serologically presumptive cases reported at the Kansas City conference did little to settle this issue. The comparative study merely emphasized: that wide variations existed between lots of antigens from either growth phase; consequently, results on the same sera varied markedly from laboratory to laboratory; the importance of interpreting serologic findings with the type and

TABLE 42-III

Significant Developments in the Serologic Diagnosis of Histoplasmosis, 1950–1959
(Human Sera)

Item	Date	Test(s)	Antigen(s)	Reference
1	1951	CF*	HYP and BYP	Grayston *et al.*
2	1952	CF	HYP and H	Grayston, J.T.
3	1952	CF, CA TP	HYP, BYP B, C, H	Kansas City Conf.
4	1953	CF, CA TP	HYP, BYP B, C, H	Campbell and Binkley
5	1953	CF	H	Schubert *et al.*
6	1954	TP	HYP and H	Salvin and Furcolow
7	1955	CF and TP	HYP and H	Furcolow and Brasher (Salvin and Schubert)**
8	1955	CF and CA	HYP, BYP C, H	Sutliff and Campbell
9	1956	CF	HYP and BYP	Hill and Campbell
10	1957	CF	HYP	Schubert *et al.*
11	1958	AG	B and H	Heiner, D.C.
12	1959	CF and CA	HYP, BYP C and H	Campbell, C.C.

* See legends Table 42-I.
** Performed the serologic tests.
AG—agar-gel diffusion.

stage of infection or disease; and it introduced the possibility that circulating antibody might be increased following the application of skin tests. Nevertheless, from all serologic studies presented at this conference, it was clear that the YP antigens were superior to the histoplasmins used by the different investigators for demonstrating CF antibody in the primary case. It was equally clear that certain histoplasmins were reactive in certain chronic cases in which YP antigens were unreactive. Some of these items in Tables 42-III and 42-IV were outgrowths of the issues emphasized at the Kansas City conference. Thus in the interest of standardization, Campbell and Binkley (1953) summarized their four years' experience with a ground yeast phase histoplasma antigen (Campbell and Saslaw, 1949[a]) and thereafter in CF tests used suspensions of whole yeasts as employed by Salvin (1947), Grayston (1952), and Hazen and Tahler (1951). They also added histoplasmin to their battery of antigens used in all routine CF tests (Hill and Campbell, 1956), which from the beginning had been carried out for blastomycosis and coccidioidomycosis as well as histoplasmosis. This is essentially the schema used by all major laboratories performing CF tests routinely at the present time. Not only are civilian populations almost as mobile as military ones in this jet transportation age, but with experience patterns of cross reactions began to emerge which, if understood, frequently were more diagnostically helpful than CF reactions with antigens of the specific etiologic agent (Campbell and Binkley, 1953; Campbell, 1960). Investigators from the Public Health Service similarly returned from the Kansas City conference to begin their still continuing investigations into the causes of antigenic variations in both growth phases (Schubert, Ajello, Stanford and Grant, 1953; Schubert, Ajello, Cooper and Runyon, 1955; Schubert, Ajello and Hall, 1957). Also in the interests of standardization, they adopted the 50 percent endpoint method of complement fixation (Schubert, *et al.*, 1955).

By the mid-1950's, the serologic tests—especially the CF—despite all acknowledged crudities and deficiencies, were being used in surveys to determine the incidence of chronic histoplasmosis in tuberculosis sanatoriums (Furcolow and Brasher, 1955) and in Veteran's Administration and Armed Forces pulmonary disease installations (Sutliff and Campbell, 1955). The incidence of histoplasmosis found in these two preliminary surveys was so striking that each led to far more extensive surveys for histoplasmosis in sanatoriums and VA-AF hospitals by these senior investigators and others. Both histoplasmin and YP antigens were used in these CF tests. In the mid-1950's also the serologic tests with both antigens were being used to explore the possibility that the high percentage of fevers of undetermined origin being observed on the Isthmus of Panama might be primary histoplasmosis, despite the fact that only one additional disseminated case had been reported from the Canal Zone (Draheim, Mitchell and Elton, 1951) since Darling's original three. This did indeed prove to be the case (Young, Cleve and Mastellari, 1957; Campbell, 1959). These findings led in turn to the establishment in 1958 of a laboratory on the Isthmus specifically to study histoplasmosis, which was cojointly and successively sponsored by the Walter Reed Army Institute of Research and the National Institute of Allergy and Infectious Diseases, N.I.H. While these investigations contributed nothing further to the improvement of serologic antigens or tests, rapid diagnosis of the primary cases by means of serologic tests led, as they had for years in the United States, to "gumshoe" epidemiological studies of the sources in nature from which these cases were recently acquired. The epidemiologic studies unequivocally confirmed the recent findings of Emmons (1958) that bats as well as avian species were linked with the distribution of microfoci of *H. capsulatum* in nature (Shacklette, Diercks and Gale, 1962). The importance of this finding in advancing knowledge of the geographic distribution of *H. capsulatum* on a global basis requires no further comment at this conference! All of this is beyond a report on the history of the development of serologic antigens and tests, per se, but not beyond the realm to which the availability of serologic tests has continuously contributed to the overall information on histoplasmosis, epidemiologically and ecologically as well as clinically.

Item 11, Table 42-III, introduces the use of agar-gel (AG) diffusion tests to the serologic diagnosis of histoplasmosis (Heiner, 1958) and to a more critical study of the complexity and multiplicity of components comprising the antigens of both growth phases of *H. capsulatum* and other antigenically related mycotic pathogens. This report is notable not only for the introduction of a much simpler test than the CF that can be used in any laboratory with designated lots of histoplasmin, but also because it was the first serologic procedure for histoplasmosis to be developed *en toto* in sera from human cases. This, to the investigators of only a decade before who searched long for even one human serum, was indeed a key to the progress that had been made.

Stimulation of Circulating Antibody Following Skin Test

Heiner's (1958) findings also revealed that application of a single skin test could boost circulating antibody demonstrable in AG tests to at least one of the components of histoplasmin. Campbell, McDearman, Hill, Ulrich, Sutliff, Wier, Taylor and Andrews (1960), in a cooperative case-finding study for histoplasmosis in VA-AF hospitals, were at approximately the same time, beginning to note a surprisingly high percentage of increases in antibody level with histoplasmin in CF and CA tests following a single skin test with this substance.

Thus, an old problem which was thought to have long since been resolved in well-controlled studies of small populations (Prior and Saslaw, 1952; Saslaw and Campbell, 1953; Salvin, Weber, Lackman, Nishio and Menges, 1954) had reappeared in the skin and serologic testing of larger populations. The earlier studies (Table 42-IV) had each indicated that three or more skin tests in rather rapid succession were required before level of demonstrable circulating antibody was materially increased in subsequent serologic tests. Later studies suggested that the earlier findings had merely been wrongly interpreted (Campbell and Hill, 1964). The stimulation of circulating antibody to a single "diagnostic" skin test, however, was extremely important in the interpretation of diagnostic serologic tests. The findings of Heiner (1958) and of Campbell *et al.* (1960) thus prompted a series of studies to reinvestigate this matter (McDearman and Young, 1960; Nicholas, Wier, Kuhn, Campbell, Nolte and Hill, 1961; Sigrest, Lummus, Campbell, Busey and Allison, 1963; Campbell and Hill, 1964; Kaufman, Terry, Schubert and McLaughlin, 1967). Each study revealed that a single skin test did indeed stimulate the production of circulating antibody demonstrable in all types of tests employed in a certain percentage of healthy histoplasmin skin test positive persons. This was particularly evident in the presence of histoplasmins as the serologic test antigens. However, McDearman and Young (1960) and Sigrest *et al.* (1963) presented evidence that such antibody was demonstrable in the presence of certain lots of YP antigen also.

Interpretation of serologic tests with histoplasmin has thus changed markedly. This has led not only to a more accurate interpretation of the serologic

TABLE 42-IV

Chronology of the Studies to Determine Effect of Single Histoplasmin
Skin Test on Subsequent Serologic Results

Item	Date	Test(s)	Antigen(s)	Reference
1	1952	CA*	H*	Prior and Saslaw
2	1953	CF and CA	HYP, BYP C, H	Saslaw and Campbell
3	1954	CF	HYP and H	Salvin *et al.*
4	1960	CF and CA	HYP, BYP C, H	Campbell, McDearman *et al.*
5	1960	HA, CF and CA	HYP and H	McDearman and Young
6	1961	CF and CA	HYP, BYP C, H	Nicholas *et al.*
7	1963	CF	HYP and H	Sigrest *et al.*
8	1964	AG, CF and CA	HYP and H	Campbell and Hill
9	1965	AG and CF	H	Schubert and Wiggins
10	1967	AG and CF	HYP and H	Kaufman *et al.*

* See legend Tables 42-I and 42-III.
HA = hemagglutination.

tests, but also to the wiser and more discriminate use of the skin test as a "diagnostic" tool (Campbell, 1968). Most importantly it has led to more critical examination of histoplasmins, especially in regard to the *h* and *m* components described by Heiner (1958). The basic studies of Schubert and Wiggins (1965) and Wiggins and Schubert (1965) are outstanding in this respect. In May of this year Kaufman, McLaughlin and Terry (1969) reported preliminary results with a histoplasmin deficient in the *m* component which did not stimulate antibody in subsequent CF tests but which still elicited positive skin tests in dermally sensitive persons.

Other Types of Serologic Tests

Table 42-V summarizes the chronological development of various types of serologic tests. As noted, all early tests and antigens were developed in sera of experimentally infected or hyperimmunized animals and preceded the studies with human sera in Tables 42-I and 42-III. None has been used nearly as extensively as the CF, and some have not been used at all except by their innovators. The latter applies to perhaps the simplest test of all— direct agglutination (Cozad, 1958; Cozad and Larsh, 1960). In fact, mycologists seem to have deliberately eschewed the simpler types of serologic tests and gone directly to those that were more complex. Although suspensions of whole yeast cells as particulate antigens could have been used in agglutination as in the CF, particles—collodion, erythrocytes, latex—of any other type onto which soluble antigens could be absorbed have been the only ones tried. There is no explanation for this except that in the beginning when we were unable to cultivate the yeast phase as expertly as we do now, we had difficulties with spontaneous agglutination. However, Cozad and Larsh

TABLE 42-V

Chronology of Tests Developed in Animals Experimentally Infected With
H. capsulatum Prior to Trial in Human Cases

Date	Test	Sera	Antigen(s)	Reference
1945	TP*	Rabbit	H*	Scheff, G.J.
11/47	TP and CF	Rabbit	HYP, BYP C and H	Salvin, S.B.
1/48	TP and CF	Rabbit	HYP and H†	Salvin and Hottle
2/48	CF	Guinea pig	H and B	Tenenberg and Howell
7/48	CF	Rabbit	HYP and BYP	Saslaw and Campbell
9/48	CA	Rabbit	H and B	Saslaw and Campbell
10/48	CF	Rabbit	HYP and BYP‡	Campbell and Saslaw
1949	HA	Rabbit	H	Norden, A.
1958	LA	Rabbit	H and B	Carlisle and Saslaw
1958	Agg	Rabbit	HYP	Cozad, G.C.
1959	FA	Rabbit	HYP	Gordon, M.A.
1960	CTA	Rabbit	HYP	Cozad and Larsh

* See legend, Table 42-I.

† Seven types of antigen from one strain of *H. capsulatum* were used in this study.

‡ Saline extract of ground yeasts used for approximately three years in human sera by Campbell and associates.

LA = latex particle agglutination.

Agg = direct agglutination.

FA = fluorescent antibody.

CTA = Capillary tube agglutination.

(1958, 1960) seem to have succeeded. There is also indication that mycologists were not immune to "faddism," and in their continuing search for that simpler test than the CF, they adapted the most recent test to be described to their own purposes.

However, different tests are used for different purposes. The fluorescent antibody test for histoplasmosis, though first investigated by Gordon (1959), has since been much more extensively used by Kaufman, Schubert and Kaplan (1962), Kaufman and Kaplan (1963) and Kaufman and Blumer (1968). Similarly, as shown in Table 42-VI, while Heiner (1958) was the

TABLE 42-VI

Chronology of Serologic Tests Developed Completely in Sera From Human Cases of Histoplasmosis

Date	Test(s)	Antigen(s)	Reference
1958	AG*	H and B*	Heiner, D.C.
1958	HA†	H and B	McDearman et al.
1961	AG	H	Schubert et al.
1962	LA (Commercial)	H	Hill and Campbell
1963	Micro AG	H	Goldin and McMillen
1965	AG and CF	HYP and H	Wiggins and Schubert
1966	AG and IE	H	Walter et al.

* See legend, Tables 42-I–42-V.

† This procedure differs so markedly from Norden's (Table 42-V) it merits separate listing.

IE = immunoelectrophoresis.

first to apply agar-gel diffusion in the diagnosis of histoplasmosis, it was Schubert, Lynch and Ajello (1961) and Schubert and Wiggins (1963) who first assessed the use of these tests as screening devices in broad populations and related reactions with CF titers observed in the same cases.

In conclusion, the author would like to state that she is well aware that this may be a biased historical review, although she has made every effort to be objective. The latter is not always easy when one has been so personally involved since the beginning of the development of serologic tests for histo-plasmosis. It is, therefore, hoped that readers will advise as to important omissions and correct any flagrant biases. The evolution of histoplasmosis from a rare, "tropical" fatal disease to the common global infection we rec-ognize at the present time has been one of the most exciting chapters in in-fectious diseases in this quarter of a century in which serologic tests were available. It would be regrettable if the record were not kept or set straight while others of us who also were deeply involved in these developments are still around to do so.

References

Ajello, L. (1967). Comparative ecology of respiratory mycotic disease agents. *Bact. Rev.*, *31*:6-24.

Campbell, C.C. (1947). Reverting *Histoplasma capsulatum* to the yeast phase. *J. Bact.*, 54:263-264.

Campbell, C.C. (1948). Yeast phase antigens in a complement fixation test for histo-plasmosis. Proceedings Seminar on Histoplasmosis (Md.), Sept. 13, pgs. 59-68.

Campbell, C.C. (1959). Serological diagnosis and epidemiological aspects of histoplas-mosis. In *Fungus Diseases and Their Treatment*. London, Butterworth, pp. 142-157.

Campbell, C.C. (1960). The accuracy of serologic methods in diagnosis. *Ann. N.Y. Acad. Sci.*, 89:163-177.

Campbell, C.C. (1968). Use and interpretation of serologic and skin tests in the respira-tory mycoses: current considerations. *Dis. Chest*, 54:49-54.

Campbell, C.C. and Binkley, G.E. (1953). Serologic diagnosis with respect to histo-plasmosis, coccidioidomycosis and blastomycosis and the problem of cross reactions. *J. Lab. Clin. Med.*, 42:896-906.

Campbell, C.C. and Hill, G.B. (1964). Further studies on the development of com-plement fixing antibodies and precipitins in healthy histoplasmin-sensitive persons following a single histoplasmin skin test. *Am. Rev. Resp. Dis.*, 90:927-934.

Campbell, C.C. and Saslaw, S. (1948). The use of yeast phase antigens in a comple-ment fixation test for histoplasmosis. II. Results with ground antigens. *J. Lab. Clin. Med.*, 33:1207-1211.

Campbell, C.C. and Saslaw, S. (1949a). Use of yeast-phase antigens in a complement fixation test for histoplasmosis. III. Preliminary results with human sera. *Public Health Rep. (Wash.)*, 64:551-560.

Campbell, C.C., McDearman, S.C., Hill, G.B., Ulrich, E., Sutliff, W.D., Wier, J.A., Tay-lor, R.R. and Andrews, C.E. (1960). Histoplasmosis case findings: II. Serologic aspects: Report of VA-Armed Forces cooperative study. In Transactions of 19th Conference Chemotherapy of Tuberculosis, pgs. 287-302.

Carlisle, H.N. and Saslaw, S. (1958). A histoplasmin-latex agglutination test. *J. Lab. Clin. Med., 51:*793-801.

Christie, A. (1958). The disease spectrum of human histoplasmosis. *Ann. Intern. Med., 49:*544-555.

Christie, A., and Peterson, J.C. (1946). Pulmonary calcification and sensitivity to histoplasmin, tuberculin and haplosporangin. *J.A.M.A., 131:*658-660.

Conant, N.F. (1941). A cultural study of the life-cycle of *Histoplasma capsulatum* Darling. *J. Bact., 41:*563-579.

Converse, J.L. (1955). Growth of spherules of *Coccidioides immitis* in a chemically defined liquid medium. *Proc. Soc. Exp. Biol. 90:*709-711.

Cozad, G.C. (1958). A study of the whole yeast cell agglutination test in rabbits experimentally infected with *Histoplasma capsulatum. J. Immun., 81:*368-375.

Cozad, G.C. and Larsh, H.W. (1960). A capillary tube agglutination test for histoplasmosis. *J. Immun., 85:*387-390.

Dack, G.M. (1948). Statement. Proceedings of the Seminar on Histoplasmosis (Md.), Sept. 13, pg. 1.

Draheim, J.H., Mitchell, J.R. and Elton, N.W. (1951). Histoplasmosis. Fourth case report from the Canal Zone. *Am. J. Trop. Med., 31:*753-760.

Emmons, C.W. (1948). Histoplasmosis in animals. Proceedings of the Seminar on Histoplasmosis (Md.), Sept. 13, pgs. 24-26.

Emmons, C.W. (1949). Isolation of *Histoplasma capsulatum* from soil. *Public Health Rep., 64:*892-896.

Emmons, C.W. (1958). Association of bats with histoplasmosis. *Public Health Rep., 73:*590-595.

Emmons, C.W., Olson, B.J. and Eldridge, W.W. (1945). Studies of the role of fungi in pulmonary disease. I. Cross reactions of histoplasmin. *Public Health Rep., 60:*1383-1394.

Furcolow, M.L. and Brasher, C.A. (1955). Chronic progressive (cavitary) histoplasmosis as a problem in tuberculosis sanatoriums. In Transactions of the VA Conference on Chemotherapy of Tuberculosis., Atlanta, Georgia, Feb. 7-10. (*Am. Rev. Tuberc. Pulmon. Dis., 73:*609-615, *1956*).

Furcolow, M.L., Bunnell, I.L. and Tenenberg, D.J. (1948). A complement fixation test for histoplasmosis. II. Preliminary results with human sera. *Public Health Rep., 63:*169-173.

Goldin, M. and McMillen, S. (1963). A micro-method for the agar-gel precipitin test for histoplasmosis. *Amer. Rev. Resp. Dis., 87:*592-593.

Gordon, M.A. (1959). Fluorescent staining of *Histoplasma capsulatum. J. Bact., 77:*678-681.

Grayston, J.T. (1952). A study of the complement fixation reaction in histoplasmosis (1952). *J. Lab. Clin. Med., 40:*90-101.

Grayston, J.T., Loosli, C.G., and Alexander, E.R. (1951). The isolation of *Histoplasma capsulatum* from soil in an unused silo. *Science, 114:*323-324.

Hazen, E.L. and Tahler, E.D. (1951). Quantitative complement fixation tests for evidence of histoplasmosis and blastomycosis. In Annual Report of the N.Y. State Department of Health, Division of Laboratories and Res. (Albany). pp. 73-74.

Heiner, D.C. (1958). Diagnosis of histoplasmosis using precipitin reactions in agar gel. *Pediatrics, 22:*616-627.

Hill, G.B. and Campbell, C.C. (1956). A further evaluation of histoplasmin and yeast phase antigens of *Histoplasma capsulatum* in the complement fixation test. *J. Lab. Clin. Med., 48:*255-263.

Hill, G.B. and Campbell, C.C. (1962). Commercially available histoplasmin sensitized latex particles in an agglutination test for histoplasmosis. *Mycopathologia,* 18:169-176.

Kaufman, L. and Blumer, S. (1968). Development and use of a polyvalent conjugate to differentiate *Histoplasma capsulatum* and *Histoplasma duboisii* from other pathogens. *J. Bact.,* 95:1243-1246.

Kaufman, L. and Kaplan, W. (1963). Serological characterization of pathogenic fungi by means of fluorescent antibodies. I. Antigenic relationship between yeast and mycelial forms of *Histoplasma capsulatum. J. Bact.,* 85:986-991.

Kaufman, L., Schubert, J.H. and Kaplan, W. (1962). Fluorescent antibody inhibition test for histoplasmosis. *J. Lab. Clin. Med.,* 59:1033-1038.

Kaufman, L., McLaughlin, D. and Terry, R.T. (1969). Immunological studies with an *m*-deficient histoplasmin. *Bact. Proc.,* M (M)23:14 (abstract).

Kaufman, L., Terry, R.T., Schubert, J.H. and McLaughlin, D. (1967). Effects of a single histoplasmin skin test on the serological diagnosis of histoplasmosis. *J. Bact.,* 94:798-803.

McDearman, S.C. and Young, J.M. (1960). The development of positive serologic tests with *Histoplasma capsulatum* antigens following single histoplasmin skin tests. *Amer. J. Clin. Path.,* 34:434-438.

McDearman, S.C., McClure, V.P., Cherry, E.D. and Ulrich, E.W. (1958). Hemagglutination of histoplasmin-sensitized erythrocytes by sera from patients with culturally proven histoplasmosis. 58th General Meeting Soc. Amer. Bact., Chicago. *Bact. Proc.* 151.

Miller, H.E., Keddie, S.M., Johnstone, H.G. and Bostick, W.L. (1947). Histoplasmosis. Cutaneous and membranous lesions, mycologic and pathologic observations. *Arch. Derm. Syph.,* 56:715-739.

Nicholas, W.M., Wier, J.A., Kuhn, L.R., Campbell, C.C., Nolte, L.R. and Hill, G.B. (1961). Serologic effects of histoplasmin skin testing. *Amer. Rev. Resp. Dis.,* 83: 276-279.

Norden, A. (1949). Agglutination of sheep's erythrocytes sensitized with histoplasmin. *Proc. Soc. Exp. Biol. (N.Y.),* 70:218-220.

Palmer, C.E. (1945). Nontuberculous pulmonary calcification and sensitivity to histoplasmin. *Public Health Rep.,* 60:513-520.

Parsons, R. J. and Zarafonetis, C.J.D. (1945). Histoplasmosis in man; a report of 7 cases and a review of 71 cases. *Arch. Intern. Med.,* 75:1-23.

Peterson, J.C. (1948). Histoplasmosis in man. *Proceedings of the Seminar on Histoplasmosis* (Md.), Sept. 13, pp. 17-23.

Prior, J. A. and Saslaw, S. (1952). Effect of repeated histoplasmin skin tests on skin reactivity and collodion agglutination. *Amer. Rev. Tuberc.,* 66:588-593.

Public Health Monogr., 39 (1956). (Various authors—see text.)

Salvin, S.B. (1947). Cultural studies on the yeast-like phase of *Histoplasma capsulatum* Darling. *J. Bact.,* 54:655-660.

Salvin, S.B. (1947a). Complement fixation studies in experimental histoplasmosis. *Proc. Soc. Exp. Biol. (N.Y.),* 66:342-345.

Salvin, S.B. and Furcolow, M.L. (1954). Precipitins in human histoplasmosis. *J. Lab. Clin. Med.,* 43:259-274.

Salvin, S.B. and Hottle, G.A. (1948). Serologic studies on antigens from *Histoplasma capsulatum* Darling. *J. Immun.,* 60:57-66.

Salvin, S.B., Weber, R.W., Lackman, D.B., Nishio, J. and Menges, G. (1954). Influence of repeated histoplasmin skin tests on precipitins and complement-fixing antibodies. *J. Lab. Exp. Med.,* 44:56-62.

Saslaw, S. (1948). The use of collodion particles for demonstrating antibodies against histoplasmin. Proceedings of the Seminar on Histoplasmosis (Md.), Sept. 13, pp. 48-54.

Saslaw, S. and Campbell, C.C. (1948). The use of yeast phase antigens in a complement fixation test for histoplasmosis. I. Preliminary results with rabbit sera. *J. Lab. Clin. Med.*, 33:811-818.

Saslaw, S. and Campbell, C.C. (1948a). A method for demonstrating antibodies in rabbit sera against histoplasmin by the collodion agglutination technic. *Proc. Soc. Exp. Biol. (N.Y.)*, 68:559-562.

Saslaw, S. and Campbell, C.C. (1949). A collodion agglutination test for histoplasmosis. *Public Health Rep.*, 64:424-429.

Saslaw, S. and Campbell, C.C. (1953). Effect of histoplasmin skin testing on serologic results. *Proc. Soc. Exp. Biol. (N.Y.)*, 82:689-691.

Scheff, G.J. (1945). Biological and immunological properties of *Histoplasma capsulatum*. No. 650. *Yale J. Biol. Med.*, 18:41-54.

Schubert, J.H. and Wiggins, G.L. (1963). The evaluation of serologic tests for histoplasmosis in relation to the clinical diagnosis. *Amer. J. Hyg.*, 77:240-249.

Schubert, J.H. and Wiggins, G.L. (1965). Preliminary studies of *h* and *m* components of histoplasmin for skin tests and serology. *Amer. Rev. Resp. Dis.*, 92:640-641.

Schubert, J.H., Ajello, L. and Hall, J. (1957). Variation in complement fixation antigenicity of different yeast phase strains of *Histoplasma capsulatum*. *J. Lab. Clin. Med.*, 50:304-307.

Schubert, J.H., Lynch, Jr., H.J. and Ajello, L. (1961). Evaluation of the agar-plate precipitin test for histoplasmosis. *Am. Rev. Resp. Dis.*, 84:845-849.

Schubert, J.H., Ajello, L., Stanford, S. and Grant, V.Q. (1953). Variation in complement fixation antigen production by different strains of *Histoplasma capsulatum* grown on two media. *J. Lab. Clin. Med.*, 41:91-97.

Schubert, J. H., Ajello, L., Cooper, J.S. and Runyon, L.C. (1955). Evaluation of histoplasmin and yeast phase antigens derived from a single strain of *Histoplasma capsulatum* in the complement fixation test. *J. Bact.*, 69:558-562.

Shacklette, M.H., Diercks F.H. and Gale, N.B. (1962). Recovery of *Histoplasma capsulatum* from bat tissues. *Science, 135*:1135.

Sigrest, M.L., Lummus, F.L., Campbell, G.D., Busey, J.F. and Allison, F., Jr. (1963). Effect of diagnostic skin testing on antibody levels for histoplasmosis. *New Eng. J. Med.*, 269:390-394.

Smith, C.E., Saito, M.T., Beard, R.R., Rosenberger, H.G. and Whiting, E.G. (1949). Histoplasmin sensitivity and coccidioidal infection. I. Occurrence of cross reaction. *Amer. J. Public Health*, 39:722-736.

Smith, C.E., Saito, M.T., Beard, R.R., Kepp, R.M., Clark, R.W. and Eddie, B.U. (1950). Serological tests in the diagnosis and prognosis of coccidioidomycosis. *Amer. J. Hyg.*, 52:1-21.

Smith, C.E., Whiting, E.G., Baker, E.E., Rosenberger, H.G., Beard, R.R. and Saito, M.T. (1948). The use of coccidioidin. *Amer. Rev. Tuberc.*, 57:330-360.

Stewart, R.A. and Meyer, K.F. (1932). Isolation of *Coccidioides immitis* (Stiles) from soil. *Proc. Soc. Exp. Biol. Med.*, 29:937-938.

Sutliff, W.D. and Campbell, C.C. (1955). Serologic serum tests for the systemic mycosis. Plans for a cooperative study. In Transactions 14th Conference on the Chemotherapy of Tuberculosis, *VA, Army, Navy*. Atlanta, Georgia, Feb. 7-10, pp. 285-288.

Tenenberg, D.J. and Howell, A., Jr. (1948). A complement fixation test for histoplasmosis. I. Technic and preliminary results on animal sera. *Public Health Rep. (Wash.)*, 63:163-168.

Van Pernis, P.A., Benson, M.E. and Holinger, P.H. (1941). Specific cutaneous reactions with histoplasmosis: preliminary report of another case. *J.A.M.A., 117*:436-437.

Walter, J., Tosh, F.E. and Chin, T.D.Y. (1966). Significance of precipitin bands in sera of chronic cases of human histoplasmosis by micro-Ouchterlony and immunoelectrophoresis tests. *Bact. Proc., M145*:62.

Wheeler, W.E., Friedman, V. and Saslaw, S. (1950). Simultaneous nonfatal systemic histoplasmosis in two cousins. *Amer. J. Dis. Child., 79*:806-819.

Wiggins, G.L. and Schubert, J.H. (1965). Relationship of histoplasmin agar gel bands and complement fixation titers in histoplasmosis. *J. Bact., 89*:589-596.

Young, R.V., Cleve, E.A. and Mastellari, A.V. (1957). Acute pulmonary histoplasmosis on the Isthmus of Panama. *Arch. Intern. Med., 100*:430-435.

Zarafonetis, C.J.D. (1948). Complement fixation studies with yeast-phase antigen in histoplasmosis. Proceedings of the Seminar on Histoplasmosis (Md.), Sept. 13, pgs. 33-47.

Zarafonetis, C.J.D. (1949). Complement fixation studies with yeast-phase antigen in experimental histoplasmosis. *Amer. J. Med., 6*:666.

Zarafonetis, C.J.D. and Lindberg, R.B. (1941). Histoplasmosis of Darling: observations on antigenic properties of causative agent. *Univ. Hosp. Bull. (Ann Arbor), 7*:47-48.

Chapter 43

An Interpretation of Serologic Tests in *Histoplasma capsulatum* Infections

SARA C. McDEARMAN

ABSTRACT

Results indicate that serologic tests, with carefully selected antigens, are important in both the diagnosis and prognosis of clinical disease resulting from *Histoplasma capsulatum* infections. Their greater use, if not demanded, is definitely recommended.

SINCE 1945, considerable effort has been directed toward the study of *Histoplasma capsulatum* antigens and the development of sensitive and specific serologic tests. There have been many and excellent reports in which serologic tests have been employed, and the results of those studies leave little doubt that serologic tests are reliable and useful tools in studying the various aspects of histoplasmosis. References to those earlier studies have been omitted here because a careful and thorough review is given in another article in this publication (Campbell, 1971).

The present study deals with the use and evaluation of serologic tests in a series of hospitalized patients, some in whom *H. capsulatum* was demonstrated by culture and some in whom histoplasmosis was suspected from the clinical and serologic findings. During the past thirteen years approximately 117,000 sera have been tested in our laboratory. The sera were received from eighty-three different Veterans Administration Hospitals, local Memphis hospitals, and a few other scattered hospitals. The data collected from these studies are the subject of the present report and will be considered in three sections. First, serologic data from a group of 426 culturally proven histoplasmosis patients are presented. Secondly, similar data from a group of 9,419 seropositive patients, but not proven culturally, are discussed. Finally, detailed data including serologic, mycologic, and clinical are presented from a group of 141 culturally proven histoplasmosis patients studied in our own hospital.

Materials and Methods

In 1956 this laboratory was established in the Veterans Administration as a central laboratory for the study of serologic tests in histoplasmosis. The primary stimulus for the development of this laboratory was the formation of the Veterans Administration-Armed Forces Histoplasmosis Cooperative

Study Group. Several studies have been reported from the group. (Veterans Administration-Armed Forces Cooperative Study on Histoplasmosis, 1961, 1964, and 1968). The serologic testing for those studies was performed in this laboratory.

This report includes data obtained during the past thirteen years. Serum specimens from eighty-three different Veterans Administration Hospitals, both study group and nonstudy group, were studied. There was no uniform plan for finding the histoplasmosis cases. In some hospitals serologic surveys were performed. In other hospitals clinical findings prompted the submission of serum samples. All patients were hospitalized at the time serologic tests were first performed. Mycologic and histologic studies were done in the individual hospitals.

Two groups of patients are presented. One group includes 426 patients in each of whom the diagnosis was established by the isolation of *H. capsulatum*. These are known as the proven cases. The other group of suspected cases includes 9,419 seropositive patients in whom histoplasmosis was suspected because of the clinical and serologic findings. Patients from whom *H. capsulatum* were identified only by histochemical methods are not included in this study. Clinical data given here were obtained from the patients' clinical records and were the evaluations made by the responsible physicians.

Serologic Tests

Each serum was tested with the battery of serologic tests that included five complement fixation (CF) tests and one hemagglutination test (HA). The antigens used in the CF tests were as follows:

Y-GW = *H. capsulatum* yeast antigen from GW human strain.
Y-VC = *H. capsulatum* yeast antigen from VC human strain.
HM   = Histoplasmin culture filtrate, pooled human strains.
B   = *Blastomyces dermatitidis* yeast phase, human strains pooled.
C   = Coccidioidin. Prepared and furnished by Dr. Milton Huppert, Veterans Administration Hospital, San Fernando, California.

Except for the coccidioidin, these antigens were prepared in this laboratory by methods given in earlier reports (Campbell and Saslaw, 1949; Hill and Campbell, 1956; Emmons, Olson and Eldridge, 1945; Martin, 1935). The same organism strains have been used throughout the past thirteen years. The National Communicable Disease Center tube or microtiter LBCF technique (Laboratory Branch Complement Fixation Method, 1965) was used.

The HA test employed a carbohydrate antigen prepared from either *B. dermatitidis* or *H. capsulatum*. The technique and antigen preparation are described in a report from this laboratory (McDearman, 1962).

The term *seropositive* is used throughout to indicate positive CF reactions with any or all of the *H. capsulatum* antigens: Y-GW, Y-VC, and HM. *Sero-negative* indicates a negative reaction with all three of these antigens. Reactions with the *B. dermatitidis* and coccidioidin antigens and the HA test are discussed separately. The term *strain* designates different isolates of *H. capsulatum.*

Results and Discussion

Culturally Proven Cases of Histoplasmosis

In this section data from the 426 cases of culturally proven histoplasmosis are discussed. These cases were accumulated during the past thirteen years in the various hospitals as noted in Table 43-I.

The largest single group of patients (254 or 60%) was studied in Memphis hospitals. There were forty-one other Veterans Administration Hospitals that contributed 172 or 40.0% of the cases. There were 58 cases (13.6%) from Veterans Administration Hospitals located outside the histoplasmosis high-incidence area (central United States—Mississippi, Ohio River valleys). The number of sera tested shows the amount of repeat testing done (5,540 sera from 426 patients). The largest number of sera tested from any single hospital was from our own. Of the 26 patients in this group, 40 (9.3%) had single sera tested and 203 (47.7%) had more than ten sera tested.

Forty of the 426 patients (with 303 sera) had serum titers of only 1:8 or 1:16. High serum titers are correlated with more extensive lung involvement. Serum titers of 1:8 and 1:16 are generally considered to be low, and there is a great tendency to forget the possibility of active lesions in these

TABLE 43-I

Geographic Distribution and Sera Tested of the 426 Histoplasmin Patients

Patient Groups	Patients		Sera Tested	
	Number	Percent	Number	Percent
Memphis Hospitals:				
VA*	141	33.1	3417	61.7
WTCD*	97	22.8	571	10.3
Other	16	3.8	86	1.5
VA Hospitals:				
Study-Group*	96	22.5	1086	19.6
Non-Study-Group†	76	17.8	380	6.9
Total	426	100.0	5540	100.0

WTCD = West Tennessee Chest Disease Hospital.

* Study group hospitals—Ann Arbor, Cincinnati, Jackson (Miss.), Kansas City, Little Rock, Memphis VA, Nashville, Oteen (N.C.), WTCD (Memphis), Wood (Wis.).

†Nonstudy group hospitals (33 VA Hospitals in 22 States)—California, Connecticut, Florida, Georgia, Illinois, Iowa, Kansas, Kentucky, Louisiana, Maryland, Massachusetts, Michigan, Missouri, Nebraska, New York, North Carolina, Ohio, Oklahoma, Pennsylvania, Texas, Virginia, West Virginia.

TABLE 43-II

Serologic Patterns of the 426 Histoplasmosis Patients

Serologic Patterns	Patients with Sera Reacting	
	Number	Percent
I. Y+HM+B	150	35.2⎫ 66.9
II. Y+HM	135	31.7⎭
III. Y +B	37	8.7⎫ 29.3
IV. Y	88	20.6⎭
V. Seronegative	16	3.8
Total	426	100.0

Y = Either GW or VC yeast antigen.

patients. Certainly these patients must be studied as carefully, if not more so, as those with high serum titers.

In Table 43-II the 426 histoplasmosis patients are classified into five different serologic patterns. The pattern for any patient was determined by the greatest number of antigens with which any serum reacted. For example, multiple sera from one patient were tested; one or more sera reacted with the three antigens Y-(GW or VC), HM and B; as the patient improved clinically, his sera reacted only with one of the *H. capsulatum* yeast antigens; this patient, then, was classified in serologic pattern I. These serologic patterns are given in an order that correlates with clinical disease activity. Pattern I is found in patients with the most extensive, active lesions. Pattern IV, with only a yeast antigen reacting, is found in patients with minimally active lesions. There were no cases with only the HM, B or HM plus B antigens reacting.

Two thirds of these 426 patients are classified in patterns I and II that correlate with extensive, active disease. Note that both the yeast and mycelial *H. capsulatum* antigens are reactive in these patterns that correlate with extensive, active disease. The *B. dermatitidis* antigen reacts with sera taken during the acute stages when infiltrates are present, with or without the presence of cavities. The extent of parenchymal lung involvement appears to determine the presence and persistence of antibodies to this cross-reacting fungal antigen.

The HA test has been mentioned only briefly up to this point. The data in Table 43-II show that sixteen patients (3.8%) were seronegative when tested with the Y-GW, Y-VC and HM antigens. There were, however, eight of those seronegative patients in whom the HA was the only positive test. There were 12 of the 426 patients from whom sera were positive first with the HA test, and only the later sera were positive with the *H. capsulatum* CF tests. In 4 of these 12 patients the only positive sputum cultures were obtained during the time the HA test was positive; sputum cultures were negative when the CF tests became positive.

Also from Table 43-II the sensitivity of the different antigens can be calculated. Yeast antigens, either the GW, VC, or both, reacted with sera from 410 or 96.8 percent of the 426 cases. The HM antigen reacted with sera from 285 or 66.9 percent of the 426 patients. There were a large number of serum reactors with the *B. dermatitidis.*

Both of the yeast antigens reacted with sera from 329 (77.2%) of the cases and sera from 68 (16%) reacted only with the GW antigen. There were 13 cases (4%) with sera reacting only with the VC antigen; 10 of these patients were from hospitals outside of Tennessee. This reaction of the VC antigen with sera from outside patients has been one of the unusual but unanswered findings in this study.

It must be remembered that multiple sera were tested from most patients and that the serum pattern of a patient was determined by the serum reacting with the most antigens. Thus, if this series had included only patients with minimal lesions, sensitivity of the HM antigen would have been much less than the 66.9% given. The sensitivity of any of these antigens is correlated with the type and stage(s) of the disease process.

Seropositive Suspected Cases of Histoplasmosis

The 9,419 patients with positive *H. capsulatum* serologic tests were accumulated during the past thirteen years from many different but mostly Veterans Administration Hospitals. The list of states in which these patients were treated, and the number of patients from each are as follows: Tennessee, 3,872; Texas, 807; Ohio, 478; New York, 467; California, 421; Arkansas, 390; Mississippi, 365; North Carolina, 303; Missouri, 289; Illinois, 260; Minnesota, 256; Kentucky, 240; Michigan, 234; Wisconsin, 116; Oklahoma, 113; Kansas, Virginia, each, 97; Louisiana, 93; Nebraska, 63; Maryland, 62; West Virginia, 59; Washington, District of Columbia, 52; Georgia, 49; Florida, 40; Iowa, 39; South Carolina, 32; Indiana, 30; Massachusetts, Pennsylvania, each, 14; Alabama, New Mexico, each, 11; Washington, 10; Arizona, 8; Colorado, Delaware, each, 7; Nevada, New Jersey, each, 5; Maine, New Hampshire, Wyoming, each 1. Care must be used in interpreting these data because the figures presented do not by any means represent a true statistical incidence of the infection in the various areas given. The distribution is as expected, with the greatest concentration of cases in the central states, and sporadic areas occurring over most of the United States. It seems reasonable to assume that those 9,419 patients harbored *H. capsulatum* at the time of seropositivity, and that some of those, 9,419 seropositive patients (especially those 2,015 in patterns I and II) had clinically active histoplasmosis at the time of testing.

Table 43-II shows the serologic patterns of the culturally proven cases of histoplasmosis, and Table 43-III shows the same serologic patterns of the 9,419 seropositive, suspected cases of histoplasmosis. Approximately 2,000 (21.4%) of the 9,419 seropositive patients fall into patterns I and II. But,

TABLE 43-III

Serologic Patterns of the 9,419 Suspected Cases of Histoplasmosis

Serologic Patterns	Patients with Sera Reacting		
	Number	Percent	
I. Y+HM+B	402	4.3 ⎫	21.4
II. Y+HM	1613	17.1 ⎭	
III. Y +B	551	5.8 ⎫	78.6
IV. Y	6853	72.8 ⎭	
Total	9419	100.0	

Y = Either GW or VC yeast antigen.

two thirds of the 426 culturally proven patients fall into these same two serologic patterns. This difference is easily explained. Patterns I and II classify those patients with sera reacting with both *H. capsulatum* yeast and mycelial antigens. In chronic pulmonary histoplasmosis positive cultures are more often obtained at the time when antibodies to both yeast and mycelial antigens are present. For the same reasons it is not surprising to find the larger proportion of the seropositive patients, 78.6 percent of the 9,419 patients, with serologic patterns having only the *H. capsulatum* yeast or the yeast plus the *B. dermatitidis* antigens reacting. Patients with these serologic patterns usually have minimal lesions and the isolation of *H. capsulatum* from them is much more infrequent.

Culturally Proven Histoplasmosis Patients from the Memphis Veterans Administration Hospital

In this section more detailed data from the 141 proven histoplasmosis cases treated in this hospital are discussed. All of these patients were hospitalized for one or more periods. When not hospitalized, they were followed regularly as outpatients. They were studied with serologic, mycologic, and clinical studies for varying periods: 21 patients, less than one year; 76 patients, one to four years; 34 patients, five to nine years; 10 patients, more than ten years. No attempt is made in this report to classify these or any of the patients in this study into disease types. In Table 43-IV the data relating to clinical findings were taken from the patients' clinical records as recorded by the physicians.

There were 4,317 sera tested from these 141 patients (Table 43-I). Only 2 patients had single sera and 115 (81.6%) had more than ten sera tested. The serologic patterns are no different than those of the entire group of 426 patients shown in Table 43-II. There were 6 of our 141 patients who were seronegative, but 3 of these 6 had positive HA tests.

There were approximately 4,300 specimens, mostly sputa, cultured from these patients. It might be of interest that in our Microbiology Laboratory positive *H. capsulatum* cultures are obtained from approximately 13 percent of our seropositive patients. We believe that this is a relatively high proportion of positive cultures, and that it results from both a capable microbiology staff and an energetic one. It certainly must be emphasized and emphasized again that repeated specimens for culture are an absolute must.

Individiual Patient Profiles

Table 43-IV includes the individual profiles of nine patients in this hospital. Serologic, mycologic, and clinical data are presented to show the correlations discussed earlier with some of the data.

Patient No. 1. (L. W.) is presented for the following points: clinical relapse, serologic relapse, treatment by desensitization with histoplasmin, difficulty of obtaining positive sputum cultures. The Y-GW antigen was positive with medium titers during the first hospital admission, when bilateral infiltrates were present; the titer decreases were parallel with the x-ray clearing and other clinical symptoms. The Y-GW antigen remained negative throughout the asymptomatic period (to 1959) even though old fibrocalcific infiltrates were present. The Y-GW antigen became positive again with the clinical relapse in October 1959; there was rapid clearing of the lung lesions and clinical symptoms with amphotericin B treatment, and the Y-GW titer decrease was again parallel. The Y-VC antigen was temporarily positive but without relation to disease process. The HM antigen was positive with the first two sera when acute infiltrates were present. Note particularly the two (only) positive sputa. Desensitization with histoplasmin did not increase or prolong the serum titers.

Patient No. 2. (D. McC.) gives another example of clinical, mycologic, and serologic relapse. The infiltrates demonstrated on the first hospital admission in 1959 probably represented an endogenous spread from the questionably active lesion noted seventeen years previously; if so, it shows that *H. capsulatum* organisms can survive in some form for long periods causing little tissue damage and apparently no antigenic stimulus, but under suitable conditions are capable of reactivation and restoration of at least some of their biologic properties.

Only the Y-GW antigen was positive, and in low titer, during the first admission, when minimal infiltrates were present without cavities; the skin test applied on June 8 could have stimulated this minimal titer, but note that sputa were already positive. With the clinical and mycologic relapses in April, 1966, all of the serologic tests except the *B. dermatitidis* CF were positive; they remained positive for more than two years, during which only moderate clinical improvement was achieved.

Patient No. 3. (P. McG.) demonstrates the high serum titers with multiple antigens when multiple cavities are superimposed with infiltrates. With

TABLE 43-IV

Individual Patient Profiles

Date		Serologic Tests					*H. capsulatum* Cultures	Remarks
		Y-GW	Y-VC	HM	B	HA		
1955	May 23	16		8	—		2S−, 3G−	Patient No. 1. L. W.
	June 6	64		16	—		2S−	
	Aug. 11	32		—	—		1S−	Treated in tuberculosis sanatorium
	Sept. 28	16		—	—		1S−	1953, 1954; cultures for AFB were
	Oct., Nov.	16		—	—		1S−	negative. First admission this VA
	Dec. 6, 14	8		—	—			Hospital, May 1955: infiltrates
1956	Jan. 17	8		—	—			both lungs; no cavities; clinical
	Feb.–Dec. (4 Sera)	—		—	—		4S−	diagnosis histoplasmosis; histo-
								plasmin desensitization Sept. 23–
1957	June 12	—	—	—	—			Dec. 15, 1955; discharged asymp-
1958	Mar. 25	—	—	—	—	—	1S−	tomatic, some lung clearing. 1957–
1959	Oct. 22	8	—	—	—	—	2S+	1958: asymptomatic, old fibrocal-
	29	16	—	—	8	—	1S−	cific infiltrate. Hospital readmis-
	Nov.–Dec. (8 Sera)	64	16	—	—	32		sion Oct. 21, 1959: new infiltrates,
								multiple cavities L lung, same old
1960	Jan.–May	16	—	—	—	32	9S−	infiltrate R lung, asymptomatic
	Aug. 11	—	—	—	—	8	1S−	and no cavities by Feb. 1960. Part-
	Nov. 15	—	—	—	—	—		time work May–Nov. 1960. Apr.
1961	Feb.–Nov. (4 Sera)	—	—	—	—	32	3S−	1961, works regularly; same old
								fibrocalcific infiltrate. 1966–1969:
1962	Apr., Nov.	—	—	—	—	16	1S−	infiltration LUL unchanged, no
1963	Apr.	—	—	—	—	—	1S−	evidence of cavities; feels well,
1964	Apr.	—	—	—	—	—	1S−	works regularly.
1965	Apr. 15	—	16	—	—	—	1S−	
	Oct. 7	—	—	—	—	—	1S−	ST+Oct. 23, 1959.
	Nov. 4	—	16	—	—	—		
1966	Jan. 11	—	—	—	—	—	1S−	Amphotericin B: Nov. 1959–Feb.
	June 28	8	—	—	—	—		1960.
1967	Oct. 10	—	—	—	—	—	1S−	
1968	Mar. 3	—	—	—	—	8	1S−	
	59 Sera Tested							
1959	June 5						1S+	Patient No. 2. D. McC.
	9						1S+	
	12	—	—	—	—	—	1S−	Calcified nodular densities RUL of
	18	8	—	—	—	—	2S−	questionable activity on 1942 rou-
	30	16	—	—	—	—	1S−	tine x-ray. First hospital admis-
	July 6	—	—	—	—	—	1S+	sion June 3, 1959: infiltrate RUL,
	Aug.							no cavities; discharged Nov. 1959,
1965	June (27 Sera)	—	—	—	—	—	25S−	improved. Outpatient follow-up:
								no change pulmonary condition.
1966	Apr. 26	16	64	32	—	8	2S+	Hospital readmission Apr. 26,
	May 9	8	64	32	—	16	3S+	1966: new infiltrate LUL with
	16	—	32	16	—	16	4S−	cavity; same old infiltrate RUL.
	June 5	16	64	64	8	8	1S−	Discharged Sept. 1966: some im-
	16	8	64	32	—	—	1S−	provement; return to usual activ-
	July–Nov. (6 Sera)	8	64	32	—	8	7S−	ities. 1967–1968: works little,
								chronic complaints, no x-ray
1967	May	—	8	16	—	—		change.
	Oct.	16	8	16	—	—	1S−	
1968	July	16	16	16	—	—	3S−	ST+June 8, 1959.
	Dec.						3S−	
	45 Sera Tested							Amphotericin B: July 6–Nov. 2, 1959; May 5–Aug. 26, 1966.

S=sputum; G=gastric; BW=bronchial washing; ST=skin test; L=left; R=right; LUL=left upper lobe; RUL=right upper lobe; +=positive; −=negative.

TABLE 43-IV (*Continued*)

Individual Patient Profiles

Date	Serologic Tests					H. capsulatum Cultures	Remarks
	Y-GW	Y-VC	HM	B	HA		
1964 Nov.	−	−	−	−	−	1S−	Patient No. 3. P. McG.
1965 Sept.	−	−	−	−	−	3S−	
Nov.	−	−	−	−	−	2S−	First hospitalization: Nov. 15–20, 1964; x-ray negative. Second hospitalization: Sept. 15–Nov. 10, 1965; RUL emphysematous bullae. Third hospitalization: May 23–July 29, 1966; infiltrates and multiple small cavities RUL, mottled appearance L lung, partial resolution at discharge. Fourth hospitalization: Oct. 10, 1960–Feb. 18, 1969; new infiltrates LUL, same infiltrates RUL; no change by discharge.
1966 May 24	512	256	64	32	128		
June 1	128	128	32	16	128	2S+	
13	128	64	32	16	64	2S+	
20	128	64	32	8	64	3S+	
July–Sept.	128	64	16	8	64	8S−	
Nov. 1	64	32	16	8	128	3S−	
1967 Feb. 28	−	8	−	−	32	1S−	
Apr. 25	64	16	−	−	64		
June 13	−	8	−	−	16	1S−	
Nov. 21						1S−	
1968 Apr. 23						1S−	
Oct. 7	128	64	−	−	−	1S+	
10	64	64	−	−	−	1S+	
14	128	64	64	−	−	2S+	ST+June 3, 1966.
26	128	32	64	−	−	3S+	
Nov., Dec.	128	32	64	−	−	1S+, 10S−	Amphotericin B: June 19–July 12,
1969 Jan.	128	64	32	−	−	10S−	1966; Nov. 4, 1968–Feb. 7, 1969.
June	32	8	8				
31 Sera Tested							
1955 Dec. 14	−	−	−	−	−	3S−	Patient No. 4. A. D.
1956 Feb. 28						Lung−	
1958 July 28	−		−	−	−	3S−	Several hospitalizations between 1946 and 1959 for tuberculosis; sputum cultures positive for AFB; antituberculosis drugs; discharged Mar. 1960, and resumed farming. Readmission Sept. 1961: chronic pulmonary histoplasmosis; multiple cavities with superimposed infiltrates L lung only. Clinically well Aug. 1965–1967. Lung tissue of Feb. 1956, re-examined Nov. 1961, with special stains: negative histologically for *H. capsulatum*.
1959 Aug. 28	−	−	−	−	−	3S−	
1961 Sept. 27	32	−	−	−	64		
Oct. 6	128	32	−	8	64	5S+	
20	64	64	16	−	64		
Nov. 9	128	64	64	8	128		
Dec. 8	128	128	64	32	64		
1962 Jan. 12	128	128	32	8	32		
Aug. 7	64	64	16	32	64		
Nov. 8	32	16	−	64	64	20S−	
1963 Jan., Nov. (3 Sera)	32	16	−	8	16		
1964 May, Nov.	32	8	16	8	16		
1965 Jan., Aug.	32	16	−	−	64		Histoplasmin ST's:
1966 Aug.	32	−	−	8	32		Nov. 1951, negative.
1967 Aug.	32	−	−	8	32		Dec. 1955, positive.
35 Sera Tested							Sept. 1959, positive.
							Amphotericin B: Nov. 8, 1961–Mar. 30, 1962.
1961 Feb. 20–23						3S+	Patient No. 5. L. A.
Mar. 3	−	−	−	−	64	1S+	
9	−	−	−	−	32	1S+	Employed at airport; exposure to propeller drafts; hometown park known as "Home of Birds."
16	−	−	−	−	128	1S+	
23	−	−	−	−	32		

S = sputum; G = gastric; BW = bronchial washing; ST = skin test; L = left; R = right; LUL = left upper lobe; RUL = right upper lobe; + = positive; − = negative.

TABLE 43-IV (Continued)

Individual Patient Profiles

Date	Serologic Tests					H. capsulatum Cultures	Remarks
	Y-GW	Y-VC	HM	B	HA		
30	8	—	—	—	32		Hospital admission Feb. 17, 1961: multiple cavities LUL, diffuse infiltrates bilaterally; some lung clearing by May 1961.
31	8	—	—	—	16		
Apr. Dec. (11 Sera)	16	—	—	—	16	16S—	
1962 Mar. 13	16	—	—	—	8		Expired Mar. 15, 1963; autopsy cultures negative for *H. capsulatum*; diagnosis: pulmonary fibrosis, emphysema, inactive histoplasmosis.
June 13	8	—	—	—	—		
Nov. 28	—	—	—	—	—		
	20 Sera Tested						ST+Feb. 23, 1961.
							Amphotericin B: Mar. 13–July 21, 1961; sulfonamide, Mar. 1961.
1958 July 1	512	32	32	128	128	1S+, 4S—	Patient No. 6. W. C.
Aug. (5 Sera)	256	32	16	64	64	1S+, 3S—	Visited corn crib two weeks before symptoms. Acute, "flu-like" symptoms four weeks before hospital admission on June 27, 1958. Acute disease, miliary infiltrates throughout both lungs; rapid symptomatic improvement; no changes of lung lesions on discharge Sept. 24, 1958. Worked regularly 1959–1961. Granular infiltrates still present Sept. 1960, but clear by Aug. 1961. Lungs clear, asymptomatic and working regularly 1961–1969.
Sept. (3 Sera)	256	8	8	32	32	1S—	
Nov.	256	—	—	32	8	1S—	
1959 Feb.–Nov. (5 Sera)	256	—	—	32	—	3S—	
1963 Feb., Aug. (2 Sera)	128	—	—	—	16	3S—	
1964 Feb.	64	—	—	—	—		
Aug.	256	32	—	—	—	5S—	
1965 (10 Sera)	128	32	8	—	—		
1969	64	8	—	—	—		
	37 Sera Tested						ST+June 27, 1959.
							Amphotericin B: Aug. 4–Sept. 19, 1958.
1959 Feb. 24	—	—	—	—	8		Patient No. 7. R. H.
Mar.						3S+, 4S—	
Apr. 13	—	—	—	—	8		Chronically ill one year; May 1959: acute cystic emphysema, no infiltrates. Hospital admission Feb. 16, 1959: Infiltrates bilaterally; no cavities.
17	32	—	—	—	16		
28	—	—	—	—	16		
May 7	—	—	—	—	8		
May 21	—	—	—	—	8	1S—	Asymptomatic and lungs almost clear by July 1959.
July 2	—	—	—	—	8		
29	—	—	—	—	16		
Oct. 2	—	—	—	—	—		Amphotericin B: May 5–July 31, 1959.
	12 Sera Tested						
1958 Mar. 15	—	—	—	—	64		Patient No. 8. E. N.
Apr. 1						1S+	
3–11						4S—	"Flu" one week before hospital ad-

S=sputum; G=gastric; BW=bronchial washing; ST=skin test; L=left; R=right; LUL=left upper lobe; RUL=right upper lobe; +=positive; —=negative.

TABLE 43-IV (*Continued*)

Individual Patient Profiles

Date	Serologic Tests					H. capsulatum Cultures	Remarks
	Y-GW	Y-VC	HM	B	HA		
14	128	—	16	—	128	1BW+	mission of Mar. 15, 1968; extensive infiltrates and multiple cavities bilaterally. Marked improvement lung lesions by June 1958; by Sept. 1958, only residuals.
June 24	16	—	—	—	32	1S—	
Aug. 29	—	—	—	—	8		
1959 Jan. 10	—	—	—	8	—	1S—	
30	—	—	—	—	—		
1960 Feb. 5	—	—	—	—	—	1S—	
7 Sera Tested							Amphotericin B: May 6–Aug. 28, 1958.
1959 Aug. 26	32	—	—	—	—		Patient No. 9. J. N.
28	16	—	—	—	8		1954 hospitalization for diabetes; chest x-ray "normal." 1956 hospitalization for diabetes; chest x-ray: increased density L lung, considered inactive; rest of lungs clear. Third hospitalization Aug. 13–Dec. 18, 1959: same "old" lesion L; multiple cavities with infiltrates RUL. Lobectomy, RUL Oct. 12, 1959. By Oct. 27 considerable clearing on R, L lung clear. On discharge Dec. 18, asymptomatic and chest clear. Outpatient follow-up to 1969: asymptomatic, chest clear.
Sept. 3, 4						2S—	
9						2BW—	
18	32	—	—	—	8		
Oct. 12						Lung 2+	
Oct. 28, 29						2S—	
Nov. 16	—	—	—	—	16	1S—	
1960 June 10	—	—	—	—	32	1S—	
1962 Jan.	—	—	—	—	16	2S—	
(3 Sera)							
Dec. 19	—	—	—	—	32	2S—	
1963 Jan. 7	—	—	—	—	64	3S—	
1966 June 7	—	—	—	—	8		
1969 Feb. 10	—	—	—	—	—	1S—	
12 Sera Tested							ST's: Aug. 31, 1959, negative. Sept. 16, 1959, positive. Oct. 28, 1959, positive.

S = sputum; G = gastric; BW = bronchial washing; ST = skin test; L = left; R = right; LUL = left upper lobe; RUL = right upper lobe; + = positive; — = negative.

resolution of the lung lesions and clinical symptoms in late 1966 and 1967, the titers decreased, some to negative. High serum titers to multiple antigens were obtained again with the clinical and mycologic relapse. Positive sputum cultures tended to parallel the HM titers.

Patient No. 4. (A. D.) had culturally proven tuberculosis, recovered, and then developed histoplasmosis in 1961. Sputum cultures and a histologic section of lung were negative for *H. capsulatum* at the time tuberculosis was active (1958-1961). High serum titers to all antigens correlated with the multiple cavities and superimposed infiltrates. The patient was said to be clinically well by 1965, but low serum titers with some antigens remained.

Patient No. 5 (L. A.) is of interest for the possible source of the *H. capsulatum* infection—exposure to propeller drafts at an airport located near a "Home of Birds." Serologically, the important finding is the positive HA tests during the only time that sputum cultures were positive. The Y-GW antigen became positive later and only in low titers. The negative HM CF test may be the result of the early administration of amphotericin B and early clearing of the pulmonary lesion (May 1961). It is possible that the skin test (Feb 23) stimulated the Y-GW antibodies first demonstrated approximately one month later. If so, the skin test did not stimulate HM antibodies. In this respect note that the positive sputa were obtained before the Y-GW antibodies were demonstrated.

Patient No. 6. (W. C.) became acutely ill two weeks after visiting a corn crib, presumably the specific source of his *H. capsulatum* infection, and the first serum was taken six weeks later. There was rapid symptomatic improvement and some resolution of the miliary lesions. During the early acute state with extensive lung involvement there were high titers with all antigens. The Y-VC was "spotty." The HM decreased rapidly to negative. Note the positive *B. dermatitidis* CF continuing for some time. Note, too, that the Y-GW antibodies have persisted for the longest time, eleven years to the last test date. It is usually difficult to obtain positive cultures in patients with acute miliary lesions. There were only two positive sputa obtained from this patient.

Patient No. 7. (R. H.) had acute pulmonary infiltrates without cavities and had rapid x-ray and symptomatic improvement. The single serum with Y-GW antibodies is no doubt due to the rapid clinical improvement. This patient also had only the positive HA test when the positive sputa were obtained. The HA test remained positive for six months but was negative by the ninth month.

Patient No. 8. (E. N.) shows the temporary presence of antibodies in acute pulmonary disease with rapid and marked regression of the disease. There were only two positive cultures. The HA test was again the first positive test in this patient with acute disease. There were only two positive Y-GW sera and one positive HM serum.

Patient No. 9. (J. N.) shows the prompt decrease to negative in Y-GW antibodies following surgery. The active lesion was removed. The old lesion in the left lung may have been responsible for the continuing positive HA test. Note that many sputa were cultured but that *H. capsulatum* were isolated only from the surgically removed lung tissue.

In histoplasmosis, as in other infectious diseases, an academic diagnosis demands the isolation and identification of the causative organism. But in many diseases this is either not possible or not practical. In the present report data is given to support the use of serologic tests with *H. capsulatum* antigens in determining both the diagnosis and prognosis in this fungus disease.

References

Campbell, C.C. and Saslaw, S. (1949). Use of yeast-phase antigens in a complement fixation test for histoplasmosis. *Public Health Rep.*, 64:551-560.

Campbell, C.C. (1971). History of the development of serologic tests for histoplasmosis. Histoplasmosis. Proceedings of the Second National Conference. Pp. 341-357. Charles C Thomas, Fort Lauderdale, Fla.

Emmons, C.W., Olson, B.J. and Eldridge, W.W. (1945). Studies of the role of fungi in pulmonary disease. I. Cross reactions of histoplasmin. *Public Health Rep.*, 60:1383-1394.

Hill, G.B. and Campbell, C.C. (1956). A further evaluation of histoplasmin and yeast phase antigen of *Histoplasma capsulatum* in the complement fixation test. *J. Lab. Clin. Med.*, 48:255-263.

Laboratory Branch Task Force (1965). Part I. Laboratory branch complement fixation method. *Public Health Rep.*, 74:1-30.

McDearman, S.C. (1962). A modified histoplasmin in the hemagglutination test for histoplasmosis. *Amer. J. Med. Tech.*, 28:146-160.

Martin, D.S. (1935). Complement fixation in blastomycosis. *J. Infect. Dis.*, 57:291-295.

Smith, C.E., Whiting, E.G., Baker, E.E., Rosenberger, H.G., Beard, R.R. and Saito, M.T. (1948). The use of coccidioidin. *Amer. Rev. Tuberc.*, 57:330-360.

Veterans Administration-Armed Forces Cooperative Study on Histoplasmosis. (1961). I. Frequency of histoplasmosis among adult hospitalized males. *Amer. Rev. Resp. Dis.*, 84:663-668.

Veterans Administration-Armed Forces Cooperative Study on Histoplasmosis. (1964). II. Chronic pulmonary histoplasmosis treated with and without Amphotericin-B. *Amer. Rev. Resp. Dis.*, 89:641-650.

Veterans Administration-Armed Forces Cooperative Study on Histoplasmosis. (1968). III. Chronic pulmonary histoplasmosis treated with Amphotericin-B alone and with Amphotericin-B and Triple Sulfonamide. *Amer. Rev. Resp. Dis.*, 97:96-102.

Chapter 44

Cellular Immunologic Studies
in Histoplasmosis

CHARLES H. KIRKPATRICK, JOHN W. CHANDLER, JR., TERRILL K. SMITH,
AND W. MARCUS NEWBERRY, JR.

ABSTRACT

Lymphocytes from patients with various clinical forms of histoplasmosis were studied for their capacity to respond to stimulation with histoplasmin *in vitro*. Subjects with positive cutaneous tests and no history of clinical infection and patients recovered from mild infections showed marked responses to antigenic stimulation, while patients recovered from chronic or severe acute infections were less reactive. In some cases this impairment may have been related to antibodies in the serum.

It is postulated that the decreased responses are due to a defect in interaction of the antigen with receptor sites on the lymphocyte surface, and this defect is related to the magnitude of antigenic exposure at the time of infection.

WHEN lymphoid cells from sensitized subjects are exposed to antigens *in vitro*, a fraction of the cell population is induced to undergo morphologic and biochemical changes. These events are presumably triggered by interaction between the antigenic determinants and receptor sites on the cell surfaces. The nature of these receptors is essentially unknown, although they have qualitative characteristics analogous to antibody molecules. Recently Paul, Siskind and Benacerraf (1968) reported that the magnitude of the antigen-induced secondary responses *in vitro* was related to the dose of the primary immunization, an observation suggesting quantitative properties of the receptors.

The report describes studies of antigen-induced biochemical changes in peripheral blood lymphocytes from patients with various forms of histoplasmosis. The amount of DNA synthesized by the cells was found to be related to the type and severity of the clinical infection, and in some cases the responses were also influenced by serum antibodies. Certain aspects of this investigation have been described elsewhere (Newberry, Chandler, Chin and Kirkpatrick, 1968).

NOTE. These studies were supported in part by USPHS Clinical Research Center Grant FR-67 and Program Project Grant GM-15756.

371

Materials and Methods

Clinical Material

Healthy volunteers with positive or negative histoplasmin skin tests were selected from employees of the University of Kansas Medical Center or the National Communicable Disease Center Kansas City Field Station. None of the subjects had a history suggesting clinical infection with *Histoplasma capsulatum* or a positive serological test for yeast or mycelial phase antigens. The subjects with negative skin tests were retested at the conclusion of the study to determine any change in cutaneous reactivity. None of the participants had any other disorder known to alter the immune response.

Clinical features of the patients with acute or of chronic histoplasmosis are summarized in Table 44-I. The severity of the infections in patients with acute histoplasmosis is varied greatly; however, all patients recovered spontaneously. Sera from these patients usually contained complement-fixing antibodies. The diagnosis of chronic histoplasmosis had been confirmed by culture in each case, and all but one patient had cavitary pulmonary disease. Each of these patients had been treated with amphotericin B and was culturally negative at the time of study. All patients with clinical histoplasmosis had positive histoplasmin skin tests.

TABLE 44-I

Clinical and Serological Features of Patients with Chronic Histoplasmosis

Case No.	Extent of Illness	Years Since Diagnosis	Reciprocal of CF Titer	
Acute			H	Y
1	mild	1	16	16
2	mild	2	8	64
3	mild	1.5	8	4
4	mild	11	0	0
5	mild	1	0	32
6	mild	10	0	0
7	mild	5	0	8
8	severe	0.5	8	256
9	severe	1	64	4
10	severe	0.25	8	128
11	severe	2	0	16
12	severe	1	0	8
13	severe	2	0	128
Chronic				
14	mucocutaneous	0.5	0	0
15	pulmonary	7	0	0
16	pulmonary	10	0	0
17	pulmonary	4	16	32
18	pulmonary	5	8	32
19	pulmonary	6	0	0
20	pulmonary	8	0	8

H=mycelial phase,   Y=yeast phase.

Antigens

The histoplasmin (Lots HKC-5 and HKC-43) was obtained from the Kansas City Field Station, NCDC. The antigens had been subjected to potency testing in sensitized animals and were diluted 1:500 for cutaneous testing in humans. To prepare the antigen for use in lymphocyte cultures, it was exhaustively dialyzed against phosphate-buffered saline (PBS) to remove merthiolate, and sterilized by millipore filtration. The nitrogen content, determined by the Kjeldahl method (Kleiner and Orten, 1966), was 2140µg/ml for HKC-5 and 94 µg/ml for HKC-43.

For studies of the effects of antigen concentration on lymphocyte responses, histoplasmin (Lot HKC-43) was dialyzed against phosphate-buffered saline, then against PBS containing 20% polyvinyl pyrrolidone until the volume was reduced by 90 percent. The nitrogen content was determined on the concentrate, and appropriate dilutions were made.

Serological Tests

Sera from all subjects were studied for complement-fixing antibodies (Mayer, Osler, Bier and Heidelberger, 1946) against the yeast (Y) or mycelial (H) phase antigens of *H. capsulatum*.

Lymphocyte Cultures

Blood was collected into heparinized syringes and the leukocytes were separated by differential centrifugation and sedimentation (Kirkpatrick and Ruth, 1966). A lymphocyte-rich suspension was obtained by incubating the cell suspensions in prescription bottles for 30 minutes at 37°C. The cells were suspended in Eagle's minimal essential medium supplemented with 20% inactivated autologous and homologous serum, 1-glutamine, penicillin, and streptomycin at a concentration of 1×10^6 lymphocytes per milliliter. In addition to antigen-stimulated cultures, controls containing no additives or 0.1 ml of phytohemagglutinin-M (Difco) that had been diluted to 10 ml were run. The cultures were incubated at 37°C in an atmosphere of 5% CO_2-95% O_2 for five days. Twenty-four hours before harvesting tritiated thymidine (6.7 C/mmol), 1µCi/p ml, was added to each culture. The cells were collected by centrifugation, washed with buffered saline, and the proteins were precipitated with cold trichloracetic acid (TCA). The TCA was extracted with cold methanol, and the pellet digested with Hyamine 10-X overnight at room temperature. An aliquot of the digest was counted in a liquid scintillation spectrometer.

The results were expressed as the ratio E/C, the mean dpm per million lymphocytes in stimulated cultures to the mean dpm per million lymphocytes in control cultures.

Results

Serological Studies

The complement-fixing activity against yeast and mycelial phase antigens was determined on sera collected at the time of the lymphocyte cultures. All but two of the members of the acute histoplasmosis group had CF antibodies, while only three of the eight subjects with chronic histoplasmosis had positive tests (Table 44-I).

DNA Synthesis in Lymphocyte Cultures

Preliminary studies with HKC-5 demonstrated that maximal responses in DNA synthesis were observed when cultures were stimulated with antigen containing 4.3μg of nitrogen and labeled at 96 hours. All experiments with HKC-5 were conducted under these conditions. Phytohemagglutinin-stimulated cultures were processed in the same manner, although the peak responses occurred at 72 hours.

Every subject was not available for all phases of this investigation, and the studies with HKC-5 were conducted with five members of each clinical category. Addition of histoplasmin to lymphocytes from healthy skin test positive subjects produced marked increases in DNA synthesis (Table 44-II). In contrast, only small increases in DNA synthesis (mean E/C, 4.9) were observed with cells from skin test negative people. The patients who had recovered from acute histoplasmosis could be divided into two groups. Cases 1 through 3 had mild infections and *in vitro* lymphocyte responses comparable to healthy skin test positive subjects. In contrast, cases 8 and 9 had more severe clinical illnesses and poor *in vitro* responses. The patients with chronic histoplasmosis (cases 14-18) also showed depressed responses with a mean E/C value of 18.7. Phytohemagglutinin produced similar increments of stimulation in all patients regardless of their clinical classification.

Role of Serum Factors

To elucidate the role of serum factors in the *in vitro* responses, experiments were done in which washed lymphocytes and sera from histoplasmosis patients were interchanged with washed cells and sera from skin test positive subjects in whom no CF antibodies were detectable. The results of this study are summarized in Table 44-III. In three cases the responses of cells from skin test positive subjects were depressed by blood group compatible serum from patients with clinical histoplasmosis (experiments 1 and 2). Cells from histoplasmosis patients showed greater responses to histoplasmin when cultured in serum from healthy skin test positive subjects, although in two studies (experiments 4 and 5) the increases in reactivity were small.

TABLE 44-II

Results of Stimulation of Lymphocytes With 4.3 µg/ml of Histoplasmin, HKC-5

Group	Case No.*	Lymphocyte Response (E/C)
Skin test negative	1	1.0
	2	2.3
	3	9.0
	4	7.8
	5	4.4
		mean = 4.9
Skin test positive	1	62.5
	2	66.7
	3	57.3
	4	120.5
	5	81.0
		mean = 77.6
Acute histoplasmosis	1	51.1
	2	51.8
	3	76.0
	8	5.8
	9	10.1
Chronic histoplasmosis	14	18.4
	15	22.6
	16	24.0
	17	5.6
	18	22.7
		mean = 18.7

* Case numbers for histiplasmosis patients correspond to those of Table 44-I.

TABLE 44-III

Effects of Serum From Patients with Histoplasmosis and Healthy Skin Reactive (STP) Subjects on Lymphocyte Responses to HKC-5

Expt. No.	Lymphocytes	Serum	E/C	Increment
1	STP	Autologous	57.3	0
	STP	Acute-8	80.1	+22.8
	STP	Acute-9	13.0	−44.3
2	STP	Autologous	66.7	0
	STP	Chronic-18	25.4	−41.3
	STP	Acute-9	21.4	−45.3
3	Chronic-16	Autologous	24.0	0
	Chronic-16	STP	161.5	+137.5
4	Chronic-17	Autologous	5.6	0
	Chronic-17	STP	11.0	+5.4
5	Acute-9	Autologous	10.1	0
	Acute-9	STP	27.8	+17.7

Donor and Case No.* — Thymidine Incorporation

* Case numbers correspond with Table 44-I.

Effects of Antigen Concentration

The effects of a wide range of antigen doses on lymphocyte DNA synthesis was studied with HKC-43. This antigen was somewhat less active *in vitro* than HKC-5. The highest concentrations of antigen employed were between 163μg and 200 μg of nitrogen, and in many experiments this dose produced little or no stimulation and may have been cytotoxic. Cells from healthy skin test positive individuals usually showed maximal stimulation with an antigen dose containing 10μg of nitrogen per milliliter (Figure 44-1). Although it is not shown in the figure, cells from skin test negative subjects had E/C values of 1.0 or less with all concentrations of this antigen.

Cells from most patients with severe acute or chronic histoplasmosis responded poorly to all doses of histoplasmin and were qualitatively similar to results with HKC-5.

The largest increments of stimulation were observed in the patients who had recovered from mild acute infections. Their responses were generally greater at every concentration of antigen studied with the exception of the 163μg to 200μg level. Of particular interest were the large responses to the 1.0μg and 0.1μg doses which produced weak responses in the cells of most patients from other categories.

A statistical comparison of the results is shown in Table 44-IV.

Discussion

Exposure of higher animals to antigenic substances initiates a series of biological reactions which culminates in synthesis of new proteins with antibody activity or differentiation of a population of lymphoid cells that participate in delayed hypersensitivity. In man the proliferative responses observed when lymphocytes from sensitized subjects are challenged with antigen *in vitro* bear close correlation to delayed cutaneous hypersensitivity and have been useful in studying clinical syndromes with associated immunological abnormalities.

The relative roles of humoral and cellular immune mechanisms in host resistance to organisms such as fungi are poorly understood. Recently it has been postulated that the syndrome of chronic mucocutaneous moniliasis is related to failure of lymphocytes to elaborate mediators of delayed hypersensitivity (Chilgren, Meuwissen, Quie, Good and Hong, 1969; Kirkpatrick, Schimke and Chandler, 1970). Although proof of this hypothesis is lacking, it is supported by the observations of impaired delayed cutaneous reactivity and lymphocyte transformation in moniliasis patients in whom the serological responses were normal.

In this investigation, the immunologic consequences of exposure to *H. capsulatum* were studied. Incidental contact with the organism by residents

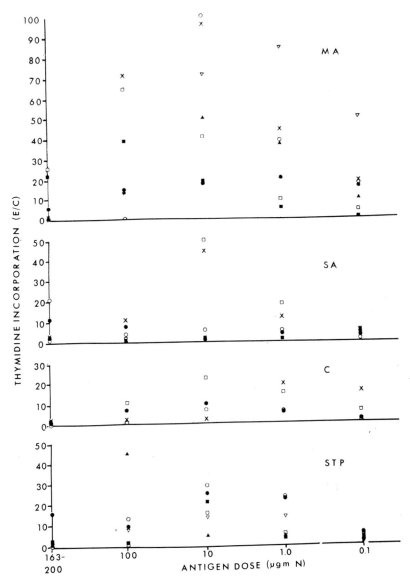

FIGURE 44-1. Thymidine incorporation by lymphoid cells following stimulation with HKC-43 histoplasmin. The peak response with the skin test positive subjects (STP) occurred with $10\mu g$ of antigen nitrogen. Chronic histoplasmosis patients (E) and those who have recovered from severe acute infections (SA) responded poorly to the antigen. In contrast, patients with mild acute histoplasmosis (MA) were exceptionally responsive to the antigen and in most cases responded to the lowest dose studied.

of an endemic area produces no clinical syndrome or serological response, but may be detected by cutaneous tests. In other cases the dose of infecting organisms is excessive and clinical infections occur. Mild forms of histoplasmosis are associated with development of delayed hypersensitivity and serological responses, and spontaneous recovery is the rule. When challenged *in*

TABLE 44-IV

Comparison of the Areas Circumscribed by the Dose-Response
Curves in Experiments Using HKC-43

Group	P
Mild acute histoplasmosis	
vs. healthy skin test positive	0.01>P>0.001
vs. severe acute histoplasmosis	0.02>P>0.01
vs. chronic histoplasmosis	0.05>P>0.02
Severe acute histoplasmosis	
vs. healthy skin test positive	P>0.40
vs. chronic histoplasmosis	P>0.70
Chronic histoplasmosis	
vs. healthy skin test positive	P>0.50

vitro, lymphocytes from healthy skin test positive subjects or patients re-covered from mild acute infections showed marked proliferative responses and DNA synthesis (Figure 44-1 and Table 44-II).

In contrast, the histoplasmin-induced responses by cells from patients with severe acute or chronic histoplasmosis were depressed. Although the mechanism of this impairment has not been defined, a role for serum anti-bodies was suggested by the serum-cell exchange experiments. Washed cells cultured in antibody-free serum showed increased responses and responsive cells were impaired when cultured in the presence of antisera. However, the degree of depression could not be correlated with antibody titer. Further-more, patients with chronic histoplasmosis had impaired responses in sera that contained no antibody activity.

An explanation for the depressed responses in patients chronic infections may derive from the experiments of Paul *et al.* (1968). It was observed that the antigen dose employed for primary immunization of guinea pigs influ-enced the affinity of the antibody synthesized and the dose of antigen re-quired to induce secondary proliferative responses *in vitro*. Animals primed with large doses of antigen produced low-affinity antibodies and required more antigen for the secondary *in vitro* responses. If the receptors on the cell surface are functionally similar to antibodies, more antigen would be required to accomplish the critical interaction required to stimulate DNA synthesis.

The factors that influence the severity of a clinical infection with *H. cap-sulatum* are only partially understood, but probably include coexisting dis-eases, drug therapy, and other poorly defined host factors. Certainly, it is not possible to make a direct association between the clinical form of the disease and the dose of infecting organisms. However, the results of these studies indicate that the type of disease does relate to the behavior of lym-phocytes when challenged with histoplasmin *in vitro*, and the results are compatible with a model employing high- and low-affinity cellular recep-tors.

Among the other alternatives, it is considered unlikely that the defect has a genetic basis because the lymphocytes respond to phytohemagglutinin, and washed cells cultured with serum from skin test positive subjects showed normal responses to histoplasmin. Furthermore, the impaired responses may reflect depletion of the cell population that can recognize and respond to the antigen. This phenomenon, an example of high dose tolerance (Dresser and Mitchison, 1968), would probably not adequately explain partial suppression that had apparently persisted for years.

Intact cutaneous reactivity in subjects with impaired lymphocyte function is readily explained in view of the current models of delayed hypersensitivity (David, 1968). Interaction of a sensitized lymphocyte with antigen stimulates release of a number of mediators that in turn produce the lesions of cellular hypersensitivity. Only a small number of the cells in the lesions are actually antigen-reactive cells, while most cells accumulate as a result of nonspecific factors (Feldman and Najarian, 1963).

The relationship of impaired lymphocyte responses to the clinical course of infection with *H. capsulatum* is unknown. It is possible that a modification of lymphocyte function induced by primary exposure to large doses of antigen impairs host resistance and predisposes the patient to disseminated or chronic infection.

References

Chilgren, R.A., Meuwissen, H.J., Quie, P.G., Good, R.A. and Hong, R. (1969). The celluar immune defect in chronic mucocutaneous moniliasis. *Lancet, 1*:1286-1288.

David, J.R. (1968). Macrophage migration. *Fed. Proc., 27*:6-12.

Dresser, D.W. and Mitchison, N.A. (1968). The mechanism of immunologic paralysis. In Dixon, J.F. and Kunkel, H.G. (Eds.). *Advances in Immunology*. New York, Academic Press, pp.129-181.

Feldman, J.D. and Najarian, J.S. (1963). Dynamics and quantitative analysis of passively transferred tuberculin hypersensitivity. *J. Immun., 91*:306-312.

Kirkpatrick, C. H. and Ruth W. E. (1966). Chronic pulmonary disease and immunologic deficiency. *Amer. J. Med., 41*:427-461.

Kirkpatrick, C.H., Schimke, R.N. and Chandler, J.W. Jr.: 1970. Chronic mucocutaneous moniliasis with impaired delayed hypersensitivity. *Clin. Exp. Immun. 6*:375-385.

Kleiner, I.S. and Orten, J.M. (1966). *Biochemistry*. St. Louis, C. V. Mosby, p. 136.

Mayer, M.M., Osler, A.G., Bier, O.G. and Heidelberger, M. (1946). The activating effect of magnesium and other cations on the hemolytic function of complement. *J. Exp. Med., 84*:535-548.

Newberry, M.W., Jr., Chandler, J.W., Jr., Chin, T.D.Y. and Kirkpatrick, C.H. (1968). Immunology of the mycoses. I. Depressed lymphocyte transformation in chronic histoplasmosis. *J. Immun. 100*:436-443.

Paul, W.E., Siskind, G.W. and Benacerraf, B. (1968). Specificity of cellular immune responses. *J. Exp. Med., 127*:25-42.

Chapter 45

Circulating Human Phagocytes and
Histoplasma capsulatum

PHILLIP HOLLAND

ABSTRACT

Ultrastructural observations of the sequence of intracellular events which occur following phagocytosis of *Histoplasma capsulatum* by motile human blood phagocytes is similar to those previously observed following bacterial-phagocyte interaction. These preliminary *in vitro* cultural results indicate that the circulating neutrophil and monocyte possess fungicidal capacity for *Histoplasma* and suggest that these cells are important human defense mechanisms against this pathogen. These results further suggest that in patients in whom quantitative or qualitative blood leucocyte defects exist, dissemination of fungal infection as well as bacterial sepsis may occur.

AS has long been known, systemic histoplasmosis is characterized by involvement of the reticuloendothelial system (Darling, 1906), and confirmation of the suspected presence of this infection may be obtained by identification of the yeast phase of *Histoplasma capsulatum* in blood and bone marrow mononuclear cells (Dodd and Tompkins, 1934). Numerous *in vivo* observations have emphasized the efficiency of the fixed and wandering bone marrow macrophage in phagocytizing this fungus (Christie, 1958; Holland and Holland, 1966). Recognition and study of the intracellular events involved in phagocytosis and kill of bacteria by blood polymorphonuclear leukocytes and monocytes has recently increased (Hirsch and Cohn, 1960; Hirsch, 1962; Zucker-Franklin and Hirsch, 1964; Holmes, Quie, Windhorst and Good, 1966; Rabinovitch, 1968; Karnovsky, 1968). Little attention, however, has been directed to the significance of these motile phagocytes as host defense mechanisms against blood-borne fungi.

In order to evaluate the cellular events following interaction of human blood neutrophils and monocytes with *Histoplasma* and the phagocytic capacity of each cell type, *in vitro* cultures were initiated and cellular pellets were examined by electron microscopy following 60-minute incubation.

Yeast phase *H. capsulatum* were obtained by subculturing the filamentous form to blood agar slants which were sealed after inoculation and incubated at 37°C for five to seven days. The fungi were removed from the slants, suspended in Hank's saline, and dispersed with the use of a vortex mixer. The suspension was then adjusted to give a final concentration of 1×10^7 yeast cells per milliliter.

Preparation of a suspension of polymorphonuclear leukocytes was performed following collection of venous blood from histoplasmin skin test negative normal adult subjects in 6% dextran solution containing heparin. Erythrocyte sedimentation was allowed at room temperature for 60 minutes and the leukocyte-rich supernate was harvested and mixed with an equal volume of Hank's saline. The cell suspension was centrifuged; the pellet obtained was subsequently washed twice and resuspended to give a final concentration of 1×10^7 leukocytes per milliliter. Pure suspensions of blood monocytes were obtained from the same subjects using the method of Bennett and Cohn (1966). The incubation mixture consisted of fungi and motile phagocyte in a ratio of 1:1, 10 percent fresh isologous serum and TC 199 media. The suspension was tumbled in a rotary incubator at 37°C for 60 minutes. Cellular pellets of the incubated suspension were obtained by centrifugation, fixed, thin sectioned, and examined with a Phillips electron microscope.

The electron microscopic observations of human polymorphonuclear leukocytes following ingestion of *H. capsulatum* shows striking morphologic variation, presumably dependent on the time after individual cell phagocytosis has occurred. Fine structure characterization of the yeast phase of *H. capsulatum* has been previously reported (Edwards, 1959). The wall of the fungi is relatively thick but does not contain a capsule as the name implies. An ovoid nucleus, primitive mitochondria, and osmophilic granules are present. In some polymorphonuclear leukocytes, numerous lysosomes were seen surrounding intact phagocytized fungi. In other polymorphonuclear leukocytes, the intracytoplasmic fungi were surrounded by a large digestive vacuole, and lysosomes were observed to empty into these membrane-bound structures. Many fungi enclosed in digestive vacuoles had undergone loss of cytoplasmic membrane integrity and disorganization of the cytoplasmic matrix. In these polymorphonuclear leukocytes significant lysosomal degranulation was observed. In other cells further deterioration of the fungi was present, and within the digestive vacuole only a membrane "ghost" of the *Histoplasma* remained. Similar electron microscopic observations of digestive vacuole formation and lysis of the organism was observed in blood monocytes incubated with *Histoplasma*. Thus, the *in vitro* interaction of this fungus with blood polymorphonuclear leukocytes and monocytes may be morphologically characterized by phagocytosis, digestive vacuole formation, and subsequent lysis of an ingested organism.

A quantitative evaluation of the effectiveness of human blood polymorphonuclear leukocytes and monocytes in phagocytizing *Histoplasma* was then performed. Each of six incubation mixtures contained a 1:1 ratio of *Histoplasma* to phagocytes. Cultures were terminated at 60 minutes and

1,000 cell counts were performed on Wright's stained smears. The percent of polymorphonuclear leukocytes containing one or more phagocytized *Histoplasma* was 46. The percent of blood monocytes phagocytizing *Histoplasma* was 68. The average number of organisms per polymorphonuclear leukocyte was 1.8. The average number of organisms per blood monocyte was 2.4. These results indicate that the blood monocyte phagocytic index for *Histoplasma* exceeds that of the blood polymorphonuclear leukocyte.

An *in vitro* evaluation of the effectiveness of human blood polymorphonuclear leukocytes and monocytes in killing the yeast phase of *H. capsulatum* was then performed. Incubation mixtures contained a 5:1 phagocyte to *Histoplasma* ratio and 10% fresh isologous serum. *Histoplasma* complement fixation titers were negative and H and M precipitin bands to *Histoplasma* antigen were absent in the six normal subjects studied. Five of six were histoplasmin skin test negative. The phagocyte-*Histoplasma* suspension was rotated end over end in a 37°C incubator for one hour. Following centrifugation, the viability of nonphagocytized organisms in the supernate as well as the viability of intracellular organisms was determined following lysis of the phagocyte. Identical controls without phagocytes were prepared. The specimens were plated in appropriate dilutions on tryptocase soy agar plates, and colonies were counted after fourteen days' incubation at room temperature. The number of viable intracellular organisms and viable organisms in the supernate were totalled, compared with identical controls without phagocytes, and the percent of phagocytes' kill capacity determined. The average percent of *Histoplasma* killed by polymorphonuclear leukocytes from the six subjects studied was 46 and the percent killed by blood monocytes was 52. These results indicate that both circulating cells possess fungicidal capacity against *H. capsulatum*.

References

Bennett, W.E. and Cohn, Z.A. (1966). The isolation and selected properties of blood monocytes. *J. Exp. Med.*, *123*:145-159.

Christie, A. (1958). The disease spectrum of human histoplasmosis. *Ann. Intern. Med.*, *49*:544-555.

Darling, S.T. (1906). Protozoan general infection producing pseudotubercles in lungs and focal necrosis in liver, spleen and lymph nodes. *J.A.M.A. 46*:1283-1285

Dodd, K. and Tompkins, E.H. (1934). Case of histoplasmosis of Darling in infant. *Amer. J. Trop. Med.*, *14*:127-137.

Edwards, M.R., Hazen, E.L. and Edwards, G.A. (1959). The fine structure of the yeast-like cells of *Histoplasma* in culture. *J. Gen. Microbiol.*, *20*:496-503.

Hirsch, J.G. and Cohn, Z.A. (1960). Degranulation of polymorphonuclear leucocytes following phagocytosis of microorganisms. *J. Exp. Med.*, *112*:1005-1014.

Hirsch, J.G. (1962). Cinemicrophotographic observations on granule lysis in polymorphonuclear leukocytes during phagocytosis. *J. Exp. Med.*, *116*:827-833.

Holland, P. and Holland, N. (1966). Histoplasmosis in early infancy. *Amer. J. Dis. Child.,* *112*:412-421.

Holmes, B., Quie, P.G., Windhorst, D.B. and Good, R.A. (1966). Fatal granulomatous disease of childhood. An inborn abnormality of phagocytic function. *Lancet, 1*:1225-1228.

Karnovsky, M.L. (1968). The metabolism of leucocytes. *Seminars Hemat., 5*:156-165.

Rabinovitch, M. (1968). Phagocytosis: the engulfment stage. *Seminars Hemat., 5*:134-155.

Zucker-Franklin, D. and Hirsch, J.G. (1964). Electron microscope studies on the degranulation of rabbit peritoneal leucocytes during phagocytosis. *J. Exp. Med., 120*:569-575.

Part VI
Prevention and Treatment

Chapter 46

Vaccine Development in Histoplasmosis

ERNEST W. CHICK

ABSTRACT

Immunoprotection against histoplasmosis appears to be unrelated to humoral antibodies as currently detected. Whole yeast cells, living and killed, and a variety of fractions from yeast cells have been used as antigens. These have shown some protective effect. The use of purified antigenic fractions may be expected to provide better sensitivity and specificity. With the development of techniques to study cellular immunity, it is now possible to evaluate mechanisms of immunity in histoplasmosis to an extent never before possible.

THE objective of modern medicine is to keep people well, or when illness does occur to stop the disease process as quickly as possible and restore the individual to as nearly normal productive life as possible. The greatest advances in this objective may be seen in the field of infectious disease. In the United States infectious disease is no longer the major killer it once was. Many of the diseases which were epidemic and devastating one or two centuries ago are no longer seen. The eradication of some of these diseases has been due to improved environmental health. But for many it was the development of a protective vaccine that led to this dramatic extinction.

When an infectious disease remains at a significant level of cases, when it produces morbidity and mortality which creates a sociologic or economic drain, then there is a need to consider the potential of vaccine development. Histoplasmosis is estimated to have infected well over 30 million people in the United States and to newly infect some 500,000 people each year. Fortunately most of these infections are benign or at most symptomatically short lived. But significant numbers do develop disease which requires medical treatment, or may progress to death. The implications sociologically and economically to the family in terms of lost productivity and income and the expense of medical care, to the population at large in this day of third-party payment and welfare programs are enormous.

From a practical standpoint, consideration of the wide distribution of *H. capsulatum* in soil, of the fact that eradication of the fungus from soil is not generally feasible, and of the benign infection produced most often, vaccination of the general population for histoplasmosis would not be feasible. Vaccination of select population groups at high risk would appear desirable. Such vaccination would, hopefully, prevent their developing disease.

If one accepts the hypothesis that overt disease occurs in individuals whose "immune mechanism" is incompetent in some way, as contrasted to asymptomatic or benign infection in individuals with competent "immune mechanisms," then immunoprotection of these individuals would be desirable if some means can be developed to identify them before they are exposed to the fungus.

Protection against infection appears to be unrelated to humoral antibodies as detected by current methods (Hill and Marcus, 1957; Salvin, 1956; Salvin, 1960; Furcolow, 1965). This is strikingly demonstrated by analysis of mortality and serologic activity of patients with clinical histoplasmosis. In 36 cases of disseminated histoplasmosis, 20 patients with serologic titer of 1:8 or greater had 60 percent mortality as compared to a 44 percent mortality in 16 patients with negative serologic titer. In another series of 83 patients with histoplasmosis, 58 patients had a strongly positive serologic titer of greater than 1:32. A 28 percent mortality was observed in this group as compared to 16 percent mortality in 25 patients with a negative titer (Furcolow, 1965).

Chandler, Smith, Newberry, Chin, and Kirkpatrick (1969) have characterized the immunoglobulin and antibody responses in histoplasmosis. They found relatively normal IgM and IgG levels and antibody activities in these fractions in patients with chronic cavitary histoplasmosis, which they felt provided some evidence against deficient humoral immune mechanisms in patients with chronic histoplasmosis. The possibility of production of qualitatively or quantitatively abnormal immune globulin could not be ruled out, however. Further investigation with newer methods and techniques may clarify the relationship of currently demonstrable humoral antibodies and the presence or absence of host resistance to disease and to relationships with cellular immunity.

Most of the experimental work on immunoprotection in histoplasmosis has been based on survival-death ratios of the animals, usually mice or guinea pigs. Antigens utilized have included living yeast cells, killed yeast cells, cell wall fractions, and cytoplasmic fractions.

Sublethal infection of animals has been found to be more effective in immunization than killed cells (Salvin, 1956, 1960; Rowley and Huber, 1956). This was thought related to multiplication of the fungus in tissue resulting in simple numerical greater quantities of yeast, to production of an immunizing substance in the tissue by the living fungus, or to altering of the immunizing substance in the process of killing the yeast (Salvin, 1960).

Marcus and Rambo (1955) and Salvin and Ribi (1955) found killed yeast cells to increase resistance to infection; however, Rowley and Huber (1956) obtained somewhat conflicting results. Salvin and Ribi (1955) found cell wall fractions gave about the same protection against challenge as whole cells; both cell walls and whole cells gave greater protection than cytoplasmic fractions. The increasing resistance to challenge after immunization with cell wall fraction of yeast or by sublethal infection developed more rapidly than did counteracting hypersensitivity (Salvin, 1956).

The influence of immunization on phagocytosis has been studied by a variety of techniques. Hill and Marcus (1960) immunized mice with whole cell yeasts. Phagocytosis was determined by the use of radioisotope-labeled yeasts. Immunized mice showed a greater digestion of yeast than normal mice. This intracellular digestion appeared to be independent of mediation by circulating or added antibody.

Salvin (1958) injected mice with live yeast, killed yeast, yeast cell wall, and yeast cytoplasm. Leucocytes obtained from the buffy coats of each group were placed intraperitoneally in normal mice and challenged with live yeast. Cells from donors immunized with live yeast, killed yeast, and yeast cytoplasm contained more challenge yeast than cells from normal animals. Cells from cell wall immunized donors did not show an increase in challenge yeast. Animals immunized with yeast cytoplasm appeared more susceptible to infection, possibly related to the induction of an allergic or toxic state.

Hill and Marcus (1957) injected P-32-labeled yeast into immunized, chronically infected mice and into normal mice. After twenty-four hours, radioactivity counts of the spleen were less in immunized than normal animals, indicating an increased rate of destruction of yeast. *In vitro* immunized cells phagocytized more yeast than normal cells.

Newberry, Chandler, Chin and Kirkpatrick (1968) studied lymphocyte transformation in normal individuals, both histoplasmin positive and negative, and patients with acute and chronic histoplasmosis. Lymphocyte transformation was determined by incorporation of radioactive thymidine into DNA. Thymidine uptake was greater in normal histoplasmin-positive donors than in normal histoplasmin-negative donors. Acute histoplasmosis patients reacted similarly to normal histoplasmin-positive donors, while chronic histoplasmosis patients reacted similarly to normal histoplasmin-negative donors. The authors felt that lymphocyte transformation appeared to be depressed according to the severity of the clinical illness as well as by the presence of serum antibodies.

These studies indicate that cellular phagocytosis and immunity may be basic in resistance to histoplasmosis. Certainly further study of cellular immunity is greatly needed.

Recently more emphasis has been placed on the need for a purified antigen fraction which might provide immunoprotection without perhaps undesirable hypersensitivity. The use of protein and of polysaccharide antigenic fractions in skin and serologic testing has been reviewed by Salvin (1963) and by Campbell (1967).

Knight, Hill and Marcus (1959) found that a polysaccharide fraction of *H. capsulatum* was not as effective as whole yeast cell in preventing mortality following challenge in mice. Using inhibition of extrapulmonary spread, Bauman and Chick (1969a) found encouraging immunoprotection by a polysaccharide-rich fraction of the cell wall.

The use of end point in studies of immunoprotection may be influential in interpretation of results. Salvin (1960) has pointed out that vaccinated mice may be resistant to infection and survive a lethal challenge dose, but still have viable organisms in their tissues. Since most normal, presumably, immunologically competent individuals infected may have a benign dissemination, as indicated by splenic calcification (Schwarz, Silverman, Adriano, Straub and Levine, 1955), protection against extrapulmonary dissemination may offer a workable end point of evaluating immunoprotection.

The use of the hamster, which is highly susceptible to *Histoplasma* infection, and the quantitation of yeast "spilled over" from the lung to spleen following intratracheal challange (Bauman and Chick, 1969b) provides an intriguing experimental model. Using this model, Bauman and Chick (1969a) found that a polysaccharide-rich fraction of yeast cell walls from four strains of *H. capsulatum* provided promising levels of protection against extrapulmonary spread. Compared to normal control hamsters, even when splenic "spill over" of yeast occurred, the number of culturally demonstrable organisms in the spleens of immunized animals was significantly less than controls. It is noteworthy that different strains produced antigen factions that varied in immunogenicity.

Strain variation and relation to immunogenicity of antigen produced has not been studied to any significant extent in the literature. Such strain differences may account for some of the varying results obtained with vaccines in the literature. Comparative studies are greatly needed.

Further work is needed on purified antigens. It still remains to be shown whether protein or polysaccharide antigenic fractions will provide better immunoprotection without undesirable hypersensitive reactions or influence on skin tests or serologic tests. Mechanisms of immunoprotection, humoral or cellular, require intensive study. It is hoped that answers will be forthcoming in the near future.

References

Bauman, D.S. and Chick, E.W. (1969a). Immunoprotection against extrapulmonary histoplasmosis in hamsters. *Amer. Rev. Resp. Dis.*, 100:82-85.

Bauman, D.S. and Chick, E.W. (1969b). An experimental model for studying extrapulmonary dissemination of *Histoplasma capsulatum* in hamsters. *Amer. Rev. Resp. Dis.*, 100:79-81.

Campbell, C.C. (1967). Serology in the respiratory mycoses. *Sabouraudia*, 5:240-259.

Chandler, J.W., Jr., Smith, T.K., Newberry, W.M., Jr., Chin, T.D.Y. and Kirkpatrick, C.H. (1969). Immunology of the mycoses. II. Characterization of the immunoglobulin and antibody responses in histoplasmosis. *J. Infect. Dis.*, 119:247-254.

Furcolow, M.L. (1965). Histoplasmosis. In Samter, M. and Alexander, H.L. *Immunologic Diseases*, Boston, Little Brown, pp. 448-454.

Hill, G.A. and Marcus, S. (1957). Nature of resistance in mouse histoplasmosis (Abstract) *Bact. Proc.*, 57:81-82.

Hill, G.A. and Marcus S. (1960), Study of cellular mechanisms in resistance to systemic *Histoplasma capsulatum* infection. *J. Immun.*, 85:6-13.

Knight, R.A., Hill, G. and Marcus, S. (1959). Immunization of mice with polysaccharides of *Histoplasma capsulatum. Proc. Soc. Exp. Biol.*, 100:356-358.

Marcus, S. and Rambo, R.F. (1955). Comparative aspects of immunization of mice against systemic mycoses. *Bact. Proc.*, 55:92.

Newberry, W.M., Jr., Chandler, J.W., Jr., Chin, T.D.Y. and Kirkpatrick, C.H. (1968). Immunology of the mycoses. I. Depressed lymphocyte transformation in chronic histoplasmosis. *J. Immun., 100*:436-443.

Rowley, D.A. and Huber, M. (1956). Growth of *Histoplasma capsulatum* in normal, superinfected, and immunized mice. *J. Immun., 77*:15-23.

Salvin, S.B. and Ribi, E. (1955). Antigens from the yeast-phase of *Histoplasma capsulatum*. II. Immunologic properties of protoplasm vs. cell walls. *Proc. Soc. Exp. Bio. Med.,* 90:287-294.

Salvin, S.B. (1956). Acquired Resistance in Experimental Histoplasmosis. *Trans. N.Y. Acad. Sci., 18*:462-468.

Salvin, S.B. (1958). The influence of leucocytes from sensitized mice on resistance to *Histoplasma capsulatum. Amer. J. Hyg., 68*:233-241.

Salvin, S.B. (1960). Resistance of animals and man to histoplasmosis. In Sweany, H.C. (Ed.). *Histoplasmosis*. Springfield, Thomas, pp. 99-112.

Salvin, S.B. (1963). Immunologic aspects of the mycoses. *Progr. Allerg., 7*:213-331.

Chapter 47

Histoplasmosis
When to Treat and When Not to Treat

JOHN H. SEABURY

ABSTRACT

This paper presents a few categories of histoplasmosis which demand treatment and raises questions about other forms of the disease. It is emphasized that the life history of histoplasmosis is insufficiently known to permit documented guidelines.

Acute or chronic disseminated histoplasmosis should be treated aggressively. Progressive pulmonary histoplasmosis warrants specific therapy. There are good clinical reasons for giving amphotericin to the patient with acute inhalational disease.

Questions are raised concerning the usefulness of skin and serological reactions in their present forms as guides to therapy. The parallelism between histoplasmosis and tuberculosis is emphasized.

Finally, the position of amphotericin B as a therapeutic agent is discussed briefly. If an agent such as isoniazid were available for the treatment of histoplasmosis, there would be little argument about what and when to treat.

WHEN to treat and when not to treat are two questions which I cannot answer with authority. Indeed, I can present only guidelines in a few categories which are probably acceptable to the experienced clinician. Beyond this, I must ask questions and express my own prejudices.

Acute or chronic disseminated histoplasmosis should be treated aggressively, even though we know a few patients will recover spontaneously. I believe therapy should be of longer duration than is possible now.

Progressive pulmonary histoplasmosis seems to warrant specific therapy just as much as progressive pulmonary tuberculosis. Studies of pathogenesis indicate surely that both have involvement outside of the lungs.

What about acute inhalational histoplasmosis? Most of the affected suffer considerably, recover completely, but undergo a significant period of postinfection asthenia. The usual duration of clinical illness is about twenty-one days. Signs beyond this suggest dissemination. Should we treat to interrupt the duration or plunge in when signs of illness persist into the fourth or fifth week? The same questions have been raised in relation to coccidioidomycosis, a disease with many similarities but a much better understood life history. There are diverse opinions, the negative colored, perhaps, by the unpleasantness of amphotericin.

How should we manage the patient with limited pulmonary histoplasmosis, especially when noncavitary, who has little or no constitutional symptoms? Is the patient with apparently stable chronic pulmonary histoplasmosis in a different category? These patients not only are infected, but they have disease. Their future is as unknown to me as is the future of the adult patient who develops primary tuberculosis. If this statement appears to be inconsistent with present knowledge, let me explain.

Let me first attack our knowledge of the fate of the adult who converts his tuberculin test or develops primary tuberculosis. First of all, we cannot rely on statistics garnered forty years ago. Recent studies of disease following tuberculin conversion apply mainly to infants and children. In general, the host determines the course of infection much more than the agent. Host factors today in the United States are not the same as forty years ago. Furthermore, we are still unable to assort host factors in a manner which lends predictability to the course of an infection. Statistics in diseases with a low or moderate rate of progression will have little applicability to the individual until host factors can be tabulated with predictability.

Secondly, I attach no reliability to individual or mass testing with commercially available intermediate PPD of 5 TU strength. Our patient experience is numerically significant. I have been using 10 TU for the past ten years with approximately 20 to 25 percent negative reactors (less than 1 cm induration) among suspects whose sputum or bronchial exudate was culturally positive.

Finally, I would like to ask a question. How many patients reported as having primary tuberculosis have had a cultural diagnosis? Are our criteria for diagnosis prior to treatment as rigid as those for histoplasmosis?

Can we predict the fate of the patient with primary histoplasmosis? How many patients with progressive disease have evidence of old histoplasmosis? Just as reinfection tuberculosis now challenges us in the population over fifty rather than in the midtwenties age group, as it did forty years ago, so it will require a lifetime of significant statistics to answer these questions.

Can we predict the rate of future active disease following histoplasmin conversion? Dr. Furculow has, but on the assumption that histoplasmin reaction is reasonably specific. I do not dispute the assumption, but I question it. Cross reactivity with blastomycosis and coccidioidomycosis poses no problem of magnitude, but what about *Sepedonium*? This fungus is common in the soils around Kansas City, and I have isolated it from sputum in Louisiana. Can this fungus, and perhaps others, provoke delayed cutaneous reactivity to histoplasmin to an extent such that mass surveys are unreliable?

Do serological findings or biopsy cultures have a precise significance? If not precise, are they truly useful? I am unwilling to accept the serological methods generally available as reliable guides to therapy. If one considers all of our patients with proven histoplasmosis (except those with acute dissemination), treated or untreated, 29 percent had negative serology. I expect dissent at this conference. Evidence of extrapulmonary spread can, I believe, be found in almost all cases of acute inhalational disease if intensively and properly sought by cultural methods. In short, I am implying that the pathogenesis of histoplasmosis at this stage is essentially the same as for primary tuberculosis. Whether the consequences are similar is still unknown.

Answers to at least some of these questions are essential before one can approach the matter of treatment scientifically. It is rather pointless to argue about which patient with chronic pulmonary histoplasmosis should be treated and which observed until we have valid statistical comparisons of such magnitude and duration that host factors, which in themselves are unstable, become smoothed out. One must go back to preantimicrobial years to recall the "good chronic" of pulmonary tuberculosis who survived for years without great changes in either his chest roentgenogram or his intermittently positive sputum. There were small exacerbations and remissions, yet the slow trend was toward either pulmonary insufficiency or death from tuberculosis. No one would suggest observation only today.

We are living in a time of indiscriminate antibiosis, perhaps in its broadest sense. I am sure that if we had an antifungal agent similar in effectiveness, toxicity and side effects to isoniazid, this paper would not be on this program. It would be replaced by one asking whether all histoplasmin converters should be treated in the great campaign for eradication.

Reasonably good treatment is available. Each physician is trying to equate the hazards and discomforts of amphotericin against the risks of the disease. My assignment does not include an appraisal of the toxicity of amphotericin, but this is very pertinent to a decision as to what to treat and what not to treat. I believe the toxicity of amphotericin has been greatly exaggerated by misuse, inadequate long-term studies and confusion of side effects with toxicity. Until we have a much greater knowledge of the risks of some forms of histoplasmosis, we cannot broaden, scientifically, our indications for treatment with amphotericin. We must rely on judgment and prejudice. I think it most important to increase our knowledge of the life history of histoplasmosis and to pool our studies of dosage and toxicity of amphotericin. Finally, until something better comes along, we must use amphotericin. It would be in the interest of the public to restrict its use to designated centers.

Chapter 48

Amphotericin B, Basic Techniques and Dosage for Histoplasmosis

N. ALEXANDER SALIBA

ABSTRACT

The most widely used treatment in the severe forms of histoplasmosis is intravenous amphotericin B. The duration of a particular course of treatment and the total dosage employed have differed in the various experiences reported. This presentation refers to the two largest studies with amphotericin B, namely, those of the United States Public Health Service Mycoses Therapy Group and the Veterans Administration. The total dosage for a single course during previous and current studies has ranged roughly between .5 gm and 3.2 gm. Amphotericin B is given usually three times per week for approximately sixteen weeks, but an optimum dosage has not been defined. The experience at our hospital in the treatment of over one hundred patients is also briefly presented.

In spite of potential renal toxicity and other side effects, most cases of severe histoplasmosis need treatment with amphotericin B, and following this, improvement can be documented in a majority of them.

Continued follow-up and study of patients will provide additional information toward the future management of histoplasmosis, either with amphotericin B, or any other antifungal agents that may become available.

AMPHOTERICIN-B is the most effective antifungal agent with which we have had the widest experience at the present time. Aware of the potential toxic effects of this drug, but also well acquainted with the type of extensive disease encountered in our hospital, we have instituted a program of treatment for patients with significant disease (1) on whom the diagnosis is proved, and (2) on those who are strongly suspect and whose symptoms and chest x-ray are unstable.

Many clinicians have reported extensively on the use of amphotericin B, particularly in histoplasmosis (Lehan, Yates, Brasher, Larsh and Furcolow, 1957; Sutcliff, 1960; Seabury and Dascomb, 1958). Many are attending this second national conference on histoplasmosis and will have some additional comments. The most frequent method of treatment has been by intravenous infusion given three times a week (daily in seriously ill patients). Basically, the initial dose most frequently used is 10 mg diluted in 5% dextrose in water, and gradually increased to 50 mg per infusion; some have given a final dosage as high as 1 mg/kilo weight per infusion. Treatment continues at this dosage level, three times per week for approximately sixteen weeks.

Although there is more general agreement about the need of amphotericin B in severe histoplasmosis and the mode of administration, there is less uniform agreement with regard to the total dosage of amphotericin B to be given over a particular course of treatment. In the Veterans Administration Armed Forces Cooperative Study on Histoplasmosis (1964) and the USPHS Mycoses Cooperative Study (1963) the total dosage of amphotericin B has ranged roughly between .5 gm and 3.2 gm in individual cases. In the former group different dosages are being used in a comparative study; in the latter an average course is 2.4 gm of amphotericin B. Most clinicians have reported side effects in many of their patients, consisting of chills, fever, gastrointestinal disturbances, headaches, thrombophlebitis, muscular weakness, and so on. Most of these were controlled to a large extent with the use of acetylsalicylic acid, antihistamines, Compazine®, and small doses of corticosteroids. In our hands, 20 to 25 mg of hydrocortisone with each infusion has proved very effective, and many patients now take their treatments with no major difficulties (Saliba and Beatty, 1962). In the early days of amphotericin B, individual treatments were prolonged to six hours or longer, most of our patients now can take the medication in a period of approximately one hour.

Rise in BUN (blood urea nitrogen) and decrease in hemoglobin during treatment has been frequently reported, these studies usually returning to normal limits following completion of treatment.

The USPHS Mycoses Therapy Group has used amphotericin B in a few hundred patients with a long period of follow-up in most of them. An untreated group has served as a control, either because these patients had disease prior to the advent of amphotericin B, or because they refused treatment. At the fifth anniversary from the date of diagnosis, 40 percent of the adequately treated histoplasmosis patients were clinically improved, compared to 20 percent in the untreated group (Table 48-I). The percentage of those whose disease progressed showed practically no difference. As regards mortality, at five years 19 percent had died of histoplasmosis in the untreated group compared to 9 percent among those adequately treated. There was no difference in the nonhistoplasmosis deaths (Figs. 48-1, 48-2). Thus, there is no doubt about the need of amphotericin B treatment in the severe form of histoplasmosis (Furcolow, 1963; Campbell, Einstein, Kravetz and Utz, 1969).

At our hospital, standard treatment has followed a protocol of the USPHS Mycoses Cooperative Study, and a course of intravenous amphotericin B has usually amounted to approximately 2.4 gm given in intermittent doses over a period of sixteen weeks. We have treated over one hundred patients, mostly histoplasmosis cases, with some examples of blastomycosis, aspergillosis, or cryptococcosis.

Besides the standard treatment for proven histoplasmosis as described

TABLE 48-I

Chronic Pulmonary Histoplasmosis Comparison of Treated and Untreated Cases at Anniversary
(Surgically Treated and Tuberculosis Cases Omitted)

Anniversary	Status at Anniversary	Untreated (%)	Inadequately Treated (%)	Adequately Treated (%)
1	Improved	27	49	63
	Progressed*	44	27	20
2	Improved	25	43	60
	Progressed	54	35	35
3	Improved	22	37	51
	Progressed	52	36	32
4	Improved	21	34	46
	Progressed	54	45	36
5	Improved	20	34	40
	Progressed	36	48	38

* Includes progressed by x-ray, dead from Histoplasmosis, transferred to treatment (untreated cases only), required surgery, and relapsed categories.

above, we have considered treatment in other situations as follows:

1. Patients who suffered a relapse following an original full course of amphotericin B usually received a second full course for significant reactivation, or approximately .5 to 1 gm of amphotericin B in milder cases.
2. For surgical cases treatment was given either when a diagnosis was made following definitive resectional surgery or pre- and post-operatively. The dosage range in these cases was 0.5 to 2.5 gm, but most received less than 2 gm (Beatty, Levene, Saliba and Coelho, 1962).
3. Likewise, some patients with evidence of clinical deterioration, and whose diagnosis was strongly suspect but not mycologically proved, have usually been treated with approximately 1 gm of amphotericin B.

In an effort to prevent relapses, we attempted a new approach for a period of approximately two years in a selected small number of patients with advanced pulmonary histoplasmosis. Besides the original course of amphotericin B, these patients received 0.5 gm amphotericin B given over a period of three to four weeks at approximately six-month intervals for about two years. These patients cooperated well, the treatment was well tolerated, and they returned regularly for outpatient clinic evaluation. However, it will be several years before we can demonstrate if this particular group of patients has a better long-term prognosis.

All this has lead us to attempt an analysis of different types of patients, with the possibility that some patients might do just as well clinically at a lower dosage of amphotericin B as they would at a dosage range of about 2.5

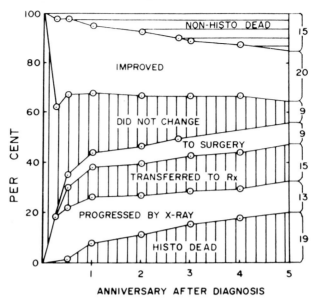

FIGURE 48-1. Chronic pulmonary histoplasmosis status of 104 untreated cases at anniversary (surgically treated and tuberculosis cases omitted).

gm. The importance of this is obvious, because those patients who relapse could then be retreated without additional risk of major renal toxicity.

We have also undertaken a study of renal biopsies whenever these could be carried out, or detailed examination of renal tissue at necropsy. We had

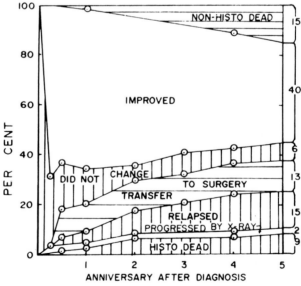

FIGURE 48-2. Chronic pulmonary histoplasmosis status of 187 adequately treated cases at anniversary (surgically treated and tuberculosis cases omitted).

TABLE 48-II

Mycoses Deaths

Patient	Year Diagnosis	Amphotericin mg	Cause of Death	Renal Findings
V.R. (57)	1967	735	ruptured aortic aneurysm	focal calcification tubules
L.G. (62)	1967 (BL.)	490	resp. acidosis, volvulus cancer	tubular changes w/regeneration basement membrane thickening
W.A. (61)	1967	2335	pulmonary embolism, CCF w/arrhythmia	focal tubular necrosis calcification, basement membrane thickening renal calculi
J.H. (65)	1967	1420	cardiorespiratory failure, respiratory acidosis, pneumonia	focal tubular necrosis w/calcification basement membrane thickening
J.B. (65)	1965 (died 1968)	1965—2330 66–67—570×3	cardiorespiratory failure, pulmonary emboli	(biopsy) focal tubular necrosis calcification basement membrane thickening (autopsy) same
G.P. (71)	1963	1655	resp. acidosis, cor pulmonale	some tubular changes basement membrane thickening
M.H. (71)	1963	1150	myocardial infarction	focal tubular necrosis, mild calcification

This shows the mycoses patients who died in the past several years in relation to the necropsy renal findings and the total amphotericin B dosage they had received. None of these patients had renal failure.

seven deaths among our mycoses patients (Table 48-II), but although renal changes were described in the necropsy specimens, no patient was ever in renal difficulties. This toxicity should certainly not be overemphasized, but on the other hand, it need not be underemphasized; rather, one should continue to explore different methods of amphotericin B usage. There is some evidence suggesting that the degree of nephrotoxicity is apparently related to the total dosage of amphotericin B (Butler, Bennett, Alling, Wertlake, Utz and Hill, 1964; Utz, Bennett, Brandriss, Butler and Hill, 1964). Renal tubular acidosis with renal vasoconstriction and nephrocalcinosis has been described by McCurdy, Frederic and Elkinton (1968).

On the other hand, in the USPHS Mycoses Therapy Group there is some evidence suggesting that inadequately treated patients did less well at their fifth anniversary than those who received adequate dosage. That is, the adequately treated group had fewer deaths, fewer patient relapses, and more patients that registered improvement. However, with longer periods of follow-up these differences become less marked. Further analysis and data collected over longer periods of time may provide additional valuable information toward the future management of histoplasmosis until such time as other antifungal agents become available.

References

Beatty, O.A., Levene, N., Saliba, N.A. and Coelho, J. (1962). Surgical therapy of chronic pumonary histoplasmosis with and without Amphotericin-B. *J. Thorac. Cardiovasc. Surg.* 44:228.

Butler, W.T., Bennett, J.E., Alling, D.W., Wertlake, P.T., Utz, J.P., and Hill, G.J. (1964). Neprotoxicity of Amphotericin-B. *Ann. Intern. Med., 61:*175.

Campbell, G.D., Einstein, H.E., Kravetz, H.M. and Utz, J.P. (1969). Indications for chemotherapy in the pulmonary mycoses. *Dist. Chest, 55:*160.

Furcolow, M.L. (1963). The use of Amphotericin-B in blastomycosis, cryptococcosis, and histoplasmosis. *Med. Clin. N. Amer., 47:*1119.

Lehan, P.H., Yates, J.L., Brasher, C.A., Larsh, H.W. and Furcolow, M.L. (1957). Experiences with the therapy of sixty cases of deep mycotic infections. *Dis. Chest, 32:* 597.

McCurdy, D.K., Frederic, M. and Elkinton, J.R. (1968). Renal tubular acidosis due to Amphotericin-B. *New Eng. J. Med., 278:*131.

Saliba, N.A. and Beatty, O.A. (1962). Treatment of mycotic infections. hydrocortisone in the control of Amphotericin-B toxicity. *Dis. Chest, 41:*214.

Seabury, J.H. and Dascomb, H.E. (1958). Experience with Amphotericin-B for the treatment of system mycoses. *Arch. Intern. Med., 102:*960.

Sutliff, W.D. (1960). Amphotericin-B therapy of histoplasmosis. *Amer. Rev. Resp. Dis., 81:*950.

U.S.P.H.S. Cooperative Mycoses Study (1963), Comparison of treated and untreated severe histoplasmosis. *J.A.M.A., 183:*823.

Utz, J.P., Bennett, J.E., Brandriss, M.W., Butler, W.T. and Hill, G.J. (1964). Amphotericin-B toxicity. *Ann. Intern. Med., 61:*334.

Chapter 49

Amphotericin B: Review of Recent Pharmacological Developments

JOHN P. UTZ

ABSTRACT

In earlier work amphotericin B, given intravenously in dosage of from 0.5 to 1.5 mg/kg/day, produced serum levels exceeding by factors of from 2 to 25, the minimal inhibitory concentration for major pathogenic fungi. Although drug could be detected in cerebrospinal fluid following intravenous administration, peak levels were frequently below the minimal inhibitory concentration of the causative fungus, and "trough" levels were undetectable. Drug administered intrathecally could be detected twenty-four hours later.

More recent work has demonstrated that with such doses (but specifically 45 daily and 90 mg every other day), "trough" concentrations were similar, but peak serum concentrations were, as expected, greater with the larger dose. At doses of 100 mg every other day peak values were not significantly better than those obtained with 50 mg daily. In dosages of 20 to 25 mg daily or 40 to 50 mg every other day, serum peak and trough values were higher with every other day administration. Drug could be detected in serum as late as 32 days, and in the urine as late as 19 days, after the last dose of drug. Preexisting renal disease as well as increased blood urea nitrogen and serum creatinine values related to drug did not appear to increase serum drug levels in any consistent way. It seems more likely that higher peak serum levels of drug may have produced more nephrotoxicity. The customary practise of intrathecal administration every 48 to 72 hours, at dosages commonly employed (0.5-1.0 mg), did not result in detectable cerebrospinal fluid levels during trough periods. Administration of smaller amounts of drug, 0.2 to 0.3 mg, if given daily and expressed slowly (over a period of 6 hours) from an Ommaya reservoir, appeared to give better levels and less signs of meningeal irritation.

M OST of our information on the pharmacology of amphotericin B has been gained over ten years ago in the fundamental studies by Louria (1958), Littman (1959), Winn (1959), Seabury and Dascomb (1960) and Newcomer *et al.* (1960). These authors demonstrated that with the intravenous administration of daily doses of from 0.37 to 2.4 mg/kg, maximum serum levels ranged from none detected to 3.65μg/ml. It was early appreciated that as late as 24 hours after administration drug could be found at "trough" levels of from 0.3μg to 12.0μg/ml. It was also shown that peak levels appeared to be inversely related to the renal function, as measured by blood urea nitrogen or serum creatinine values. These data are relevant to the minimal inhibitory concentrations of the causative fungi and serum levels of

1µg/ml exceeded by factors of from 25 to 2 the minimal inhibitory concentrations of the drug against such fungi as *Histoplasma capsulatum, Coccidioides immitis, Blastomyces dermatitidis, Candida* species, *Sporothrix schenckii*, and *Cryptococcus neoformans*.

Seabury (1959) and Newcomer (1960) showed, in addition, that with daily doses of from 0.25 to 1.2 mg/kg, administered intravenously, levels in the cerebrospinal fluid were considerably lower and ranged from less than 0.04µg to 0.56µg/ml. However, these values in some instances exceeded the minimal inhibitory concentrations for some of the pathogenic fungi causing meningitis.

Seabury and Dascomb (1958) and Littman (1958) showed, in two patients not receiving drug concommitantly by the intravenous route, that with doses of 0.5 and 1 mg administered intrathecally, cerebrospinal fluid drug levels 24 hours following injection, were 0.33µg and 0.45µg/ml.

Howard (1960) using cell culture techniques showed that at a concentration of 0.1µg/ml in the media and with *H. capsulatum*, extracellular multiplication was inhibited, and the multiplication intracellularly was slightly suppressed. At a level of 0.05µg/ml multiplication was minimally affected extracellularly and unaffected intracellularly.

Within the past year Bindschadler and Bennett (1969) have reported important new contributions to our knowledge of the pharmacology of this drug. It is especially noteworthy that their studies demonstrate that immediately after the end of an intravenous infusion no more than 10 percent of the injected dose is present in the serum. If one assumes that the concentration in the extracellular fluid is at a level similar to that in the serum, still no more than 40 percent of the injected dose can be accounted for. Although the authors do not present data on the amount of drug intracellularly, it is reasonable to assume from studies above that the remaining drug cannot be accounted for by amounts that are biologically active intracellularly. Amounts of drug detectable biologically in cerebrospinal fluid and parotid gland fluid are, as previously mentioned in part, low or immeasurable.

The mystery is further intensified by the observation that in patients receiving daily infusions of the same dose of drug, only about 2 to 5 percent of the injected dose appeared in the urine in a biologically active form.

In all patients studied for periods ranging from two hours to thirty-two days after a last dose of drug ranging from 30 to 80 mg, serum levels could be detected in all patients on the seventh day, in both of two patients studied on approximately the twentieth day, and in one patient studied after thirty-two days. The authors have interpreted these data as suggesting that the drug is deposited in certain sites, and then released slowly when the serum concentration falls sufficiently.

In further studies of patients receiving either 45 mg every day or 90 mg every other day, trough serum values were similar. Not unexpectedly, however, mean peak serum levels were higher with the double dosage given every other day. When 100 mg doses were given every other day, peak values were no higher than of those obtained with 50 mg every day, whereas the mean trough values were significantly lower. With doses of 20 to 25 mg daily or 40 to 50 mg every other day, trough and peak values were higher with every other day administration.

In view of what has been said before, it is difficult to explain why repeated administrations of the same dose of drug did not result in increasingly higher serum concentrations, or in changes in the trough concentrations.

In eight patients amphotericin B was present in urine for from four to nineteen days after a last dose of drug of from 30 to 80 mg intravenously.

In three patients with preexisting renal disease, there was not a decreased excretion or increased serum concentration of the drug. (Indeed, it has been our own personal observation over a number of years that amphotericin B therapy can predictably lower serum creatinine and blood urea nitrogen values when such abnormalities are based, at least inferentially, on fungal infection of the kidney.)

Drutz *et al.* (1968) have argued persuasively for daily intravenous doses of from no more than 15 to 40 mg (0.25-0.50 mg/kg). Bindschadler and Bennett's data, however, suggest that such lower doses daily give lower peak and trough values than higher levels every other day. Drutz *et al.* point of lesser toxicity with such lower dosages was not countered, however.

Much of the new information regard to the pharmacology of amphotericin B injected into the cerebrospinal fluid has been obtained through the use of the Ommaya reservoir (Witorsch *et al.*, 1965). It has been customary when drug is given intratheracally at this site, as well as at cisternal and lumbar sites, to give the drug no more frequently than every 48 to 72 hours. However, Bindschadler and Bennett showed that trough levels obtained were usually below the minimal inhibitory concentrations of the infecting fungus. When the frequency of injection was increased to every 24 hours, and the dosage reduced to 0.2 to 0.3 mg, trough concentrations were improved. However, such frequent therapy was accompanied by an elevation in the cerebrospinal fluid protein and by a decline in glucose. Data were limited to two patients, but it was suggested that manual depression of the Ommaya reservoir over a 6-hour period following infusion reduced such side effects. (It is of parenthetic interest that the amount of drug present in the cerebrospinal fluid following intravenous infusion does not appear related detectably to protein content.)

References

Bindschadler, D.D. and Bennett, J.E. (1969). A pharmacologic guide to the clinical use of amphotericin B. *J. Infect. Dis.*, 120:427-436.

404 *Histoplasmosis*

Drutz, D.J., Spickard, A., Rogers, D.E. and Koenig, N.G. (1968). Treatment of disseminated mycotic infections. A new approach to amphotericin B therapy. *Amer. J. Med.*, 45:405-418.

Howard, D.H. (1960). Effect of mycostatin and fungizone on the growth of *Histoplasma capsulatum* in tissue culture. *J. Bact.*, 79:442-449.

Littman, M.L. (1959). Cryptococcosis (Torulosis) Current concepts and therapy. *Amer. J. Med.*, 27:976-998.

Louria, D.B. (1958). Some aspects of the absorption, distribution, and excretion of amphotericin B in man. *Antibiot. Med. Clin. Ther.*, 5:295-301.

Newcomer, V.D., Sternberg, T.H., Wright, E.T., Reisner, R.M., McNall, E.G. and Sorenson, L.J. (1960). The treatment of systemic fungus infections with amphotericin B. *Ann. N.Y. Acad. Sci.*, 89:221-239.

Seabury, J.H. and Dascomb, H.E. (1958). Experience with amphotericin B for the systemic mycoses. *Arch. Intern. Med.*, 102:960-976.

Winn, W. A. (1959). The use of amphotericin B in the treatment of coccidioidal disease. *Amer. J. Med.*, 27:617-635.

Witorsch, P., Williams, T.W., Jr., Ommaya, A.K. and Utz, J.P. (1965). Intraventricular administration of amphotericin B: Use of subcutaneous reservoir in four patients with mycotic meningitis. *J.A.M.A.*, 194:699-702.

Chapter 50

Histoplasmosis and Amphotericin B: Results of a Limited Experience

JOHN H. SEABURY

ABSTRACT

Of thirty patients treated for histoplasmosis with amphotericin B, half had disseminated disease. Initial treatment failed in 20 percent. All deaths (4) occurred among patients with disseminated disease, but ony half of these died from histoplasmosis. Two of the initial treatment failures have been retreated and are now sputum negative.

The average daily dose of amphotericin for the whole group was approximately 0.5 mg/kg. Dosage since 1964 has been considerably less than that used earlier. No reduction in efficacy has been detected.

HISTOPLASMOSIS is seen with lesser frequency in New Orleans than blastomycosis. Cryptococcosis is recognized about as often as histoplasmosis. An intriguing feature of our experience is the relative frequency of disseminated disease. Half of the thirty patients considered here had disseminated disease, whereas in north Louisiana the pulmonary form is much more common.

This small group of patients is limited to those treated by us in Charity Hospital. Patients treated in other hospitals under our guidance or consultation are not included, even though they would approximately double the cases for analysis. This restriction is imposed for two reasons: (1) patients not under our continuous supervision were not always treated in a manner acceptable to us, and (2) follow-up has been grossly inadequate.

Table 50-I summarizes the results of treatment with amphotericin B. The group is too small to make percentages meaningful, but initial treatment failed in 20 percent. The patient whose death has been attributed to treatment will be discussed briefly.

A Caucasian female, forty-two years old, had been treated for several years with corticosteroids for rheumatoid arthritis. Approximately nine months before referral to Charity Hospital, she developed daily fever. Within a few months, hepatosplenomegaly, anemia, and thrombocytopenia were recognized. No diagnosis was made until a diffuse pulmonary infiltrate of the "interstitial" type appeared together with pancytopenia. Bone marrow examination revealed *Histoplasma capsulatum*. When received by us, she presented with high fever, anasarca, universal petechiae, hypoproteine-

TABLE 50-I

Results of Treatment of Histoplasmosis With Amphotericin B
(Half of the Patients Had Disseminated Disease)

	Histoplasmosis
Primary cures	23
Late deaths	4
2 *from* histoplasmosis	
2 *with* histoplasmosis	
Death from treatment	1
Living relapses	2
	—
Total	30

mia, and pancytopenia. The initial infusion contained 5 mg of amphotericin B. During the infusion she developed hyperpyrexia and pulmonary edema. This was followed by diffuse erythema, shock, and death. We believe death was precipitated by a Herxheimer type of reaction, but we have no proof. Autopsy revealed the most extensive dispersion and highest concentration of *H. capsulatum* that we have seen.

All deaths occurred among patients with disseminated disease, although only half (2) died from histoplasmosis. These are included in Table 50-IV. Inadequate duration of treatment may have been a factor in one of the two deaths from histoplasmosis. Some may argue that daily dosage was also suboptimal in this patient. We do not think so.

Two patients who relapsed and are still living are tabulated in Table 50-II. One has been treated three times with amphotericin and once with saramycetin. The other has been re-treated only once. Both had chronic fibrocavitary histoplasmosis, one with intercurrent tuberculosis. Both are now sputum negative. They have been given 3 gm of sulfadiazine daily since their last retreatment. One cannot evaluate its role in their present status.

Our experience with pulmonary histoplasmosis is insufficient to lend much weight to opinions which we have formed. Nevertheless, I am express-

TABLE 50-II

Patients with Histoplasmosis Who Relapsed After Primary Treatment With Amphotericin B and Are
Still Alive (Both Patients Had Chronic Pulmonary Disease)

	Histoplasmosis
Living Relapses	2
1 treated '60–'61, sputum+'64;	
spread '66, retreated '67.	
1 treated '61.	
retreated R02-7758, '63	
retreated '64	
retreated '65	

TABLE 50-III

Dosage of Amphotericin B in Patients Treated for Histoplasmosis (Note Reduction in Average Dose Since 1964)

	Dosage (mg)
Median dose/kg/day	0.55
Average dose/kg/day	0.496
Average dose/kg/day	
'56–'63	0.54
'64–'68	0.32

ing them as points for discussion. Treatment with amphotericin during a range of 90 to 160 days does not seem to result in as much radiographic clearing or cavitary closure in chronic fibrocavitary histoplasmosis as was achieved by chemotherapy of similar duration in the same type of tuberculosis. Disease of short duration responds well. We believe that histoplasmosis and tuberculosis are sufficiently alike in their pathogenesis and pathology that duration of treatment will be similar when a relatively nontoxic agent for histoplasmosis becomes available.

The daily dose of amphotericin administered to these patients is shown in Table 50-III. The average daily dose for the whole group is approximately 0.5 mg/kg. It will be interesting, and perhaps important, to compare our dosage and results with others working in this field.

The average daily dose prior to 1964 and that from 1964 to 1968 are tabulated separately for the purpose of discussion by this conference. The daily dosage used by us in the treatment of all mycoses except sporotrichosis has been significantly reduced since 1964. This has been done because toxicity and side effects have been consistently more severe in recent years than we noted with either the insoluble suspension or the earlier lots of the colloidal suspension. We like the blood urea nitrogen to remain below 50 mg%. We

TABLE 50-IV

Tabulation of Dose and Duration of Amphotericin B in All Treatment Failures

Initial Rx	*Deaths and Relapses*	
0.93 mg/kg/d	141d	D*
0.64mg/kg/d	120d	R
0.62mg/kg/d	85d	R&D
0.56mg/kg/d	125d	R
0.57mg/kg/d	78d	D
0.49mg/kg/d	90d	D*

* = Died from histoplasmosis
D = died.
R = relapse.
d = days.

do not tolerate persistent nausea or severe anorexia. In addition to a lower daily dose, we have found it necessary to decrease the daily increments of amphotericin in seeking an acceptable maintenance level. The daily increase now is usually 2 mg for adults.

The reduction in daily dosage has been accompanied by some increase in the duration of treatment. However, many patients will not accept the duration we would like, primarily for economic reasons.

Our experience with histoplasmosis alone is too meager to allow comparison of results using our present low daily dosage treatment with those obtained by the moderate dosages of the past. If one considers all of our patients with systemic mycoses, the number is sufficient to justify a tentative evaluation. We can detect no lessening of the effectiveness of treatment.

Discussions with physicians who use amphotericin infrequently yield a somber view of the antibiotic. The many difficulties and serious toxicity reported seem to stem from three errors. The first is due to poor control of the infusion. It is started by a nurse, and neither the uniformity of suspension nor evenness of flow is regulated. The second and third errors are due to the package insert. Dosage is increased too rapidly, and everyone seems to struggle for a too high level of 1.0 to 1.5 mg/kg. We believe this insert should be revised.

Chapter 51

Therapeutic Trials of Amphotericin B for the Treatment of Histoplasmosis

WHEELAN D. SUTLIFF

ABSTRACT

During the past ten years amphotericin B was the treatment of choice for histoplasmosis as well as for other deep or systemic mycoses. However, the general acceptance of amphotericin has been modified for most physicians by acute awareness of unfavorable factors such as expense, toxicity, and some limitations as to its effectiveness. The quality of the information about the effectiveness of amphotericin B, therefore, needs discussion as one aspect of its continuing evaluation. During the ten- to twelve-year period the clinical classifications of histoplasmosis were redefined, starting from the comprehensive early designations "kaleidoscopic" or "protean" which denied uniform subdivision, to the current three major subdivisions used by several authors, namely, acute pulmonary, chronic pulmonary, and extra-pulmonary or disseminated histoplasmosis.

Acute pulmonary histoplasmosis cases seldom required amphotericin B therapy because the prognosis was generally good and the course mild.

The fatality rate of disseminated histoplasmosis was believed to be nearly 100 percent before amphotericin became available, but recoveries were known to occur. In disseminated histoplasmosis of children the recovery of only a small number of treated cases was accepted by most observers as evidence of the effectiveness of amphotericin B. Similar data were recorded of the results of amphotericin B therapy of adult disseminated histoplasmosis.

Chronic pulmonary histoplasmosis was the last clinical type of disease to be described, (Sutliff, Hughes, Ulrich and Burkett, 1953). The only study of amphotericin B therapy of histoplasmosis using randomized matched cases was carried out by the Veterans Administration-Armed Forces Cooperative group (Histoplasmosis Cooperative Study No. 2, 1964) who compared treated cases with those admitted and similarly observed in the same hospital during the same time. A striking increase in sputum culture conversions, a decrease in the number of cases with radiologic progression, and a slight increase in cases with changes in serologic titers were demonstrated in treated cases, as compared with controls.

It is believed generally, as a result of these studies, that amphotericin B has a favorable effect on the course of disseminated and chronic pulmonary histoplasmosis. The conclusion is based largely on the judgment of a succession of clinical investigators, and was confirmed by observation of one matched series of treated and control cases.

A REVOLUTION in the therapy of histoplasmosis and other systemic mycoses was begun when Lehan, Furcolow, Brasher and Larsh (1951), Seabury and Dascomb (1958), and Utz, Louria, Feder, Emmons and McCullough (1958) reported the treatment of groups of cases with amphotericin B in 1957 and 1958. During the following ten years amphotericin B was the treatment of choice for histoplasmosis as well as for other deep or systemic mycoses. However, the general acceptance of amphotericin B was modified for most physicians by acute awareness of unfavorable factors such as expense, toxicity, and some limitations as to its effectiveness. The quality of the information about the effectiveness of amphotericin B, therefore, needs discussion as one aspect of its continuing evaluation.

The clinical data supporting the use of amphotericin B for the treatment of histoplasmosis varied from individual case reports to prospective studies with or without matched controls. Information of value was obtained from all these sources. During the ten- to twelve-year period the clinical classifications of histoplasmosis were redefined, starting from the comprehensive early designations "kaleidoscopic" or "protean" which denied uniform subdivision, to the current three major subdivisions used by several authors, namely, acute pulmonary, chronic pulmonary, and extrapulmonary or disseminated histoplasmosis. These subdivisions were found to be necessary in the analysis of amphotericin B therapy because the indications for treatment and the results of treatment varied for each of these three major clinical types of histoplasmosis.

During this ten-year period the facilities for mycologic and serologic diagnosis improved under the impact of the availability of an effective therapy. Such combined diagnostic and therapeutic changes were factors believed by some of the investigators of that period to present a challenge to the interpretation of the effect of therapy. Newcomer, Sternberg, Wright and Lessner (1959) stated this and other difficulties as follows: the small overall number of cases and the need for prolonged follow-up would result in inadequate experience of the natural course of the disease to compare with the results of treatment. They were skeptical of cooporative efforts and they were somewhat pessimistic as to the possibility of objective evaluation of antifungal therapy. From our present position of vantage, with respect to evaluation of antibiotic therapy of the systemic mycoses, I should like to pay my respects to the workers, most of whom are in this room, who elected to try to overcome these obstacles and to unravel the clinical problems of the therapy of the systemic mycoses. They (or should I say "we?") have persisted against formidable odds, have accepted data as we found it, and made the most of it.

Acute Pulmonary Histoplasmosis

Acute pulmonary histoplasmosis cases seldom required amphotericin B therapy because the prognosis was generally good and the course mild. These cases included primary symptomatic or asymptomatic cases. Groups of cases and individual cases in which primary infection or reinfection resulted from obvious exposure to environmental sources were also included. Asymptomatic infections were manifested as mild atypical pneumonias, hilar lymphadenopathy, miliary pulmonary involvement, and resulting pulmonary calcifications. The treatment of an occasional acute pulmonary case whose condition was severe enough to require therapy was reported by Rubin, Lehan and Furcolow (1957) and by Baum and Schwarz (1960) with favorable results. The small total number of reported treated cases was evidence that no need was recognized to treat the average patient with acute pulmonary histoplasmosis.

Disseminated Histoplasmosis of Infants and Children

Disseminated histoplasmosis produces fever insidiously in infants and children, with the gradual development of hepatosplenomegaly, leukopenia, and anemia. The same symptoms occur in adults, together with granuloma or gumma formation, usually in the oropharynx. The fatality rate was believed to be nearly 100 percent before amphotericin became available, but recoveries were known to occur.

Heyn and Giammona (1959) reported the recovery of one three-month-old infant following amphotericin B treatment and cited nine previous recoveries from the literature without amphotericin B, five of which were treated with ethyl vanillate. It was assumed that this one recovery demonstrated the effectiveness of amphotericin B. Moffet, Jannar and Cramblett (1959) reported two cases, four months and four years of age, that recovered following amphotericin B (Table 51-I). Little (1962) treated nine cases from three months to four and one-half years of age with amphotericin B, of which eight recovered and one died. The recovery of only a small number of treated cases was accepted by most observers as evidence of the effective-

TABLE 51-I

Amphotericin B Therapy of Disseminated Histoplasmosis

Author	Treated			Untreated		
	Number Cases	Re-covered	Died	Number Cases	Re-covered	Died
Moffet *et al.*, 1959 (Infants, children)	2	2	0			
Little, 1962 (Infants, children)	9	8	1			
Utz *et al.*, 1958 (Adults)	3	3	0	4	0	4
Drutz *et al.*, 1968 (Adults)	5	2	3*			
National Communicable Disease Center (Furcolow *et al.*, 1963)	22†	17	5	24‡	4	20

* Died of systemic diseases other than histoplasmosis.
† 9% less than 10 years of age.
‡ 33% less than 10 years of age.

ness of amphotericin B. No comparable series of preamphotericin B cases was available, and no critical analysis of such data was attempted.

Disseminated Histoplasmosis of Adults

Similar data were recorded of the results of amphotericin B therapy of adult disseminated histoplasmosis. Utz *et al.* (1958) reported three recovered cases in adults following treatment with amphotericin B, with four- to eighteen-month follow-up, and cited four previous consecutive deaths occurring before amphotericin B was available. Drutz, Spickard, Rogers and Koenig (1968) described five cases in adults treated with the aid of amphotericin B blood level determinations, all of whom recovered. The total number of adult cases was too small for profitable use of randomized controls. About half of the Seabury *et al.* (1958) cases from Charity Hospital in New Orleans were disseminated, and one-half were chronic pulmonary infections. The combined figures demonstrated that both forms had good results. Of 24 cases, 19 improved, 1 relapsed, and 4 died, three of disease other than histoplasmosis, and only one of histoplasmosis.

Comparisons were made as opportunities presented. Center for Disease Control studies, (Furcolow, 1963) described 22 amphotericin B treated disseminated histoplasmosis cases of all ages with 17 recoveries. Although they were not comparable, they were compared with 24 untreated patients of all ages, mainly from records made before amphotericin B became available, with only 4 recoveries. The contrast was overwhelming. It was concluded that amphotericin B was an effective therapeutic agent for extra-pulmonary disseminated histoplasmosis.

Chronic Pulmonary Histoplasmosis

Chronic pulmonary histoplasmosis was the last clinical type of disease to be described (Sutliff, Hughes, Ulrich and Burkett, 1953). Chronic pulmonary histoplasmosis was characterized by infiltrations usually involving the apices of the lung and by cavitation. The course was associated with acute symptoms only at intervals, and was usually prolonged for months or years. It rarely led to systemic dissemination, and death was more often due to secondary complications than to active spread of histoplasmosis. The patients were over forty years of age and had complicating disabilities and a high fatality rate from conditions other than histoplasmosis. The effect of therapy was less readily recognized in chronic pulmonary histoplasmosis than in other clinical forms because the pulmonary lesions did not resolve completely and pulmonary insufficiency did not always disappear. One can see from the attached table (Table 51-II) that the Center for Disease Control and the Veterans Administration-Armed Forces Cooperative Studies, in which

TABLE 51-II

Amphotericin B Therapy of Chronic Pulmonary Histoplasmosis

Author	Number of Cases	Death Histoplasmosis %	Death Histoplasmosis %	Improved %	Unimproved %
National Communicable Disease Center (Furcolow *et al.*, 1963)					
>25 mg/kg	89	16	8	59	17
<25 mg/kg	55	12	24	32	28
VA-Armed Forces Co-op Study (Histoplasmosis Cooperative Study) No. 2, 1964; No. 3, 1968	52*	0	13	84	3

* Six cases also sulfonamides.

cases were treated serially, had good results (Furcolow, 1963; Histoplasmosis Cooperative Study No. 3, 1968; Sutliff, unpublished data—20 cases). As a matter of fact, all observers, even those with reports of single cases that are not tabulated here, noted the control of progression of pulmonary lesions. About one half of the Seabury *et al.* (1958) cases were chronic pulmonary histoplasmosis, and the overall figures cited above were quite favorable, and are believed to have applied to both clinical types of disease.

Untreated cases were described by Baum and Schwarz (1962) and by the Center for Disease Control (Furcolow, 1963), and the lack of comparability to the amphotericin B treated cases was stated. Comparisons were made, however, and it must be allowed that the ready acceptance of amphotericin B as the therapy of choice for chronic pulmonary histoplasmosis was well supported by uncritical perusal of these reports. The studies illustrate, however, some of the fallacies which have been described in the use of statistics by physicians. The untreated cases cited by the Center for Disease Control group (Furcolow, 1963), both in the disseminated histoplasmosis as well as the chronic pulmonary histoplasmosis groups, were collected without regard to certain possible sources of error. Many of the untreated disseminated cases were observed before amphotericin B therapy was available. They were diagnosed before specific methods were either widely or selectively applied, some as long as ten years before therapy provided motivation for heightened clinical suspicion and special attention to mycology. The untreated disseminated cases were collected from sources other than the pulmonary disease sections at hospitals in which nearly all of the cases treated with amphotericin B were found. As a result, there were greater numbers of infants in the untreated series as compared with the greater number of adults in the treated series of disseminated cases.

It may be assumed that some of the cases of chronic pulmonary histoplasmosis diagnosed years before amphotericin B therapy was available differed from those diagnosed with the aid of increased clinical suspicion and routine or selectively applied cultures. As culture facilities became more accessible, chronic pulmonary cases which had been overlooked for months or years were diagnosed, and cases of long duration and extensive involvement that were subject to prolonged hospitalization were first recognized when the hospital staff became aware of the disease. It seems possible that some severe cases died during the period before amphotericin B therapy was introduced, whereas less severe cases persisted long enough to be included in the treated series, thus weighting the untreated series with excess deaths and weighting the treated series with cases of relatively good prognosis. While such speculations of possible sources of error do not provide evidence of fallacies, it is to avoid such sources of criticism that matched series of cases may be employed.

Random selection of matched cases during the same overall time period was designed to counteract the irregular weighting of treated and untreated series collected from different institutions during different time periods.

The only study of amphotericin B therapy of histoplasmosis using randomized matched cases was carried out by the Veterans Administration-Armed Forces Cooperative group (Histoplasmosis Cooperative Study No. 2, 1964) which compared treated cases with those admitted and similarly observed in the same hospital during the same time (Table 51-III). A striking increase in sputum culture conversions, a decrease in the number of cases with radiologic progression, and a slight increase in cases with changes in serologic titers were demonstrated in treated cases, as compared with controls. As an example, in Table 51-IV it may be seen that all patients had sputum cultures positive for *Histoplasma capsulatum* before therapy, and that 11 of the control subjects and 13 of the drug-treated patients had confirmation of the positive culture within three weeks before treatment began. One drug-treated patient had a "negative" sputum specimen within three weeks before treatment, but another specimen was positive on culture early in the course of treatment. This was considered to be consistent with the presence of persistent infection. At each period of observation most control cases remained positive. Only three of fourteen control subjects developed negative sputum cultures, one at six weeks, and two at the end of four

TABLE 51-III

Randomly Selected Chronic Pulmonary Histoplasmosis Cases Treated With
and Without Amphotericin B

	Number Cases	Culture Conver- sions	X-ray Before Rx.		X-ray After Rx.		Deaths	
			Regres- sion	Progres- sion	Regres- sion	Progres- sion	Histo- plasmosis	Nonhisto- plasmosis
amphotericin B	16	15	4	7	11	0	0	3
No amphotericin B	14	1	6	6	5	4	3	1

TABLE 51-IV

Relationship of Cultures for *Histoplasma capsulatum* to Therapy

	Control (14 Cases)			Drug Therapy (16 Cases)		
	Positive	*Negative*	*Not Done*	*Positive*	*Negative*	*Not Done*
Before therapy	14	0	0	16	0	0
After therapy (at 6 weeks)	10	1	3	2	13	1
After therapy (at 4 mo.)	9	2	2	1	9	6
Total negative, at least two weeks	—	3	—	—	16*	—
Permanent results	13†	1	0	1	15	0

* Two cases of mycologic relapse, one of which subsequently reverted to negative.
† Two cases had negative cultures followed by mycologic relapse.

months (Table 51-IV). Mycologic relapse occurred in the first two, leaving one in fourteen control subjects whose sputum remained negative by culture for *H. capsulatum*. By contrast most of the treated cases became negative at each period of observation. Only one case relapsed and fifteen of sixteen cases remained negative. The cases were observed for an average of three years. Other facets were brought out during the study, particularly the observation that sputum conversion sometimes occurred in twenty-four hours or within one week.

Discussion

These studies give evidence that histoplasmosis responds to amphotericin B antibiotic therapy. During their accomplishment the technique of therapeutic trials in this field of activity was sharpened. Randomization was used, even though blind or double-blind techniques were not feasible. Observation of matched series of chronic pulmonary histoplasmosis and other systemic mycoses have been continued by the Veterans Administration-Armed Forces Cooperative Study Group. One study showed combined sulfonamide and amphotericin B therapy was too toxic to continue (Histoplasmosis Cooperative Study No. 3, 1968). Another, while not complete, is devoted to the testing of doses smaller than the standard used by most investigators. Improvements were devised and incorporated into recent protocols of the Veterans Administration-Armed Forces Cooperative Studies for the use of new therapeutic agents.

The large studies without matched controls were of value because they defined the course and results of the disease under therapy in a comprehensive manner. Such series of unmatched cases, however, did not result in convincing data on the course of untreated cases that was comparable to the treated series. Polarization of opinions and unnecessary controversy resulted. One authority on histoplasmosis therapy emphasized the severity of the untreated disease and thereby risked exaggerating the differences in fatality rates in treated and untreated patients. Another authority emphasized the proportion of patients who, if left untreated, would recover without amphotericin B therapy, but did not provide for rational separation of cases needing treatment from those that did not.

The randomized studies, even if they have had no other impact on the accepted picture of histoplasmosis, have demonstrated that the disease may be sufficiently uniform in a given series to demonstrate differences which are due to therapy, and that such differences are best observed through frequent cultures for *H. capsulatum*. The procedures of prospective chronic pulmonary histoplasmosis therapy trials have been improved to provide for selection of cases characterized by (1) repeatedly positive cultures, (2) cavitary pulmonary lesions, and (3) for comparisons of any new therapeutic agent with the performance of a standard agent so that none of the cases are untreated.

It is generally believed, as a result of these studies, that amphotericin B has a favorable effect on the course of disseminated and chronic pulmonary histoplasmosis. The conclusion is based largely on the judgment of a succession of clinical investigators, and was confirmed by observation of a matched series of treated and control cases.

References

Baum, G.L. and Schwarz J. (1960). Clinical experiences with amphotericin B. *Antibiot. Ann.*, 638-643.

Baum, G.L. and Schwarz, J. (1962). Chronic pulmonary histoplasmosis. *Amer. J. Med.*, 33:873-879.

Drutz, D.J., Spickard, A., Rogers, D.E. and Koenig, M.G. (1968). Treatment of disseminated mycotic infection. *Amer. J. Med.*, 45:405-418.

Furcolow, M.L. (1963). Comparison of treated and untreated severe histoplasmosis. A National Communicable Disease Center cooperative mycoses study. *J.A.M.A., 183:* 823-829.

Heyn, R.M. and Giammona, S.T. (1959). Disseminated histoplasmosis treated with amphotericin B. *Amer. J. Dis. Child.*, 98:253-255.

Histoplasmosis Cooperative Study No. 2. (1964). Chronic pulmonary histoplasmosis treated with and without amphotericin B. *Amer. Rev. Resp. Dis.*, 89:641-650.

Histoplasmosis Cooperative Study No. 3. (1968). Chronic pulmonary histoplasmosis treated with amphotericin B alone and with amphotericin B and triple sulfonamide. Veterans Administration-Armed Forces Cooperative Study on Histoplasmosis. *Amer. Rev. Resp. Dis.*, 97:96-102.

Lehan, P.H., Furcolow, M.L., Brasher, C.Q. and Larsh, H.W. (1951). Therapeutic trials of the newer antifungal agents. *Antibiot. Ann.*, 467-469.

Little, J.A. (1962). Intravenous amphotericin B therapy in children with histoplasmosis. *J. Kentucky Med. Assoc.*, 60:965-966.

Moffet, H.L., Jannar, S. and Cramblett, H.G. (1959). Successful therapy of disseminated histoplasmosis through the use of amphotericin B. *J. Iowa Med. Soc.*, 49:625-631.

Newcomer, V.D., Sternberg, T.H., Wright, E.T. and Lessner, R.M. (1959). Current status of amphotericin B in the treatment of systemic fungus infection. *J. Chron. Dis.,* 9:353-374.

Rubin, H., Lehan, P.H. and Furcolow, M.L. (1957). Severe non-fatal histoplasmosis: report of a typical case with comments on therapy. *New Eng. J. Med.,* 257:599-602.

Seabury, J. H. and Dascomb, H.E. (1958). Experience with amphotericin B for the treatment of systemic mycoses. *Arch. Intern. Med.,* 102:96-101.

Seabury, J.H. and Dascomb, H.E. (1964). Results of the treatment of systemic mycoses. *J.A.M.A.,* 188:509-513.

Sutliff, W.D., Hughes, F., Ulrich, E. and Burkett, L.L. (1953). Chronic pulmonary histoplasmosis. *Arch. Intern. Med.,* 92:571-586.

Sutliff, W.D. Unpublished data (20 cases).

Utz, J.P., Louria, D.B., Feder, N., Emmons, C.W. and McCullough, N.B. (1958). A report of clinical studies in the use of amphotericin B in patients with systemic fungal disease. *Antibiot. Ann.,* 685-701.

Utz, J.P., Tregar, A., McCullough, N.B. and Emmons, C.W. (1959). Amphotericin B: intravenous use in patients with systemic fungal disease. *Antibiot. Ann.,* 628-634.

Chapter 52

Evaluation of Amphotericin B Therapy of Histoplasmosis

FRED E. TOSH, IRENE L. DOTO, GEORGE A. SAROSI,
AND JAMES D. PARKER

ABSTRACT

Amphotericin B has been found effective in the treatment of the various severe forms of histoplasmosis. Although acute pulmonary histoplasmosis cases usually recover without specific therapy, the occasional severe infection will respond to a short course of treatment of fourteen to twenty-one days. In a series of disseminated cases of histoplasmosis, the mortality was 83 percent among untreated cases and only 23 percent among cases receiving amphotericin B. Among a group of chronic pulmonary histoplasmosis cases, there were significantly more deaths among untreated patients than among those receiving amphotericin B. Of the 238 chronic pulmonary histoplasmosis cases treated with amphotericin B, 3 were treatment failures, and 33 relapsed during a five-year follow-up period. Relapse was not related to the total dose of drug given, but death was. There were significantly fewer deaths among those patients who received over 35 mg/kg of body weight of drug than among those who received less.

PRIOR to the introduction of amphotericin B in 1956, there was no effective therapy for histoplasmosis and there was little hope of recovery for patients with the more severe forms of the disease. Since 1956, there have been many reports describing the efficacy of amphotericin B in histoplasmosis and other fungal infections. Many of these reports describe only single cases. In 1957, a group of tuberculosis and chest disease hospitals joined together under the auspices of the Center For Disease Control to collect information on the course of histoplasmosis and to study the effectiveness of amphotericin B therapy. Most of the data in this report were obtained through the Center For Disease Control Cooperative Mycoses Study.

Materials and Methods

A previous paper has described the operation of the Center For Disease Control Cooperative Mycoses Study (Center Cooperative Mycoses Study, 1963). Briefly, the diagnosis of histoplasmosis was verified at the Central Office in Kansas City, Kansas, by culture or by examination of slides of pathologic material and identification of the fungus.

The protocol for the study recommended giving 50 mg of amphotericin B intravenously three times a week for a total of sixteen weeks for a total of 2400 mg. Because of side effects and toxicity of the drug, it was not always possible to follow the schedule recommended in the protocol. Some patients refused to continue the drug while others left the hospital against medical advice before completion of the recommended course of therapy. The group of patients not treated with amphotericin B consists of some diagnosed before the advent of the drug and others who refused therapy.

The participating hospitals sent monthly reports of signs and symptoms, 14×17 inch PA chest films, and if possible, sputa for fungal cultures, and sera for fungal complement fixation tests while the patient was in the hospital. Thereafter, an attempt was made to obtain follow-up information at six-month intervals for a year, and then yearly for five years, and then every two years. Death certificates, autopsy reports, or both, were obtained on all patients who died.

Chest films were reviewed yearly by a panel of three or five chest physicians from the participating hospitals. These films were evaluated as to progression or regression of the disease in comparison with initial or pretreatment roentgenograms, without knowledge of therapy in the patient.

A relapse is defined as the reappearance of *Histoplasma capsulatum* in cultures of sputum or other specimens, or a worsening of the chest film and symptoms without other apparent cause after termination of therapy. A treatment failure is defined as a persistence of the organism in cultures throughout and after therapy. Length of follow-up is the period of time from the first positive culture in the untreated cases and start of therapy in treated cases to the last chest film, culture, or patient response by questionnaire.

Most patients entered in the Cooperative Mycoses Study had either disseminated or chronic pulmonary histoplasmosis. Through the investigations of epidemics and referred patients, the Mycoses Section of the Kansas City Laboratories has collected data and follow-up of a large number of acute pulmonary histoplasmosis cases. Since acute pulmonary histoplasmosis is usually a self-limited disease, amphotericin B has been recommended in only a few of the more severe cases. The diagnosis in the acute pulmonary cases was based on isolation of the organism from clinical materials in an occasional case and a combination of a positive skin test, serological test, compatible x-ray findings and confirmation of the point source of infection in the remainder.

Results

Acute Pulmonary Histoplasmosis

The number of acute pulmonary histoplasmosis cases treated with amphotericin B has been limited. The drug was recommended in only those patients who had been ill for two weeks or longer with fever, anorexia, weight loss, and extensive pulmonary involvement visible by chest roentgenogram. The recommended course of therapy was short, ranging from fourteen to twenty-one days, starting with low daily doses of amphotericin B, increasing the daily dose gradually to 1 mg/kg body weight, then giving the drug every other day. The response to therapy was very good with a decrease in fever after three to four days of therapy, return of appetite, and general improvement. After completion of the short course of therapy, the patients continued to improve with weight gain and gradual clearing of the chest film.

Disseminated Histoplasmosis

The most clear-cut evaluation of amphotericin B therapy has been in the treatment of disseminated histoplasmosis. In 1963, the National Communicable Disease Center Cooperative Mycoses Study reported 20 deaths among 24 cases of untreated disseminated histoplasmosis. Of 22 cases of disseminated histoplasmosis treated with amphotericin B, there were only 5 deaths, and 2 of these were due to causes other than active histoplasmosis. Two patients in the treated group relapsed and were re-treated.

Chronic Pulmonary Histoplasmosis

Of the patients with chronic pulmonary histoplasmosis admitted to the NCDC Cooperative Mycoses Study, those with tuberculosis, blastomycosis, and other concomitant infiltrative pulmonary disease were eliminated, leaving 238 who received amphotericin B therapy alone. The total dose of amphotericin B ranged from 3 mg/kg body weight to 108 mg/kg. Eighteen patients received less than 10 mg/kg and 17 received 50 mg/kg or more, while the remainder received 10 to 49 mg/kg. For comparison, there were 100 chronic pulmonary histoplasmosis cases who did not receive amphotericin B therapy.

Deaths and relapses or progression among the treated and untreated cases during the first five years of follow-up are shown in Table 52-I. Of the

TABLE 52-I

Deaths and Relapses or Progression Among Treated and Untreated Chronic Pulmonary Histoplasmosis Patients Within the First Five Years of Follow-up

Amphotericin Therapy	*Total Patients*	*Relapsed or Progressed*		*Died*	
		No.	*%*	*No.*	*%*
Treated	238	36	15	69*	29
Untreated	100	57	57	46†	46

* Includes 11 patients who died after relapse.
† Includes 35 patients who had progression and died.

TABLE 52-II

Relapses Among Treated Chronic Pulmonary Histoplasmosis Patients
Within the First Five Years of Follow-up

Length of Follow-up (Years)	No. of Patients at Start of Year	Relapses	
		Number	Percent
1	238	12	5
2	202	8	4
3	172	7	4
4	147	5	3
5	123	1	1

treated cases, 33 (14%) relapsed and 3 were treatment failures. Among the 100 untreated cases, 57 (57%) continued to have *H. capsulatum* in their sputum or had progression of their disease as evidenced by chest roentgenogram. Fifty-one of the 57 remained positive or had progression of their disease during the first year after diagnosis. During the five-year follow-up period, there were 69 deaths (29%) among the patients receiving amphotericin B therapy and 46 deaths (46%) among the 100 untreated cases.

Since the treated and untreated groups were not comparable with respect to age, extent of disease, and duration of follow-up, the partial correlation coefficients were calculated. This method of analysis substantiated our conclusions of significantly more deaths in the untreated group than in the group receiving amphotericin B. Also, in the treated group, death was inversely related to the dose of amphotericin B. Significantly more of the patients receiving less than 35 mg/kg of body weight of amphotericin died (39%) than of those receiving more than 35 mg/kg (26%).

Relapse was not related significantly to dose of amphotericin B, stage of disease at diagnosis, or to any of the other variables except duration of follow-up, to which it was related inversely; that is, most relapses occurred early in the follow-up. Table 52-II shows that over one-half the relapses occurred in the first two years of follow-up; however, this was the period of time during which most of the patients were under observation. There was no significant difference in yearly relapse ratios during the first five years of follow-up, although there was a trend downward in that the ratio dropped from 5 percent during the first year to 1 percent during the fifth year.

Discussion

The use of amphotericin B in acute pulmonary histoplasmosis is not usually necessary, but in the occasional severe case without improvement after approximately two weeks of illness, amphotericin appears useful. Definite improvement was noted after only a few doses of the drug in the small number of cases observed. Fourteen to twenty-one days of therapy were given and, although the patients may have recovered without this, there is little doubt that the length of illness was shortened by the use of the drug.

Amphotericin has had a very marked effect on the course of disseminated histoplasmosis. In the NCDC Cooperative Mycoses Study, mortality among untreated disseminated cases was 83 percent compared to only 23 percent among those receiving amphotericin B. Other investigators have also reported good results with amphotericin B in disseminated histoplasmosis (Seabury and Dascomb, 1960; Little, 1962; Drutz, Spickard, Rogers and Koenig, 1968).

Most patients having chronic pulmonary histoplasmosis respond to amphotericin B therapy with sputum becoming negative for *H. capsulatum*, x-ray improvement, and improvement in their general condition. Failure to respond to the initial course of amphotericin B occurred in only 3 of the 238 patients. Relapses occurred in 33 or 14 percent of the treated group. There was no relationship between the total amount of drug received in the initial course of treatment and relapse. The majority of the relapses occurred during the first two years of observation, although the ratio of relapses to the number of patients followed ranged from 5 percent during the first year to 1 percent during the fifth year of observation.

In a randomized study of chronic pulmonary histoplasmosis treated with and without amphotericin B (Veterans Administration-Armed Forces Cooperative Study on Histoplasmosis, 1964) there was a good response in the treated patients while all but one of the untreated patients continued to have active disease as indicated by positive sputum cultures.

Even though considerable experience has been gained in the use of amphotericin B in treatment of histoplasmosis, there is a lack of information regarding the total dose that should be given and the length of time it should be given for the treatment of the different types of histoplasmosis. Our data show no relationship between total dose and relapse, although there was a relationship between total dose and deaths, there being more deaths in the group receiving less than 35 mg/kg body weight. One report (Drutz, Spickard, Rogers and Koenig, 1968) indicated that daily dosage could best be regulated by blood level determinations. The authors found that some patients maintained an adequate blood level and had a good response to therapy on a daily dose that was one fourth to one half of the usually recommended 1 mg/kg of body weight. The smaller daily doses resulted in fewer side reactions and a smaller total dose during the course of treatment, which could be helpful in avoiding significant renal damage in patients who may require several courses of amphotericin B for relapses.

Amphotericin B is an effective drug in the treatment of histoplasmosis, but there is a need for more precise information regarding the optimum daily dose, treatment schedules, and the total dose of drug to be used in treating the various types of histoplasmosis.

References

Communicable Disease Center Cooperative Mycoses Study (1963). Comparison of treated and untreated severe histoplasmosis. *J.A.M.A. 183*:823-829.

Drutz, D.J., Spickard, A., Rogers, D.E. and Koenig, M.G. (1968). Treatment of disseminated mycotic infections; A new approach to amphotericin B therapy. *Amer. J. Med., 45*:405-418.

Little, J.A. (1962). Histoplasmosis in childhood. *Quart. Rev. Pediat., 17*:32-36.

Seabury, J.H. and Dascomb, H.E. (1960). Experience with amphotericin B. *Ann. N.Y. Acad. Sci., 89*:202-220.

Veterans Administration-Armed Forces Cooperative Study on Histoplasmosis (1964). Histoplasmosis Cooperative Study II. Chronic pulmonary histoplasmosis treated with and without amphotericin B. *Amer. Rev. Resp. Dis., 89*:641-650.

Chapter 53

Status of Saramycetin, Hamycin, and 5-Fluorocytosine as Antifungal Agents

JOHN P. UTZ

ABSTRACT

From *in vitro* and especially *in vivo* studies saramycetin appears by the subcutaneous route to be a promising agent in the treatment of human infections with *Histoplasma capsulatum*, *Blastomyces dermatitidis* and perhaps *Sporothrix schenkii* and *Aspergullus fumigatus*. The drug will be available soon for further clinical investigation in patients with chronic cavitary histoplasmosis in a cooperative study. Hamycin has so far proved a useful agent by the oral route in a number of patients with blastomycosis, some with rather severe form involving lung and bone. Its present status is limited to investigation in a single center on an experimental basis. 5-Fluorocytosine appears to have marked chemotherapeutic activity in some patients with *Cryptococcus neoformans* and *Candida albicans* infections by the oral route of administration. At present it is available for clinical investigation on an experimental basis.

Saramycetin

THE antifungal agent, saramycetin, first described under the code name of X-5079C (Grunberg, Berger and Titsworth, 1961) is produced by the microorganism *Streptomyces saraceticus* when grown in a submerged culture on a soybean, flour, sugar, salts medium. Distinctive chemical characteristics include its polypeptide nature, sulfur content of 12 to 14 percent, and solubility of the sodium salt in water. Its molecular weight is estimated at 14,000. On hydrolysis large amounts of cystine are produced, in addition to heterocyclic sulfur acids, for which the name, saramycetic acid, has been proposed.

Chemotherapeutic activity was shown by these authors in experimental infections with *Histoplasma capsulatum* and *Blastomyces dermatitidis* in mice, with a curative dose subcutaneously for 50 percent (CD_{50}) of 2 to 5 mg/kg for the former and 15 to 20 mg/kg for the latter. Against *Candida albicans* the drug exerted no activity at doses of 200 mg/kg. These studies were confirmed and extended by Emmons (1961) who found the drug active in experimental *Coccidioides immitis* and *Sporothrix schenkii* infections in mice. He pointed out as well the remarkable therapeutic index: in acute toxicity studies the lethal dose for 50 percent of mice (LD_{50}) varied in different lots from 650 to 3300 mg/kg. This contrasted strikingly with the therapeutic dose of 5 mg/kg sufficient to prevent death in mice from otherwise fatal *H. capsulatum* infections.

It was appreciated early that there was a considerable greater activity *in vivo* than *in vitro*. *H. capsulatum* was able to grow in broth containing saramycetin in a concentration of 65,000µg/ml (Lones and Peacock, 1961). The difference in activity could not be explained on the basis of conversion to a more active form in mammalian tissue (Berger, Goldberg, Sternbach and Mueller, 1962; Gale, Kandall, and Welch, 1963). However, saramycetin was inactivated in modified Sabouraud's medium at temperatures of 30°C, so that in forty-eight hours 25 percent activity was lost, and at eight days 82 percent was lost. Activity of the drug was markedly decreased also by increased acidity, especially at pH values less than 6 (Lones and Peacock, 1963). However, in HeLa cell cultures growth of *H. capsulatum* was markedly suppressed for six days at concentrations (3µg/ml) achievable in serum. Relatively little is known about the mechanism of action. Gale (1963) showed that *Mucor corymbifer* has a markedly thickened wall when grown in the presence of saramycetin. This effect could be counteracted by the presence of sulfite and cystine.

In studies most recently summarized by Witorsch, Andriole, Emmons and Utz (1966), thirteen courses of therapy were given to eleven patients with histoplasmosis. With six courses there was objective clinical improvement and inability to culture the microorganism from specimens previously positive. There was relapse following two of these courses. Clinical response only was observed in three courses, and no effect was noted in four courses in three patients. The first of these, a patient with severe disseminated disease, received only two days of therapy. In the second patient treatment was discontinued after only five days, owing to a rapidly increasing alkaline phosphatase value. The third patient has a ten-year history of meningitis, which remained refractory to multiple courses of various antifungal agents. In this study the drug was administered every six hours with doses ranging from 3 to 17 mg/kg, but with most patients receiving 3 to 5 mg/kg per day. The total dosage varied from 42 mg to 38 gm per course, but in only five courses was the total dose more than 20 gm.

Sutliff (1964) administered saramycetin to three patients with chronic pulmonary histoplasmosis refractory to prior amphotericin B therapy. His total dosages ranged from 11.4 to 21.9 gm. In all three patients *H. capsulatum* could not subsequently be cultured from sputum beginning at times ranging from twelve to fifty-four days after commencement of therapy. In one patient only minimal changes were noted on the chest films. All three patients improved subjectively, one gained twenty pounds in weight, one became free of hemoptysis, and a third reported a substantial improvement in well-being.

Drouhet, Sureau, Destombes, Berod and Tapie (1962) treated a patient with severe disseminated histoplasmosis with saramycetin in dosage of 50 mg four times daily for fifteen days. *H. capsulatum* could not be recovered from palatal lesions previously positive. However, he had a relapse of his disease following therapy.

Procknow (1962) treated a patient with severe disseminated histoplasmosis with a total of 4.4 gm of saramycetin during a period of twenty-two days before the patient succumbed to an acute mycardial infarction. Prior to starting therapy, *H. capsulatum* had been isolated from oral ulcers, sputum, blood, bone marrow, and urine, but following three weeks of therapy, the organism could not be cultured from any source. At autopsy, microorganisms resembling *H. capsulatum* were seen in large numbers in adrenal granulomas, in small numbers in the spleen, kidneys, and blood, but not at all in liver, bone marrow, lymph nodes, or oral lesions.

Hamycin

Hamycin, an antibiotic produced by *Streptomyces pimprina*, resembles amphotericin B in being a polyene, and has a virtually identical ultraviolet spectrum and percentage composition of carbon, oxygen, and nitrogen. It differs from it, however, in that hamycin is soluble in methanolic calcium chloride, has a different infrared spectrum, and is more readily absorbed from the gastrointestinal tract, according to some observers. In studies of experimental *H. capsulatum* infections in mice (Williams, Bennett and Emmons, 1965) with a single intraperitoneal injection of the drug five days a week for four weeks (20 injections), in a dosage of approximately 2 mg/kg per day, two of ten mice survived, and in one of these *H. capsulatum* could not be cultured from the liver or spleen. In contrast with higher doses of drug and with the vehicle controls, all mice were dead of disease or drug within two weeks.

On our service six patients with histoplasmosis have received hamycin therapy. Of these, three had the chronic cavitary pulmonary form, and three had severe disseminated form. Two of the three patients with chronic cavitary disease failed to respond clinically, and *H. capsulatum* continued to be cultured from the sputum. The third patient improved clinically and the microorganism could no longer be cultured, but relapse occurred approximately eighteen months after institution of therapy. In the three patients with severe disseminated disease, there was remarkable clinical improvement in two and a failure to culture *H. capsulatum* from specimens previously positive. However, both of the patients relapsed. In the third patient no detectable clinical improvement occurred, and treatment had to be discontinued because of gastrointestinal intolerance. Two forms of drug have been employed. The first, a pressed tablet containing 125, 225, and 250 mg of drug. With this therapy, no serum levels were detected before a dosage of

10 mg/kg was reached. Thereafter, levels were not increased even though the dose was augmented to a maximum of 50 mg/kg per day. Serum levels ranged from 0µg to .09µg/ml. Following this a micronized preparation in capsular form was employed in doses of from 10 and 20 mg/kg per day. With the larger doses the serum concentrations ranged from trace to .125µg/ml. Analysis of the results of serum determinations revealed that the number of patients treated was too small to be statistically significant, but it was suggested that the pressed powder, micronized regimen produced better results than the pressed tablet alone (Utz, Witorsch, Williams, Emmons, Shadomy and Piggott, 1967; Utz, Shadomy and Shadomy, 1968).

5-Fluorocytosine

5-Fluorocytosine is an odorless, white, crystalline solid whose melting point is about 295°C with decomposition. Its molecular weight is 129.1, and it is fairly soluble in water (15% at 25°C). *In vitro* it exerted a variable chemotherapeutic effect against a number of fungi, notably, *C. albicans* and *A. niger*. Albino mice infected intravenously with *C. albicans, Cryptococcus neoformans, H. capsulatum* or *B. dermatitidis*, received the drug by the intraperitoneal or oral route. Chemotherapeutic activity was seen against *C. albicans* and *C. neoformans*, but not against *H. capsulatum* or *B. dermatitidis* (Grunberg, Titsworth, and Bennett, 1964).

5-Fluorocytosine has not thus far been tried in human histoplasmosis, and inview of the lack of laboratory studies to show effectiveness, it is unlikely to be used. However, the drug is active in some patients with *Cryptococcus* meningitis and severe *Candida* septicemias (Tassel and Madoff, 1968; Utz, Tynes, Shadomy, Duma, Kannan and Mason, 1969).

References

Berger, J., Goldberg, M.W., Sternbach, S.M. and Mueller, M. (1962). Antibiotic X-5079C. Ger. 1, 122, 670, Jan. 25, 1962. *Chem. Abstr.*, 56:14744 b.

Drouhet, E., Sureau, B., Destombes, J., Berod, J., and Tapie, P. (1962). Histoplasmose bucco-pharyngée chronique récidivante evoluant depuis 8 ans. Activitée thérapeutique l'amphotericine B et de l'antiobiotique X-5079C. *Bull. Soc. Franc. Dermat. Syph., 69:* 46-53.

Emmons, C.W. (1961). Chemotherapeutic and toxic activity of the antifungal agent X-5079C in experimental mycoses. *Amer. Rev. Resp. Dis.*, 84:507-513.

Gale, G.R., Kandall, S.M. and Welch, A.M. (1963). Observations on mechanism of action of the antifungal peptide, RO 2-7758. *Proc. Soc. Biol. Med.*, 113:179-182.

Gale, G.R. (1963). Effects of the antifungal peptide RO 2-7758 on morphology of *Mucor corymbifera. J. Bact.*, 85:823-827.

Grunberg, E., Berger, J. and Titsworth, E. (1961). Chemotherapeutic studies on a new antifungal agent X-5079C, effective against systemic mycoses. *Amer. Rev. Resp. Dis.*, 84:504-506.

Grunberg, E., Titsworth, E. and Bennett, J.E. (1964). Chemotherapeutic Activity of 5 Fluorocytosine. *Antimicrobial Agents and Chemotherapy—1963*. Ann Arbor, American Society for Microbiology, pp. 566-568.

Lones, G.W. and Peacock, C. (1961). Effect of the antifungal agent X-5079C on the growth of *Histoplasma capsulatum in vitro. Amer. Rev. Resp. Dis.,* 84:529-533.

Lones, G. W. and Peacock, C. (1963). Factors Affecting the Activity of Antibiotic X-5079C Against *Histoplasma capsulatum in vitro. Antimicrobial Agents and Chemotherapy—1962*. Ann Arbor, American Society for Microbiology, pp. 861-866.

Procknow, J.J. (1962). Effectiveness of X-5079C in the treatment of disseminated histoplasmosis and blastomycosis. *J. Lab. Clin. Med.,* 60:1005.

Sutliff, W.D. (1964). Antifungal Antibiotic RO 2-7758 Therapy of Chronic Pulmonary Histoplasmosis Cases Refractory to Amphotericin B. *Antimicrobial Agents and Chemotherapy—1963*. Ann Arbor, American Society for Microbiology, pp. 741-744.

Tassel, D. and Madoff, M.A. (1968). Treatment of *Candida* sepsis and *Cryptococcus* meningitis with 5 fluorocytosine. *J.A.M.A.,* 206:830-832.

Utz, J.P., Witorsch, P., Williams, T.W., Jr., Emmons, C.W., Shadomy, H.J. and Piggott, W. (1967). Hamycin: chemotherapeutic studies in systemic mycoses of man. *Amer. Rev. Resp. Dis.,* 95:506-509.

Utz, J.P., Shadomy, H.J. and Shadomy, S. (1968). Clinical and Laboratory Studies of a New Micronized Preparation of Hamycin in Systemic Mycoses in Man. *Antimicrobial Agents and Chemotherapy—1967*. Ann Arbor, American Society for Microbiology, pp. 113-117.

Utz, J.P., Tynes, B.S., Shadomy, H.J., Duma, R.J., Kannan, M.M. and Mason, K.N. (1969). 5 Fluorocytosine in Human Cryptococcosis. *Antimicrobial Agents and Chemotherapy—1968*. Ann Arbor, American Society for Microbiology, pp. 344-346.

Williams, T.W., Jr., Bennett, J.E. and Emmons, C.W. (1965). Chemotherapeutic and Toxic Activity of Hamycin in Experimental Mycoses. *Antimicrobial Agents and Chemotherapy—1964*. Ann Arbor, American Society for Microbiology, pp. 737-741.

Witorsch, P., Andriole, V.T., Emmons, C.W. and Utz, J.P. (1966). The polypeptide antibiotic agent (X-5079C): further studies in 39 patients. *Amer. Rev. Resp. Dis.,* 93: 876-888.

Chapter 54

Surgical Treatment
of Pulmonary Histoplasmosis

FELIX A. HUGHES, JR., CHARLES E. EASTRIDGE,
AND PADIATH A. ASLAM

A total of 43 patients with histoplasmosis who were treated surgically are presented. There were 23 patients with a chronic pulmonary type, 16 with pulmonary granulomas, and 4 with symptomatic calcified mediastinal granulomas, and 4 with symptomatic calcified mediastinal granulomas. In the twenty-three with chronic disease, there were 16 lobectomies, 5 segmental resections, and 6 plombage thoracoplasties. Wedge resection was used in sixteen with undiagnosed pulmonary granulomas, and excision was used in four with mediastinal granulomas. All cases were proven by culture or pathologic demonstration of the organisms.

Surgical conservatism without specific chemotherapy has been satisfactory in resecting solitary pulmonary or mediastinal granulomas that are due to histoplasmosis. No evidence of dissemination was noted following wedge resection of pulmonary granulomas or incision and evacuation of mediastinal granulomas. Chronic progressive histoplasmosis as indicated by cavitary or infiltrative disease justifies the use of amphotericin B as coverage during resection. In those with cavitary disease who are unable to withstand resection, good results may be obtained by resorting to collapse therapy combined with amphotericin B.

SURGICAL treatment for histoplasmosis is usually indicated in those patients with undiagnosed parenchymal granulomas in the cancer age group, symptomatic granulomas within the mediastinum, or in chronic progressive disease.

The most common reason for recommending operation in residual histoplasmosis was to either exclude bronchogenic carcinoma or to eliminate symptoms arising from complications of the inflammatory process. In contrast, surgical treatment is indicated in chronic progressive disease to remove the irreparably damaged lung tissue as well as the foci of infection.

The progressive nature and serious prognostic import of untreated chronic progressive histoplasmosis has been amply demonstrated by Furcolow (1963), and the need for specific medical and surgical treatment has been emphasized (Sutliff, Hughes, Ulrich and Burkett, 1953; Hughes, Whitaker, Lowry, Polk, Foley and Fox, 1954; Hughes, Burwell and Pate, 1956; Carr and Sutliff, 1964). The use of amphotericin B has been shown to improve prognosis when used in severe active disease (Furcolow, 1963; Sutliff, Andrews, Jones and Terry, 1964), and appears to favorably influence the results of surgery in chronic disease (Gryboski, Crutcher, Holloway, Mayo,

Segnitz and Eiseman, 1963; Polk and Bailey, 1960; Takaro, 1967; Changwoo, Kilman, Vasko and Andrews, 1969).

The purpose of this presentation is to review our experience in the surgical treatment of forty-three patients with histoplasmosis over the past twenty-three years.

Materials and Methods

There were 43 patients with histoplasmosis seen on the Thoracic Surgical Section over a twenty-three-year period. These fell into two distinct groups: there were 32 referred for diagnosis and treatment of suspicious lung lesions, and 11 with active histoplasmosis referred for surgical consideration following medical treatment.

All patients had before operation a general medical and routine laboratory evaluation which included smear and culture studies for acid-fast bacilli and fungi. In those with clinical evidence of reduced pulmonary reserve, ventilatory studies as well as blood gas determinations were carried out.

Following resection, histopathologic and culture studies were obtained from the resected tissue. Calcified nodes were decalcified, sectioned, and stained with methenamine silver technique in order to demonstrate *Histoplasma capsulatum* organisms. In those with proven active histoplasmosis, complement fixation tests were performed, and elevated titers were found in dilutions ranging from 1:8 to 1:520. These tests, when repeated, were found useful in following the course of the disease as well as confirming the clinical diagnosis.

Amphotericin B was not used to "cover" the risk of resection as Isoniazid is used in resections for tuberculosis. It was used, however, preoperatively and postoperatively in two patients with active histoplasmosis, and in six it was given sometime during the course of the active disease. In general, an attempt was made to effect a medical cure, and if this did not succeed, then surgical treatment was utilized in those deemed suitable because of localized disease.

Results

In five patients, a plombage thoracoplasty was performed rather than resection because of either bilateral active histoplasmosis, restricted pulmonary function, or severe arteriosclerotic heart disease. One of the five later required a contralateral plombage thoracoplasty for disease in the opposite lung. Two patients had resections performed later at the time of plombage removal. These resections were done for a persistent cavity in one and an intracavitary aspergilloma in the other (Fig. 54-1).

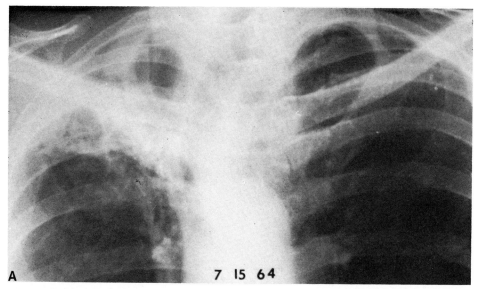

FIGURE 54-1A. Posterior anterior chest roentgenograms. FIGURE 54-1A. Residual right upper lobe cavity with intermittent hemotysis following treatment with amphotericin B.

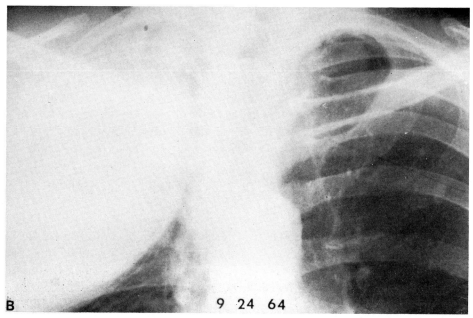

FIGURE 54-1B. A lucite plombage in the right upper thorax with collapse of the cavity.

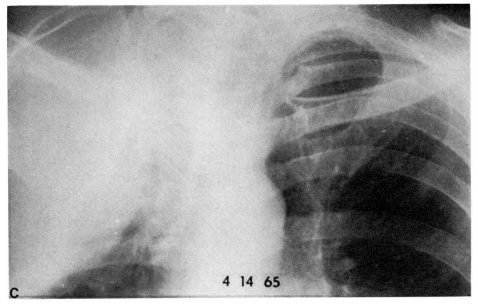

4 14 65

C

FIGURE 54-1C. The appearance of the chest following removal of the plombage and a right upper lobectomy. Intracavitary aspergillus was present.

Of the five patients with active disease treated by plombage thoraco-plasty, four remained well, and one died three years later from histoplasmo-sis. Two required a second operation, one a contralateral plombage, and the other a right upper lobectomy at the time of plombage removal. Four patients in this group received amphotericin B during the course of treatment. In the one with recurrent disease, amphotericin B was given in both the pre-operative and the postoperative periods.

Five lobectomies were done on 4 of the 6 patients with diagnosed active disease, resulting in sputum conversion immediately in 3 and within two years in the remaining 1. Segmental resection was the only treatment in 2 (Table 54-I). Of these, 1 had an immediate sputum conversion, and the other sputum converted to negative within one year. Two complications oc-curred in this group. In one there was a contralateral spread requiring lo-bectomy, and in the other there was a residual pleural space requiring a tho-racoplasty.

Of the 12 patients with undiagnosed active disease at operation, lobec-tomy was done in 10 and segmental resection in 2. A complicating bron-chopleural fistula and empyema occurred in 1, requiring a modified Schede thoracoplasty for correction. None of them received amphotericin B, and all remained well following the resectional surgery (Table 54-II).

There were sixteen who had wedge resections for coin lesions (Table 54-III). All of these have remained well despite the lack of medical coverage.

TABLE 54-I

Chronic Pulmonary Histoplasmosis

Case	Diagnosis	Operation	Complications	Secondary Operations	Drugs	Comment
1	Sputum	LUL	Recurrent RUL disease	RUL	E.V.	Well
2	Sputum	Segmental	Recurrent disease	Thoracoplasty	MRD112	Well
3	Sputum	LUL, Segmental decortication	Fistula and empyema	Drainage	0	Died 11 years later cor pulmonale
4	Sputum	Plombage	Recurrent RUL disease	Plombage	0	TB previously, well
5	Sputum	Plombage	Persistent cavity	LUL	Amphotericin B(pre and post)	Well
6	Sputum	Plombage	0	0	Amphotericin B(pre and post)	Well
7	Sputum	Plombage	Progressive disease	0	Amphotericin B(pre and post)	Died 3 years later Histoplasmosis
8	Sputum	Plombage	Recurrent disease	RUL	Amphotericin B(preop.)	Intracavitary Asperigullus
9	Sputum	Segmental	0	0	Amphotericin B(preop.)	Well
10	Sputum	RUL	0	0	Amphotericin B(preop.)	Active 1 year postoperative, now well
11	Sputum	RUL	0	0	Amphotericin B(preop.)	Well

TABLE 54-II

Chronic Pulmonary Histoplasmosis
(Diagnosis from Specimen)

Case	Diagnosis	Operation	Complications	Secondary Operation	Drugs	Comment
1	Tissue culture	Segmental	Fistula & Empyema	Thoracoplasty	0	Died emphysema 8 years later
2	Tissue culture	RUL	0	0	EV	Died TB 2 years later
3	Tissue culture	RUL	0	0	0	Well
4	Tissue culture	Segmental	0	0	0	Well
5	Tissue culture	RUL	Fistula & empyema	Drainage	0	Well
6	Tissue culture	RUL	0	0	0	Well
7	Tissue culture	RUL	0	0	0	Well
8	Tissue stains	RUL	0	0	Amphotericin B(postop)	LUL 8 mo. previously for TB
9	Tissue stain	RUL	0	0	0	Intracavitary Aspergillus—Died leukemia 2 years later
10	Tissue stain	LUL	0	0	0	Well
11	Tissue stain	RUL	0	0	0	Intracavitary Aspergillus-well
12	Tissue stain	RUL	0	0	0	Well

TABLE 54-III

Coin Lesions Removed by Wedge Resection

Case	Site	Diagnosis	Results
1	LUL	Tissue culture	Good
2	LLL	Tissue culture	Good
3	RUL	Tissue culture	Good
4	LLL	Skin test	Good
5	LLL	Tissue stain	Good
6	RLL	Tissue stain	Good
7	LUL	Tissue stain	Good
8	LLL	Tissue stain	Good
9	LLL	Skin test	Good
10	LUL	Tissue stain	Good
11	RLL	Tissue culture	Good
12	RUL	Tissue stain	Good
13	LLL	Tissue stain	Good
14	LUL	Tissue stain	Good
15	LUL	Tissue stain	Good
16	LUL	Tissue stain	Good

In four patients with complications associated with calcified nodes secondary to histoplasmosis, lobectomy was required in two for atelectasis and bronchiectasis, and in the others simple excision of the eroding calcified nodes resulted in cessation of hemoptysis (Table 54-IV).

Discussion

The majority of patients in this series were referred with suspicious lesions within the lung or with unexplained hemoptysis. Despite careful evaluation by bronchoscopy, skin tests, sputum smears and cultures, and special roentgenograms, the diagnosis was rarely established clinically. In many, resections were performed primarily to exclude the diagnosis of bronchogenic carcinoma (Fig. 54-2).

The solitary nodule when it occurs in men, especially those past middle

TABLE 54-IV

Calcified Mediastinal and Hilar Granuloma due to Histoplasmosis

Case	Clinical Findings	Preoperative Diagnosis	Operation	Operative Findings	Results
1	Recurrent ML infections Atelectasis middle lobe	Carcinoma	RML	Atelectasis Bronchiectasis	Good
2	Recurrent hemoptysis Rib notching Decreased femoral pulse	Coarctation aorta Constricting calcified glands	Repair coarctation Excision calcified hilar glands	Coarctation aorta Eroding calcified gland	Good
3	Recurrent right lower lobe pneumonia Hemoptysis	Bronchiectasis	RLL	Contracted lobe	Good
4	Hemoptysis Endobronchial mass	Bronchial adenoma	Excision calcified glands	Eroding calcified gland	Good

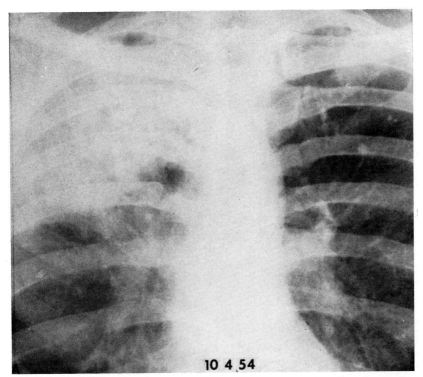

10 4 54

FIGURE 54-2A. Posterior anterior chest roentgenograms. FIGURE 54-2A. An undiagnosed right upper lobe infiltrate.

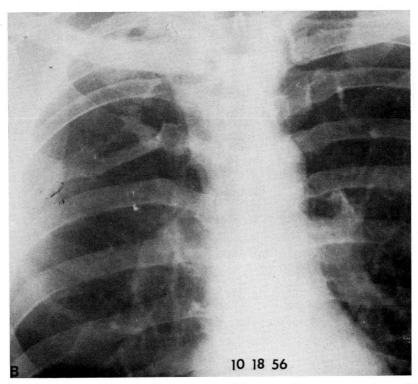

10 18 56

FIGURE 54-2B. The chest following right upper lobectomy for pneumonic form of histo-plasmosis.

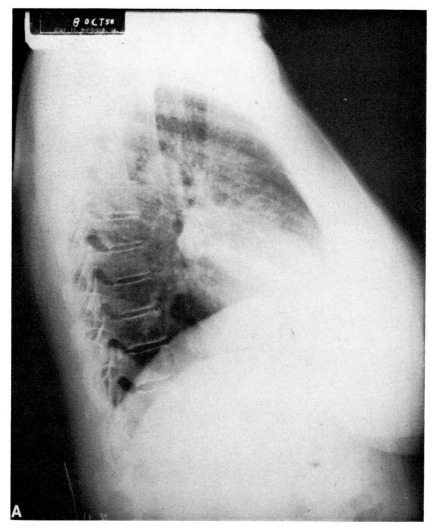

FIGURE 54-3A. Right lateral chest roentgenogram showing atelectasis of the right middle lobe and calcified mediastinal granulomata.

age, usually presents a difficult diagnostic problem. If these nodules can be identified as stable granulomas, then resection is not indicated. Stable granulomatous nodules usually represent a stage of healing, and dissemination is unlikely. The solitary nodules which we feel are safe to observe without resection are (1) those with solid calcification, (2) those with a large central core of calcium, (3) those with concentric rings of calcification, and (4) those heavily stippled with evidence of stability for one year. If the diagnosis is uncertain, these nodules are removed by wedge resection, with clamps isolating the area from the circulation. Frozen section diagnosis is obtained immediately from a portion of the nodule, while the rest of the specimen is used for bacteriologic and fungus cultures. There were no significant postoperative complications in this series. This clinical experience reemphasizes the benignity of surgical resection for localized histoplasmosis granuloma. The recorded incidence of wedge resections in this and previous studies indicates that conservation of pulmonary tissue is justified and dissemination is not apparent despite the fact that these lesions are often surrounded by satellite nodules.

Mediastinal granulomas due to *H. capsulatum* are responsible for a wide spectrum of chest disorders. These granulomata when heavily calcified have a high incidence of complications. The most common complications encountered in this group were hemoptysis, tumorlike endobronchial projections, broncholiths, and atelectasis followed by bronchiectasis (Fig. 54-3).

The pathological sequence of mediastinal granulomas seems to be an early granulomatous inflammatory change in the lymph nodes draining a given region of the lung. Overwhelming infection leads to capsular involvement and involvement of adjacent nodes by an inflammatory reaction. The

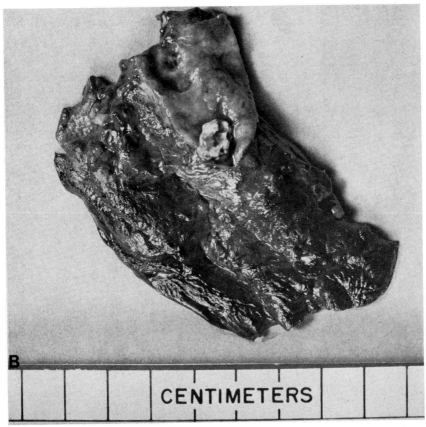

FIGURE 54-3B. Photograph showing a contracted right middle lobe with obstructing broncholith and bronchiectasis. Decalcification and staining revealed *Histoplasma capsulatum* organisms.

resulting proliferative fibrotic reaction may not only encompass groups of lymph nodes but may also involve the surrounding mediastinal structures. As in other granulomatous reactions, there is central caseation and liquefaction followed in time by calcification of the necrotic elements. Even though these totally calcified lesions may be quiescent for years, there is a local erosive property which may become manifested at any period.

Resection of mediastinal or hilar granulomas is often required to stop bleeding, rule out endobronchial tumors in partial erosion, or to remove destroyed lung tissue resulting from bronchial obstruction. Since these calcified granulomas are usually attached to other important mediastinal structures by dense fibrous tissue, they can rarely be removed *in toto* with the capsule intact. The operative technique used therefore is to open the mass, evacuate the contents, and excise as much of the wall as possible, leaving the attached portion intact.

In patients with chronic progressive histoplasmosis, the indications for resection should parallel in general those used for pulmonary tuberculosis. There is ample clinical and pathological evidence to indicate that cavitary or fibrocaseous histoplasmosis suggests poor tissue response to this reinfection-type disease, and the threat of subsequent progression is great. Resection accomplishes the removal of the damaged lung tissue with its contained foci of infection, thereby interrupting the general progression of the disease (Fig. 54-4).

In the past eight years, amphotericin B has been used in preoperative preparation of those patients in whom *H. capsulatum* is recovered from the sputum by smear or culture. It is used in the postoperative period only in those with reactivation manifested by a positive sputum or radiological evidence of spread.

Before amphotericin B became available, the complications following resection in cavitary disease were frequent in contrast to the lack of complications encountered in noncavitary disease. Of the complications encountered, bronchopleural fistulae, empyema, and residual air spaces were the most frequent.

There was a special group of five patients with cavitary disease in whom resection was contraindicated because of the extent of the disease, lack of pulmonary reserve, or severe cardiovascular disease. In this group, plombage thoracoplasty was used in combination with antimycotic drugs. The results obtained were good. This type of thoracoplasty was chosen because collapse of the underlying cavities could be accomplished with a minimal loss of pulmonary function and reduced stress on the cardiovascular system (Fig. 54-5).

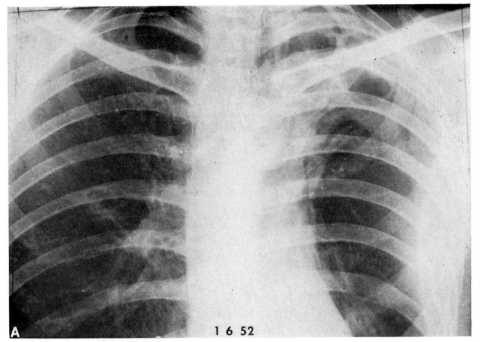

FIGURE 54-4A. Posterior anterior chest roentgenograms. FIGURE 54-4A. Large left upper lobe and small right hilar cavity with a left pleural effusion resulting from histoplasmosis.

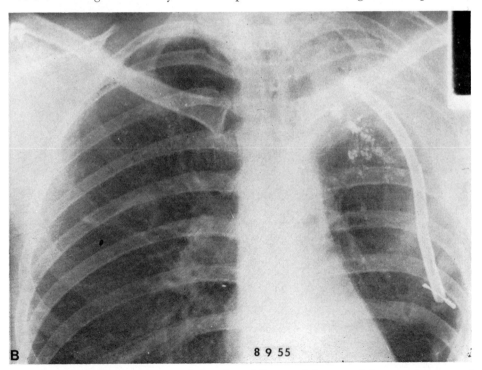

FIGURE 54-4B. The appearance of the chest following left upper lobectomy, segmental resection superior segment left lower lobe, and decortication. Following resection the right hilar cavity showed enlargement.

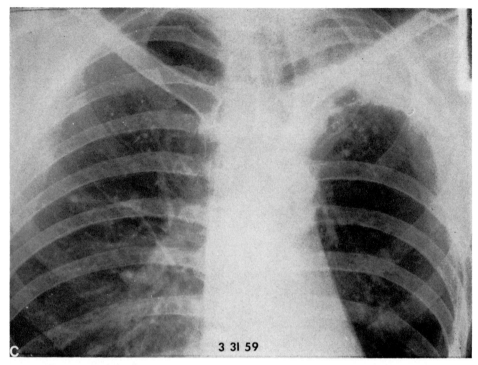

FIGURE 54-4C. The appearance of the chest four years following recovery.

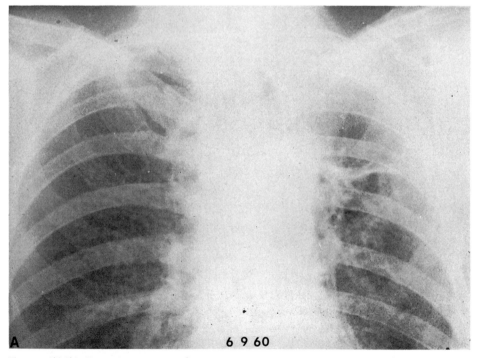

FIGURE 54-5A. Posterior anterior chest roentgenograms. FIGURE 54-5A. A large left upper lobe cavity due to histoplasmosis.

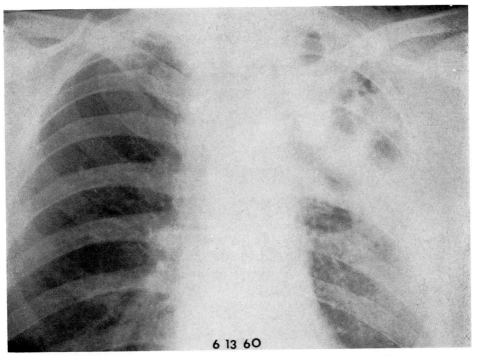

Figure 54-5B. The appearance of the chest following a lucite plombage.

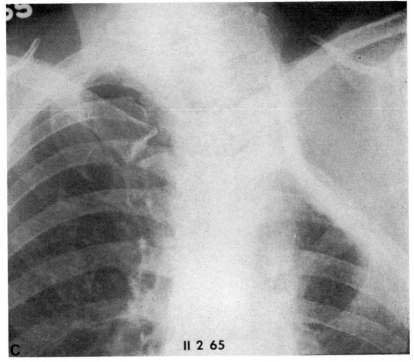

Figure 54-5C. The appearance of the chest five years following removal of the plombage and a left upper lobectomy.

References

Carr, D. and Sutliff, W.D. (1964). The Treatment of Mycotic and Parasitic Diseases of the Chest. *Histoplasmosis*. Springfield, Thomas, pp. 31-54.

Changwoo, Ahm, Kilman, J.W., Vasko, J.S. and Andrews, H.C. (1969). The therapy of cavitary pulmonary histoplasmosis. *J. Thorac. Cardiovasc. Surg.*, 57:42-51.

Committee on Fungus Diseases, Subcommittee on Therapy, Indications for chemotherapy in the pulmonary mycoses. *Dis. Chest*, 55:160-162, 1969.

Furcolow, M.L. (1963). Comparison of treated and untreated severe histoplasmosis. *J.A.M.A.*, 183:823-829.

Gryboski, W.A., Crutcher, R.R., Holloway, J.B., Mayo P., Segnitz, R.H. and Eiseman, B. (1963). Surgical aspects of histoplasmosis. *Arch. Surg.*, 87:590-599.

Hughes, F., Burwell, J. and Pate, J. (1956). The surgical treatment of chronic pulmonary histoplasmosis. Transactions of the 15th Conference on Chemotherapy of Tuberculosis. pp. 313-320, Feb. 1956. Veterans Administration Central Office, Department of Medicine and Surgery, Washington, D.C.

Hughes, F.A., Whitaker, H., Lowry, C., Polk, J., Foley, F. and Fox, F. (1954). Resection for mycotic pulmonary disease. *Dis. Chest*, 25:334-349.

Polk, J.W. and Bailey, A.H. (1960). Surgical treatment of histoplasmosis with case reports. *Minn. Med.*, 43:665-669.

Sutliff, W.C., Andrews, C.E., Jones, E. and Terry, R.T. (1964). Histoplasmosis cooperative study II. Chronic pulmonary histoplasmosis treated with and without amphotericin B. *Am. Rev. Resp. Dis.*, 89:641-650.

Sutliff, W.D., Hughes, F.A., Ulrich, E. and Burkett, L.L. (1953). Active chronic pulmonary histoplasmosis. *Arc. Intern. Med.*, 92:571-586.

Takaro, T. (1967). Mycotic infections of interest to thoracic surgeons. *Ann. Thorac. Surg.*, 3:71-93.

Chapter 55

Surgery for Cavitary Histoplasmosis

JOHN W. POLK

ABSTRACT

A short résumé of our experiences with cavitary histoplasmosis has been presented. Thirty-eight patients had pulmonary resection with amphotericin B. There were seven postoperative complications in this group and nine patients showed progression of their disease over a long period of time. A second group of thirty-eight patients were presented having surgery and therapy with amphotericin B, either pre- or post-operatively. In this group, the progression of the disease was nil, but the postoperative complication rate was around 20 percent. This figure is similar to the figure for those without amphotericin B coverage. In spite of this, however, we feel that amphotericin B should be given to all patients in whom the diagnosis is established prior to surgical resection, or in postoperative period when the diagnosis is made from the resected specimen. It appears to be most beneficial here in preventing progression of the disease.

THE organism *Histoplasma capsulatum* causes a specific fungus infection which presents many and complicated clinical manifestations. The symptoms vary from the picture seen in epidemic histoplasmosis causing flu-like symptoms to the complication picture of disseminated disease. Between these extremes we have chronic progressive cavitary histoplasmosis, focalized lesions, right middle lobe syndromes, extensive infiltrations, and almost any other type of pulmonary manifestation that has been described for other diseases. In fact, pulmonary histoplasmosis, like pulmonary tuberculosis, often mimics other diseases.

Since chronic progressive cavitary histoplasmosis is the most frequent type of disease that we see as surgeons, this phase of the disease will be discussed. It is important to remember prior to the advent of amphotericin B therapy, approximately 80 percent of the people with chronic progressive cavitary pulmonary histoplasmosis expired within five to six years. Selected groups did well with localized pulmonary resections, but the recurrence rate was high.

Cavitary histoplasmosis is the most frequent form of the disease for which we have performed surgical resection. Seventy-six patients have had varying surgical procedures and were in this category. Forty of the patients in this group had positive sputum for *H. capsulatum* and definite diagnosis of cavitary histoplasmosis established preoperatively. In nineteen patients the diagnosis of cavitary histoplasmosis was strongly suspected because of roentgenological evidence of cavitary disease with positive histoplasmin skin test, negative skin test for tuberculosis, and a positive serology test. The diagnosis in the remaining seventeen was made postoperatively from the resected specimen. Seven of this last group had been diagnosed as pulmonary tuberculosis by positive sputum cultures. Resectional surgery had been performed as part of the treatment for the cavitary tuberculosis. Both tubercle bacilli and *H. capsulatum* were found on the pathological examinations of the resected lung. Bronchogenic carcinoma was the diagnosis in three of these patients; again, *H. capsulatum* was demonstrated in the resected tissue.

TABLE 55-I

Results of Treatment in Seventy-Six Cases of Cavitary Histoplasmosis

	Number of Points	*Postoperative Complications No. (96)*	*Late Mortality due to Histoplasmosis No. (90)*
Surgery only	38	7 (18)	3 (8)
Surgery plus adequate preoperative amphotericin B	9	4 (44)	0
Surgery plus adequate post-operative amphotericin B	5	1 (20)	0
Surgery plus inadequate post-operative amphotericin B	6	1 (20)	1
Surgery plus adequate pre- and post-operative amphotericin B	15	3 (20)	1 (6.5)
Surgery plus inadequate pre- and post-operative amphotericin B	3	1 (33)	0

Since the advent of amphotericin B, the life expectancy of a patient with cavitary disease has improved remarkably. Furcolow (1963) and Sutliff, Andrews, Jones and Terry (1964) reported encouraging results in the treatment of chronic cavitary histoplasmosis with amphotericin B, as shown by sputum conversion, x-ray improvement, and reduced mortality. We recommend that a total dose of 2 gm of amphotericin B be given before we feel that the patient has had adequate therapy. Patients described by Sutliff (1964) and Furcolow (1963) who were treated adequately have reduced the mortality rate to 15 percent as compared to an inadequately treated group with four-year mortality rate of 25 percent and recurrence rate much higher. Diveley and McCracken (1966) reported twenty-nine cases of surgically treated cavitary histoplasmosis without amphotericin B coverage, and Polk, Cubiles and Buckingham (1957) reported good results on seventeen of twenty-one operative cases for cavitary histoplasmosis. In one of the later reviews, Ahn, Kilman, Vasko and Andrews (1969) reported a 9.6 percent mortality among a group of 114 patients treated surgically without amphotericin B coverage. In our complete group of 38 patients treated surgically without amphotericin B coverage, there have been 2 immediate postoperative deaths due to respiratory failure and 3 late deaths due to progression of disease in an average follow-up of sixty months. (There have been 8 other patients with recurrence.)

Levene, Slesh, Torres and Saliba (1968) reported 24 cases of surgically treated, cavitary histoplasmosis; 10 patients had concomitant amphotericin B and surgical therapy, and 12 patients had only postoperative amphotericin B therapy. They reported 6 postoperative complications in each group. They concluded that amphotericin B offers little protection to immediate postoperative complications but appears to have a beneficial effect in the long-term results. We have mentioned our thirty-eight patients who had definitive surgical procedures without amphotericin B coverage. Thirty-eight patients also received combined treatment with amphotericin B and surgery. Of these, nine patients had what we considered adequate preoperative amphotericin B. There were four postoperative complications but no mortality. Five patients had surgery plus adequate postoperative amphotericin B therapy, with one minor postoperative complication in this group. Again, there were no deaths. Six patients had surgery and what we considered inadequate postoperative amphotericin B. There was one complication in this group and one late death due to progression of disease. Fifteen patients had adequate pre- and post-operative amphotericin B therapy plus surgery. In this group, there were three postoperative complications. Three patients had inadequate pre- and post-operative amphotericin B plus surgery. Again, there was one postoperative complication.

From the above-mentioned figures we have developed the same conclusions as Levene *et al.* (1968), that is, that even though our series and his are small, amphotericin B seems to offer little protection to the immediate postoperative complications but is beneficial value in the long-term results, especially when we consider progression of the disease as our primary target.

References

Ahn, C., Kilman, J.W., Vasko, J.S., and Andrews, N.C. (1969). The therapy of cavitary pulmonary histoplasmosis. *Thorac. Cardiovas. Surg.*, 57:43.

Diveley, W. and McCracken, R. (1966). Cavitary pulmonary histoplasmosis treated by pulmonary resection. *Ann. Surg.*, 163:921.

Furcolow, M.L. (1963). A Communicable Disease Center Cooperative Mycosis Study. Comparison of treated and untreated severe histoplasmosis. *J.A.M.A. 183*:823-829.

Levene, N., Slesh, M.Z., Torres, J. and Saliba, N.A. (1968). Surgical aspects of chronic progressive cavitary pulmonary histoplasmosis. *Ann. Thorac. Surg.*, 5:23-29.

Polk, J.W., Cubiles, J.A. and Buckingham, W.W. (1957). The surgical treatment of chronic progressive pulmonary histoplasmosis. *J. Thorac. Surg.*, 34:323.

Sutliff, W.D., Andrews, C.E., Jones, E. and Terry, R.T. (1964). Histoplasmosis Cooperative Study. Chronic pulmonary histoplasmosis treated with or without amphotericin B. *Amer. Rev. Resp. Dis.*, 89:641.

Chapter 56

Result of Surgical Treatment in Chronic Pulmonic Histoplasmosis

NATHAN LEVENE, ALLONZO-RULLODA BORJA, THOMAS RUFFIN HOOD,
AND N. ALEXANDER SALIBA

ABSTRACT

Thirty-three cases of surgically treated histoplasmosis were reviewed. Seven were noncavitary while twenty-six were cavitary pulmonary histoplasmosis. Among the noncavitary histoplasmosis only one had a complication. There were no reactivations or mortality. The over all complication among the cavitary histoplasmosis is 46 percent. Adjuvant amphotericin B treatment given preoperatively and postoperatively decreased the incidence of complications. The greatest benefit from the amphotericin B treatment appears to be the marked reduction of postoperative reactivation. The long-term result justifies surgery as shown by the number of patients who resumed working (36%) and those who became symptom free (28%). There was only one fatality (3.6%), and this occurred sixty-five months after operation.

THE current treatment of chronic cavitary pulmonary histoplasmosis is amphotericin B and surgical resection (Ahn, Kilman, Vasko and Andrews, 1969; Beatty, Levene, Saliba and Coelho, 1962; Katz, 1960; Levene, Slesh, Torres and Saliba, 1968; Takaro, 1967; Yates, Langeluttig and Brasher, 1960). Although claims of good results have been reported in the past in the surgical resection of localized histoplasmosis, there is no justification at present for such procedure in cavitary disease without adjuvant amphotericin B coverage.

In the chronic phase of the disease amphotericin B is at best only a suppressive drug with recurrences after cessation of treatment in a number of cases (Veterans Administration-Armed Forces Cooperative Study, 1964). About one half of the resected surgical specimens are still positive for *Histoplasma capsulatum* even after the administration of amphotericin B. Surgical resection offers additional definitive treatment which may hopefully reduce the incidence of reactivation. The necessity for removal of significant localized disease is greatly influenced by the relentless and progressive course it follows, marked by exacerbations, remissions, dissemination, parenchymal destruction, incapacitation, and ultimately even death. It is reported that amphotericin B, if used alone, decreases the mortality to 15 percent (Furcolow, 1963), and if used along with surgery, the mortality is further reduced to 6 percent (Ahn *et al.* 1969).

We have reviewed a series of thirty-three cases of surgically treated histoplasmosis that we have encountered, and these will serve as the basis for this presentation.

Clinical Material

Thirty-three cases of pulmonary histoplasmosis treated by resection from 1955 to July, 1969, were reviewed. There were 27 males and 6 females. The youngest patient is eleven years and the oldest is sixty-three years. Seven were between 30 to 39 years (21%), 11 between 40 to 49 years (33%) and 8 between 50 to 59 years (27%). Seven cases were noncavitary granulomatous lesions, while twenty-six were chronic cavitary cases. Because of their divergent postoperative behavior, the noncavitary and cavitary lesions will be divided into Group I and Group II, respectively, and discussed separately. The average postoperative follow-up is 54 months in twenty-five cases, 2 to 6 months in seven cases and less than 2 months in one case.

Result

Group I. Noncavitary Granulomatous Pulmonary Histoplasmosis (Seven Cases)

They generally follow a benign postoperative course. Two cases had lobectomy; one, segmenectomy; three, wedge resection; and two, exploratory thoracotomy and biopsy. There was one complication, but no incidence of reactivation or mortality. The long-term follow-up includes 4 who are well and working, 2 symptom free, and 1 whose status could not be determined.

Group II. Chronic Progressive Cavitary Pulmonary Histoplasmosis (Twenty-Six Cases)

For the purpose of this study, anything that was even suggestive of a postoperative complication or a reactivation has been appropriately labeled as such. Other reports may not have had this liberal interpretation, and this may explain our relatively higher complication rate (Table 56-I).

In the outline of complications 5 patients had no preoperative amphotericin B but received treatment postoperatively; 12 had pre- and post-operative amphotericin B; 9 cases had no treatment at all, and 1 was lost to follow-up immediately after discharge (Table 56-II). The dosage range of amphotericin B given with surgery was 540 mg to 2500 mg, most patients receiving less than 2 gm. The reactivation rate at least two months after surgery was 23 percent, and this is seen in (Table 56-III) in relation to amphotericin B treatment.

This analysis points to the significant decrease in complications and reac-

TABLE 56-I

Surgical Procedure and Associated Complication in Chronic Cavitary Pulmonary Histoplasmosis

Procedure	Cases	Complications
Lobectomy	11	5 (45%)
Lobectomy and segmental resection	3	3 (100%)
Two lobes	1	1
Pneumonectomy	2	0
Segmental resection	7	3 (43%)
Wedge resection	2	0
Total	26	12 (46%)

tivation in those patients who received both pre- and post-operative amphotericin B. We, therefore, feel that in all suspect cases such as those with positive serology, amphotericin B coverage should be seriously considered whenever pulmonary surgery is carried out for a more definitive diagnosis.

Long-term Result

Nine cases were back working following discharge. Seven were asymptomatic but not working, but these include two housewives doing routine house chores. One is symptomatic with pulmonary insufficiency and in two the disease has not been eliminated. The current status in six is unknown. One died sixty-five months after the initial resection from acute superior vena cava obstruction.

Discussion

Although the vast majority of primary infection with *H. capsulatum* is mild and self-limiting, a certain proportion of cases either disseminate or

TABLE 56-II

Frequency and Type of Complications Related to Amphotericin B Treatment in Surgical Resection (Chronic Cavitary Histoplasmosis)

Types of Complications	No Preoperative But Postoperative Amphotericin B	Pre and Postoperative Amphotericin B	No Amphotericin B*
None	1	8	5
Empyema		1	2
Spread first month	0	0	0
Bronchopleural fistula	3		1
Hydropneumothorax		1	
Air space	1	2	1
Total number of cases	5	12	9

* One of the cases has no follow-up after discharge from the hospital.

TABLE 56-III

Reactivation Following Surgery in Relation to Amphotericin B Coverage
(Chronic Cavitary Histoplasmosis)

Treatment	Cases*	Reactivation After 2 Months
No preoperative but with postoperative treatment	5	2 (40%)
With pre- and post-operative treatment	12	1 (8%)
No amphotericin B treatment	8	3 (37%)

* One of the cases has no follow-up after discharge from the hospital.

progress to the chronic phase of the disease. The mortality of untreated disseminated histoplasmosis is about 83 percent. In the chronic phase, one-third are dead in 3.6 years without treatment. Of those that survive, two-thirds are at least 50 percent incapacitated (United States Public Health Service Cooperative Mycosis Study, 1961). The disseminated form is essentially a medical problem; however, the indolent, relentless course that the chronic type pursues demands more definitive treatment. In the disseminated phase, amphotericin B is recognized as the drug of choice, whereas in the chronic phase amphotericin B is at best only suppressive. Conversion of sputum usually occurs several weeks after the institution of amphotericin B treatment, sometimes to recur after the discontinuance of the drug. Therefore, destroyed areas of lung should be considered for resectional surgery when feasible.

In the surgical resection of histoplasmosis the same principles were applied as in any other thoracic surgery, yet in spite of this, our complication rate in histoplasmosis has been consistently higher than in other thoracotomies. These included air space, empyema, bronchopleural fistula and hydropneumothorax. Contrary to other reports, we believe that these complications are inherent to the disease process, rather than those which generally occur in thoracic surgery.

The overall complication rate in cavitary disease is (46%). The most frequent is postresectional air space (30%) and bronchopleural fistula (30%). Empyema occurred in three cases. No spread of disease occurred in the immediate postoperative period. The cases with preoperative and postoperative amphotericin B treatment had a slightly lower complication rate (30%) than those with no treatment at all (50%). Those with no preoperative treatment but with postoperative treatment have an incidence of 80 percent complications (Table 56-II). We cannot explain the reason for the higher complication rate for those with only postoperative amphotericin B treatment compared to those without any treatment. All complications were treated accordingly and there was no postoperative mortality.

Reactivation after resection is rarely mentioned in other reports. Long-term follow-up in our series has shown that this can occur after surgery. In chronic untreated cases, the progression of the disease is 23 percent in the first year, 29 percent in the second year, and 64 percent in the sixth year (Furcolow, 1963). In our series of surgically treated cases without preoperative but with postoperative amphotericin B treatment, the reactivation rate is 40%, while those not treated at all have reactivation rate of 37 percent (Table 56-III). Only 8 percent of the cases who had preoperative and postoperative amphotericin B treatment developed reactivation. In this particular phase of the disease amphotericin B treatment seems to provide the most benefit. The only mortality (3.8%) occurred in a fifty-six-year-old man who had the right upper lobe and middle lobe removed and later developed empyema which required thoracoplasty. He had a protracted course and eventually died 65 months later from acute superior vena caval obstruction.

The end result of 36 percent working and 28 percent asymptomatic justifies the performance of surgery in an otherwise progressively debilitating and fatal disease. The decrease in complications and reactivation, more than justifies the use of amphotericin B.

References

Ahn, C., Kilman, J.W., Vasko, J.S., and Andrews, H.C. (1969). The therapy of cavitary pulmonary histoplasmosis. *J. Thorac. Cardiovasc. Surg., 57*:42-51.

Beatty, O.W., Levene, N., Saliba, A. and Coelho, J.C. (1962). Surgical therapy of chronic pulmonary histoplasmosis with and without Amphotericin B. *J. Thorac. Cardiovasc. Surg., 44*:228.

Furcolow, M.L. (1963). A communicable disease center cooperative mycosis study. Comparison of treated and untreated severe histoplasmosis. *J.A.M.A., 183*:823-829.

Katz, S.C. (1960). Chronic fibrocavitary histoplasmosis. *G.P. 21*:137.

Levene, N., Slesh, M.Z., Torres, J. and Saliba, A. (1968). Surgical aspect of chronic progressive cavitary pulmonary histoplasmosis. *Ann. Thorac. Surg., 5*:23-29.

Takaro, T. (1967). Mycotic infections of interest to thoracic surgeons. *Ann. Thorac. Surg., 3*:71.

United States Public Health Service Cooperative Mycosis Study (1961). Cause and prognosis of untreated histoplasmosis. *J.A.M.A., 177*:292.

Veterans Administration-Arm Forces Cooperative Study (1964). Histoplasmosis cooperative study. *Amer. Rev. Resp. Dis., 89*:641-650.

Yates, J.L., Langeluttig, V.H. and Brasher, C.A. (1960). Medical Management of Histoplasmosis. *Histoplasmosis*. Springfield, *Thomas*, pp. 449-470.

Part VII
Quo Vadis

Chapter 57

Unanswered Clinical Problems in Histoplasmosis

MICHAEL L. FURCOLOW

ABSTRACT

The purpose of this paper is to describe some of the many unanswered problems which remain in the diagnosis and treatment of histoplasmosis, in particular, the need for further studies in immunology of the disease highlighted by some recent papers that have been presented at this conference, and the possibility of genetic, immunologic, and other deficiencies playing a large part in the outcome of the disease, and the need for better evaluation of the therapeutic agents which are presently in use, and the development, if possible, of new agents. The racial and other differences in immunity certainly need to be investigated as well as the differences in sex. The effect of cortisone on dissemination on the disease needs to be investigated further. In short, there are many unanswered clinical problems which are highlighted in this presentation.

ONE might begin the discussion of unanswered clinical problems by posing the simple question as to why some people become ill with histoplasmosis, some remain well, and some die. It used to be that we were satisfied to accept the proposition that there was a difference in peoples' "immunity" and that this accounted for their different response in terms of illness to various infections. I expect this dates back to the days of Webster, when by testing in various groups of mice, he found that there were certain mice that were immune to bacterial infections, others that were immune to viral infections, and a third group, lesser group, who were relatively immune to both infections. In this day and age, however, such simplistic definitions are no longer acceptable; we have now gone down into such questions as, is the immunity or susceptibility to histoplasmosis mediated by a cellular or a humeral antibody or a combination of both? For instance, there are some schools of thought, among whom Dr. Wheeler is one, who feel that a mononuclear cell loaded with *Histoplasma* organisms is not a healthy cell doing its job of killing the *Histoplasma* organisms but an incompetent cell that is loaded with organisms which it cannot handle, and in many ways the cell is protecting the organisms rather than letting them be available to the other more competent cells which have destroyed their organisms and have a nice clean clear cytoplasm. There are indeed other people who say that the ability to form certain substances in its cell wall is what protects the *Histo-*

plasma yeast cells residing inside the cell from being harmed by the drugs which we give. There are still others who think that the enzymes and other substances in the cell decide whether the organism is going to live or die once it is ingested.

Another interesting question is why the *Histoplasma* organism gets into the monocytes rather than into the polycytes. Certainly the polycytes appear to be first on the scene in most animals, and it appears possible that even in tuberculosis, the polycytes ingest the tubercle bacilli and sometimes destroy them and sometimes not. Whether this mechanism operates in histoplasmosis or not has never been substantiated. There usually is not a leukocytolysis in histoplasmosis, but it appears peculiar that the polymorphonuclear cell, the so-called first line of defense, would completely ignore these fungus organisms and allow them to be ingested by the more slow-moving and sluggish mononuclear cells of the reticuloendothelial system.

All of this, of course, is conjecture, but I must say that there are evidences appearing that there may be more to this than conjecture. For instance, work reviewed by Kirkpatrick at this Conference shows that some hints are beginning to emerge of differences in lymphocytic transformation and changes in immune globulin and antibody activities associated with active and chronic histoplasmosis. It does not appear that anything has as yet become evident that would serve to indicate beforehand which members of a given population will have severe illness in contrast to those who will have a relatively mild clinical response or even a subclinical infection.

Perhaps the genetic composition of the individual has a large part to do with the severity of the disease, though no evidence of this had been brought forward. It should be remembered, however, that there have been repeated suggestions of genetic differences in resistance to tuberculosis. This appears to be substantiated in studies by Puffer (1946). If this genetic susceptibility to pulmonary disease in tuberculosis is accepted, it might also be applicable to histoplasmosis. This again represents an unexplored field.

Differences in clinical responses are still to a large extent unexplored. For instance, the exact determination of which cases should be treated has not been shown by laboratory or other means. Those cases are most often treated which appear to be very severe or life endangering. It is quite probable, if we had a good gauge of telling which cases were going to progress early in the game, that we could do much better with instituting treatment.

The whole matter of amount or kind of treatment is still largely unanswered. Is it necessary to treat for any given period of time? Is the present continuous treatment the most desirable, or would it be better to have intermittant therapy over a longer period? Is the dosage presently used for amphotericin excessive or too small? Does the appearance of breakdowns occuring suggest intermittant therapy might be better? It is apparent that combined therapy at least with sulfas has not been successful, but combined therapy with other agents might be more effective, particularly with sara-mycetin. Alternating therapy might also be thought of as a possible improvement over the present status by employing one drug for a week or two, followed by another, and then switching back again. All of these problems are underlined by the fact that amphotericin is not really the easiest drug to use, and indeed it might be better to control the dosage of the drug by the serum levels of inhibition of the particular organism concerned, as has been suggested by Drutz *et al.* (1968). On the other hand, this is a rather complex way of doing things, and the facilities are not always available.

Coming to the toxicity of amphotericin itself, is it possible that it could be alleviated by some substances, such as mannitol, which have a sparing action on the kidneys, or would it be possible to use much smaller doses of amphotericin by the use of some compound such as benemid which would deter the excretion of the amphotericin, thus maintaining higher blood levels for longer periods of time? Again these are unexplored problems.

Then, it is quite clear that some persons, even those who develop clinical disease, may not require therapy but will improve under simple bed rest as shown by Goodwin *et al.* (1966). The separation of these patients from those who will go on to extensive lung damage if they are untreated is a vital clinical need.

One might even, at the most basic level, say that it is not at all clear what the effects of age, sex, and race are on the incidence of disease when one acquires infection with *Histoplasma capsulatum*. There have been no good clinical studies of the frequency with which disease opposed to infection occurs. In spite of attempts in Panama by Young *et al.* (1957) and in Lexington, Kentucky (Doto *et al.*, 1967), all the studies leave something to the imagination in terms of precise clinical follow-up. Indeed this is not surprising, since we lack similar information for as old a disease as tuberculosis, that is, no one is able to accurately determine the incidence of development of pulmonary lesions or clinical illness with acquisition of infection with tuberculosis. Nor do we have this information available for histoplasmosis or blastomycosis or the other mycotic diseases.

What is the relationship of infecting dosage to severity of illness and to dissemination beyond the lungs? It is thought that in tuberculosis the dosage is not terribly important but the susceptibility of the individual is what determines the clinical illness, and this theory has also been applied to histoplasmosis. However, dosage in histoplasmosis may be more important; although, again the evidence appears to favor the immunity of a host as the most important deciding factor rather than the number of organisms inhaled.

One might conjecture on the differences in pathogenesis of these mycotic diseases and try to point these up as directions for future work which might solve some of our basic problems. If one looks at the five systemic granulo-

matous diseases that are markedly similar, namely tuberculosis, histoplasmosis, North and South American blastomycosis and coccidioidomycosis, there
are extremely interesting similarities and dissimilarities. In all these infections, following the inhalation of the organism, there is growth in the lung
and the regional lymph nodes. It appears that almost always there is some
leakage of organisms into the general bloodstream at this time. Obviously,
the rate and amount of leakage would vary with different individuals and
perhaps with different organisms, but at any rate, it is clear in histoplasmosis
since Schwarz, Silverman, Adriano, Straub and Levine (1955) showed almost a one to one relationship between infection and calification in the
spleen. This would indicate that in almost everyone the disease dissemi-
nates. It would seem quite likely that a similar course of events occurs in the
other mycotic diseases, although this is not so well established. The interesting thing is that in histoplasmosis so few bad results come about from this
dissemination, whereas in all of the other diseases at least some occurance of
localized disease due to the early dissemination tends to occur after sensitivity is developed and the organisms have been localized. It is the development of skin test sensitivity about ten days to two weeks after infection that
limits the further development and spread of the organism, not only systemically but locally.

Coming now to clinical acute disseminated disease, this seems to occur
only in a small percentage of those who develop infection. In coccidioidomycosis this has been estimated by Fiese (1958) as about one half of 1 percent, but it has never been statistically supported on any of the other studies. It is interesting that tuberculosis and coccidioidomycosis tend to go to
the meninges during the early disseminating stage, and as does occasionally
blastomycosis. The same three tend to go to the bone and skin, but resulting
in more chronic infection than in the meninges. Neither of these types of
involvement occur with histoplasmosis, or almost never. One might say that
while early dissemination appears from pathologic evidence to be more
common in *Histoplasma* infection, this dissemination is certainly the most
innoculous of all the five granulomatosis diseases. Why should this be so?
Why should tuberculosis and histoplasmosis tend to develop delayed
chronic cavitary type of disease in the lungs and North American blastomycosis less commonly, whereas coccidioidomycosis, and as far as we know
South American blastomycosis, do so only rarely? Why should acute cavitation occur so commonly in coccidioidomycosis, less frequently in tuberculosis, and rarely in histoplasmosis? Finally, another and last question, why
should the calification occur so frequently with histoplasmosis, and yet histoplasmosis tends to be the most common of the mycotic diseases involved
in chronic disease of the lung? Is it the frequency of containing the organisms in the lung in the beginning that in some way gives us a greater immunity that later on leads to a greater number of breakdowns, or am I ask-

ing too many questions of you young people here? We should leave a few for the Third National Histoplasmosis Conference, which we trust will not be so long in production as this one.

A fascinating facet of the clinical studies of histoplasmosis is the difference in racial susceptibility between tuberculosis and histoplasmosis. Why is it that the Negro has so much higher susceptibility to tuberculosis and so much higher resistance to histoplasmosis than the white race. On the other hand, it appears that the Philippinos and Negroes both appear to suffer more severe coccidioidomycosis than other races. This does not appear to be at all true for histoplasmosis. The same might be said of the sexes, why is it that females in both tuberculosis and histoplasmosis rarely suffer from the advanced form of the disease, although the infection rate among males and females is fairly closely similar in any given area.

Although Dr. Tosh has discussed the problem of reinfection in histoplasmosis at this conference, it seemed to me that he did not touch on an important question relating to the possibilities that a large part of the deleterious response to infection is due to reinfection. I am speaking particularly of allergic reaction to reinfection. You are all aware that in Mexico, Gonzelas-Ochoa (1959) reports as high as 28 percent deaths occuring fairly soon (2-3 days) after inhalation of large numbers of organisms presumably in persons who had been previously positive. These could well have been allergic deaths. Also, Smith and Tegeris (1958) have reported that treatment with cortisone combined with other treatment appeared to be beneficial in some of the acute phases of infection. I am wondering whether these were not in fact reinfection cases in which a large component of the response was allergic rather than infectious. This brings up the interesting observation we made in the epidemic in Arkansas in which we thought we were able to separate two types of response based on absenteeism from the school. It appeared that there was a peak of absenteeism occurring about two or three days after the supposed date of exposure, and then a second peak occurring about 17 days after this date of exposure. If you will look at Figure 57-1 from this epidemic I think you can visualize the two groups. The presumption was, since this was an area of fairly high endemicity of histoplasmosis, that the primary rise in absenteeism was associated with the allergic response to reinfection, whereas the secondary rise in absenteeism was due to primary infection. The x-ray and serologic data are interesting in the two groups. There is even a suggestion in the early Cincinnati water tower epidemic, which must have occurred among sensitized persons, that the onset was earlier than one would have expected based on known times of exposure and illness (4-5 days) (Sabin, 1951). These clinical matters are very important in as much as if the patients' illness is largely due to an allergic response to infection, the treatment in this case would probably be some corticosteroid to suppress the immediate allergic problem, whereas if his re-

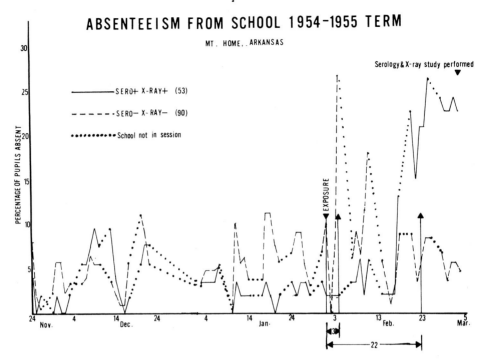

FIGURE 57-1. Chart of absenteeism in Mt. Home Schools showing two different peaks of absenteeism with peaks at about three and twenty-two days.

sponse was truly of an infectious nature, this would be completely contraindicated.

By way of conclusion, I would ask, What is the relationship of histoplasmosis and chronic pulmonary fibrosis? You remember that the fibrosis of the mediastinum that occurs with histoplasmosis is quite different from the type seen after primary infection. Could there be a relationship?

References

Chandler, J.W., Jr., Smith, T.K., Newberry, W.M., Jr., Chin, T.D.Y., and Kirkpatrick, C.H. (1969). Immunology of the mycoses. II. Characterization of immunoglobulin and antibody responses in histoplasmosis. *J. Infect. Dis.,* 119:247-254.

Doto, I.L., Furcolow, M.L., Varga, D.T., Tosh, F.E., and Griffith, R.L. (1967). Seasonal histoplasmin conversion rates in Lexington, Kentucky. *Arch. Environ. Health, 15*: 357-383.

Drutz, D.J., Spickard, A., Rogers, D.E. and Koenig, M.G. (1968). Treatment of disseminated mycotic infections. *Amer. J. Med., 45*:405-418.

Fiese, M.J. (1958). *Coccidioidomycosis.* Springfield, Thomas.

Gonzales-Ochoa, A. (1959). Histoplasmosis premaria pulmonar aguda en la Republica Mexicana. Estudio de 74 casos. *Rev. Inst. Salud. Enfermedades Trop.,* 19:341-350.

Goodwin, R.A., Snell, J.D., Hubbard, W.W. and Terry, R.T. (1966). Early chronic pulmonary histoplasmosis. *Amer. Rev. Resp. Dis.,* 93:47.

Newberry, W.M., Jr., Chandler, J.W., Jr., Chin, T.D.Y. and Kirkpatrick, C.H. (1968). Immunology of the mycoses depressed lymphocyte transformation in chronic histoplasmosis. *J. Immun., 100*:436-443.

Puffer, R.R. (1946). *Familial Susceptibility to Tuberculosis.* Cambridge, Harvard University Press.

Sabin, A.B. (1951). Abstract: Miliary Granulomatous Pneumonitis in a Group of Men Exposed to Pigeon Excreta. Trans. 47th Annual Meeting National Tuberculosis Association. pp. 290-291.

Smith, D.T. and Tegeris, A.S. (1958). Acute disseminated pulmonary histoplasmosis treated with cortisone and MRD 112. *Ann. Intern. Med., 48*:1414-1420.

Young, R.V., Cleve, E.A. and Vincente-Masterellari, A. (1957). Acute pulmonary histoplasmosis on the Isthmus of Panama. *Arch. Intern. Med., 100*:430-435.

Chapter 58

Need for Reporting and Surveillance of Mycoses

TOM D. Y. CHIN

ABSTRACT

Surveillance methods in communicable disease control have been applied and found effective for the investigation and control of many infectious diseases. Application of these methods, however, have not been fully utilized in the control of histoplasmosis and other mycotic infections.

An adequate reporting system is the first step necessary in implementing a surveillance program. At present histoplasmosis is a reportable disease in only about one fourth of the states. The need for more complete reporting is evidenced by the estimation that each year about one-half million people in the United States acquire this fungus infection, and frequently the source of infection can be determined by appropriate epidemiological investigations.

The Ecological Investigations Program of the Center for Disease Control publishes a Mycoses Surveillance Report to encourage development of a more adequate system of national surveillance of histoplasmosis, blastomycosis, coccidioidomycosis, cryptococcosis, and other mycotic infections. Through these reports, we hope to stimulate interest and cooperation among physicians and health authorities concerning reporting and surveillance of mycotic infections.

SURVEILLANCE is an important activity in communicable disease control. According to current usage, the term refers to continuous watch over the occurrence and spread of a disease in a population through systematic collection, evaluation, and dissemination of epidemiologic data and other pertinent information. The modern concept of disease surveillance, as distinct from surveillance of persons, was first applied in about 1950 to malaria control in the United States. Since then, the application of this concept became firmly established in 1955 when surveillance was developed for investigation of poliomyelitis in connection with the Salk vaccine program (Langmuir, 1963). Today, surveillance methods have been applied and found effective for the investigation and control of a number of infectious diseases, including viral hepatitis, salmonellosis, viral encephalitis, smallpox, measles, and rubella.

The first step in implementing a surveillance program is to develop an adequate reporting system. In this country the mechanism of reporting diseases such as poliomyelitis, diphtheria, and tuberculosis is well developed. The basic process consists of prompt reporting of all definite and suspect

460

cases of a specific communicable disease to a local health department followed by field investigation at the local level. The data are then assembled and forwarded to a central location, such as a state health department, where they can be evaluated and the information disseminated.

Although many infectious diseases, including anthrax, Rocky Mountain spotted fever, tularemia, and trichinosis, are reportable diseases in many of the states, histoplasmosis is not reportable in about three fourths of the states. Yet, it has been estimated that about thirty million people in the United States have been infected with the fungus *Histoplasma capsulatum*. It is probable that about 500,000 people each year acquire the infection, and about one third of those who become infected develop a clinical illness lasting from two days to two weeks. Furthermore, a certain number of the infected persons, perhaps as many as one thousand per year, develop disseminated disease, which is usually fatal unless properly treated (Furcolow, 1935). Also, in clinical diagnosis, pulmonary histoplasmosis is frequently confused with pulmonary tuberculosis. Studies have shown that many patients with chronic histoplasmosis have been admitted to tuberculosis hospitals and sanatoriums. Serologic surveys of patients admitted to these hospitals in areas of high histoplasmin sensitivity indicated that 7.6 percent of the patients had positive serologic tests for histoplasmosis. Active pulmonary histoplasmosis could be documented by sputum examinations in about one fourth of these patients (Furcolow *et al.*, 1962). Thus it has been estimated that as many as three to four thousand patients with cavitary histoplasmosis are admitted to tuberculosis sanatoriums each year.

Histoplasmosis is a preventable disease. The infection is acquired by inhalation of spores of *H. capsulatum*, and the sources of infection in many of the outbreaks of histoplasmosis have been found to be associated with soil contaminated with droppings of bats, chickens, starlings, blackbirds, and other avian species. The disease can be prevented by avoiding contact with these sources, by wetting down the soil before working in known contaminated areas, or by treatment of infected soil with chemicals such as formaldehyde (Tosh *et al.*, 1966).

The feasibility of chemical decontamination to control histoplasmosis has been well illustrated by the studies conducted in Mason City, Iowa, where two major outbreaks of histoplasmosis had occurred in association with a starling roost located in the center of the city (D'Alessio *et al.*, 1965; Tosh *et a'.*, 1936). After the second outbreak, a five-acre area which was the site of the contaminated starling roost was treated with a 3 percent formaldehyde solution. Studies indicated that the chemical treatment was highly effective in eliminating the fungus from the soil (Tosh *et al.*, 1967), and histoplasmin skin testing of children in the community suggested that the starling roost site was no longer a source of infection.

Histoplasmosis is a major cause of pulmonary mycotic infection in the

United States. The infection is highly prevalent in the Mississippi, Missouri, and Ohio River valleys. The source of infection can frequently be determined by epidemiologic investigation; therefore, all persons with acute histoplasmosis should be promptly reported. The disease can be readily diagnosed by appropriate clinical studies supported by histoplasmin skin test and serology, and in some cases by isolation of the fungus. Amphotericin B is available for treatment of the chronic pulmonary and disseminated forms of histoplasmosis. Furthermore, the infection can be controlled by treatment of the known sources with appropriate decontaminating procedures.

Recently, the Ecological Investigations Program of the Center for Disease Control published a Mycoses Surveillance Report. The purpose of this report is to encourage development of a more adequate system of national surveillance of histoplasmosis, blastomycosis, coccidioidomycosis, cryptococcosis, and other mycotic infections. The first issue of this report summarizes presently available information received from state and local health departments and other pertinent sources. It contains information on the current status of histoplasmosis and coccidioidomycosis, number of reported deaths attributed to systemic mycotic infections, number of cases of actinomycosis, blastomycosis, coccidioidomycosis, cryptococcosis, and histoplasmosis optionally reported to the Public Health Service, results of serological tests performed by public health laboratories for the detection of systemic mycoses and information on the CDC Mycoses Study.

One of the aims of the Mycoses Surveillance Report is to stimulate more active reporting of cases and outbreaks of mycotic infections. Since reporting of disease is normally made by physicians, it is hoped that those who are working in the field of mycology will encourage physicians to report cases of mycotic infections seen in their practice to health authorities. It will also be helpful to urge health authorities to consider listing histoplasmosis, blastomycosis, coccidioidomycosis, cryptococcosis, and perhaps others among those to be reported.

The Mycoses Section of the Kansas City Laboratories is interested in receiving reports of special field and laboratory investigations of mycotic infections as well as routine case investigations. The information submitted will be included in future issues of the Mycoses Surveillance Report, which will be distributed periodically to health departments, other agencies, and research workers.

References

D'Alessio, D.J., Heeren, R.H., Hendricks, S.L., Ogilvie, P. and Furcolow, M.L. (1965). A starling roost as the source of urban epidemic histoplasmosis in an area of low incidence. *Amer. J. Resp. Dis.,* 92:725-731.

Furcolow, M.L., Schubert, J., Tosh, F.E., Doto, I.L. and Lynch, H.L., Jr. (1962). Serologic evidence of histoplasmosis in sanatoriums in the U.S. *J.A.M.A.,* 180:109-114.

Furcolow, M.L. (1965). Environmental aspects of histoplasmosis. *Arch. Environ. Health,* 10:4-10.

Langmuir, A.D. (1963). The surveillance of communicable disease of national importance. *New Eng. J. Med., 268:*182-192.

Tosh, F.E., Doto, I.L., D'Alessio, D.J., Medeiros, A.A., Hendricks, S.L. and Chin, T.D.Y. (1966). The second of two epidemics of histoplasmosis resulting from work on the same starling roost. *Amer. J. Epidem., 94:*406-413.

Tosh, F.E., Weeks, R.J., Pfeiffer, F.R., Hendricks, S.L. and Chin, T.D.Y. (1966). Chemical decontamination of soil containing *Histoplasma capsulatum. Amer. J. Epidem., 83:*262-270.

Tosh, F.E., Weeks, R.J., Pfeiffer, F.R., Hendricks, S.L., Greer, D.L. and Chin, T.D.Y. (1967). The use of formalin to kill *Histopasma capsulatum* at an epidemic site. *Amer. J. Epidem., 85:*259-265.

Chapter 59

The Need for an Improved Serologic Test for Histoplasmosis

CHARLOTTE C. CAMPBELL

ABSTRACT

In the contemporary age of massive upheavals of soil and increasingly aggregat-
ing human populations, *Histoplasma capsulatum* as an air pollutant probably
causes more cases of histoplasmosis than all of those traceable to direct exposure
to identifiable microfoci in nature combined. With the correspondingly high incidence of undifferentiated respiratory infection, the need for a simple reliable
serologic test which can be carried out routinely in all laboratories becomes increasingly urgent. Recent developments in the production of replicable antigens
suggest reliable antigens may soon be available for this purpose.

A S noted in an earlier report to this conference (Campbell, 1971), the development of serology for the diagnosis and study of histoplasmosis is
essentially one continuous plea for improved tests and antigens. There have
been many attempts to replace the cumbersome complement fixation with a
simpler procedure that could be carried out in any laboratory. However, the
type of test per se is not the crux of the matter. It is the fact that *Histoplasma capsulatum* contains a multiplicity of serologically reactive components in both growth phases. These are inconsistently reproduced in successive preparations from the same strains. Indeed, it is not unusual for duplicate flasks inoculated with the same suspension and incubated and harvested under precisely identical conditions to yield antigens of widely varying composition, qualitatively as well as quantitatively. Thus it is because of
the inability to replicate antigens of both growth phases, except by chance,
that serology of histoplasmosis has remained in the hands of a few experienced investigators who are cognizant of the antigens' deficiencies and the
difficulties in even remotely replicating successive lots of the preparations
for serologic tests. As a result, even the less than perfect antigens that are
available in specialized centers for the serology of histoplasmosis have been
used very little by the average clinician. This, in itself, is a sad commentary
on an infection and disease whose microfoci in nature are as ubiquitous and
widely distributed globally as *H. capsulatum* (Ajello, 1967).

The present report is to emphasize (1) some of the more recent developments in histoplasmosis, the infection and disease, which make wide application of improved serologic procedures not only desirable but mandatory

and (2) some of the developments in the laboratory which indicate that reproducible antigens for meaningful analysis and thus greatly improved serologic study might yet be a reality in the near future.

Histoplasma capsulatum as an Air Pollutant

The most compelling reason for the widespread availability of a simple, reliable serologic test for histoplasmosis is the now undeniable evidence that a high percentage of persons acquiring clinical histoplasmosis in the present era are victims of *H. capsulatum* as an air pollutant. They have had no direct exposure to microfoci such as bird roosts, old chicken houses, or bat caves, but only to air into which particles of the fungus have been released from such microfoci by the bulldozers and other instruments of construction that are commonplace everywhere in all of our daily lives. As exemplified by the outbreaks of histoplasmosis in Montreal (Leznoff, Frank, Telner, Rosensweig and Brandt, 1964), Greenwood, South Carolina (Sellers, Price and Newberry, 1965), and Mason City, Iowa (Tosh, Doto, D'Alessio, Medeiros, Hendricks and Chin, 1966), *H. capsulatum* is far more important as an air pollutant in this contemporary era of massive upheavals of soil and increasingly densely aggregated human populations, and probably accounts for an infinitely greater number of cases than all of those traceable to direct exposure to microfoci in nature combined. When this contemporary situation is viewed along with the high incidence of undifferentiated respiratory infection, the urgent need for a simple reliable serologic test for histoplasmosis that can be carried out in any laboratory is clear.

However, this is only one aspect of the current situation. The outbreaks cited above also illustrate the frequency with which histoplasmosis may present, in which the chief complaints are not respiratory but allergic. Thus simple reliable serologic tests for histoplasmosis should be as available to the dermatologist as to the general practitioner.

Finally, in this contemporary era in which we must consider *H. capsulatum* as an air pollutant and no respector of "occupational" groups or the many who do not indulge in "spelunking" or other exotic hobbies or professions that would bring them into direct contact with its known microfoci, we must also consider the chronic diseases of aging. This, too, is a relatively contemporaneous concept from which *H. capsulatum* can not be dismissed. How much of blindness, mental disorientation, or malfunctioning hearts, livers, or kidneys is an expression of unrecognized infection by *H. capsulatum* or insults inflicted by its products—perhaps years after its actual invasion? And this we shall never know or even be able to investigate unless serologic tests become widely available to determine the true incidence of histoplasmosis in all of its protean manifestations. In the existing circumstances there cannot be the slightest doubt that the incidence of histoplasmosis is increasing. And in this context it is not unreasonable to project into a future in which histoplasmosis—and other respiratory mycoses acquired in a similar fashion—proves to be not only among the most important of the infectious diseases but also the most difficult to control. Improvements in the standards of living which do much to minimize man-to-man transmitted diseases paradoxically are precisely those which increase the incidence of the respiratorily acquired mycoses. Histoplasmosis is certainly among the most important of these because of the broad global distribution of the microfoci of *H. capsulatum*. In contrast to diseases of deprivation, histoplasmosis since it was first described during the construction of the Panama Canal, has been associated with economic progress and expansion. It would be well if we did not overlook this in an era when we must relentlessly expand to contend with an exploding human population. *H. capsulatum* as an air pollutant is a very different thing than *H. capsulatum* left undisturbed in its own ecological microfocus. It thus behooves us to begin to look more to the submerged portion of the iceberg wherein histoplasmosis strikes densely aggregated hundreds and thousands and less to the pinnacle of suspecting histoplasmosis only in the comparative few with traceable direct and recent exposure to bird roosts or bat caves. Clearly, the need for widely available serologic tests for the rapid diagnosis of histoplasmosis is very great in this contemporary age of expansion and undifferentiated respiratory infection.

Developments Toward Reproducibility of the Antigens

For years it has been clear that the variations in antigenic composition stemmed from variations in the organism itself, since everything else in antigen production could be and was rigidly standardized and controlled. Thus, the studies of Berliner (1968) reported earlier to this conference have great significance for the consistent reproducibility of serologic antigens as for many other aspects of histoplasmosis. Her discovery that all primary isolates of *H. capsulatum* comprise two morphological types, one of which will rapidly overgrow the other if not separated, was astounding to those of us who had attributed this phenomenon to uncontrollable pleomorphism that inevitably occurred in stock cultures with which antigenic preparations were initiated. We now have evidence not only that the A and B types differ markedly in their pathogenicity for experimental animals (Daniels, Berliner and Campbell, 1968) but in their antigenic composition as well (Reca, unpublished data). Thus, with this basic observation of the organism itself, a large step was taken toward an intelligent control of strains used in antigen production and in markedly reducing variations in composition of successive preparations. That this important step was so long in coming is a warning that bacteriologic techniques do not always suffice for the more complex fungi.

Goodman, Sprouse, and Larsh (1968), in their efforts to minimize the "hit-and-miss" methods of harvesting histoplasmins, found a close relationship between increasing skin test component(s) and increasing total protein coupled with decreasing total carbohydrate. Schubert and Wiggins (1965) have done much to elucidate the *h* and *m* components described by Heiner (1958).

Thus, while the routine serologic tests for histoplasmosis are not greatly improved over those available fifteen years ago, considerable progress is being made in the laboratories toward the reproducibility of antigens. Commercial production can then be undertaken with confidence, making it finally possible for the tests to be used on the wide scale demanded. In this respect, development of vaccine should also be more seriously entertained than at present. For *H. capsulatum* as an air pollutant, as earlier noted, is not a respector of occupational groups and may indeed produce as much infection and disease as influenza at the present time.

References

Ajello, L. (1967). Comparative ecology of respiratory mycotic disease agents. *Bact. Rev., 31:*6-24.

Berliner, M.D. (1968). Primary subcultures of *Histoplasma capsulatum*, I. Macro and micro-morphology of the mycelial phase. *Sabouraudia,* 6:111-118.

Campbell, C.C. (1971). History of the development of serologic tests for histoplasmosis. *Proceedings of the Second National Conference on Histoplasmosis,* Springfield, Thomas.

Daniels, L.S., Berliner, M.D. and Campbell, C.C. (1968). Studies on rabbits infected with *Histoplasma capsulatum* yeasts from different filamentous types of the same strain. *J. Bact.,* 96:1535-1539.

Goodman, N.L., Sprouse, R.F. and Larsh, H.W. (1968). Histoplasmin potency as affected by culture age. *Sabouraudia,* 6:273-284.

Heiner, D.C. (1958). Diagnosis of histoplasmosis using precipitin reactions in agar gel. *Pediatrics,* 22:616-627.

Leznoff, A., Frank, H., Telner, P., Rosensweig, J. and Brandt, J.L. (1964). Histoplasmosis in Montreal during the fall of 1963 with observations on erythema multiforme. *Canad. Med. Assoc. J.,* 91:1154-1160.

Reca, M.E. (1969). Unpublished data.

Schubert, J.H. and Wiggins, G.L. (1965). Preliminary studies of *h* and *m* components of histoplasmin for skin tests and serology. *Amer. Rev. Resp. Dis.,* 92:640-641.

Sellers, Jr., T.F., Price, Jr., W.N. and Newberry, Jr., W.M. (1965). An epidemic of erythema multiforme and erythema nodosum caused by histoplasmosis. *Ann. Intern. Med.,* 62:1244-1262.

Tosh, F.E., Doto, Irene L., D'Alessio, D.J., Medeiros, A.A., Hendricks, S.L. and Chin, T.D. (1966). A second of two epidemics of histoplasmosis resulting from work on the same starling roost. *Amer. Rev. Resp. Dis.,* 94:406-413.

Chapter 60

The Need for Improved Antimycotic Therapeutic Agents

JOHN P. UTZ

ABSTRACT

For the systemic mycotic and related microbiological infections, clinically available and chemotherapeutically active drugs include iodides (sporotrichosis), sulfonamides (nocardiosis), penicillin (actinomycosis), 2-hydroxystilbamidine (blastomycosis), and amphotericin B (the remainder). With each of these agents and with virtually all infections, notable failures occur frequently, and death is not uncommon with many. In addition each of them have side effects which range from mildly irritating and not requiring discontinuation of treatment to irreversible renal damage. A continuing search for new antifungal agents can thus be justified on the basis of lack of efficacy and of serious side effects.

ALTHOUGH iodides have been used in sporotrichosis since the beginning of the century, and sulfonamides for nocardiosis since the mid-1930's, and penicillin for actinomycosis since the mid-1940's, the development of amphotericin B and its usefulness in a number of fungal infections date to 1957. It was thus warmly welcomed and relatively gratefully received as a boon by both physicians and patients in the treatment of such disease as cryptococcal meningitis, severe disseminated histoplasmosis, and widely disseminated forms of blastomycosis.

Because of the understandable tendency of physicians to report treatment successes rather than failures, it is somewhat more difficult to document the lack of efficacy of the therapeutic agents presently available. I believe it is fair to say, however, that by this first criterion, treatment failure, present agents are inadequate, and a need exists for newer ones. I am sure that many other physicians have shared my current experience, treating a patient with actinomycosis, who is allergic to penicillin, who has relapsed repeatedly after courses of therapy with erythromycin, tetracycline, and most recently an orally absorbed form of a cephalosporin, cephalexin. It is also sobering to reflect on the 50 percent case fatality rate, commonly spoken of and probably insufficiently lamented, in the treatment of nocardiosis. The death from coccidioidal meningitis just this month of a highly effective and skilled psychiatric physician, who had acquired his infection approximately six years ago while on service with the army in the southwest, provides a topical and graphic example of our inadequacies in the treatment of this disease. Although there are great difficulties in the culture of the causative microorganisms, the clinical features of cerebrorhinophycomycosis are so dramatic and virtually pathognomonic that the diagnosis can be made readily and early in the course. Nevertheless, most case reports are of a fatal illness, and disease is properly considered a fulminant process relatively unresponsive to chemotherapy. Although response to treatment in blastomycosis is prompt and gratifying, relapse following therapy continues to be a disappointing feature. In our patients relapse rates have varied from 19 percent with amphotericin B to 75 percent with saramycetin. Although aspergillosis in this country seems to be less important than in Europe, the isolates of *Aspergillus* we have studied in our laboratory have been far more resistant than other genera, and experience in eliminating this microorganism from sputum has been disappointing. Although there has been an intriguing case report of improvement related to estrogens in an *Allescheria boydii* infection (Mohr and Muchmore, 1968), a rather limited experience with treatment of this disease with more specific antifungal agents has been for the most part unsuccessful. The multiple fungi associated with mycetoma have rendered this disease virtually untreatable chemotherapeutically, although some strains of *Actinomyces* and *Nocardia* isolated from lesions have been sensitive to drugs previously mentioned. *Candida* endocarditis represents so commonly a fatal disease (76% treated with amphotericin B, 100% untreated) (Utz, 1968) that recovery of a patient, with whatever therapy, would probably warrant publication in the medical literature. *Candida* sepsis, a far more common form of severe *Candida* infection, is associated with case fatality rates only slightly less (50% treated, 76% untreated). Although therapy in cryptococcal meningitis has probably been the most dramatic and satisfactory example of the successful use of amphotericin B, there still remains a hard core of approximately 15 percent of patients who are unaffected by treatment and die. Chronic cavitary histoplasmosis is still an infection in which such relatively nonspecific therapy as surgery seems clearly indicated. Cladosporiosis is classically a disease of the central nervous system, from which a few patients have apparently recovered after drainage or surgical resection of an abscess, but for which there exists no satisfactory chemotherapeutic agent at present.

The second testimonial for the need for newer chemotherapeutic agents is the toxicity of those presently available to us. We have already spoken of the allergy, unfortunately now common, to penicillin. Although sulfadiazine, the most commonly employed agent in nocardiosis, is relatively nontoxic, care should be taken to avoid using the longer acting members of the sulfonamide drugs, which have been associated with such severe reactions as erythema multiforme (the Stevens Johnson syndrome). 2-Hydroxystilbamidine has been rarely accompanied by the cranial fifth neuropathy that so often and so severely plagued patients who received the parent compound, stilbamidine. Nevertheless, the intravenous administration of the drug is occasionally followed by alarming, though fortunately rarely serious, symptoms as breathlessness, palpitation, dizziness, fainting, headache, and nausea. The administration of iodides is accompanied by acneiform skin lesions, nausea, increased salvitation, coryza, sneezing, increased bronchial secretions ("head cold"), and swelling of the parotids.

With saramycetin there has been considerable differences in local tenderness with the drug according to the lot employed. The preparation recently available to us for study in two patients seems to have been attended by more local tenderness than was seen in the better lots used in the previous study. The other major side effects have been changes in liver function (Andriole, Utz and Sabesin, 1961; Witorsch, Andriole, Emmons and Utz, 1966). In all thirty-nine courses of therapy in which the test was performed, sulfobromophthalein retention was increased, with maximum values ranging from 12 to 69 percent. The conjugated and unconjugated serum bilirubin values were elevated in thirty of forty-three courses of therapy. In marked contrast the serum glutamic oxalacetic transaminase (SCOT) was increased in only nine of forty-one courses of therapy. On histopathologic examination changes were nonspecific and variable.

Considerably less experience with hamycin has nevertheless resulted in the appreciation that in virtually all patients a dosage of 15 to 20 mg/kg per day of the micronized preparation is attended by such symptoms as nausea, vomiting, and diarrhea. In one patient it was necessary to discontinue the drug and use amphotericin B. One singular exception was a woman who took 40 mg/kg for a period of two weeks. More recently we have become aware of rather marked hypokalemia requiring 20 to 40 milliequivalents of potassium chloride intravenously (because of vomiting) in three patients.

Experience with 5-fluorocytosine is even more limited. However, in the approximate one hundred patients treated thus far, the most commonly observed changes have been leukopenia, elevation in the SGOT or the serum glutamic pyruvate transaminase values. One of our patients complained of bad dreams.

It is however, with amphotericin B that the toxicity of the antifungal agents reaches its zenith. A great number of separate articles and, indeed, a whole symposium (Utz, Bennett, Brandriss, Butler and Hill, 1964) have been devoted to its toxicity. The patient complains bitterly of fever, chills, nausea, vomiting, malaise, and anorexia. In one controlled study (Tynes, Utz, Bennett and Alling, 1963) as high a proportion as 80 percent of infusions were accompanied by such manifestations. More importantly the drug has marked nephrotoxic effects including cylindruria, increased blood urea nitrogen and serum creatinine, and decreased clearances of urea, creatinine, inulin, and para-aminohippurate. In the study of (Butler, Bennett, Alling, Wertlake, Utz and Hill, 1964) 88 percent of eighty-one patients had evidence as late as four years after treatment of persistent renal function abnormality. Histopathologic study of renal tissue in ten patients at biopsy and sixteen patients at necropsy showed necrosis and calcification of the convoluted tubules. More recently, McCurdy, Frederick and Elkinton (1968) have described renal tubular acidosis in five of six treated patients. Anemia is also common, and in one study (Brandriss, Wolff, Moores and Stohlman, 1964) there was a decrease in the hematocrit of at least 10 units in 76 percent of thirty-seven courses of therapy. Red cell survival studies in five of these patients showed a slightly shortened survival time, presumably due to underlying infection, which hemolytic process was not increased by treatment. The normochromic, normocytic anemia was considered due to decreased red cell production resulting in turn from bone marrow suppression. Hypokalemia, although not well understood in derivation, is a most important manifestation, since its side effects are so dramatic, dangerous, and alarming to the patient. These have consisted of muscle weakness, often severe, and of electrocardiographic changes and arrhythmias.

References

Andriole, V.T., Utz, J.P. and Sabesin, S.M. (1961). Altered sulfobromophthalein metabolism in man induced by antibiotic X-5079C. *Amer. Rev. Resp. Dis.*, 84:538-548.

Brandriss, M.W., Wolff, S.M., Moores, R. and Stohlman, F., Jr. (1964). Anemia induced by amphotericin B. *J.A.M.A.*, 189:663-666.

Butler, W.T., Bennett, J.E., Alling, D.W., Wertlake, P.T., Utz, J.P. and Hill, G.J. (1964). Nephrotoxicity of amphotericin B. Early and late effects in 81 patients. *Ann. Intern. Med.*, 61:175-187.

McCurdy, D.K., Frederick, N. and Elkinton, J.R. (1968). Renal tubular acidosis due to amphotericin B. *New Eng. J. Med.*, 278:124-131.

Mohr, J.A. and Muchmore, H.G. (1968). Maduromycosis due to *Allescheria boydii*. *J.A.M.A.*, 204:335-336.

Tynes, B.S., Utz, J.P., Bennett, J.E. and Alling, D.W. (1963). Reducing amphotericin B reactions: a double blind study. *Amer. Rev. Resp. Dis.*, 268:938-940.

Utz, J.P. (1968). Treatment of *Candida* infections. In Winner, H.I. and Hurley, R. (Eds.). *Symposium on Candida Infections*. Edinburgh and London, E. and S. Livingstone, pp. 221-224.

Utz, J.P., Bennett, J.E., Brandriss, M.W., Butler, W.T. and Hill, G.J. (1964). Amphotericin B toxicity. *Ann. Intern. Med.*, 61:334-354.

Witorsch, P., Andriole, V.T., Emmons, C.W. and Utz, J.P. (1966). Antifungal agent X-5079C. Further studies in 39 patients. *Amer. Rev. Resp. Dis.*, 93:876-888.

Chapter 61

Need for Direct Soil Isolation Procedures for *Histoplasma capsulatum*

COY D. SMITH

ABSTRACT

The use of the indirect mouse method for the isolation of *Histoplasma capsulatum* from soil is expensive, time consuming, and has many limitations. This method measures only infection versus noninfection. Also animal susceptibility may vary with animal strain and may vary even within the same strain of animals because of such factors as age and sex. The use of direct cultures would eliminate many of these undesired variables and allow quantation of the number of viable particles of the fungus in the soil.

Direct culture method of isolating *H. capsulatum* from soil would enable investigators to better study the action of soil sterilization or eradication procedures and the interaction of this fungus growing in the presence of the other organisms in soil. It is very difficult to do basic ecology experiments when the only reliable method of isolating the fungus from soil is the indirect mouse method.

Experimental evidence demonstrates that *H. capsulatum* can be recovered more efficiently from contaminated soil by direct culture using the modified oil flotation technique. A higher number of colonies was isolated by diluting the oil by this method than with saline dilutions without oil.

Better results using direct culture of *H. capsulatum* from naturally infected soil were also obtained when the soil was allowed to dry somewhat by storing for two to four weeks in the laboratory prior to culturing.

At the present time the use of direct culture for the isolation of *H. capsulatum* is not as sensitive or as reliable as the indirect mouse method.

*H*istoplasma capsulatum was first isolated from soil using direct culture by Furcolow and Larsh (1952). The isolation was made on Elm bark agar medium after over four hundred attempts were made using various substrates and techniques. The next reported isolations using direct culture methods were made by Smith and Weeks (1964). The success of these isolations was credited primarily to a new medium, i.e. yeast extract (Smith, 1964). Subsequently, it has been found that the medium was not primarily the reason the isolations were made but because of some undetermined condition.

Many investigators have spent and are still spending much time and effort at attempts to develop a suitable method. Little progress thus far has been made in these efforts. At the present time investigators still use an indirect animal method for the isolation of *H. capsulatum* from soil. The mouse is the most common animal used for this purpose, since it is relatively inexpensive, easy to work with, and highly susceptible to histoplasmosis. Animals are usually injected intraperitoneally or intravenously with the suspect soil either diluted in a physiological salt solution or processed through a flotation method of one type or another (Emmons, 1949; Larsh, Hinton and Furcolow, 1952; Smith and Furcolow, 1964). Another method of indirect isolation is an exposure method described by Hinton, Larsh and Silberg (1957). All the above methods rely on the animals becoming infected with the pathogenic fungus and later growing the organism from their tissues.

Since all the above methods appear to do the job, why is there a need for direct isolation other than being a more expedient method? In the first place, use of animals as an indirect method is more time consuming. The animals are held for four weeks prior to autopsy when cultures are made, and it requires an additional two to four weeks before the fungus will grow and can be identified; therefore, a total lapse of time up to eight weeks may occur before the results are known. Upon investigating suspect epidemics, time is often critical when treatment of patients or preventive measures must be taken. The use of animals makes the procedure more costly, and all laboratories do not have access to them. An additional factor in the use of animals is that another variable is added, since they are highly susceptible to infection, they may already have histoplasmosis acquired by airborn inhalation before being used, especially if they are in an endemic area. It is a well-known fact that the MLD_{50} of most infections agents varies in animals even within the same species and may be influenced by age, sex, and so on. Certainly the minimal infective dose can vary in histoplasmosis as easily and laboratories do not use the same strain, age and sex of mice.

H. capsulatum is a slow-growing organism compared to most common fungi and bacteria found in soil. In the laboratory on culture medium it is very susceptible to antagonistic products produced by other organisms; therefore, a culture plate does not have to be overgrown to inhibit growth of *H. capsulatum.*

What is so different about natural soil reservoirs to allow this fungus to apparently grow and survive well? If we had an effective direct culture method, then studies could be conducted to study the interaction of other microflora and *H. capsulatum* in soil. The soil characteristics, physical and chemical, which favor or restrict the growth of the fungus could be better defined through direct culture methods. Indeed the ecology of this fungus could perhaps be studied more readily. There is a need for quantitating growth in soil directly rather than in infective units, as is currently being done especially when trying various soil eradication procedures. Infective units may change considerably in different types of contaminated soil.

Current Status of Direct Isolation

H. capsulatum has been isolated by direct culture from naturally infected soils several times during the past two years in our laboratory. At no time has any of the techniques used been sensitive enough to rely upon as a routine method. Only after soils were processed by the oil flotation method (Smith, 1969) and dilutions of the oil plated was it possible to isolate the fungus with any consistency from natural soil. The medium used was yeast extract (Smith, 1964) containing penicillin, 100 units, streptomycin, 50µg, polymixin B, 10µg, and cycloheximide, 0.5 mg/ml. After obtaining these results, experiments were conducted to determine if culturing the oil was a more effective method than saline dilutions.

Materials and Methods

A known amount of *H. capsulatum* was added to 25 gm of fertile garden soil. The number of viable particles was determined on the same day as the experiment was done. Colony plate count techniques were used for this determination.

The seeded soil was processed by the modified oil flotation method. After blending and prior to the addition of oil, a sample of the saline suspension was withdrawn, dilutions of 10^{-1}, 10^{-2}, and 10^{-3} were made, and each was cultured on ten yeast extract agar plates; Of this inoculum 0.1 ml was used per plate. After the oil had been added, the mixture was shaken for 15 minutes, serial dilutions were made of the oil in sterile oil, and cultured. The cultures were incubated for 22 days at 29°C, then plates were examined for *H. capsulatum*.

Results

Efficacy of two different techniques for reisolating the fungus from contaminated soil is shown in Table 61-I. The number of viable particles of *H. capsulatum* added to the 25 gm of soil was found to be 6.7×10^4 per gm. There were no isolations of *H. capsulatum* obtained from culturing the 10^{-1} and 10^{-2} dilutions of saline. The 10^{-3} dilution of saline yielded an average of 0.4 colonies per plate from ten plates. Therefore, even though the lower dilutions contained more viable particles of the fungus, none was recovered because of overgrowth or inhibition of other organisms in the soil.

It is not known how many viable particles of *H. capsulatum* were in each dilution of the oil. Previous studies indicate that it will float and concentrate the fungus from a saline suspension (Smith and Furcolow 1964). There

TABLE 61-I

Efficacy of Two Methods for Culturing *H. capsulatum* from 25 gm Garden Soil After Seeding with
6.7×10^4 Viable Particle (Mycelia Form) per Gram

No. of Viable Particles Recovered From:	Dilution Cultured		
	10^{-1}	10^{-2}	10^{-3}
Saline suspension	0	0	4.0×10^3
Oil suspension	0	4.1×10^3	2.2×10^4

were no isolations obtained by plating the oil at a 10^{-1} dilution, but an average of 0.4 colonies per plate were obtained at the 10^{-2} dilution. However, at the 10^{-3} dilution an average of 2.2 colonies per plate were isolated. Therefore, at this dilution over five times the number of colonies were isolated by plating the oil suspension compared to saline. These results reflect the amount of contamination present which either overgrow or inhibited growth of *H. capsulatum*. These data show that dilutions of oil are better for recovery of the fungus than saline dilutions. This explains our improved results using naturally infected soils. The oil concentrates *H. capsulatum* but does not concentrate all the microflora in soil to an equal degree.

Another technique which appears to help direct isolation of *H. capsulatum* from soil is to collect it and let it remain at room environment and dry in the containers for at least two to four weeks. In experiments using this technique the number of colonies isolated of *H. capsulatum* from natural soils have been higher, with a decrease in contamination. The technique was originally suggested by Emmons (1949) in order to reduce mouse deaths resulting from bacteria. It also probably explains the "unknown conditions" of the two soils used by Smith and Weeks (1964) which enabled them to isolate the fungus with ease. These two soils had remained in the collection cartons for six weeks in the laboratory before attempts were made to isolate *H. capsulatum* from them by direct culture. Our results with this drying method suggest that the use of moisture-retaining plastic bags to store soil may be deleterious.

Storage of soils prior for use in direct culture attempts, however, does not shorten the time lost by using the indirect animal method. Also it is not known how this treatment affects the population of *H. capsulatum*. Apparently this fungus is not as sensitive to drying as shown with *Blastomyces dermatitidis* (Smith and Furcolow, 1967). However, some loss of viability may occur, or in contrast, the organism may increase in numbers. At any rate it would be unusual that drying would have no effect and the fungus to remain *status quo*. Therefore, another disadvantage to using this technique is the influence it may have on the numbers of viable particles of *H. capsulatum* as well as other soil organisms.

References

Emmons, C.W. (1949). Isolation of *Histoplasma capsulatum* from soil. *Public Health Rep., 64:*892-896.

Emmons, C.W. (1960). Saprophytic reservoirs of *Histoplasma*. In Sweany, H.C. (Ed.). *Histoplasmoses*. Springfield, Thomas, 76-87.

Furcolow, M.L. and Larsh, H.W. (1952). Direct isolation of *Histoplasma* from soil. *Proc. Soc. Exp. Biol. Med., 80:*246-248.

Hinton, A., Larsh, H.W. and Silberg, S.L. (1957). Direct exposure of mice to soils known to contain *Histoplasma capsulatum*. *Proc. Soc. Exp. Biol. Med., 94:*176-179.

Larsh, H.W., Hinton, A. and Furcolow, M.L. (1952). Efficiency of the flotation method in isolation of *Histoplasma capsulatum* from soil. Proceedings of the Conference on Histoplasmosis. *Public Health Monogr., 39:*74-80.

Smith, C.D. (1964). Evidence of the presence in yeast extract of substances which stimulate growth of *Histoplasma capsulatum* and *Blastomyces dermatitidis* similarly to that found in starling manure extract. *Mycopathologia, 22:*99-105.

Smith, C.D. (1969). Unpublished data.

Smith, C.D. and Furcolow, M.L. (1964). Efficacy of three techniques for isolating *Histoplasma capsulatum* from soil, including a new flotation method. *J. Lab. Clin. Med., 64:*342-348.

Smith, C.D. and Furcolow, M.L. (1967). The susceptibility of *Blastomyces dermatitidis* to drying. *Proc. Soc. Exp. Biol. Med., 125:*263-266.

Smith, C.D. and Weeks, R.W. (1964). Isolation of *Histoplasma capsulatum* from soil by direct culture. *Proc. Soc. Exp. Biol. Med., 115:*549-551.

Chapter 62

Ecologic Eradication of Fungi: Dream or Reality?

GUENTHER STOTZKY

ABSTRACT

The activity, ecology, and population dynamics of microorganisms in soil are influenced by both the characteristics of the microbes and the physical, chemical, and biological properties of soil. One such property of the latter appears to be the clay mineral composition. For example, analysis of ninety-one soils, representing twenty-nine geographic locations in eight countries, from which *Histoplasma capsulatum* had been isolated showed that, with the exception of soils from two locations, none contained swelling three-layer clay minerals that expanded beyond 14A when homoionic to K, air-dried, and saturated with glycerol. The presence of the fungus was not related to the presence or absence of other clay mineral species or to soil pH. These results were similar to those obtained with *Fusarium* wilt of banana, in that the rate of spread of the wilt was rapid in soils not containing such clays but was slow in soils that contained them. These field observations, coupled with extensive studies conducted on various levels of experimental complexity on the differential effects of various types of clay minerals on the growth, metabolism, genetics, surface interactions, and so on, of microorganisms in pure culture and in soil, indicate that even a single environmental factor, such as the type of clay minerals present, greatly influences microbes in soil. This influence is manifested in a series of changes in other environmental factors (e.g. nutrition, pH, ionic strength and composition, osmotic pressure). These studies also suggest that alteration of the soil environment, and thereby of the soil microbiota, by addition of expanding three-layer clay minerals might be an effective method of enhancing the biological control of *H. capsulatum* in soil.

THE elimination, or perhaps more realistically, the reduction in the rate of spread of a fungus or any other organism from a natural environment implies the enhancement or alteration of those factors—physical, chemical, biological—already operating to control the activity, ecology, and population dynamics of the organism in that habitat. The factors, however, must be defined before alteration of an organism's environment can be considered. In the ecosystem under consideration here (i.e. the soil and the soil microbiota, including *Histoplasma capsulatum*), these factors are probably the same as those that influence microbes in any habitat, except that the solid phase pre-

NOTE. The preparation of this report was supported in part by Public Health Service Research Grant No. AI-08476, from the National Institute of Allergy and Infectious Diseases.

dominates and therefore probably plays a greater role than in other habitats. Although individual chemical (e.g. organic and inorganic nutrients, growth factors, ionic composition), physical (e.g. moisture, temperature, pressure, radiation, atmospheric composition, pH, Eh, particulates), and biological (e.g. cooperation, antagonism, characteristics of the organisms) factors can be listed without much difficulty, their influence cannot be assumed nor studied as easily, inasmuch as their expression usually results not from the action of a single variable, but rather from the sum of numerous interactions (Stotzky, 1968). For example, the water content of the soil cannot be altered without concomitantly influencing the atmospheric composition; changes in pH are accompanied by changes in Eh and ionic composition; pressure and temperature are interrelated. Consequently, stressing one environmental factor causes a change not only in that factor but simultaneously and subsequently in several, with the result that the entire environment is altered.

Another consideration is that microbes, regardless of their habitat, are aquatic creatures. Even in soil, most microbial activity is probably restricted to water films encompassing particulates and to capillaries between particles, and although filamentous forms can grow through the voids between water films, the filaments are coated with water, and feeding probably occurs only in sites of accumulated water.

The assumption must also be made that *H. capsulatum*, based on its apparent restricted geographic distribution, is not, except in soils where it has become established, a *normal* soil inhabitant. Consequently, it should be considered a soil invader, to borrow from Waksman's and Garrett's classifications of soil-borne plant root-infecting fungi (Garrett, 1956). A corollary question to this assumption is how the fungus becomes established as an inhabitant in some soils but not in others. There are two main mechanisms by which an invader can become an inhabitant. One is for the organism to adapt, either physiologically or genetically, to the environment. Although most microbes are capable of some degree of adaptation, this process is relatively slow and haphazard, even in eucaryotic organisms, and is basically dependent upon the genetic plasticity of the organism, with the environment's role being primarily and perhaps only to select certain adaptations. Consequently, assuming that distribution and introduction of the pathogen into soil are not limiting factors, adaptation to all environments should occur, and the fungus should be present much more universally in soil than present isolations indicate. As it appears not to be universally present, the importance of adaptation in the establishment of the pathogen as a soil inhabitant appears to be minor.

The second mechanism by which an organism can become established in a specific habitat is for that habitat to change so that the antagonistic capabilities of the indigenous population are reduced sufficiently to enable the invader to become so entrenched that it can withstand the onslaught of the indigenous population when the latter regains its full capabilities (Stotzky, 1967). Inherent in this mechanism is the assumption that distribution and physical introduction of the organism into the habitat has occurred and that the organism has sufficient flexibility to adapt to and exploit its new environment.

Assuming the second alternative, the next question then is what environmental stresses are involved in such periodic reductions in the activity of the indigenous soil population. It is here that much more must be learned about which environmental factors influence microbes in soil and how this influence is exerted.

One such factor appears to be the clay mineralogical composition of the soil. The initial indication that clays influence the ecology of fungi in soil resulted from studies to explain the differential rate of spread of *Fusarium* wilt of banana. The causal fungus, *Fusarium oxysporum* f. *cubense* (E. F. S.) Snyd. and Hans., is soil-borne, invades the plant through the roots, and becomes distributed in the vascular system, resulting eventually in wilting and death. The rate of disease spread, expressed as the effective banana-producing life of a plantation, differs considerably from one soil to another: wilt-susceptible bananas can generally be produced on "short-life" soils for three to ten years and on "long-life" soils for more than twenty years, with some soils being in continuous banana cultivation for more than seventy years.

Analyses of soils from plantations in Honduras, Guatemala, Costa Rica, Panama, Colombia, Ecuador, and the Cameroons showed no correlations between the effective banana-producing life and eighteen chemical and physical properties of the soils. A high correlation, however, was apparent with the clay mineralogy of the soils: a particular species of clay mineral was present in almost all long-life soils, but was absent from almost all short-life soils (Stotzky *et al.,* 1961; Stotzky and Martin, 1963; Stotzky, 1967). The distinguishing clay was a crystalline, three-layer, hydrous alumino-silicate, which when homoionic to K ions, air-dried, and then solvated with glycerol, expanded to give either a distinct x-ray diffraction peak at a *d* value greater than 14.5 A or a peak between 14 and 14.5 A which was skewed toward higher spacings. Although a species name was deliberately omitted, the distinguishing clay mineral tended toward montmorillonite in the montmorillonite-vermiculite sequence. All soils, regardless of their disease history, contained various combinations of other clay minerals, but there was no correlation between their presence or absence and the rate of spread of the disease.

To determine whether the apparent correlation with clay mineralogy was unique to this plant disease or was indicative of a basic ecological phenomenon, the clay mineralogy of approximately ninety soils, representing twenty-nine geographic locations in eight countries, from which *H. capsulatum* had been isolated was analyzed. The results were similar to those obtained with

TABLE 62-I

Clay Mineralogy of Soils from Which *Histoplasma capsulatum* Has Been Isolated

Location	Samples	Clay Minerals				
		M	V	Mi	I	K
Augusta, Georgia	1			+		+
Tennessee	1			+		+
Sturgis, Mississippi	1			none		
Selma, Alabama	1			none		
Laurens County, South Carolina	2		+			+
Mississippi Co., Arkansas	4				+	+
Washington, District of Columbia	4		+	+	+	+
Clarksburg, Maryland	9		+	+		+
Libertytown, Maryland	2		+	+		+
Walkersville, Maryland	1			+	+	+
Washington Co., Maryland	11		+	+	+	+
Conesus Lake, New York	1			+	+	+
Alexandria Bay, New York	1				none	
Milan, Michigan	2		+	+	+	+
Lima, Ohio	2			+	+	+
Lexington, Kentucky	6		+	+	+	+
Bryantsville, Kentucky	1			+	+	+
Mexico, Missouri	3			+	+	+
Kansas City, Missouri	1			+	+	+
Bellevue, Iowa	1			+	+	+
Mason City, Iowa	3			+	+	+
Grand Island, Nebraska	1			+	+	
Transvaal, South Africa	9			+		+
Mbujimayi Area, Congo	12			+	+	+
Tingo Maria, Peru	1		+	+		+
Lara, Venezuela	1			+		
Oropuche, Trinidad	1			+		
Madden Lake Cave, Panama	6	+				+
Emilia-Romagna Reg., Italy	2	+	+	+	+	+
Total Number of Soils	91					

V = vermiculite; Mi = mica; I = illite; K = kaolinite; M = "montmorillonite."

Fusarium wilt of banana, in that the distinguishing clay mineral was absent from all soils, except from those from two locations (Table 61-I). Neither the presence or absence of other clay minerals, nor the pH, which ranged from 5.4 to 8.0, was related to the distribution of the fungus.

Although there were no "controls" in this correlation comparable to the long-life banana soils, and there are undoubtedly numerous areas having soils which contain neither *H. capsulatum* nor the distinguishing clay mineral, its absence in so many soils from which the pathogen has been isolated strongly indicates a causal relationship. Furthermore, differences in clay mineral composition were apparent between soil samples from which the pathogen was isolated and those usually associated with the general area from which the samples were derived: in many locations, montmorillonite was present in the general area, whereas this clay species was absent in the samples containing the pathogen (Stotzky and Post, 1967).

These studies indicated that the clay mineral composition of soils was related to the ecology of at least these two pathogens and that the distribution and physical introduction of their propagules do not seem to be limiting factors. The rate of spread of *Fusarium* wilt of banana did not appear to be related to the frequency or intensity of natural floodings, to the use of surplus irrigation waters from fields with high disease incidence on low incidence fields, nor to the use of diseased planting stock, as both long- and short-life plantations were in many instances simultaneously planted with rhizomes obtained from the same areas, which sometimes had previously been abandoned to the disease. Although *H. capsulatum* appears to be associated with animal droppings, primarily those of birds and bats, the essentially unrestricted geographic distribution of animal manures and the high saprophytic ability of the fungus suggest that type and availability of energy sources are not primary limiting factors in its ecology (Ajello, 1967; Goos, 1965). Moreover, the widespread distribution of avian and chiropteran habitats indicates that the potential exists for the dispersal and introduction of propagules of *H. capsulatum* into almost any soils. The apparent differences between the potential and actual distributions of these two pathogens appear, therefore, to be related to factors that influence their establishment and subsequent development in, rather than to their introduction into, soil.

To determine whether the clay mineralogy of soils was one of these factors and, if so, the mechanisms by which clays influence microorganisms, the effects of various clay minerals differing in physicochemical characteristics on growth and activity of microorganisms in pure culture and in sterile and nonsterile soils are being investigated. In pure culture systems, essentially only montmorillonites from some one hundred samples of clay minerals and similar particles stimulated the respiration of bacteria and actinomycetes, primarily by maintaining the pH of the environment suitable for sustained growth (Stotzky, 1966, 1966a; Stotzky and Rem, 1966, unpublished).

Montmorillonite also appears to "protect" microbes, especially bacteria, against hypertonic osmotic pressures: reductions in metabolic activity with increasing solute concentrations were less in the presence of montmorillonite; at high solute concentrations, the activity increased in proportion to the amount of montmorillonite present (Stotzky and Rem, 1966, unpublished). This effect may be involved in the apparent restricted distribution of *H. capsulatum*, in view of the reports by Smith and Furcolow (see report in this volume) that bird droppings contain a high salt content and that the fungus grows and sporulates best in media containing approximately 3% NaCl. Inasmuch as this salt concentration is inhibitory to many terrestrial bacteria, the apparent correlation between bird droppings and the distribution of *H. capsulatum* may reflect an osmotic inhibition of soil bacteria in some soils which would enhance establishment of the fungus. This inhibi-

tory effect of manure would be minimized in soils containing montmorillonite, as the bacteria would be protected against the increased osmotic pressure and thereby retard the establishment of the fungus.

Bacteria and actinomycetes also spread almost twice as rapidly through
soils naturally containing the expanding three-layer clay mineral usually absent from short-life banana soils and from soils whence *H. capsulatum* has
been isolated, whereas fungi spread almost twice as rapidly in soils not containing such clay. The addition of montmorillonite to the latter type of soils
also enhanced the spread of bacteria and retarded that of fungi. The competitive effects of bacteria against fungi also appeared to be more pro-
nounced in soils containing the distinguishing clay mineral (Stotzky, 1965;
Stotzky and Post, 1965, unpublished). The better growth of bacterial auxo-
trophs and the increased conjugation of bacteria in soils containing montmorillonite (Weinberg and Stotzky, 1970, 1970a) add another dimension to the
differential role of clay minerals in the adaptation and ecology of microbes
in soil.

In nonsterile soil systems, autotrophic (i.e. nitrification) activity was enhanced by increasing increments of montmorillonite but not of kaolinite
(Macura, Kunc, and Stotzky, unpublished), and the presence of montmorillonite markedly stimulated both the rate and extent of heterotrophic utilization of some substrates (e.g. aldehydes), but not of others (e.g. glucose,
oleate) (Kunc and Stotzky, 1968, 1970, unpublished).

The rates of disease spread were also significantly lower when plant species susceptible to soil-borne root-infecting pathogens were grown in the
greenhouse in soils naturally containing the distinguishing clay mineral or
amended with montmorillonite (Stotzky, unpublished).

Because the physiology of sorbed and nonsorbed cells may differ, and the
adsorption of substrates and metabolites by clays might affect their availability and activity—both phenomena which could profoundly influence the
ecology of microbes in soil—surface interactions between clay minerals, microorganisms, and organics are being studied. Such interactions are apparently influenced by the type and physicochemical characteristics of the clay
and by the cation status of the ambient environment, which affects the elec-
trokinetic potentials of all components (Santoro and Stotzky, 1967, 1967a,
1967b, 1968, 1968a; Stotzky and Bystricky, 1969). The adsorption of proteins and other organics appears to be related more to their molecular
weight and to the valency of the cation on the exchange complex of the clay
than to the ambient pH and isoelectric point of the organics (Colom and
Stotzky, unpublished; Harter and Stotzky, 1969, unpublished). These factors, in addition to the mechanisms and sites of adsorption of organics by
clays, apparently influence the relative availability of organics as substrates
for or inhibitors of microbes in soil (Stotzky, 1968).

It is apparent from these studies that a single environmental factor, such as the type of clay minerals present, will greatly influence the activity, ecology, and population dynamics of microbes in soil, and that this influence is manifested in a series of changes in other environmental factors (e.g. pH, nutrition, ionic environment). Moreover, it is also apparent that the definition of the influence of even a single factor in as complex an environment as soil requires studies on various levels of experimental complexity.

These studies also suggest at least one possible method of altering the soil environment for the purpose of eradicating or controlling *H. capsulatum*, i.e. the incorporation of montmorillonite. Although some success in controlling the pathogen has been achieved with fungicides (Smith *et al.*, 1964; Tosh *et al.*, 1966, 1967), the duration of their control has not yet been established, and, as fungicides kill organisms already present in soil but do not alter the environment for long, the pathogen could establish itself again upon reinoculation. The history of fungicide use against plant pathogens indicates that, after an initial reduction in both the saprophytic and pathogenic soil microbiota, most microorganisms reestablish themselves, sometimes at levels higher than those present prior to fumigation (Bollen, 1961; Domsch, 1964; Garrett, 1956). The necessity for repeated fumigation against soil-borne plant pathogens attests to the short duration of control and suggests that for long-term control it is necessary not only to kill the pathogen but also to alter the environment and thereby the ecology and population dynamics of the nonpathogenic soil microbiota, so that reestablishment of the pathogen is deterred. Such an approach to eradication of *H. capsulatum* from soil would not only be cheaper and more permanent, but would also reduce the introduction of high concentrations of chemicals into the biosphere.

Regardless of what methods are used to alter the ecology of *H. capsulatum* in soil, more information than presently available (Goodman and Larsh, 1966) about the factors that influence the ecology and population dynamics of the pathogen in soil is necessary. Does the apparent restricted geographic distribution of *H. capsulatum*, as indicated by both isolation from soil and histoplasmin sensitivity, imply environmental control in areas where it is not present (Ajello, 1967)? Why are large areas endemic to histoplasmosis, as indicated by skin testing, and the fungus has not been isolated from soils in these areas? Conversely, why can the pathogen be isolated from soils in some areas where the human population is predominantly histoplasmin negative (see reports by Edwards and Ajello in this volume)? Why is it impossible sometimes to isolate *H. capsulatum* and other pathogens from stored or *in situ* soils that were once positive (Ajello, 1967), and why, in some areas, does there appear to be a seasonal incidence of isolation from soil? Does this imply an influence of climate on the competitive soil microbiota which in turn results in fluctuations in the pathogen population, or does it imply recurring alterations in the forms in which the pathogen exists in soil at different times? What are the propagules that the fungus produces to persist and proliferate in soil and what mechanisms (e.g., fungitoxins, lysis) does the soil microbiota use to control the fungus? Is the correlation between the presence of manures and the isolation of *H. capsulatum* more apparent than real, especially as the fungus is present in many areas devoid of dung (see MacKinnon in this volume)? What stimulators of the pathogen and/or inhibitors of the competitive soil microbiota are present in manures, and should more biochemical and microbiological studies be devoted to this aspect, especially in view of the apparent involvement of creatinine in the frequent occurrence of *Cryptococcus neoformans* in bird droppings (Staib, 1961)? Does the apparent correlation between manure and the isolation of *H. capsulatum* in some areas reflect only a secondary effect, with the clay mineralogy, through its influence on the competitive bacterial microflora, being a primary determinant, and the droppings either stimulating the fungus or inhibiting the competitors? When manure is present, the pathogen may grow better, but if montmorillonite is also present, the stimulation of the pathogen is masked by the stimulation of the competitors by the clay, with the net result that establishment of the fungus is retarded. The stimulatory or inhibitory substances in manure may also be adsorbed and rendered ineffective by montmorillonite, or the clay may negate the effect of the high solute concentrations derived from droppings and thereby indirectly prevent the establishment of the fungus.

From even these few possibilities, it is apparent that too little is known about the chemical, physical, and biological factors that influence *H. capsulatum* in soil. Until these factors are better defined, ecological eradication of this pathogen will be a trial and error situation at best. Only after more is learned about the activity, ecology, and population dynamics of microbes in soil will the ecological eradication of *H. capsulatum* approach being a realistic dream.

References

Ajello, L. (1967). Comparative ecology of respiratory mycotic disease agents. *Bact. Rev., 31*:6-24.

Bollen, W.B. (1961). Interactions between pesticides and soil microorganisms. *Ann. Rev. Microbiol., 15*:69-92.

Domsch, K.H. (1964). Soil fungicides. *Ann. Rev. Phytopath., 2*:293-320.

Garrett, S.D. (1956). *Biology of Root-Infecting Fungi.* Cambridge, England, Cambridge University Press.

Goodman, N.L. and Larsh, H.W. (1966). Environmental factors and growth of *Histoplasma capsulatum* in soil. *Mycopathologia, 17*:145-156.

Goos, R.D. (1965). Growth and survival of *Histoplasma capsulatum* in soil. *Canad. J. Microbiol., 11*:979-985.

Harter, R.D. and Stotzky, G. (1969). Adsorption of proteins by montmorillonite. *Agron. Abstr.*, p.75.

Kunc, F. and Stotzky, G. (1968). Influence of clay minerals on heterotrophic microbial activity in soil. *Agron. Abstr.*, p.94.

Kunc, F. and Stotzky, G. (1970). Decomposition of some aldehydes in soil containing different amounts of montmorillonite. *Folia Microbiol.* (in press).

Santoro, T. and Stotzky, G. (1967). Effect of electrolyte composition and pH on the particle size distribution of microorganisms and clay minerals as determined by the electrical sensing zone method. *Arch. Biochem. Biophys., 122:*664-669.

Santoro, T. and Stotzky, G. (1967a). Influence of cations on flocculation of clay minerals by microbial metabolites as determined by the electrical sensing zone particle analyzer. *Soil Sci. Soc. Amer. Proc., 31:*761-765.

Santoro, T. and Stotzky, G. (1967b). Effect of cations and pH on the electrophoretic mobility of microbial cells and clay minerals. *Bact. Proc., A15.*

Santoro, T. and Stotzky, G. (1968). Sorption between microorganisms and clay minerals as determined by the electrical sensing zone particle analyzer. *Canad. J. Microbiol., 14:*299-307.

Santoro, T. and Stotzky, G. (1968a). Further observations on electrophoretic mobility of microorganisms and clay minerals. *Bact. Proc., A24.*

Santoro, T., Stotzky, G. and Rem, L.T. (1967). The electrical sensing zone particle analyzer for measuring germination of fungal spores in presence of other particles. *Appl. Microbiol., 15:*935-939.

Smith, C.D., Furcolow, M.L. and Tosh, F.E. (1964). Attempts to eliminate *Histoplasma capsulatum* from soil. *Amer. J. Hyg., 79:*170-180.

Staib, F. (1962). Kreatinin-Assimilation, ein neues Spezifikum für *Cryptococcus neoformans. Zbl. Bakt. (Orig.),* (Abstract I), *186:*274-275.

Stotzky, G. (1965). Replica plating technique for studying microbial interactions in soil. *Canad. J. Microbiol., 11:*629-636.

Stotzky, G. (1966). Influence of clay minerals on microorganisms: II. Effect of various clay species, homoionic clays, and other particles on bacteria. *Canad. J. Microbiol., 12:*831-848.

Stotzky, G. (1966a). Influence of clay minerals on microorganisms: III. Effect of particle size, cation exchange capacity, and surface area on bacteria. *Canad. J. Microbiol., 12:*1235-1246.

Stotzky, G. (1967). Clay minerals and microbial ecology. *Trans. N.Y. Acad. Sci., II:30,* 11-21.

Stotzky, G. (1968). Relevance of soil microbiology to search for life on other planets. In *Adv. Appl. Microbiol.* Eds. Umbriet, W.W. and Perlman, D. Academic Press, N.Y. *10:*17-45.

Stotzky, G. and Bystricky, V. (1969). Electron microscopic observations of surface interactions between clay minerals and microorganisms. *Bact. Proc., A93.*

Stotzky, G., Dawson, R.E., Martin, R.T. and ter Kuile, G.H.H. (1961). Soil mineralogy as a factor in the spread of *Fusarium* wilt of banana. *Science, 133:*1483-1485.

Stotzky, G. and Martin, R.T. (1963). Soil mineralogy in relation to the spread of *Fusarium* wilt of banana in Central America. *Plant Soil, 18:*317-338.

Stotzky, G. and Post, A.H. (1965). Growth rates of microorganisms in soil. *Agron. Abstr.*, p.89.

Stotzky, G. and Post, A.H. (1967). Soil mineralogy as possible factor in geographic distribution of *Histoplasma capsulatum. Canad. J. Microbiol., 13:*1-7.

Stotzky, G. and Rem, L.T. (1966). Influence of clay minerals on microorganisms: I.

Montmorillonite and kaolinite on bacteria. *Canad. J. Microbiol., 12*:547-563.

Stotzky, G. and Rem. L.T. (1967). Influence of clay minerals on microorganisms: IV. Montmorillonite and kaolinite on fungi. *Canad. J. Microbiol., 13*:1535-1550.

Tosh, F.E., Weeks, R.J., Pfeiffer, F.R., Hendricks, S.L. and Chin, T.D.Y. (1966). Chemical decontamination of soil containing *Histoplasma capsulatum. Amer. J. Epidem.,* 83:262-270.

Tosh, R.E., Weeks, R.J., Pfeiffer, F.R., Hendricks, S.L., Greer, D.L. and Chin, T.D.Y. (1967). The use of formalin to kill *Histoplasma capsulatum* at an epidemic site. *Amer. J. Epidem.,* 85:259-265.

Weinberg, S.R. and Stotzky, G. (1970). Effect of clay minerals on growth, conjugation, and genetic recombination of *Escherichia coli* in soil. 10th Internatl. Congress for Microbiology Aa-9 (abst.).

Weinberg, S.R. and Stotzky, G. (1970a). Conjugation and genetic recombination of *Escherichia coli* in soil. *Soil Biol. Biochem.* (in press).

Chapter 63

Summation

NORMAN F. CONANT

THE first conference on histoplasmosis took place seventeen years ago at Excelsior Springs, Missouri, in November, 1952. At that time several recommendations were made concerning further study of the etiologic agent *Histoplasma capsulatum* with respect to areas of endemicity, ecology, and strain variation which would be reflected in the production of histoplasmin for skin testing and as an antigen for serologic tests. Such tests would include the complement fixation test, precipitin test, and collodion agglutination test which were being used at that time for the serologic diagnosis of histoplasmosis.

Some of the above recommendations have been worked on by participants of the Second National Conference on Histoplasmosis. Further serologic tests have been investigated, namely, the agar-gel and the fluorescent antibody tests. Both of these tests have met with reasonable success. It is admitted, however, that the sharing of common antigens by other fungi makes an interpretation of these tests difficult.

The chemical analysis of crude histoplasmin has been obtained by sophisticated methods and techniques which have been applied to other infectious agents and their products. These purified products, thus obtained, have not been compared with the "old" histoplasmin in statistically significant numbers of known positive reactors to warrant their use in epidemiologic surveys. Such studies should be made.

There was some question as to cultural variations and differences in the products obtained from such cultures. It was stated that primary cultures would appear differently macroscopically and be composed of microscopic differences that were reflected in the type of spores produced, smooth or tuberculate, and the amount and character of the mycelium. Further study of the genetic characters of these different-appearing cultures might result in established strains suitable for antigenic analysis and virulence tests which could be duplicated time after time.

Although the dog poses a problem in endemic areas, there is as yet no information that would indicate animal to man transfer of the infection. The isolation of *H. capsulatum* from infected dogs, the serology of the infected animal and possible means of eradication of infection from mongrel dogs was discussed thoroughly.

The clinical and pathological aspects of histoplasmosis was thoroughly discussed by a highly competent group of physicians and pathologists. Although there is still some doubt that uveitis is a sequelae of histoplasmosis, this complication was given its "day in court." Of particular interest was the mention of erythema nodosum as a clinical feature of the disease. This was the first report of this allergic manifestation occurring in histoplasmosis; albeit only one observation was made. The eruption on the skin is known to be a favorable sign in coccidioidomycosis and carries with it an excellent prognosis. It is surprising that this clinical syndrome has not been previously reported for histoplasmosis, a disease which has a high sensitivity level.

An evaluation of amphotericin B therapy was discussed as was the use of hamycin, saramycetin and 5-fluorocytosine in the treatment of histoplasmosis. Amphotericin B was considered to be the best available drug at this time, but it was conceded that a better drug was needed.

Chapter 64

Summation

CHESTER W. EMMONS

WHAT advances in our knowledge of histoplasmosis since the first national histoplasmosis conference have been reflected in our three-day conference? Studies have revealed some of the intricacies of the genetic structure of *Histoplasma capsulatum*. Variations in the fungus have been recognized formally. I think we still do not have the last word on the A and B varieties of *H. capsulatum*. Tremendous strides have been made in elucidating the antigenic components of the fungus. It is not surprising, considering the antigenic complexity of the fungus, that interpretations of histoplasmin skin testing puzzled us twenty years ago, that such an extensive literature on serology has accumulated, and that today we still seek better methods of serologic diagnosis that we even now have. Some of the aspects of the biochemistry and physiology of the fungus are known better than they were only a few years ago.

Participants have pointed out that there are still some unresolved problems concerning the ecology of the fungus and the epidemiology of the mycosis. What is the relationship of *H. capsulatum* to birds? Is it present in their feathers? The host role of bats is more apparent. We heard some useful contributions to the nutritional requirements of the fungus. A simple method of direct isolation of the fungus from soil is being sought. Methods and costs of reducing the population or eradicating *H. capsulatum* from soil were reviewed, and the conditions under which this may be attempted safely and with hope of success were outlined.

During the past seventeen years we have learned more about clinical variations of histoplasmosis, but the relationship (if any) of the mycosis to uveitis, and the role of exogenous reinfection (generally believed to be rare) are still debated points. Discussions of therapy have been focused mainly on when, at what dose, and for how long amphotericin B should be administered. It is unfortunate that saramycetin (first reported 8 years ago) has not yet been released for extended clinical trials. The only long series of patients treated with this low toxicity antibiotic yielded inconclusive results because the supply of the drug was inadequate for maximum dose and duration of treatment.

The conference has brought into focus some of the problems which perhaps can be discussed more definitively if we hold another conference after another seventeen-year period of research. There are some obvious objectives for histoplasmosis studies which were not discussed here, and perhaps in seventeen years we shall have reached those objectives also.

Author Index

491

Subject Index

503